California Time

FREDERIC RAPHAEL

California Time

JONATHAN CAPE
THIRTY BEDFORD SQUARE LONDON

For Clare Stone

FIRST PUBLISHED 1975
© 1975 BY VOLATIC LTD

JONATHAN CAPE LTD, 30 BEDFORD SQUARE
LONDON WCI

ISBN 0 224 01124 3

SET IN 11PT EHRHARDT 453 AND 11PT EHRHARDT
SEMI BOLD
PRINTED IN GREAT BRITAIN
BY RICHARD CLAY (THE CHAUCER PRESS) LTD
BUNGAY, SUFFOLK

Καινούριους τόπους δὲν θὰ βρεῖς,
δὲν θἄβρεις ἄλλες θάλασσες.

Kavafy

(Penguin Book of Greek Verse
Poem 334, line 1 of second stanza)

It will be remembered that during his transatlantic flight Victor England watches a Western. The camera, panning the prospect, discovers a panning prospector. He shakes his sieve and there is the gleam of pay-dirt. He stops, stoops and picks out the gold on his palm. He looks round nervously. In the West, they collect percentages with a gun.

Now he is riding across desert. He enters a canyon at sunset and halts to make a fire and get some rest. He rolls himself in a blanket and lies down.

It is night. The ears of the prospector's horse prick exclamation-marks against the moonlight. Two men are silhouetted at the mouth of the canyon. The bed-roll lies still. The two men converge and, on the nod, fire point-blank into the blanket. No red design badges the *serape*. They frown; and as they frown, shots flash from behind a boulder at the edge of the canyon. The prospector has taken advantage of the cut between sunset and moonrise to light out and leave a bundle of cactus to hide its toes under the blanket. One of the gunmen has indigestion from a bullet. The other dives headlong into rubber rocks and begins a duel with the prospector, whose billing promises victory. Who is paid ten per cent of the gross to get shot in the first reel?

The gunman (close-up of narrowed eyes) tries a subterfuge. He cries out as if he too has been nickel-nicked. The prospector's hat rises, bold above the boulder, and the gunman rises too and does not miss; the crown is his, but only a hollow crown; the hat contains no head. Subterfuge has been met with subterfuge and, as the gunman holes the hat, the prospector holes the gunman.

Unscathed, the prospector steps out and climbs down his long shadow towards the two leaking gunmen. He uncorks his water-bottle and takes a cool swig. Killing dehydrates a man. Imploring eyes watch him from the stained sand. The prospector holds out the bottle to one of the dying men.

'If you think you've got time.'

The gunman reaches up, stiffens and falls back. The prospector, recognizing a losing streak when he sees one, sticks his

7

thumb through his drilled hat and shakes his insured head:
'Rough.'

Victor England keeps his head-set to his ears, but he alters the channel from time to time (as he does his wristwatch, from Greenwich to California) and so enjoys Tombstone's banjo band in a performance of the Choral Symphony and the corrupt judge speaking in the tones of the editorial staff of a News Weekly. His eyelids droop. The head-set falls from his ears and its thin arms caw and claw feebly, like an unfleshed lobster, at his neck.

At the airport, Victor is met by Praz, the Studio greeter. Due to a strike of handlers, he has had to carry his own luggage from under the plane, where a rectilinear mountain of suitcases has dwindled to a single moleskin molehill before his angry eyes. One of his cases is missing. An airline functionary comes up to him and points to the only remaining case.

'Has to be yours,' said the Passenger's Friend, who was paid for a forty-hour smile.
'That's no bag of mine,' Victor England said. 'Mine all went through in London and now one's missing. Where is it?'
'You're saying this isn't it?'
Victor England, saying nothing, said just that.
'Maybe you can trace yours on an exchange basis, sir.'
'My name is Victor England,' Victor England said.
'I'll tell you what, Mr England,' said the Passenger's Friend, 'leave it with me.'
'And when you find it, you can leave it with me.'
'All I ask is – don't allow a little thing like this to affect your travelling pleasure. If you have any kind of a problem, just come to me.'
'I will, and I have, and here I am.'
'Absolutely,' said the Passenger's Friend. His name was Dwight D. Hernandez and he was there to be shot at: his name was on a target pinned over his heart.

*

Praz tells Victor, as they take short cuts through the canyons, that he managed to smooth the way through customs with a few folded greenies – 'That's the kind of mail everybody still likes to get' – and Victor, agreeably displeased, touches his wallet. Praz seems, at this stage, to be the incarnation of the reliable old Studio servant. He has escorted all the great stars in their time and he continues to live in the light of what may be extinct but still shines if you know which channel to choose. He has the pensionable agelessness of an elderly boy who has been doing the same job for longer than anyone can remember. Whatever his servile insolence, he seems far from the blue-chinned heavy at whose description gum-chewing Jack McLeish, Captain of Detectives, sucks in his peppermint cheeks. Yet already, before the limousine arrives at the hotel, pointing his loaded questions at every hold-up, he shows indications of becoming a garrulous menace.

'Did you know Mr Carnap, Mr England, when he was on the Coast?'

'This used to be an Italian restaurant,' Victor England said.

'Because I was in Europe in the Fall and I saw Mr Carnap. I guess you must know him in London.'

'Frascati,' Victor England said, 'wasn't that the name?'

'I was in London. I was in Paris. Do you know Geneva, Mr England? Because I was in Geneva. Mr Carnap drove me personally round London. Now there's a real gentleman. The Tower of London, Windsor Palace, Hampton Court. Only one city in the world cleaner than Geneva for my money and that's Disneyland. But London gets my vote in the end, I don't care what they say. Isn't that some city? I was kind of impressed with Munich, if you know Munich.'

'I don't know Munich,' Victor England said.

'If you like a cold beer,' Praz said.

They have to stop at a green light when a motorcycle cop flags them down. Praz slides his head out from under the metal shell of the limousine, tortoise wrinkles on his marine neck, and wants to know what gives, officer. The cop digs his spur in the road and answers with a thumb: an arrowhead of his colleagues is coming down the eleven-hundred block, yellow eyes blinking at the ends of their handlebars, jaundiced escort for a cortège in which veiled fame is travelling.

'Looks like the big funeral,' Praz said, 'and I know some people who're going to be pretty sore when they hear about this.'

'I wonder what they did with Frascati,' Victor England said.

'The last bunch of mourners went to see a big-shot nailed down, they didn't get no escort, and that included some considerable stock-holders in this town. They had to contend with a nose-to-tail situation on the freeway coming home, didn't make the opening that night till it was closing. Are there going to be some questions!'

'How about if we backed up?'

'Officer, tell me something,' Praz called out. 'What kind of a cadaver do you have to be in this town before you can make a right?'

The cop fanned Praz down till he was three feet six inches high.

'How about if we backed up?' Victor England said.

'I'll tell you what they did with Frascati, Mr England,' Praz said. 'They buried him and built a bank on top of him. Who argues with the right price on his head?' Praz leaned out again. 'Because I want to get Mr England to his hotel,' he told the cop. The cop shrugged. What did England mean to him?

When Victor first goes into the hotel, there is a girl sitting in the lobby, near a potted plant with black, fleshy leaves.

It was difficult to be sure of her age or status. Was she waiting for her big chance to become a chambermaid or was she a young actress resigned to a lifetime of star-dom? She wore a long cotton dress and blood-brown ox-hide boots. The reddish material of her costume so closely matched the watered silk of the wall-covering that, for a moment, frowning from the sunshine, Victor England misread the lobby for empty. Until he blinked her into focus, she might have been a ghost designed by a clever young man. In the place of her eyes, egg-shaped sunglasses previewed the scene: two elevators and two entrance-ways alternated there. For an instant, Victor England saw a pair of himself in her yoked glance.

The girl's mirrored lenses pan him across the lobby and up to the Reception Desk, where we now discover that he can write equally well with either hand. The two signatures are entirely different, however, and the one he offers first does not tally with his credit card.

'Can there be another Mr England?' the clerk asks.

'Yes, of course,' he replies, and then obliges with his other hand.

Meanwhile, he thinks of going up to the girl. A pressure urges him towards her; it reminds him of the leaned weight of the crew behind a dolly, pending the cue to move. Should he offer her help? Why should he, he wonders, when she has done him no harm? She waits, expressionless, electrically silent, like one of those modern clocks for whose tick one can spend a lifetime listening. She prompts some emotion in him, but he cannot say what it is. Gentleness, greed, desire, contempt?

She reminded him cruelly, because prematurely, with the remote and officious punctuality of an alarm call, of the old days. That look of docility guarded by ambition, he had seen it on a thousand girls and more, girls capable of warmth and sincerity and passion and loyalty, but capable also of shrillness, malice, frigidity and love. When they were grateful, you bought and sold them; when they were spiteful, you desired and indulged them and not infrequently you married them. He had seen a thousand such girls, and more.

Her transparent youth, flawed only by a shred of innocence as blanched as a hangnail, offers him a window on the past. He can see into a world he has assumed to be lost. If she appears to look through him, he can also look through her; each offers the other a kind of access, but for the moment their presents do not coincide. They are not living in the same time, nor celebrating the same feast. Is that why he finds that he cannot, for all the weight of inclination, go up to her?

Instead he turned and shared her vision. A silver screen of light hung over the entrance to the lobby. It shimmered like the molten mouth of an oven. People and cars, mute and heat-steeped, swam past, undulating flatly, specimens on a life-size slide. Victor England, tactful as treachery (he had seen it before), smiled at the same plot as the girl, and that was as much as he could do.

His luggage is now seen entering on a low trolley hauled by a grey bellboy with all the crouching solicitude of an ambulance man with a blue-cross basket case. The stiff suitcases are covered with flowers like stylized coffins embossed with floral tributes. A meticulous murderer might be transporting his victims *en terrine*. Victor goes out into the white afternoon to remind Praz to drive straight back to the airport and check on the missing bag. He finds himself passing dollar after dollar through the slot which Praz has pressed open at the top of his blue window. The greeter seems to have turned into a teller who will never tell without money in his hand. His chin has taken on the rounded, gun-metal form of a pre-war sedan. Victor feels that Praz has access to an underworld where his case has been cached and which cash alone can unlock. Praz does not even tear off a promise as a receipt for the money. Victor's apprehensions are to prove justified. He never sees Praz again. When McLeish checks with the Studio, no one there has ever heard of him, 'Don't worry,' says the detective, 'it's probably because he's been there so much longer than anybody else.' Victor England watches the car down the dry slipway and into the stream of traffic and then he returns to the lobby.

He did not look for her, but there was no sign of the girl. He frowned at the place where she had been sitting and found that the mere chair, every line of it warped to please, like a courtier of the Louis it aped, aroused in him the same questionable emotion as had the girl herself.

Her absence is a positive feature of the lobby. He goes up to her chair and plants his clean sole on the velvet seat, above gilded buds that will never know summer, and tightens tight laces. He is about to collect his key when he spies the girl's basket tucked in a recess behind the spotted plant.

She could only just have abandoned it, for as he watched, it creaked and slumped forward, like an ungirdled stomach. Could it be that she had left her hands in it, those blunt-fingered hands which, when he reminded himself, he could see writhing on the burnt-sugar handles of her basket? Were they comforting each other, like papless puppies, in the bottom of the fibrous basket?

Why should Victor England have such a fantasy of mutilation? Are the girl's hands memorable for their bluntness or detestable because of it? Meanwhile Victor's own hand is poised to sign the register, a deckle-edged volume as heavy as the book of the dead. The owner of the hotel has come down specially to greet the distinguished director (as he is described on the secret list which the clerk allows everyone to see) and stands watching while Victor's left hand undertakes the assignment. The owner's name is Verdugo and he lives at the very top; Verdugo is, of course, the Spanish for executioner.

*

'Mr England, sir, what a pleasure! What a privilege!'

'Hullo, Ramon. How are you, Ramon?'

'Very well, Mr England. Older, but very well.'

'We're all older, Ramon.'

'Not you, Mr England, not you. All these years, you never age at all. I want the secret some day.'

'No secret. I started early.'

'And you never stopped. *That*'s the secret. You've seen our alterations? Nothing is too good for our friends. I have a new chef. He cooks everything you shouldn't have better than anyone else in the world. So, things are better.'

'Promise?' Victor England said.

'Promise. We had a whole bunch of people in the restaurant, in the Bonne Auberge, last night. Young, optimistic, go-ahead – they've got plans, they've got ideas –'

'Any messages?' Victor England said.

'Upstairs.' Verdugo pressed the elevator button.

'Everybody still have to wear a tie?' Victor wanted to know.

'In the Bonne Auberge? Of course. Absolutely. As long as I'm alive. As long as La Mission belongs to me.'

Ramon Verdugo had, at that moment, the face of a president-in-exile. He wore the dented dignity of those who have come to power by the sword and have been docked of it by the pen. There were rumours, and they hummed in the silent air like unscreened flies, that the extensions had proved more expensive than Ramon's hand-stitched pocket could afford. He had begun his career by being rewardingly involved in a racket, in another state and a lifetime earlier. It had been a complex business, as such businesses had better be, and nothing was ever proved against any angel who had wings broad enough for flight. (Only the small were fried.) Verdugo, so a ribbing columnist once said in the Rib Room, had been in it up to his ears: 'Only luckily for him he had more hair in those days. He pulled himself out by his top-knot. And what's more, nothing fell out of his pockets while he was doing it. You don't start La Missy-own with a ten cent pack of seeds.' One of the T-bones on the griddle spat in the columnist's eye and he had to go home winking.

Now Verdugo stood, in black coat and striped trousers, and watched the one-handed elevator clock that told the storeys. He liked formality and he liked to impose it. He kept a spare cravat, already looped, under the Maître d's lectern and he had been known to tighten the knot himself on a recalcitrant celebrity who banked on privilege. His employees dared a less formal style. A bearded black man, with ACME across his T-chest, was hauling a stertorous vacuum-cleaner back and forth over some new carpet like some blind and legless pet.

'We also have a new pool,' Verdugo said, 'with waves. Special waves.'

'Special waves, special trouble,' Victor England said.

The elevator opens and four laughing people are disclosed. One of them is a woman. She is in the midst of a loud, particularly brazen laugh, the sort of bar-room bark which might once have apologized for itself by turning into a cough. Her vulgarity is redeemed, or compounded, by a pair of matchless eyes, fresh from the strong-box, which can belong only to one of those great names which have been criticized so much that they are beyond praise. The three men jostle for the position nearest to their Princess, jowled babies touching base. Even the least favoured (he had been closest in the night) manages to keep a finger on her arm, as a reader might keep a place in a book. The woman continues to laugh, although the sight of Verdugo, and Victor, induces the men to show the pursed propriety with which they might have greeted a casket.

The Princess flung the shards of her derision in the air and, like a jagged juggler, cared nothing for the broken peace and the broken pieces. Victor England seemed to be struck by some of her florid shrapnel; he winced a measure of brave pain. Her face, raddled with annual rejuvenation, rode past him while his eyes, dazzled by remembered rockets, ran a retrospective that saw her swaggering down an illuminated stairway, Cedric Gibbons's decline leading to a breast-taking fall into a springing carriage of chorus boys' hands. Whereupon she rode off, one arm raised in triumph at the close shave she had had, to a storm of applause from extras with their own evening clothes.

As the elevator doors smacked their rubber lips together to end the sequence, Victor said, 'I almost didn't recognize her. The Princess, and I almost didn't recognize her.'

'Only the eyes,' Verdugo said, 'that's all she has left.'

'I guess the rest went in taxes,' Victor England said. 'She looks like she was some Madame who's bought the Princess's eyes at the closing-out sale.' He could imagine the great star, still secretly as exquisite as she had been in their youth, waking to remember that she was as blind as a Byzantine, ravished of her unique jewels and sentenced henceforth to weep from twin emptinesses. The truth was different. She still had her jewels, but she was walled up in a tower of flesh to which not even the needle could provide a key. The truth was always different. 'That was really her?'

'Weren't you two married one time, Mr England?'

'I was married all the time, Ramon. I married them all,' Victor England said. 'It was all I knew to do.'

'We always pay for our mistakes,' Verdugo said.

'Especially if we marry them,' Victor England said.

Verdugo pointed a perforated toe to a toasted ring in the carpet of the elevator. 'Since our re-fit, I've had to replace over thirty yards of carpet. And you know who does the damage more often than not? People not even staying in the hotel.' Verdugo closed his eyes like a ledger. They were the wary, weary eyes of an age-old species which knew that for all its webbed wisdom it would soon be extinct. Verdugo was the descendant of those bearded Iberian navigators, bead-bearing bastards and voracious visionaries who had set out to invent a new world. The last of them had made California the West Wing of Europe.

'No appreciation,' Verdugo said. 'People not even staying.'

'She's old,' Victor England said, ashamed to see himself still uncreased in the vanity glass on the elevator wall.

'You can spend all the money in the world,' Verdugo said. 'Who thanks you?'

The expense of renewing the fabric of La Mission has clearly taxed Verdugo hard. Even a snake can run out of skins. The executioner, reminded of his own mortality, resents the sentence he has so often and so promptly carried out on others. Verdugo's business career has required the curtailing of not a few curt, ailing rivals ('All you need to say is yes,' he is said to have said at a just-a-few-words bedside in the Cedars of Lebanon) and it may even be that there are more ruthless stories yet in the secret diaries of his success. The gentle friars who ran the original missions were installed by blades from Toledo. Certainly Verdugo has dangerous as well as loyal friends behind him:

For years he was wise enough and patient enough never to have a room for any client of the agent who had shown the door to a certain singer when he was in a trough in his career. The singer surfaced one day, as Verdugo had guessed he would, and rode into town on the crest of an unbreaking wave. Once in striking distance of his enemies he changed to a scythed chariot and rode out to settle a few old sores. Verdugo was rewarded with the word that the singer's friends were his friends and suddenly there were a lot of them. Caesar had crossed the Rubicon and whoever had crossed him was rubicund indeed. He was back on top of the heap, solo. When Caesar sang, what other voice was heard? He stayed in

Caesar's Palace thru the Ides of March and enjoyed a long, long life. Even at his farewell concerts, which had taken place recently, only fools had said goodbye.

They reach the top floor and start along the lemon chiffon carpet which leads to the big numbers.

'Mr Keyes called me this morning on my private number,' Verdugo said, 'just to be sure that everything was ready for you.'

'Is the old man in town?'

'He didn't say.'

'Is that right?' Victor England offered Verdugo the professional compliment of distrust.

'He said to be sure and give you his warmest personal regards.'

'Can I cash those here in the hotel, Ramon? How is he, Rex?'

'Like a young man still. He still loves the girls. He still rides –'

'Barbara still finds them for him?'

'When he doesn't find them for himself. What a man, I must say. Mr England, your key.'

'She's still operating?'

'Still operating. A happy and a profitable stay to you. *Salud y pesetas!*'

Verdugo hands over a key weighted to make a bigger hole in Victor's pocket than even the bill. Verdugo has opened all the doors in the suite, just as a man selling a Swiss penknife will always open all the blades before he lets you cut yourself. The sound of hammering now becomes audible. Victor England, watching the place from which it comes, cannot tell whether something is being built or torn down.

Verdugo has also turned on all the lights before bowing himself out. He seems at pains to acknowledge that it is night-time for Victor England even though bars of sunshine stripe the louvred shutters. The sideboard represents a welcome committee that is devoted by proxy: bow-belted bottles and prize produce in cellophaned baskets deliver hellos in round numbers from charge accounts all over town. Even the flowers are under transparent hoods to save them from assassination. Victor opens the ribboned envelopes and reads the cardboard love they contain. The succession of names, old neighbours leaning over the fence of time, causes him now to smile a one-winged smile, now to nod distant recognition. Sometimes he clicks his tongue and occasionally he mouths a name, as if he has just been introduced and wants to be sure he has it right. And then again a new pairing, unexpected x with unwise y, makes him frown until, with a simultaneous equation of his eyebrows, he comes up with the solution. *Him*, with *her*? What do you know? His agent, Brute Andrews, has sent the usual salute: champagne cased in sham pleasure.

Victor presses a button and the window drapes swing their evening skirts together. He stops all calls, throws himself on the spread lap of the bed and closes his eyes. Time's indigestion brings back the past. His dream, if it is a dream, turns out to be a re-run: he is again in London, in a projection room where once more a Western is being shown. It soon emerges that it is the same Western he has seen on the flight: here is the same prospector, a beard or two older, looking down on a mining-company site. A patrol of armed men keeps his head down, but already we have recognized the place where he made his first strike. His claim has been swindled from him with the help of the judge who mouthed editorials in the plane. Self-mocking, the prospector tosses his one remaining nugget from hand to hand, remounts his horse and rides slowly away.

Victor watched from the back row. He had gone, at the director's express invitation, printed white on red, and when the lights went up, the kid climbed over, kidding. 'You stayed!'

'Who said different?'

'They told me you always walked out.'

'Only when I've paid,' Victor England said.

'Then pay up,' the kid said, 'and you can go home.'

'It was good,' Victor England said.

The young man grinned, opening the top bracket of his political moustache to declare white teeth. 'So stick around. See if I care.'

The two of them stood together while the ticketless audience helped each other into coats and out of the theatre. Several men bent towards the director on their way and pressed parts of his body with effusive hands, as if they had money in him. They nodded to Victor England and gave him the postponed deference due to a High Priest who had not, on this occasion, conducted the service.

When everyone else had gone, Drakos and Victor England stood between the rows of peach-coloured *fauteuils*. Drakos flushed away his cigarette in a spinning chrome ashtray and prompted Victor with a light fist to the waistcoat.

'Now come on,' he said, 'what didn't you like?'

'There was a lot of blood.'

'Liable to happen when you make holes in people, Victor,' Drakos said, imitating, at no extra charge, a great star who was now old enough to sit back and do commercials for savings banks.

'You should know,' Victor England said.

'Right. I'm younger than you are. I've had a lot more experience. What else?'

'And then the massacre – '

'You had to like the massacre. The massacre was a bunny, wasn't it?'

'How did you do that? It looked like it was all one shot, but – '

'It was five,' Drakos said, the proud father of quins.

'O.K., you went through black once or twice, I got that much, but … *five*?'

'Five. Would I lie to you? I went through black twice. I locked the camera and matched one entire set-up frame for frame, what else did I do?'

'You tell me.'

'Not until we're married,' Drakos said, 'and maybe not even then. You really don't know?'

'You went through black three times,' Victor said. 'Now what else did I miss?'

'Most everything,' Drakos said. 'Sir, can I help you?'

A famous old man who still wore a famous young smile was standing in the doorway of the theatre.

'My wife left her glove,' he said, and went steeply down the ramp to the front. 'I have it. I have it. Forgive me.' He climbed the gradient once again. 'Peter,' he said, 'it was wonderful – just wonderful.'

'Sir,' Drakos said, 'thank you. May I say that you were the greatest bad man I ever saw? "I'm looking for a horse." Do you remember that line?'

'I remember it.'

'To have you call a Western wonderful, that's all the reward I ever need.'

'Goodnight, Peter. Goodnight, Victor.' The old man went out, holding the glove like the only fish from a long day's angling.

'That was once the quickest gun in the West,' Drakos said. 'Kerpooch! Now he can't even get it out of the holster. There's a man used to spend two whole days and nights in the saddle and you believed it. *I* believed it. Now he has to have an air cushion to sit on the can. You have a car?'

'Yes, thank you,' Victor England said.

'Can you give me a ride home?'

'With pleasure.'

'The pleasure's waiting at home,' Drakos said, guest-comic in his own show. 'I'll just take the ride. Too much blood you think?' The fist cossetted the waistcoat again. 'Now that's not something anyone could ever accuse you of, Mr England.'

Later that evening, after Drakos has first yelled 'Nazi' at a waiter who still has six ounces of German grenade in his body ('Maybe that's why you rattle when you serve,' Drakos quips) and then sent back a dish because he didn't order jugged hair, Victor England duly drives the young man home. His place is in an uncompleted business district. The chauffeur has to edge past mixers and between banks of corrugated iron before Drakos indicates for him to stop by slapping his palm on the glass and spreading his fingers in a five-spoked fan, like some one bidding at auction. He looks less to have found where he actually lives than to have decided where he might as well. Then Victor sees a girl waiting by a solitaire board of chromium buttons, the bell-pushes for a block of steel and planked concrete flats. Drakos sits in the car next to Victor and eyes the solitary girl, canvassing his companion for complicity. Victor says, 'Do you know her?' Drakos shakes his head in assent, gets out of the Rolls and walks up to the girl.

He put his hands on her accessible flesh and whispered in her ear. She feinted to strike him, but he finger-and-thumbed her wrist and worked her towards the Rolls. Victor England leaned for the handle of the door and, as she looked up, saw that it was the girl who worked in the saloon in Tombstone and was all set to marry the boy she had always loved until the judge sentenced him to a rope necktie. That was how a nice girl like her got to be in a place like this. When she spotted Victor's surprise, she threw back her head and blew bubbles of laughter in the glassed silence. Drakos stood beside her, indicating her absurdity, a magician soliciting applause for the rabbit.

He leaves the girl buckled in misfits of giggles, walks up to the car and asks Victor to come in. The girl likes him. Victor protests that he doesn't know her.

'She's in the picture,' Drakos said.
'But I still don't know her.'
'How do you think I know her?'

Drakos laughs excessively at this, aware of some hidden (or

obvious) meaning perhaps; or has the laughter itself some arcane inflection? Is it a veiled vestige of the language Drakos once spoke? He now speaks perfect English, but his laugh still has a foreign accent. It remains always in italics, like emphatic print. Victor senses that in Drakos's underlined judgment his own manners are both dated and ridiculous.

Drakos has walked back to the entrance to the flats where he pushes a bell by the triggered door and bends to kiss the metal lips through which ringers can identify themselves to those within. A buzzing click rewards his description of himself; the door springs open. Victor England sits in the unrolling Rolls and stares at the grained concrete of the building.

He wanted to apologize to Dennison, his chauffeur, who had been with him for months. He was angry, but on reflection he saw that he was angry not with Drakos (whose bespoke fan had left its prints on the glass division that made the Rolls a showroom) but with Dennison, the goat who now failed to go. Victor was obliged to sit there and watch Drakos and the girl go through the glass door and snap it shut behind them.

In private, where Victor could see them perfectly, Drakos bent the girl backwards over his arm. She might have been a traveller's hangered suit. He pulled out her breasts and switched on the nipples.

Victor clapped his hand to his chest and felt for his wallet. Did he simply crave the hard comfort of his wad, or did he imagine, for one wild, hopeful moment, that Drakos had used the girl as a decoy while he robbed him?

Why should Victor England imagine for a moment that Drakos might want to rob him? The young man is a very successful director with well-advised money everywhere, like undetected crimes. Fame, we are told, has made his twenties last longer than a decade; there is no reason why his thirties should ever end. When Victor finds that he still has his wallet, he fingers it like a growth that has not, after all, regressed. Is he disappointed not to have been robbed? Has he somehow courted the covert insults with which Drakos's insolence has not failed to degrade him? Would being robbed have given the evening a desired climax? He now feels, it is suggested, like a connoisseur who has been gulled into leaving a knowledgeable kleptomaniac alone with his collection and comes back, after an agony of absence, to find that this thief of exquisite taste has not deigned to lift a thing.

Victor England's London home is in a newly-whitened, newly-heightened, newly-brightened terrace facing a royal park. Victor feels a proud uneasiness as he approaches this flat-faced Parthenon with its grin of pillars, forever open wide, in a Nashing of plaster teeth. The terrace, with its warranted warrens, is a hive of conspirators who have never met and never will meet the victims of their conspiracy. They seldom even meet each other, yet what outsider can doubt that those who live chic-to-chic in such a place are implicated in some common plot? When money talks, it has many tongues; silent, it never appears to contradict itself.

A few nights earlier, a man was arrested near the dustbins. His arrest was not prompted by any of the tenants. He was wanted for something the authorities would have to look up, but he had been incautious enough to go out wearing a face some policeman had seen before. A dated face is always in danger: fame or the police always get you in the end. The arrested man yells accusations at the Palladian pilasters and the dormer windows whose darkness he has lightened. He holds the white sepulchre responsible for his dark and bolted future. The rich make enemies as they sleep.

Victor England stands for a while in front of the building, the poisonous – because free – oxygen mask of the night breathing into his face. He stares across at the park with its green-plumed Serpentine and its unplucked promise of flesh. The gardens are a well-known rendezvous for prostitutes of all sexes; everyone goes down there for love and money. Victor's feet itch to enter the bidding grove (shades of that leaned weight behind him), but just as he is once more fingering his wallet, to be sure that it is neither too thin for what he wants nor too thick for safety, Mr Richards, the janitor, makes silent noises behind him and emerges with a long leash of dogs whose owners are away proving how much they love their places in the country. (What year exactly, one wonders, is this? Like the films which he himself directs, Victor's world is set in the past. This year's films were always made last year.)

Mr Richards is trusted with all the tenants' keys: it is the best way they can devise of locking him in. The one man who never escapes from prison is the gaoler. Richards, we are now told, has a face that collectors sometimes think they have seen on stamps.

It was the face of a royal by-blow. He had missed a public future only by a pubic whisker. Had the unshelled oyster by which his ancestor came to life been seeded in a different Pearl, he would have been a Prince. He was a man who had missed the big prize in the lottery of fate by a single digit in a dozen.

If Richards is but a janitor instead of a monarch, the tenants still regard him with a certain respect. He is the only man who knows them all. Without him, there would be neither order nor scandal, the only proofs of rank. He is in fact a sort of citizen-King, a Scandinavian sovereign who lends dignity to others while himself pedalling a two-wheeled throne. (Richards has indeed in his time come third in the 200-kilometre professional road-race.) Without Richards, the inhabitants of the terrace could never be quite sure that they were in the right place.

Inside his own entrance, Victor looked up to see a rusty-haired man coming towards him, overcoat over arm, lashless eyes caustic with vigilance. How was he to avoid this striding figure? The passage seemed too narrow and his own spirit too tired to confront such confidence. He walked up to the stranger. It was his own reflection, drilled like a guardsman. Victor met his own unsmiling,

unboned self at the very door to his flat and the two of them went in together, good spies who had walked to their rendezvous.

Later, recalling this moment, Victor finds himself detecting minute divergences in the identity of his own image. He himself, he remembers, had his overcoat round his shoulders. Did not what passed for his reflection have its overcoat slung over its arm, just as he had until the very last second before he entered the building? Did his sudden change of appearance catch the other short? In what sense does a man's reflection spy on him, and on whose behalf?

Victor's flat, as grandly husked within the terrace's Corinthian colonnade as Cordoba Cathedral within its rouged cincture of Moorish arches, is as large as one Georgian house caught with another on its back (there is a sibling flat upstairs) and it is less a home than a showcase in which Victor and his wife, the paradigm of matching pairs, have two of everything. Even what is unique is sent away to be married.

Victor goes into the drawing-room. He is under the impression that he is looking for something. His films always insist on a plot and he himself is driven by an obscure sense of mechanical purpose. He must have a place in a plot if he is not to be edited into insignificance. What is he looking for? He goes up to the chess-set on the side table and contemplates the regular rows of peaceful pieces as if they already composed some improbable problem. The set once belonged to a great philanthropist and chess champion who allowed himself to be fool's-mated by the Nazis. Like many things and some people, Victor has acquired it at auction. The champion's effects made good prices, but no one bid for his causes.

How brilliant the pieces were with moves which had long ago won unquestioned exclamation marks! Decorative as Swiss guards, yet unstriped with Michaelangelo's gauds, they paraded in their pre-technicolor world, all black and white, and waited for the finger that would trigger those muffled muscles and send sidling bishops (promoted dunces) and beknighted horsemen into their mating game. When Victor touched them, he was mindful of the grandeur that had once commanded them. Might one not thus, hesitantly, touch the bossed bride that had known Juan's bed? Could he ever resurrect such responses as must be dormant, ripe for ruses, in that rooky woodenness?

He toys with a move or two, licensing a finger to light on the nippled nut of a pawn and stroke it to shiny readiness before returning it to its lines. The latter abrupt movement unstables a horse which falls to the floor, requiring worshipful search. Victor England appears during this scene to be a novice at chess. Is it not curious that he was once a player of considerable promise!?

Victor is assailed by an anxious sensation. Is there someone else concealed in the room? A burglar? An assassin? Who can it be? The effect of this phantom presence is to charge every move, every glance into the darker corners, with a dramatic significance. With this apprehension comes, to Victor's surprise, a sense of liberation. He is quite alone, concerned only for himself. He is ready to use the most precious of his wife's rare crystals as a missile. He has no sense of property, only of self-preservation. He does not feel at home, and by that very token he is master of his environment. He rejoices in the masterful exhilaration of the thief. He surveys the room unembarrassed by a proprietor's propriety. He becomes a critic, not a victim. It is hard to say how long this sense of glorious danger persists, but in these few moments he sees how unnecessary are all his matched necessities. The room is a burden. It is only by removing something from it that it can possibly be improved. How does one improve a tomb save by rolling back the stone? To pillage such a place would be to give it life.

The thief too was an interior decorator. Certainly the interior decorator was a thief. How often had Victor come home to find his wife and William, the charmer whom she was helping with his career, laughing together? What was the joke? What green flame lit their warmth?

'What do you really want in this room, darling?' his wife had asked him on one such evening, while her dreams put on their clothes again.

'I'll settle for perfection,' Victor said.

'Perfection!' William said. 'May I be honest?'

'You can try,' Victor England said, to pinch his wife.

'I'm not good enough yet to do anything that isn't perfect.'

'William, you're wicked,' the woman said.

That Christmas William brought Fleur three presents: an apple, an apple with a single bite out of it and an apple core. They were cast in bronze. Victor England was given the bill, and the pip.

Victor England's films, to which a classifying article by Hugh Stone, the transvestite critic, ascribes a scrupulous lack of authenticity, have perhaps something of the same painsgiving airlessness which William (bill to the wealthy) has brought to the England residence. Is it significant that when Victor has found the knight under the *chiffonnier* in the dining-room and returned it to the chessboard, he stands there for a moment trying to solve the still commotion on the board and toying with a golden fruit from the bowl of stone plums on the sideboard? He tests its unyielding ripeness and dents only his thumb. The fullness of the Orphic egg, which clearly echoes this unyolked oval, is a repeated motif not only in the airless room but also in Victor England's films, where nothing is suffered to survive save the relevant. Plot is all. Both work and life are thus crammed with unbreathable necessity, as Hugh Stone puts it. Can praise, or condemnation, go further?

Later on, we are given an extract from an interview between Victor and Hugh Stone which may have a considerable bearing on subsequent events:

Q. Tell me about your favourite character.

A. The one I liked best?

Q. Your favourite.

A. Well, I'll tell you. Mr Hyde.

Q. In *Doctor Jekyll and Mr Hyde*?

A. In *Doctor Jekyll and Mr Hyde*. He fascinated me. I hated Dr Jekyll.

Q. You hated Dr Jekyll?

A. I hated him.

Q. Why is evil more attractive than virtue, do you think?

A. Because man is evil, I guess. He's more at home when he's allowed to be himself. More natural. Only was Dr Jekyll so virtuous?

Q. You're the director!

A. I think he was phoney. That was the whole idea with the way I had the place furnished. I don't know if you remember –

Q. The windows wouldn't open.

A. The windows wouldn't open. He was always worried about dust and dirt. Everything shone. Do you remember how his wife was always feeling faint, she kept panting, she couldn't do anything?

Q. The bourgeois wife. Sickness as evasion, isn't that what you were talking about there? Virtue as flight.

A. Was I?

Q. Anyway –

A. Anyway, I was trying to convey that there wasn't any air in her life. No life in her life, I guess. She was beautiful –

Q. Is she still alive?

A. Is she still alive? My heavens, yes. Jekyll seems like the perfect husband, at least that was –

Q. That came across perfectly –

A. But he was really a killer too. He didn't have to wait to turn into Hyde. He was a killer already. He embalmed everybody, stifled them, stopped them breathing.

Q. The doctor's last office!

A. Pardon me?

Q. Closing our eyes.
A. If you like.

Now we can understand better why, before leaving his own drawing-room, Victor England feels suddenly breathless. He pours himself a dose of Evian water. A drop or two slops on the polished shoulder of the new-old *chiffonnier*. He rubs it with his fingers, as if the wood were some absorbent material. Now when he wakes up again in his suite in California, he sees that Verdugo not only switched on all the lights but also the television, which is playing soundlessly (the supplier's name is Beethoven!) in the corner of the room. By a pretty coincidence, Victor's film of *Dr Jekyll and Mr Hyde* is Gem Of The Day – courtesy, Michael Diamond and Sons – and the scene to which Victor opens his eyes is the one where Dr Jekyll, having prepared some medicine for his sick wife, accidentally picks up a phial containing poison and realizes only at the last minute, when he trips and slops a speck of it on the polished table, that he has almost made a fatal mistake. (The spot on the table turns the colour of blood.) Later, Jekyll has to steal some polish from the maid in order to expunge the obstinate stain. The scene where he steals it is deliberately ludicrous, as if to show to what absurd lengths a man must go (stealing what is, after all, his own property) once he is driven to conceal the evidence of his own humanity. Mr Hyde's naturalness gives the lie to his obsessive alter ego. One feels that one would like to see the entire film.

It is not yet quite time to return to California. We now find Victor England going silently into his wife's bedroom:

The woman was lying in the centre of the four-poster bed, the curtains loose on either side of her, fine curtains which shivered, catching cold from the draught as the door was opened. The mattress and the bed-covers rose to a crest where she lay. The bed was not unusually large, but she appeared almost out of reach. The frame supporting the pleated canopy was aflutter with gilded

wings and buttocks. The bedposts might have been candlesticks from some tastefully pillaged cathedral, their cupidinous angels seconded to sleep with a queen of lascivious chastity. The room was maintained at a given temperature. The building had its own generator (the candles at modern shrines being all electric) and its inhabitants would never be martyrs on any common grid.

Victor observes that even when his wife is asleep, if she is asleep, she seems to practise a look of unwrinkled irony which, when he first met her, it was his spring ambition to remove forever:

He believed that he could give her enough for her no longer to care so terribly about her beauty.

'I want to make you happy,' he said.

'Just that you want to is enough,' she told him.

He was proud when she said that, but he might have known; he might have known that a woman who was satisfied with a man's desire would never desire a man. She would love fingers that went no further than to adjust hems and eyes that gauged, in a held mirror, the effect of a single snip of top-pocketed scissors. She was touched by attentions that left her untouched. She promised Victor that the least thing he did would give her pleasure. How could he guess that soon it would be only the least things that she would suffer him to do? Once he wanted to give her everything; now he could only give her everything she wanted. Did not Delilah, shears in hand, whisper to the drowsy Samson that she preferred long-haired men?

Fleur is in some sense a cut flower. But she has a character of her own. For Victor England, she is not only exotic but dangerous. She is compared to a flower which a collector has nurtured for its colour but which also turns out to have more sinister potentialities: when he is looking for some deadly ingredient (for what purpose?) he discovers that his darlings' autumn contains the unregistered poison he requires. Even the pansy's face, in an unguarded moment, is badged with the skull and crossbones of the poison bottle.

Autumn is not a season which Fleur herself cares to contemplate. She remains protected, so far as possible, from anything which might endanger her subscription to summer. (A glossy magazine called *Été* is on a bedside table.) Fleur is equipped with a nervous system more sensitive to menace than the hairiest of the alarms fitted to her doors and windows. She is both jewel and setting; tender plant and tough frame.

She never rose until noon. She hoped that by leaving half the day on her plate she might diet her way to a reprieve from time's acid punctuality. She put out whatever reminded her of the caustic tick of reality. She had devised a way of both looking and not looking at things; to wince was to wrinkle. She was like one of those meticulous, ephemeral insects whom the mere shadow of a hostile presence was enough to ball into immobility. Her unflinching terror at the smallest natural shock had given her a reputation for fearlessness.

A writer who had to live in Switzerland (or Curaçao) wrote to another, who was still sufficiently unsuccessful to be able to go where he wanted, that Fleur had once carried an adored Siamese cat under her dress across a frontier, to save it from the penned penance of quarantine in unloving hands. The cat had clawed her breast, but she had been a Spartan with the pain; she had not revealed a whisker. The writer, who frequently entertained the Victor Englands in inventoried houses, did not know that Fleur had later discovered, after tests, that she was allergic to the cat's fur. In spite of the bond of its claws, she had it put down, in Mayfair. A charming man dabbed a fleck of poison on one shaved toe. Fleur's rash was better in the morning, though her eyes were swollen.

In the same way, she put down whatever might chap the smooth skin of her illusions. Whole areas of life were out of bounds. She flew over them, first class. Yet in the narrow field where she was mistress, not a blade stirred without her warrant. She had her own private line; none who knew its number ever had to give a name. Her room was murmurous with gentle assassinations. She was never out of earshot of delicious and refreshing secrets, like the Sultans of Granada who moved about in the common heat cooled by deliquescent banisters where they alone could dip unctuous fingers.

Fleur's bedroom was luminous with discarded print. She took many newspapers, but she contrived to select, with sharp squeamishness, what she would or would not see of their contents. She was never without scissors. A rabble of rejected newsprint, coarse with floods, flames and famine, littered the floor and stirred about Victor England's feet: Fleur retained only those fillets of social news which might quicken her wit or instruct her malice. Her pretty filleting made her floor an ossuary of unwanted truth from which, had any historian cared to boil it up, a stock of human misery might soon have been brewed.

As Victor England begins to undress, his foot becomes entangled in a section of a newspaper in which his wife has cut a hole just his size. He finds himself hopping around the room, ginned and bitter in a comedy of the kind no one makes any more. He dreads overbalancing and upsetting the potted promises on Fleur's cosmetic tray. He is especially fearful of falling on the one woman on whom the world has licensed him to fall. At last he manages to tear off the paper crab attached to his ankle and stumbles, hobbled by freedom, into the bathroom.

It is walled with mirrors. He sees himself placarded in every available space, like the wanted man he has always wanted to be. When he removes the last of his clothes, he is reminded, as if by the pointed red notice of a lapsed policy, that he is a man.

The winking, monocular mole nestling in the curly grass of his groin raised its head, a sleeper stirring without opening an eye. He glanced up and saw Drakos looking down at him from above the bath. Had the young genius found a tiny undetected window from which to spy on him? What calculated coincidence made Fleur stick this particular face over the draughty vent that extracted expensive, expended air from the room?

Drakos's frowning expression, Croesus creased, quickened Victor England to gaiety. He danced. Had Drakos been there in the flesh, he must have believed that Victor had seen some growing grosses. The room was small, but there seemed now to be accessible to him all the vaulted infinities which William had archly contrived in the icy walls. Victor was actually humming 'Unless It's Love' and conducting the orchestra and chorus with his water-pick, when the dove-grey telephone cooed and the operator hatched 'California'.

'Unless It's Love (Throw it away/Blow it away/Like an Old, Old Glove)' is the theme song of Victor England's greatest success and it turns out that he is less fond of it than his capering in the bathroom suggests:

There was a party one summer at the London house of a writer-producer opposed to all wars that failed to take money at the box-office. The old crowd from the Coast were out to piss on the memory of the rich-hunting Senator whose witch-hunting accusations had made them the most overdone underdogs in history. Victor had not wanted to go. He called by only because he was promised that somebody he hadn't seen for ages and never wanted to see again had threatened to drop in. What kind of a crosspatch wouldn't go a couple of miles to cut an old friend?

34

There was a band. As he came into the room, they began to play 'Unless It's Love'. It was a salute he could not return. He wanted to run someplace and hide.

He later walks home across Hyde Park, where Dr Jekyll walked the dog. His distant success hounds Victor England; he cannot shake its gold-studded collar. He thinks of 'Unless It's Love' as his chubby and now teenage baby, bursting the seams of a satin sailor-suit, its hairy arms bulging with bald toys. Early success is the mark of Cain; on the other hand, who remembers Abel?

Victor wakes up in the suite. He sees that the television is switched on (it is at this very moment that Dr Jekyll does his slow burn) and immediately extinguishes it with the crackle of a nylon sweater coming off. He presses the button and opens the drapes once more.

He had once been on a cruise and fell asleep in his cabin. On waking, he felt as he did now. When he looked out of his window – anyone could have a port-hole, he had a starboard window – he observed that the ship had heaved to. Passengers and crew were pendulous in the lifeboats. The California sky and the baffled sound of the traffic gushing in the street below brought back to him that moment of suspended time. Had he slept twenty-four hours or a few minutes? Was he a day older or was he not?

He struggles to his feet, wrestling thinness, fighting off the sensation of being two-dimensional. Has his third dimension been mis-routed in the missing bag, or is it to be expected that, back in movie-land, he should have this feeling of being a court card in a suit that isn't trumps? (Suit suggests suitcase; not to be trumps is not yet to have clinched the contract: all Victor's anxieties are encapsuled here.) We may also recall that the girl in the lobby was watching for her date – if that was what she was watching for – in a silver screen. One cannot

35

be a king or even a knave – both of them court cards – in the film capital without consenting to a loss of dimension.

The calling carbuncle, inflamed vocative, is glowing on the telephone at the bedside. Victor calls down for the message. The girl reads him a list, with all the intimacy typical of a total stranger, and he lies on the bed, allowing the names to form a patchwork quilt over him:

He was cosy with re-issued memories. Not all of them were rosy, but they had the quality unique to long and golden careers. He was lapped in reminding luxury. If there were greys and blues, they were great greys and beautiful blues. Even where there were undoubted stains, it was still undoubted vicuna they had stained.

It is not until the end of the rôle-call that the girl says, 'Oh and a man came by with your bag.' Victor makes no exclamation of either relief or pleasure.

'Was there something valuable in it?' the girl asked.
'I guess I'll find out,' Victor said. 'What else have you got?'
'That makes you just about clear, Mr England. Have a nice day now.'
The red light went out. He was left with a strange sound. It could have been the machinery of a new industry, a sound as regular and as inhuman as a heart-beat. Victor frowned. He was suspicious, as suspicious as he was of his own body, which for him resembled one of those pieces of patent equipment that could never be bought outright: no matter what you offered or how long they stood in your office, they always belonged to the company that leased them. When things went wrong, specialists came and ran tests. When a machine stopped, it was taken away. Victor England regarded his body as an unreliable gadget, on which he had spent a lot of money. He hunted the new sound like a symptom.

*

He opens the door of the suite and goes out into the yellow corridor. He tries to look out of the windows, as if the noise might be a sort of light and possess a visible source, but they are too high for him to be able to see anything but the glistening forehead of his own efforts. The sound stops. He is trembling. He puts his hand on his heart (as he did in the Rolls), as if it might have been stolen. In a moment we shall meet a crucial character in Victor England's life. But first there is a digression.

As he walks along the primrose path, he realizes that he is carrying the heavy gold key to his suite. It is attached to a weighty star like lawmen wore in the days when it proved they were good. He hesitates and then puts it in his delicate pocket. His suit is the work of a London tailor with the skill to make a dwarf tower over his contemporaries. He is said to have made a fat producer so slim that he tried to leave the shop without opening the plate-glass door and had to have fifteen additional stitches, in his forearm. (A wry writer, hearing the story, remarks, 'If they're Bob's stitches, they'll burst open on him next time the bastard lifts his arm to blow his own trumpet.') The tailor's workmanship is less perfect than his eye. His trousers haven't always proved too clever: one pair split on an actor during night shooting, 'and he was only bending down to pick up a cue'. On another occasion, Victor England himself left a sleeve in an actress's hungry hands. 'She got the job.' Victor has told himself several times that he cannot risk another hammy humiliation, but Bob, the sew-and-sew, has some curious hold on him:

Sometimes, between films, when his last thriller was frightening audiences in places too dangerous to visit and his next had scared even the Studio that was due to finance it, he would leave his deductible office and walk around the West End toy-shops looking for something he didn't need. As the bereaved return to places and people who have remained ignorant of their loss, so Victor would revisit dealers and antiquarians whose

business it is to provide old frames for new money and to whom he had once gone to furnish Fleur's happiness. He could draw comfort from their cheerful anachronisms. The past is a country to which the rich always dream of emigrating. Its customs service is marked by the dated deference required of those who serve princes, purists and pederasts.

When Victor England had acquired, after haggling with men who never haggled, one or two articles he did not really want to buy (from people who, of course, did not really want to sell them), he would arrive, often with derelict's rain on his velvet lapels, at Bob Pound's premises. The tailor might have been a relative to whom each visit was an instalment towards the payment of some shapeless, unaccountable debt. While the rain lowered scalloped blinds over the satin glass of the double windows, Victor would play the sulky Sultan on the hexagonal calfskin ottoman in the centre of the showy showroom.

'Hullo, Bobbie. How's Bobbie?'

'Not so bad. Yourself?'

'Tired.'

'What've you been doing then?'

'Waiting. Thinking. Nothing.'

'What you been buying?'

'Presents.'

'How's the missus?'

'She's at home,' Victor England said.

'How's about a coffee?'

The double-breasted girl went for coffee, frowning at the rain, and the two men sat in the planned gloom. The tailor was slim but his features were large and uneven: his eyes were ledged with bunions of flesh; his nose was yoked between yellow cheeks. Since he could not clothe his face, it alone had no style.

'Busy, Bob?'

'Busy!'

The shop, for all its egregious emptiness, bore out the

bored boast. If no customers were visible, the staff – their mouths pinned silent – worked like a brigade of chefs hot to satisfy a restaurant hungry with demanding ghosts.

'So like when are we going to get a chance to do something for you?'

'I'll tell you something I could use, Bobbie, a suit for California.'

'No problem. I can do that for you. One or three? For when would this be?'

'I'm going in ten days. One. Maybe sooner, if – '

'What you going for? Something big?'

'I'd like it to last a full week, Bobbie, this time, could it?'

'That's what you need,' Bob Pound said. 'Something really big again. The ultimate.'

'That's what they want,' Victor England said.

'I can have something for you to try by the weekend. Shall we look at some books?'

'No detachable sleeves,' Victor England said. 'O.K.?'

'They're extra,' Bob Pound said.

'Bobbie.'

'Vicky, did I ever let you down? The weekend.'

Victor England, not for the first time, had to go back to the office and get the girl to telephone another tailor, on whom he had called earlier in the day, and tell him that he had been thinking again.

What hold does Bob Pound have over Victor who hates, as we know, to be called Vicky? All that is ever clearly stated is that Bob once made Victor England a confession. Since then, Victor has been reluctant to lose touch with him; he behaves, in other words, as though the confession had been his rather than the tailor's. What has Bobbie told him that Victor would prefer not to have come out? Whatever it is, it somehow resembles the detachable sleeve (which also came out) and which remains more of a reproach to Victor than to Pound.

*

While the new suit is being cut, Victor attends a wedding in the apartment of Madame Romano. Because he has had to go to a fitting, he wears one of the suits Bob Pound has made for him in the past. Madame Romano is a renowned artist and hostess:

She was renowned as an artist among hostesses and as a hostess among artists. If she had not been born in the purple, she was determined to die in it, though not yet.

'Victor England!' she cried.

'Madame!' said Victor.

'How is he?'

'He's fine. How's she?'

'Never better. I had my check-up last week. I've got the lungs of a young girl.'

'How does she feel about that?'

She slapped him lightly with her fan. 'What a shame Fleur couldn't come. Mr Fu is doing his noodles.'

'It's her busy time in the border,' Victor said.

'*Elle adore la nature, n'est-ce pas?*' said Madame Romano, who was once a Frenchwoman, once a Russian and always an American. 'Victor, I must go and tend the Canon. He's a bundle of nerves. It's his first Jewish wedding.'

The unhappy couple are Americans, a fugitive banker and his pursuing mistress. The girl is blonde as a bone and is said to have had substantial alimony while still a virgin. The bridegroom's name is Barry Gold. He has the amiable gentility of one who has given up being Jewish as others give up smoking. He has caught it in time; all traces of circumcision have vanished from his face. The girl's maiden name is Bacon.

The ceremony is to be held in Madame Romano's drawling-room and there is to be a bedding breakfast afterwards. Madame's voice is heard telling people how much the young couple want to settle in England. 'They love London,' she keeps saying, as if to establish that there is something they love, even if it isn't each other. The ceremony is to be conducted by a consulting clergyman in a claret caddy. He emerges at last ill-humoured from behind a naughty screen, on which nymphs and shepherds are coming away in a perversion of pastoral. Garbed in his clerical choler and white doily, he looks, says a guest, like the first syllable in a charade. 'And I think I've guessed the word.'

Madame's drawling-room is stiff with her own work. There are enough screens to hide a thousand little milliners. The room is crammed with people, coming and going, mostly journalists leaning against their next column, and it is constantly being replenished by new arrivals, like a bucket that can take so much only because it leaks.

The clergyman is now seen to be dissatisfied with the stool on which the couple are to kneel. Then just as everyone appears ready for the altarcations to begin, there is a problem about identifying East. Some screens have to be moved. These hitches in the hitching remind Victor of how late it is getting and of how hungry he is. He remarks to his neighbour that he can't wait for this great lunch they are slated to have.

Victor's neighbour took a packet of fruit pastilles from his high pocket and, with his fingernail, detached the top one (purple as an art director's night) and offered it to Victor. Victor shook his head.

'I'll stick out for the noodles.'

'Noodles,' the man said. He was tall and *triste* and wore remarkable blue shoes. Was he suffering from some rare inflammation of the toes? Had he recently disembarked from a yacht? Or did he, quite simply, have round feet? He had round blue shoes, that was certain, of a gentle material. His name, he told Victor with a sigh that reminded him of how few people have a say in their own names, was Bradley Biddle.

During the service, Bradley Biddle searched the cylinder for another purple; the small change of unspent orange, red and green discs he thrust into his high pocket, amid the peppermint spots of a Sulka handkerchief that did not match his tie. 'So American, don't you think?' he said.

'What's that?' asked Victor.

'Having a religious ceremony for adultery.'

The clergyman announced that he had a few private words for the bride and groom alone. The guests pressed forward so as not to miss any of them. Was it smoke or emotion that watered their eyes? The atmosphere had certainly thickened. Madame Romano dodged behind one of her own nymphatic screens and slid from the room, unobtrusive as a battleship down a slipway. Dabbing her eyes with a dry handkerchief, she plunged in the direction of a basinful of unscripted troubles.

'What price noodles now?' Bradley Biddle said, offering a blue chip of candy. 'Could be the right thing at the right time.'

'I still believe in Mr Fu,' said Victor.

'What happens if the Messiah doesn't show? And are you sure you really want to wait till the third day?'

The large figure of Madame Romano was back, standing in tiers in the double doorway, near a rogues' gallery of signed photographs in which nearly every example of framed fame had been caught with the jewellery still about her. Royal sincerity was scribbled at the bottom.

The newly minted Golds now dropped to their knees on a long, low stool, a dachshund among furniture, closed their eyes and began to hope. Trenchant tears were of coursing down Madame Romano's cheeks. A young girl, who had come to the wedding in the hope of being introduced to her father, gushed up to her hostess and began to kiss her. Madame Romano pushed her away like a second helping.

'Mr Fooey,' Bradley Biddle said. 'Believe me. I know.'

'Dear, dear friends, everybody,' Madame Romano said. 'Please – '

'Wise up,' Bradley Biddle said. 'Have one before they go through the roof.'

'Something so utterly, utterly terrible has happened – something totally and completely unforeseen – my beloved Mr Fu – '

'Give me one of those things,' Victor England said.

'My beloved Mr Fu, the light of my life, my irreplaceable Mr Fu – you all know how I love him, how I depend on him – Mr Fu has met with an accident.'

'Oh darling,' said a Countess whose husband took title and income from a conjunction of inaccessible places, 'what is it, what's happened?' She flung all her arms round Madame Romano. 'Not our divine Mr Fu!'

'Noodles under the bridge,' Bradley Biddle said.

'There is some food in the small dining-room,' Madame Romano said, discountenanced, 'but I'm afraid it's far, far from what I had hoped to give you. Oh Barry dear and Kelly (née Bacon), do you think you can ever forgive me?'

'Fudgy, dear dear Fudgy, anything! Only what happened?'

'Mr Fu, who never to this day has done me anything but proud, left two turkeys on silver platters in the oven. You know how he does turkey. He put them in in plenty of time but, well, what with the Reverend's wonderful address, which I shall never, *never* forget – he must've been taken ill. I went in just a minute ago and there's – there's nothing at all in the kitchen except two black birds and a pool – a pool of my best Georgian silver.' Madame Romano began to melt in sympathy. 'My Paul de Lamerie!'

'Ever see hall-marked lino?' Bradley Biddle said.

'Oh Fudgy, no! But what about Mr Fu? What's happened to him?'

'I earnestly trust he's gone to commit hara-kiri.'

'I didn't know Chinamen could.'

'Pekin-style,' Bradley Biddle said.

'We do at least have some salad in the back dining-room, but – '

'To think I got a sitter for my rabbit,' Biddle said.

'Oh and your glasses, bring your glasses.'

There is a long, audible hush. They might just have entered a tunnel in the middle of a scenic railway. Bradley Biddle nudges Victor in the ribs. Victor lifts his knee in instinctive self-protection and there is the unmistakable sound of freshly wounded trousers. The consequence of his pants bursting into tears is that Victor England now feels compelled to stay at the Romano apartment at least as long as Bradley Biddle, paying rent for the rent. The only way to silence gossip is to stay with it. Biddle will not be able to talk about his comic cuts as long as Victor, remembering Byron's example, does not depart too soon and leave his reputation behind. The embarrassment occasioned by his thin elegance undoubtedly betokens something more fundamental. Victor England may not enjoy, or even be part of, London society, yet his uneasy aloofness prevents him, if absurdly (as the trousers unmetaphorically prove), from turning his back on it. He does not care to advertise the disdain which his breached breeches could so obviously symbolize. We are wedded to institutions by the sacrament of hypocrisy. Who can betray what he does not love?

Victor's mishap is doubly comic because:

... half the room would have liked nothing better than to see the other half embarrassed: Victor England's bare ass could have ridden a palm-strewn path between them, he himself mounted on it like a clever actor who rides undaunted the spirited beast he holds between his own legs.

The reference here, one assumes, is to actors who appear to be mounted, when in reality they are riding a hobby-horse that looks like an independent mount. Every dangerous twitch of the animal which they control so coolly is in fact self-induced. In addition, surely, we have another reminder of the Jekyll-and-Hyde dyad, and of that ambidexterity which means that Victor England requires two signatures of Victor England before he is completely committed: both of them, of course, his own.

During the lettuce, Victor catches sight of someone he takes to be Fleur coming into the room. (It proves to be a baulked Balkan Princess.) Hoping to hide unseamly trousers from his wife, he backs against a bucolic screen, aiming to appear like a Vatican sculpture, unbuttocked in its niche.

At last Bradley Biddle drains his neighbours' pooled Puligny and makes round tracks across the carpet. The private interiors of the flats contrast with the cold public corridors and staircases. ('Flats' is, of course, also the name given to the sections of scenery bolted together to make stage settings.) The landings and stairs are as practical as prisons, like those backstage areas screened from the limelight. The tenants here, no less than those in Victor England's own terrace, are sentenced to luxury for life, banged up in bang-up style, on condition that they stay in their places.

Victor now need no longer give Bradley Biddle the heavy attention due to a man who knows too much. All through the green lunch, Victor has stood polite sentry on Bradley Biddle's tongue so that he shall not have the chance to make him sound like a bum.

Now they wait at the kerb, with nothing in common but a desire for taxis.

'Not much of a year for lettuce, was it?' Biddle said.

'I couldn't help feeling sorry for her though,' Victor said, when a taxi was already swimming in towards him. 'She was even more embarrassed than I was. Damned pants!'

'What happened to her pants?' Biddle said.

Victor England said, 'Skip it, Biddle. I still have my sentimental side, I guess. Madame reduced to giving her guests lettuce for lunch! Didn't you feel a little bit sorry for her?'

'Nuts,' Bradley Biddle said. 'She never gives people anything *but* lettuce. She gives Royals lettuce. They come

see a blue movie – lettuce. She never gives anybody anything else.'

'Come on, Mr Fu's turkey gets better write-ups than I
do. Better than my turkeys do anyway. It's famous, for
Godsakes.'

'It ought to be famous. It's lived longer than Harry
Shap's tortoise. Harry Shap's tortoise is one hundred and
fifteen, going on one hundred and sixteen. I'll tell you
something, England. Mr Fu doesn't exist. Madame hires
two black turkeys every time she gives one of these
gangbangs of hers. Two black turkeys, a thermos of hot
silver and a can of fresh tears from the Malvern hills.'

'You sound like you've known her a long time,' Victor
England said, holding the taxi into the edge of the stream
by its doorhandle.

'Mother?' Bradley Biddle said. 'It's been a few years.
She's rubbed a soft spot in my heart. Or is it a blister?
Noodle oo, England. Oh and thanks for the cab.' Which
he proceeded to take, giving the address of a torture
chamber where he had a charge-account, before Victor
could even forget to open the door for him. 'I hope
we meet again,' Biddle leaned out to say. '*The funeral
maybe?*'

Victor flags futilely for another cab, dreaming of destinations,
and then walks round to see Bob Pound. The tailor is unembarrassed at Victor's accident. All he does is nod and smile;
the unscheduled aperture might as well be an extra amenity.
Victor almost apologizes for even mentioning his misfortune
and Bob does him something of a favour in repairing it. While
his trousers are given stitches, the revered project for a
California suit is brought out for another fitting.

The suit promised, as always, to be perfect. An under-
lining underling stood by to chalk up the smallest crease
of displeasure or to pin it into a smile. This prophylactic
acupuncture was more painful to Victor than a misfit.
They pressed him to express his smallest doubts. How

could he say that his doubts were large? He was not even convinced that the cloth was the same as he had chosen from Bob's spineless books. It felt to have the same lack of body as the pinstripe which had just split along its dotted line. Why, he wondered, was Bob's material always so unsuitable? It was as if the client were a Roman general in a triumph, saddled with a worsted slave at his back to remind him, with tendentious creaks and groans, of the perils of the purple.

Victor England buys the paraphernalia of success because nobody has ever offered him anything else. We begin to understand why he has made so many films which he has at first wanted to refuse. He is rich because no one has really made a pitch for penury. His very impatience with the trappings of wealth has allowed him to be trapped by them:

Where a man might hesitate to buy one of something he had always wanted, Victor would order four or five of what he could not be bothered to wonder whether he wanted or not. He evaded salesmanship by yielding to it. Poverty of decisive desire made him a man of property. Since he could not choose, he had everything.

This is proved when he gets back to his office. Workmen are installing a complicated hi-fi system. The chief salesman is there to show him some unlikely additional refinement. Victor agrees to have it before Mr Aplin has even begun his apologies for the price and temperament of the equipment. The man goes away, wondering where he went wrong, even though he has secured the order: Victor fails to give him the satisfaction of having overcome his resistance. He acquires goods as libertines do bastards: by an insatiable lack of precaution.

When his priced possessions fail to work properly (the hi-fi system does not go wrong only because it is never used), he simply buys new ones, even if the old are under guarantee. As a result, he scarcely has room for the many versions he has of the same defective luxury. We shall soon see what part women play in the sumptuous sum of his life. After every divorce, when he thinks that he will be able to start again from the beginning, he finds that his new house is already full of all the luxuries which furnished his previous nightmares, except a wife; and even there a new one is usually being cut free from her previous entanglements with a pair of Midas's own scissors. Victor's dream of a simple life is having just one of everything, including wives. The comedy of wealth is that the effort to reduce everything to essentials means only that more and more things become essential. Victor England's course may be followed through life like that of an ocean liner, by the four-lane highway of dumped trash that he trails behind him. His ex-wives scream like gulls.

There follows an account of Victor England's first Hollywood romance. It starts with the memory of a purchase:

Once, in a border town, Victor England bought a girl a mink coat. He was young. He had just received his first bonus. Someone, somewhere, was afraid of losing him. He had dreamed for many years, though he had not yet lived for many, of the day when he would buy a girl a mink coat. Her name turned out to be Billie-Mae Lafayette. She was a platinum blonde with dimples and a very white skin and a black patent-leather pocketbook. He fell in love with her when he saw her frowning at a menu in a downtown diner. She put him in mind of a pretty pig trying to read the top line on an oculist's chart. He was enchanted. She said she wanted to be in the movies, that was why she'd come West, and he gave her a part in the chorus. The leading man put fourteen straight custard pies in her puss before they got the key light right. When the movie was over and the legal people were drawing up a personalized calendar of his future with the Studio, he told the girl to pack her things, they were going on a vacation.

'Says who?' said the girl, who did not yet show any signs of having a purse.

'Have you ever felt fur?' the young Victor asked. Her

puckered reluctance delighted him. The milky skin was uncurdled by kisses. 'Have you ever experienced the feel of fur? I want you to have that experience for the first time, with me. Will you, Billie-Mae?'

'Victor England,' she said, 'you're going to be famous. You're going to make it. I can feel it.'

'You're going to feel it,' he said. 'You bet you are. Any minute now.'

'And how about me? What's going to happen to me?'

'You want a contract?'

'Oh Vicky,' she said, 'I didn't want to say it. I wanted to save it. I swore I was going to, but I have to: I love you, Vicky. I loved you from the first minute.'

'I love you too, Billie-Mae. Now show me your dimples.'

She smiled and did auditions with her eyes. She gave him all the angles. He loved her. He truly did. He loved the purity of her exultation. He loved her unspoiled mercenary rapture. She made success worthwhile.

He took her in his Dodge coupé down to the beach and bruised her whiteness with kisses. He ate her lipstick sandwiches while she smiled and smiled and did things to his face with her lashes. They sat there all day until the red sun went down to scorch the filleted sea.

He and Billie-Mae were not yet lovers (he had seen none of her darker dimples) when they set out for the border. He bought a package of rubber hopes and took them with his tooth things. He drove down to collect her from The Towers, where she roomed. He was happy. When he reached to kiss her, she came as smoothly to his lips as a cliché. 'Hullo, baby.'

'My Vicky,' she said. 'We're really going places, you and me!'

What was commandingly beautiful to him was that she wanted everything, without exception, that he could give her. Why should he distinguish between boundless love and boundless hunger? Had he not loved her first with a menu in her hand? They drove past a theatre where *So This Is Love* was showing. She leaned over and whispered in his ear. 'Directed by Victor England.' He glanced at her adoration and was satisfied. She was the first girl he had had who did not love him only for himself. Billie-Mae was his dream: fresh, adoring, untouched and for sale.

'You and I are going to the moon,' he said, 'in June.'

Before driving north in his Buick (he has traded in the Dodge), Victor goes to see his new agent, Rick Andrews. Rick says he'd like a ride in the new car and drives with them to the City Limits. Andrews is busy wrapping up the contract with the Studio and talks all the way about options, overage and Oscars. He does not address one word to Billie-Mae. When he says goodbye to Victor before walking back to where his Albino assistant has parked the follow-up car, he says only, 'Enjoy yourself': singular proof that the girl is not his client. Once they are alone, Victor puts his arms around Billie-Mae and promises always to take care of her. Now that he has Andrews's word that she doesn't mean a thing (he couldn't even spare a plural for her), he can be both affectionate and reassuring. It is a parody of a run-away wedding. The Best Man (as Rex Keyes has described Andrews) is an agent whose only concern is that Victor doesn't become seriously involved.

Victor knew that if he returned by himself, Andrews would never ask what had become of the body. Victor recognized him for a callous and single-minded bastard. He was sure they would have a long and happy association.

And he is right. In later years, however, Andrews learns how to be courtly. He never forgets to send flowers to Victor's wife, whoever she may be, on her birthday and on anniversaries (he knows that there can never be too few birthdays or too many anniversaries) and to admire her – 'Jesus, younger than ever!' – at barbed barbecues on Maliboob beach.

*

Victor England and Billie-Mae go to the best fur shop in the first town they come to over the border. When she sees that she is really going to get what he has promised, the simple, greedy child is overwhelmed:

He had to support her into the shop, like a princess led politically to the scaffold or to the marriage bed. She looked at him with her lovely, condemned eyes.

'No, Vicky,' she said, 'you can't. I won't let you. You're going to spoil me. They're so *precious*.'

'Precious, if I can't spoil you, why are we here?'

They wrestled for a moment out there in the open, on the boardwalk. No one on the whole North American continent, he whispered to her, would ever rescue a girl forced to such a consummation. He was licensed for ever to force a furry fate on females. He tricked her through the narrow door and set her down in front of her hunted heaven.

Victor, like Brute Andrews later, is mercilessly magnanimous. He insists that Greta, the English proprietress, parade all her stock. Corsets creaking with connivance, she displays pelt after pelt, until the showroom resembles a bloodless butcher-shop. The girl, her appetite revived, picks over the corpseless slaughter with a coroner's courtesy. It is worth remarking that earlier, on the car radio they twiddle from station to station, enjoying the opportunity for catty cutting, they have heard the news (quickly censored because 'We said we were going to have fun') that fighting has started in some unpronounceable place for some unbelievable reason. Greta says that she is afraid that England is going to be tricked into war again and we realize that the programme that they have hurriedly hurdled is one that announces the Polish campaign. In a few days world war is about to begin, but who cares? The girl plumps for a mink, descending at last from the mountain of paraded possibilities with a conclusive, sighing leap. Victor has no difficulty understanding Billie-Mae's look of cheated victory as she examines her rich shawl. No choice can be untainted by regret: one might always have chosen better, or at least differently.

'You're never going to be sorry,' Greta said.

'Never, are we, Vicky?' the girl said.

Greta winked at Victor England and buried the exposed stock. Victor was reminded of the Madame at the cat-house where Andrews took him to celebrate the end of shooting. She had hustled the unselected girls out of the chandeliered parlour, leaving Victor with one called Barbara. She gave him everything except the pleasure of having had someone else.

Billie-Mae stares at herself, then turns and walks away, looking back at her own image in the hope of jealous eyes. At last she seems convinced:

'Oh Vicky,' the girl said. 'I never knew anything could be so beautiful.' She was looking at herself full face again, motherandchild, and humming the theme from the movie. Her shoulders lifted towards each other and made an accordion of her body: she was one delicious squeeze-box in her own eyes. It needed but the gentlest pressure to bruise music from her. Victor ignored the hand she now held out to him. He could see there for the playing, but preferred to save and savour, that organ note – *oh!* – of slaked surrender which he had yet to hear from a girl.

'We'll take it,' Victor England said.

'Oh wouldn't she like it monogrammed?' Greta said, in her learned American. 'I just know she would, wouldn't you?'

'B.M.L.,' the girl said. 'Only can you do it like right away? I hate to be without it.'

'Could you call back in a couple of hours?' Greta asked Victor England. 'I shall require the services of a specialist needlewoman; I don't have those particular letters made up right now.'

'I can always change my name,' Billie-Mae said. 'Who knows? I may have to anyway, for my career. Isn't that right, Vicky?'

'I'll just bet you folks can find something to do for a couple of hours,' Greta said.

The girl was standing in a valley of glass. She reflected with her twins, framed in silver trenches either side of her. Only when they had given their bright assent did she say, 'I guess so. I'd like the dignified letters, for the monogram. English-style. Royal Georgian.'

'That'll be very tasteful. Rely on me, my dear. I wouldn't allow anything else.'

'What're you doing?' the girl said. 'I'm not taking it off. No, ma'am, not me. Not after all this.'

'Just while the needlewoman does the necessary. It has to be stitched right into the lining.'

'I want to wear it for ever,' the girl said.

'Two hours! Then you can wear it for the rest of your life.'

'Oh nuts,' the girl said. 'Excuse me, but can I use your bathroom? This thing has got me all excited. I have to tinkle.'

Victor England was left alone with the creaking Englishwoman for whom, he was forced to decide, he had conceived a sudden desire. What was the stiff attraction of this corseted lady as she put skins back in their places? When Billie-Mae returned, she stood in the mouth of the shop and gaped at the blank space between Victor and Greta. Could she have spotted the hard evidence of their unacted act?

They go to a movie to pass the two hours. At first, Victor England makes no amorous move. The girl has to insinuate her fingers in Victor's, a woman parking, and gives a wriggle of relief because he does not withdraw. The movie (they have come in more than half-way through) seems an unlikely one for a provincial theatre. Its setting and characters appear to be of a sophisticated order, with a screenplay by authors who insist on having their credit in cash. In one of the climactic scenes, the hero, dressed in a blazer and white flannels, is sitting on the deck of an ocean liner. A smart woman (designed by Molly New according to Billie-Mae) comes along the deck and stops near where he is watching an ingénue and her husband playing pingpong. The following dialogue takes place:

WOMAN: Planning to ruin another life?

MAN: All I'm planning is to challenge the winner. I sincerely trust that that will entail ruining nothing more than the crease in my flannels. If that. His backhand looks decidedly dicky.

WOMAN: You're the wickedest man in the world and I don't care who knows it.

MAN: Well, I do, so kindly keep your voice down or –

WOMAN: I shall shout if I want to.

MAN: – I shall be deluged with demands to prove it.

WOMAN: You said you loved me once.

MAN (*complacently*): Once is usually enough.

WOMAN: I would have given my life for you.

MAN: I'm sorry to say that that has never been my idea of a fair exchange.

WOMAN: Do you know why I'm on this ship crossing the Atlantic like this?

MAN: Presumably for the same reason I am. It's too far to swim.

WOMAN: How can you be so cruel when we could be so happy together. Come back to me, my darling. You'd never have to be alone again. Never. Think of it.

MAN: I've thought.

WOMAN: What will you do when you're old and grey and nobody wants you any more?

MAN: Break down and sob uncontrollably.

WOMAN: You think it's chance that's brought us together? It isn't. I've planned this moment for years. Do you know what this is?

She has pulled a gun from her reticule.

MAN: It looks dangerously like melodrama to me. I
suggest you put it away at once.
WOMAN: No jury in the world would convict me.
MAN: No jury in the world is likely to get the chance.
You're almost certain to miss. Righteous indignation has a
notoriously unsteady hand.
WOMAN: Don't you realize? I'm offering you everything
a woman can offer a man.
MAN: Of course I realize. That's exactly what makes this
whole scene so insufferably distasteful.

Billie-Mae watches the film with glistening eyes, her finger-
nails biting Victor's wrist. At the man's last remark, she turns
to him and whispers fiercely, 'I *hate* him.' Victor who has
suffered the nip of her nails with unsmiling indifference turns
to her and kisses her passionately on the mouth. The rest of
the show goes by like a dream.

'Come on,' he said at last, 'let's go see if it's ready.'

'It feels ready,' she dared to say, bold beyond the code.

'Don't do that,' he said. Touched, he twisted from her.
She followed him with high, tottering steps, up the steep
aisle. She caught him as he turned to see next week.

'Vicky, it isn't the coat is it?'

'What isn't the coat?'

'You're not sorry about the coat, are you?'

'Why, don't you want it? It already has your monogram on it.'

'I love you, Vicky,' she said, in the unsteady light of
a once-in-every-decade-there-comes-a-motion-picture
promise from an executive who swivelled into shot like
a goosed gander. 'I don't care if I never have anything
from you my whole life long.'

'It's yours,' Victor England said, going through the
swing doors past the popcorn.

'Don't think I don't want it, Vicky,' she said, wincing
at the sunshine, 'because I do, I do. Only we haven't
paid for it – '

'Are you making a contribution?' Victor England said.

'If you have any kind of second thoughts, *any* kind of second thoughts, all we have to do is run and get right straight back into that beautiful Buick and blow town. I mean it. I'll never hold it against you, never. Swear.'

'Then I'll hold it against you,' Victor England said, under a forthcoming attraction. 'You funny little piggy you!'

The strength, or weakness, of this exchange is that it can be read in several ways. Victor and Billie-Mae have just been to a sentimental movie; it is plausible that they should take their tone from it. Their conversation can, on a genial reading, be larded with girlish smiles and handsome reassurances, affectionate moues and winning winks. Surely the girl wants the fur coat; surely Victor wants her to have it. But what of the following?

... years later, cypher-breaking critics would sigh for the mythopoeic subtleties in what Victor and Billie-Mae had watched like sand running through a two-hour glass. The underrated over-eighty director, no longer alcoholically anomalous, would sit on the platform at festivals and sip ominous water while questioning his questioners.

This very film is, we shall find, the one which Peter Drakos later imitates and in which his girl stars. (When he is challenged about some jokes he has lifted, Drakos says, 'Of course I deserve solo credit. Is it my fault if they made the remake first?') Victor England's sensation, at the screening, of 'second-time around' is no illusion. 'In this town,' he remarks on another occasion, 'the unique is what hasn't happened in ten years.' Is this not a direct echo of the 'once-in-a-decade' sales-line in the trailer at the Royalty Theatre?

The suggestion that there are hidden shallows in the commonplace movie alerts us to the possibility that the scene between Victor and the girl is also susceptible to subtler soundings. Is not the girl perhaps right when she guesses that Victor is angry? If so, she proceeds to annoy him further by her placatory offer to renounce the coat. She appears unaware of the polite rage this occasions. When she says, 'I love you,' it may be that the emphasis falls on 'you' (as opposed to the coat): she fears that he has seen through her and suspects her of mercenary mercies. His response is, 'It's yours.' He would prefer her to want the coat. Only if he can be sure that her attitude is a demand, not a promise, is he willing to meet the bill. He recovers his good humour when (in the tradition of boy-mates-girl comedy) she feeds him the opportunity for the last word: 'Then I'll hold it against you.'

Now comes a cut – and there, indeed, he is: holding the cut coat against her. This apt allusion to the brisk, punning style of motion picture narration leads the reader to gloss over the more savage aspect of Victor's promise: holding things against women is, in one way *and* another, his defining characteristic.

Can one not argue that for all the years and all the lies which separate them, Billie-Mae and Fleur, lying ingeniously inert in the four-poster bed in the London house, are somehow sisters under the skin, or the fur? The London house is, remember, said to resemble a slice of flat wedding-cake and when they first take the fur from Greta's shop, we hear that it is folded into a cake-box – one of those creased cardboard contraptions which can be broken out from two dimensions into three. The name and coat of arms (both fanciful) of the shop are printed on the lid, armorially bracketed between a trapper and a tripper. Greta has folded the coat so expertly that the box can be dangled on a single finger: suddenly all that coat is no heavier than puff pastry.

They are back at the hotel:

'Guess what,' the girl said, 'she didn't even charge us for the needlewoman. Wasn't that dear of her? Oh Vicky, she must've guessed, mustn't she, about us?'

   'Guessed what?' Victor England said.

'About us,' the girl said. 'Oh Vicky, I'm so excited. I'm so *excited*. I feel like a kid. I don't know what to do.'

She drew down the shades and kicked off her shoes. She smiled over her shoulder and lifted a foot. Pretty soon she had thrown off every last stitch, dancing herself into white nudity – oh what a surprise when she showed him *her* fur! – to the tidal gush of the fretwork radio between the beds.

'Think I should have dyed this too?' she wanted to know.

Victor England was sitting in a pants-polished tub chair below the triple windows. The girl turned in front of him, with the badge of black hair curly as a French beard below her flat tummy. She did a kneesy to the left and a kneesy to the right and pushed back the hair from her smooth forehead. 'Well, Monsieur, do I pass?'

'You're cast,' Victor England said.

She stuck out nicely and kissed him on the top of his nose, arms extended backwards, all set for a dive into some musical pool. 'Am I pretty?'

'Come here,' he said.

'Am I pretty, Vicky? Now you've seen all of me, am I pretty?'

'Put it on,' he said.

'The coat?'

'Put it on.'

'Don't you like me like I am?'

'When I tell you.'

'O.K. There. O.K.? Oh Vicky, I love it. I love it.'

'I love you,' Victor England said, since she hadn't.

She threw herself into his lap and kissed him. Her breasts came out of the front of the coat, little pink eyes puckered, and he kissed them awake. She jumped up, sparkling, pressing promises on his lips and hands, keeping her place in his book, and then she said, 'Vicky, can I do something? Because I really want to do something!'

'Depends,' Victor England said.

'I'm going to – I'm going to.' She kept the lights on in her eyes as she shucked herself from the coat and, nude as an untouched photograph she had done because she was down on her uppers, so hungry she kneaded the dough, posing with her best profile while she did it, because a girl had to be looking her best, she pulled the sleeves right through her new coat till it was completely inside out and then – 'This is what!' – she put it on again, that way round, the fur against her whiteness and my! then she did a shimmy. Then she shook and then she bumped and then she said, 'Oh Vicky, Vicky, *Vicky*, oh if only I could put *you* on like this and feel you all over me – all, all, all at once like I can your fur.'

He felt skinned. He grinned and he was skinned. She turned and stuck out her derrière and looked back at him sideways and – hey nonny, nonny – her eyebrows were question marks. She pushed her hands deep into the side pockets of the coat and flipped back the panels and showed him her melons.

'Oh Vicky, Vicky! It makes me want to do things, it really does. I hope it does you? Oh Vicky, come on: let's do things we're not supposed to do.'

'*Let's do things we're not supposed to do!*' Is there, after what must be nearly thirty years, so great a difference between the California of Victor England's youth and that of Drakos's dandyish devilries? Drakos has the arrogance of a man who, having escaped from hell (though his claims in this direction need scrutiny), does not notice that heaven too has a warning over the gate. When we reach the scene at the Playa de Moriscos, it will be seen how he also is a victim of the vain evasions of which he accuses Victor after their meeting in the Santa Monica villa where they make blue movies. Is Drakos quite as revolutionary as he likes to advertise? At Barbara's establishment on Eden Drive, there is a cut-crystal sampler hanging in the lobby and inscribed with the rubric: 'Only the forbidden is permitted here.' It is said to be a trick's bespoke apology from Tiffany's, after a tiff while going down in the

elevator. The slogan, as respected as the eleventh command-
ment, has been there since cant remembers when. Drakos's
brand of amorality is, in a frayed phrase, nothing new. He,
like his hit movie, is a sort of revival, almost a sort of plagiar-
ism. (Without dwelling too long on a fragment taken out of
sequence, the fact that the police come to Barbara's house
while Victor is there on Brute's treat and shoot a man nobody
ever saw before, actually in one of the pussy parlours, is a
reminder that death and delight room on the same floor.)

The next thing we know is that Victor and Billie-Mae are
making love.

His hands left red prints on her white back and sides.
When they had finished their traffic, bumper-to-bumper
over the bed, Billie-Mae looked over her shoulder at him.
His tender triumph, as he stayed on his knees after the
service, was confused by her observant silence. Was
there something else he had to do? She waited like a
patient who hadn't been hurt enough for it to be a real
operation.
    'O.K.?' she said. 'It was for me.'
    'I don't think it was,' he said. 'Was it?'
    'Bang,' she said. 'Truly. You were wonderful. And so
gentle. I never thought you'd be so gentle.'
    'You know guys who aren't?' he said.
    'Some guys like to do all kinds of things.'
    'You say that from experience?'
    'Things you wouldn't like. You're my experience,'
Billie-Mae said. 'And a wonderful one too. Are you
always so gentle?'
    'Always,' he said. He could have killed her.
    'I never thought I could want a baby,' she said.
    'I want you to have a career.'
    'Which way do you do it if you want to have a career?'
the girl said.
    'With a smile,' Victor England said.
    'Victor,' she said, 'I'd do anything you wanted and it'd

never be dirty, not for me. Anything. You do know that, don't you? So just say, O.K.?'

He said nothing.

'I could eat you,' she said. 'I could eat you.'

She put on her bra and stood in front of him with shining eyes, her cups running over. She skipped to the window and snapped up the shades. 'Oh Vicky, wow. Vicky, wow. Vicky, look at this, will you? My God!'

He was towelling in the bathroom. He came out aproned and saw her point. The landscape was all snow. The last big flakes were just swinging into place. Not a single footprint had landed Friday on the bleached beach of this new world.

'Can you beat it? Can you beat it?'

'Can't beat that with a stick,' Victor England said.

'I declare, that's the most beautiful thing I ever saw in my life. Oh Vicky, doesn't that just prove it? We're going to be the happiest people in the world. All I want to do is make you happy. That is, if you'll let me. You will, won't you? Promise?'

'Promise,' Victor England said, thinking already of their divorce. 'Let's go out and snowball.'

'Oh Vicky and when you've made me a star – because I'm going to do everything you tell me, but everything. I'm going to be clay in your hands, I promise.'

'And in my hair,' Victor England said. 'I'll bet.'

'Naughty! Now you're being naughty,' she said. She put her arm round his towel and weighed the wallet in the centre of his skirt. 'Oh Vicky,' she said. 'When we're married, when we're *married*!'

They window-shop the snow; the world is one white sale and they are first in line for all its sheeted treasures. They go out into the creaking floss. Billie-Mae comes from a state where they never snowball and she scarcely knows what to do. Her incompetence enchants Victor England; he pelts her helpless with burst after burst of crystal shrapnel. He wants to quench her goggling giggles, yet they fill him with excited energy.

She turns and runs towards the fishbone firs behind the hotel. The sea of snow seems to rise about her as she plunges forward. (A presentiment, one cannot but think, of the moment when a blonde girl, clothed only in her own fur, fights for death in the permanent waves below the beach-house on the Playa de Moriscos.) Billie-Mae is wearing her new coat, of course; as she ploughs through the snow, it becomes a pillow of salt.

Victor England catches up. They stand facing each other, panting white laughter. Then he dumps her in the snow and turns her into a Swiss roll, over and over like a cold-stored Cleopatra. Her face is covered in white (are we intended to see a resemblance to a corpse?) and with her arms straight-jacketed in snow, she has to blow out the flakes like curds. Only when an upward slope checks her fattening descent can she fight her way out and crawl, gasping and crying, towards the hotel. Victor runs after her and straddles her and paddles her canoe to make her go faster. She rears up and he topples backwards into a cold, armless couch. Billie-Mae rises and runs, waits, and runs again to the chalet. There is a porch, on which she stands, breathing smoke, as Victor England regains his feet. As he stamps towards the steps, a deck below her, she walks her hand along the loaf of snow on the railing above his head and gives him distinguished hair.

Inside, she pulled off her coat and it fell, overweight, over the radiator.

'Oh,' she said, 'oh, oh, oh. Was that fun!' She shook her hair and blew on her fingers. 'Oh Vicky, was that fun or wasn't it?'

'You tell me,' Victor England said. 'Only not now.'

'Oh, do you want to too? I thought I was getting depraved or something. If you want to, I want to, Vicky, and that's for always. It'll be warmer with our clothes off. Oh I wish I had something new to show you every time. I wish this wasn't all there was to me, you know?'

'We can always put something in,' he said.

'Well here I am. Put something in. That was naughty! Come and get it.'

He pulled two snowballs out of his pockets.

'Oh no, no, Vicky don't! Don't you *dare*.'

She twisted and screamed under the powder that spiked her beard with salt and pepper.

'You stinker,' she said. 'You bastard. Now what're you going to do?' She watched him. 'Don't you ever do a thing like that again. Ever.'

'You really liked it that much?' Victor England said.

'If you did, baby,' she said. 'And you did, didn't you? I don't mind what you do. You have such a beautiful smile. You ought to be *in* the movies too. You ought to be both sides of the camera. Gee, I wish I had some snow though. You wait. I won't forget what you did.'

'Forget it if you like,' he said. 'Just don't forgive, O.K.?'

She leaned over and twiddled the knob to find her station. 'I'll never ask anything of you,' she said, leaving him custody of a breast.

'O.K.,' he said. 'Let's not futz around: what do you want exactly?'

'I said nothing.'

'I know. So name it,' Victor England said. 'Or doesn't it have a name?'

'It has a name all right.' Her flesh was like muscled butter, ready for spreading. 'If I *had* to ask for something – '

'Give me your arm,' he said. 'I'll twist it.'

'If you wanted to promise me just one thing ... '

'That doesn't sound like it's going to be enough to me.'

She listened to his chest and then looked over the ledge of his jaw and saw he was still there. 'Get rid of that man.'

'Man?' Victor England said. 'What man?'

'Andrews. *That* man. Promise me you'll never go near him again.'

'Why would I want to do that?'

'He was so nasty to me I thought I'd die. I honestly thought I'd die. He never said one single word in my

63

direction the whole time he was in the car with us. I might as well have been non-existent. He's a bastard.'

'He's a brute,' Victor England said, and his insincerity coined a legend.

'I knew you'd see it my way. I just couldn't go along if I knew you still had him in your life. Oh hon, you're going to be such a wonderful, famous director. We're going to be so happy, I just know we are, you and me.' She kissed him on most of his mouth and he wondered how long it would last. And that was Victor England's number one.

When they get back to Hollywood, Victor takes the coat for valuation. Only then is he brought to realize that he has been swindled. It must have been when they left the fur to be monogrammed that Greta took the opportunity to switch the expensive coat for a cheaper one. (The camouflaging roll in the snow was just what the doctoring ordered.) The price of having the handsome hand-sewn monogram turns out to have been just about half the money Victor paid for the original coat; it is now clear why the coat is said to be *cut* – cut whisky is watered whisky – and why it was boxed in a *con-trap*tion. Victor smiles at the cost of his innocence and finds himself comforting the valuer:

The furious furrier asked again and again why Victor had not come to him for a coat. He had to keep walking out into the fresh air, he was so sore. His outrage was broken up into six-word fragments, like the dialogue they gave to the producer's girl-friends with big talents the Hayes office wouldn't let anybody show on the screen. 'I could have helped you ... done a job for you ... who's more reasonable than I am? ... dollar for dollar, who's more reasonable? ... you do a thing like this ... will you please tell me something? ... I don't know what to say ... I still don't know what to say ... I'm upset, forgive me, I'm upset ... Why didn't you come to me? ... I'd appreciate an answer to that ... '

'Mr Katz, next time, I promise.'

'You'd better, Mr England, truly, because ... '

'Nobody likes to be cheated twice,' Victor England said.

Yet he leaves the shop feeling that somehow everything is worth it, even what is worthless:

You had to be somebody to be deceived like he had been deceived. Who pulls a switch on a nobody? When he told his bride of the swindle, she cried till his eyes were sore. He enjoyed her *à cheval*, while she sniffed. As he rode her into town, he was as unscarred and unscared as if he had already started to pay her alimony.

'Vicky, how can people do a thing like that?' she wanted to know.

'Practice,' he said, pushing down on her melons to dismount.

And now we are back in Ramon Verdugo's hotel. Victor turns a corner in the primrose corridor and finds that he is crossing a temporary equator. The afternoon sun has left pools of tepid light, a receding tide in which shrimps of dust swim to shadowy shores.

At first he sees no one in the waterless sea he has now entered, only the double doors of the suites, each marked with a golden number. The colour of the girl's skin is so white, so unbronzed by the call of California, that he fails to see her at all until he has gone almost all the way towards her. Is it the same transparent girl whom he encountered in the lobby? Almost certainly not: this girl's hair is of a different shade and she looks smaller. On the other hand, Victor does not attach all that much significance to size: a director can find an angle to make anyone a giant or a pygmy; a knack he has in common with Bob Pound. As for the hair, she could always be wearing a wig. If she is, it's all she is wearing:

She watched his approach as kindly as a creature in its element might watch one that was not. She was standing against the door of a suite, her hands behind her back. Her nakedness appeared so natural that it might have been made specially for her. About the chapped lips, which had kissed each other to swollen numbness, there hung the crescent of a smile that had yet to find its moon. She stood quite still, a possessed prophetess on whom were printed all the naked truths that Victor did not care to seek or dare to speak. He dropped his glance to the beige target of her sex, her only clothed part.

'Hullo, Dotty,' Victor England said. 'Is something wrong?'

'No,' the girl said. 'I'm locked out.'

'I didn't know you were still here. Nobody told me.'

'We're always here,' she said.

'Last time I heard about you, you were in Calabria. Are you well? You look well.'

'I've got a bit of a chest actually.' She coughed. 'What brings Mr England to California?'

'The same thing that brought Miss England,' Victor England said. 'People. Money. California. You forget – '

'I remember,' the girl said. 'I wasn't ever Miss England. No chance.'

'You're going to catch cold.'

'Calabria?' the girl said. 'Oh when we were doing that Western. I still have saddle-sores!'

'You rode beautifully. How's Rob?'

'He's fine. He's smashing. We both are. If I could only shake this cough. Have you seen Frank?'

'I just got in. I heard from Rex. I'm seeing Frank in the morning.'

'Only how are things out there?'

'At the Studio? You tell me.'

'I just did,' the girl said. 'Much as I know.'

'You've been here quite some while now.'

'That's how come I'm behind,' she said.

'You can't stay here. We have to find somewhere for you to live, Dotty. Do you want me to go look for somebody?'

She shook her head. 'We live here.'

'To let you back in. Or is Rob around?'

'Rob's in there,' she said. 'Why else would I be out here?'

'I don't get it.'

'He threw me out. How goes it with your project?'

'All to talk about,' Victor England said. 'Threw you out?'

'He'd love to work with you some day. It was only a spat.' She knocked. 'Rob? Do think of him.'

'I think of you both. You're always busy. You're always doing something.'

'We can always stop.'

'Let's get together, the three of us, while I'm here.'

'Call us,' she said. 'We sit here. It was such a shame that other thing fell through, but it wasn't our fault. We wanted to do it. They just couldn't work anything out.'

'There's maybe always another time.'

'At least there's always another maybe!'

'Right. Tell Rob hullo from me. You're sure I can't do anything?'

'What could you do?' she said.

'Watch that chest,' Victor England said.

The girl's name is Dotty Lampard. A few years earlier, we now learn, she was one of those golden bullets fired into the head of the old morality. She personified a new generation. She said nothing very remarkable; she did nothing very remarkable; she simply *was* remarkable.

She blew a whole season into life. People talked about her and London as if they were new-born twins. The film which carried her to frame and fortune was one of those damned triumphs which even those who hated it had walked out of at least two or three times. All that, to be sure, was a few years back now. The film, still well enough known to be referred to, like an empress or a clown, by its first and only name, had since appeared,

67

cold, sliced and pickled with commercials, on television. It was in black and white, a dissector's item, but Dotty's magic lent colour to its reputation.

Two stars were above the title when the film was first shown, but after people had seen Dotty, they never stooped to look up there again. If she was, contractually speaking, third on the bill, the movie was as unquestionably hers as the three parts of Gaul were Caesar's.

Her success was more complete for her inadequacies. Did not Greek sculptors flaw the beauty of their master-pieces lest the Gods be jealous? A discerning critic – one of the few who could see without closing his eyes – declared that only a blind flatterer could have called her acting average. Her legs, he declared, would not have doubled the tips of a tea-girl; her breasts were nothing you could not find better positioned and better shaped elsewhere. What mattered was not what she looked like but what she was. To do her justice (which was need-lessly unkind), Dotty never made any mystery of her mind or any secret of her body: she took the tartest possible inventory of both.

There was no fine print in the bargain she struck with her audience. She was all in capitals, like an ultimatum: the public surrender was immediate. Hundreds, thou-sands, millions of girls began at once to look and sound Dotty Lampard. Like all impractical fashions, her style fitted everyone.

As for Dotty herself, no oracle could have been more laconic. But if she was seldom heard to speak except in monosyllables, they were all monosyllables no one had ever heard before.

Dotty Lampard, the phenomenon, is a watershed in the idea of what a girl can be. (She shops always in the men's departments of London's stores.) Yet as a watershed, she remains on the borderline of the two areas, or eras, she defines. She typifies the liberated woman, but perhaps she more indicates the way to others than actually follows it herself. What is the feminine of Moses? If California is the Promised Land, is it not significant that we meet her first when she has been locked out? Is the coughing girl whom Victor England discovers in the corridor, the same hockey-healthy hellion who cast doubt on the virility of the middle-aged – anyone over twenty-four – by demanding of them, whatever they said, or did, that they come again? She had a directness that went against the groin. Flattery, she told a gusher, was a rose without a prick.

Life had given her few of the lines, but all of the close-ups. Her silences were all in the Dictionary of Quotations. She bit her nails but she knew how to scratch. She was a rebel who asked people what she should do. She was inimitable and the proof was you saw girls like her everywhere. If critics with a name to make declared that she was overrated even when she was unknown, she carried off, in the year following her début, one acting award after another. What else could they give her? Had there been plaques or platitudes for sentimental sedition or merely for talented tail, she might have had those instead, but the world distributed its honours in established categories and so the worldly shook their heads and decided to call her an actress. She had to cry and clutch at the same staple statues that mere legends had been voted in their time. Perhaps, compared to them, she was not really an actress, but if she was not, who cared any more who was? Was she not yet a star? Then who would look at the sky until she was? At each presentation, she wept like a schoolgirl with nine-month news and went as brazenly for her glistering armful as for an abortion. She took prizes and praise like a snub. Congratulations were candy to her diabetes: too many and she was comatose. Others had been surprised by success; she was alone in being embarrassed by it. At each predictable surprise, she put her hand to her mouth – a patient who had swallowed the thermometer, again.

Was she still amazed when she won her rumpteenth award? She was appalled. When the critic who had first run an unflattering rule over her assets voted her 'The Bubble Most Likely To Be Pricked', she sought him out at a New Year's Eve affair and made him ridiculous by tactful tactics only she could have devised: effusive endorsement, backed with intimate instances.

Victor England happens to be at that party. Fleur has already gone to bed: she isn't ready for a new year yet. The movie business is still apparently booming, so it must be several years before the California meeting with Dotty, when things are so bad that any gathering of more than three or four people has to be a funeral or bad driving. Victor comes over to where Dotty is offering unaccepted smiles, like cigarettes to a non-smoker, while the critic, who has grown to be the tallest dwarf in London (is Bob Pound his tailor?), disagrees with the way she is agreeing with him.

Victor England turned back the lapel of his lip, identifying himself, whenever she wanted him, as a fellow-sufferer. She caught only a certain coldness, which he was aiming at the critic, and greeted him warmly.

'Hullo,' she said. 'I'm Dotty Lampard. I'm a fan of yours.'

'Are you, Dotty? Not as big a fan as I am of yours.'

'Oh now,' she said, 'much much bigger! I *hope*. You always had such beautiful ladies in your films.'

'*Had?*' Victor England said. 'I sort of hoped I hadn't stopped yet.'

'And I hope I haven't started. Maybe – '

'That sounds like a cue for a song. Will you look at that queue for a drink? What do you say we go somewhere we haven't been invited and have a nice time?'

'A nice time? That sounds wonderful. I'm dressed all wrong for this. Don't you think I am?'

'I never noticed you were dressed at all,' Victor England said.

'I don't have the figure, do I?'

'No one's ever going to notice,' Victor England said. 'They'll be too busy looking at you. Dotty, I'd love for us to do something together.'

'What have you got?' she said.

'Soon as it's light I start digging.'

'You know I can't act, don't you?'

'I read the papers,' Victor England said. 'But I never believe them. You know what a writer I know said about your critic friend, don't you? "He's got three names and he still hasn't made one of them yet." '

'Oh writers,' Dotty Lampard said. 'They never like anybody. Is your new one all cast?'

'All cast and no cash,' Victor said. 'I'm still shopping a Studio.'

'You won't have any problem,' Dotty said. 'What's it called again? Anyone'd do anything with you if you asked them.'

'Will you marry me?'

'Nice title,' she said. 'Don't forget me now.'

'Forget you! Are there people who can?'

'I'm serious.'

'So am I, without my writers. What about getting out of here? Do you have a coat?'

'One day –' she began a promise, but it was broken by the hard hammer of midnight. 'Oh I hate years,' she said, and ran across the floor to where an unsmiling, very fair young man let her hang herself in the closet of his arms. The young man was also very tall and he wore spectacles. Alone among the guests, he had made no gesture towards the fancy dress which their hostess had engraved on their heartfelt felt heart invitations. He was the only person in the room somehow not at the party at all. He was there for Dotty alone. She pressed her mouth against his, like a salve, a bare misprint away from a slave.

Dotty is reported to be wearing a blue, sea-through blouse and a dirndl skirt with darned-all beneath. She is right about her figure: her legs are as short as telegrams and her breasts will never be worth a staple in her navel. 'She looks like she buys her hair by the yard,' says one fashing journalist to another. 'By the yard or in the yard?' is the quip-as-lightning reply. If Dotty were the sum of her shortcomings, she would add up to nothing, but it just so happens that the one thing she has on the plus side of her ledger is infinity. ('That's something we'd all like ten per cent of,' Brute Andrews remarks later.)

At the time of this party, Dotty's first film has, of course, already come out, but it is during the following year, while she is collecting all her Diva's dividends, that she is transformed from a force into a property: 'Something you could pull down and build on.' Victor, still busy setting up his next project, calls her agent and pries for her price, but the Studio, sore at having turned down her first picture because no one had ever heard of her, is determined not to have her now because everyone has.

'They're crazy,' Victor said.

'If they weren't, what would they be doing in the business?' Brute Andrews was mixing his own Caesar salad.

'Frank can't be that stupid,' Victor England said.

'He's not stupid. He's scared. I hear the people sneaked out of the sneak in Portland last week.'

'*Mister Big?*'

'Mister Big, heap big miss,' Brute Andrews said. 'The cards were 80–20 for euthanasia.'

'They wanted me to do it,' Victor said.

'They should've more than wanted.'

'They talked about half a million, didn't you say?'

'I wanted money,' Brute Andrews said. 'I'm not a young man any more. I need special food. Lots of lettuce.'

'They offered money.'

'You didn't want to do it,' Andrews said. 'You told me you didn't want to do it.'

'I didn't want to do it,' Victor England said. 'I thought we were talking about money.'

'The Studio is in that one up to here,' Andrews said. 'If not higher. Maybe here. You should've seen some of those cards.'

'Who's your source on this?'

'Never mind branding the media,' Andrews said. 'The trute's the trute.'

'That's not good news, Brute.'

'Since when was the truth good news?'

'All the more reason to go somewhere new for honey.'

'For honey, that's your privilege. But money always comes from the same place. The bank.'

'I'm thinking of Dotty. She has to be the most exciting thing in ages.'

'Everyone's got the hots for the girl, but today who can afford her?'

'I'm talking about box-office, Brute.'

'It makes 'em doubt their judgment, Victor, when they could have had her for nothing. Could be we'll have to trim ship and look elsewhere.'

'Heap Big Miss, huh?' Victor England said.

'If they're lucky,' Brute Andrews said.

The Studio does eventually go ahead with Victor's (never named) film, but with a star that's safe (and on Brute Andrews's sheet). To cover their timidity, the publicity people issue a denial that Dotty has been turned down for the part. How else can they put it around that they could have afforded her but have deliberately chosen not to? The selected star luckily does everything asked of her – and unluckily nothing else. The best thing that can be said of the resulting product is that no accountant ever complains about it. At this stage in her life, through no action of her own, Dotty has acquired the one sure proof of talent:

... the accolade of enemies. Because the printed word

73

was that Victor had tested and rejected her, certain groups began to smile at him in tiled restaurants with spiral staircases and waiters who played Sunday football with the patrons. They wanted to recruit him to the club where the dues amounted only to doing down Dotty. The members were executives who had bowed out so frequently that their backbones, what was left of them, could stay unsnapped in six inches of clearance; they were limbo-dancers who faced the floor. They had often held each other's jobs and would arrive sometimes in the wrong office, having forgotten they now worked for the outfit across the road. These men had seen them come and they had seen them go and they had seen them come back again, if TV rated as a second coming. The business suited them; they didn't want anything to be different, except in the money department. Dotty Lampard had changed everything and they were not men who liked everything to change.

What worries these London-based Phoenixes without fire is that Dotty seems insufficiently dedicated either to money or to fame. Her price may have been high to Victor England (and would certainly be to them, if they had anything to offer her that she could want), but the scandal is that she has been making herself available, just for fun, to flesh-in-the-pan artists who make porn-ball art films they sell on a circuit-and-see basis. How dare she give it away like that?

And what did she mean, the club wanted to know, wearing clothes pennies could buy and no one could ever sell? She picked up second-hand duds on stalls in markets, could you imagine this girl? Give her a present, she wouldn't take it. They went to her with cash and carriage. Would she hitch her star to their wagon? She walked places. Their Portuguese girls wouldn't walk down the street with the Doberman. Baby-sitters made tougher conditions. This damned Dotty wouldn't make any conditions at all. She actually walked places. 'If the world was all people like her,' one of them said, 'there'd be no sense inventing the wheel yet. The guy would starve.' They wanted to be Santa Claus – was it such a lot to ask? – and she wouldn't believe in them. She ruined the party. Could you blame them for being insulted? She wore the see-through blouses and then she looked right through *them*! She forgot their names; she called them all Mister Um. They bent to kiss her and she'd put out her hand and say 'How do you do?' They were important people; they had given an easy lifetime to the business and she didn't even know the credits for which they had soiled their souls. Had they not once had scruples and consciences and hopes? They now had no scruples, no consciences, and hopes. They were still waiting for the big one. They might be nobody today, but just wait for tomorrow. They only needed to land one big one, just one big one and then oh boy! Meanwhile? Meanwhile they did a job. In the morning, they read the Trades and shook their heads over the latest hits ('Calls himself a producer? He's a nobody, he's got nothing,' they would swear) and in the afternoons, whatever was left after Mario's last cup of Sanka, they went maybe to the races to help a friend's horse over a hurdle or else they worked out at the pedal parlour (most of them packed a paunch) and then in the evenings it was the conference call with the Coast when they said a-very-good-morning-how-goes-it to the nobodies who had nothing and promised them, no problem, to obtain unobtainable suites for their sweeties at London's hottest hotels, where they'd be sure to run up buffaloing bills on the U.K. slate and never even bother to call and say hullo until it was goodbye. And at night? At night they were free to dream of California the Golden from which marital martyrdom, incompetence or a very dear old friend had long ago expelled them.

Now Dotty's success, which seems to prove that all you need

for a hit is 'A girl, an Arriflex and a faggot,' has made life with a big cigar suddenly precarious:

Damocles looked up from his gull's eggs and there was that damned sword.

'You know what she's basically done? She's made it so nothing's dirty any more. She's laid it all right on the line.'

It was true: the whole liturgy of a long and fat generation was made obsolete by Dotty Lampard's grey breasts and waffled behind.

Innuendo was out the window.

The reference here is to the most notorious scene in her notorious (though now innocent enough) first film. She is in a bathing-suit, sitting in a cane chair while the hero makes fudge in his mother's kitchen. He talks and talks, with a young man's self-centredness, and never notices that the girl is in love with him. Dotty does not say a word throughout the scene. The young man has all the lines, but no one could ever remember a thing he said. (Despite this less-is-more lesson, Dotty's agent insists that her golden smile be capped with silver speeches in her second film.) The young man remains unaware of how besotted the girl is until, scalded with desire, she leaps up from her chair and advances on him. As she does so, the audience sees that the cane seat of the kitchen chair has imprinted a lattice-work of squares across her barely covered behind.

'What's the matter,' the young man asks, 'can't you wait?' He is, of course, referring to the fudge. The girl shakes her head, and the audience reads her mind. So doleful, so desperate, so devoted and so demanding is her expression that her fee goes through the roof in just forty-eight frames, from a standing start. In those two seconds of screen time, a certain look of demanding docility sets the fashion for what is to be known as a touch of the Dotty Lampards. Female sexual desire has found its four-letter face.

The young man goes to take the fudge off the hot-plate.

'Hungry?' he asks. This time Dotty nods. Has he finally guessed her secret? 'It's hot,' he warns her, 'do you mind?' She shakes her head. The candied candour of her appetite sets the seal on a new age. Neither wincing nor winsome, she has the directness of innocent hunger. With no warning, the young man bursts out laughing: heavy, blurting gasps of derision. Dotty is staggered. Without the smallest sign of acting, merely by being there when not wanted, the girl conveys such pain and bewilderment that the audience's hearts are twisted off the known road and go bumping down a precipice into devotion. Dotty thinks the young man is laughing at her desire; only after humiliation has stuck its finger in her eye does he realize that she does not know why he is laughing. He points at her waffled rear. She twists to share the joke, which is literally on her, and at that moment she gives the look that finally breaks the banks. The Dotty Lampard smile – 'As miraculous, as commonplace and as easily cracked as French bread,' says the critic who likes to see his name on the advertising – spreads across her face.

Now the young man wants her all right! As he comes forward stiffly to kiss her, her lips spread ruefully in a sort of flat, defeated grin and, at the same time, seem to thicken, to swell, as if under a lovely lash.

It was at once a liberation – had she not seen her own absurdity and thus risen above it? – and an enslavement. She was demeaned by her need for so banal a boy, but then what else could slake her fire? Every woman recognized in her desire the seeds of servitude. Every man glanced at the woman beside him and saw the warning flare of her nostrils: the dragon's furnace was alight. What, after all, was freedom but the awareness of slavery?

The symbolism discovered in the scene by Hugh Stone is, probably, one a rewriting writer thought of for a prodding producer and a dire director, who would both give a lot of money (as long as it wasn't too much) for the right to say they had thought of it.

Hugh Stone's comments are as follows:

The theme of bondage informs the whole sequence. The young man is unmoved both by the girl's beauty and by her devotion. And here he stands, of course, for all men who are more interested in sex as a kind of confectionery than in any mature relationship. It is the deformation of her flesh, prefiguring the sexual humiliation which he (or life) has in store for her, that alerts him to her sexual existence. He wishes, we are being told, to mark her as the chair has marked her. (Is it worth noting here that *chair* is the French for flesh? The director's first film, remember, was a documentary about transhumance in the Haute Savoie.) The young man laughs first but no one is deceived: his, unlike hers, is a crafty desire which imagines 'doing things to her' as the acme of sexual liberation. The fudge surely has a Freudian significance here: it tips us off to what he has in mind. The girl's later responses express all the ambiguities which are to be found in the new feminism. The director has orchestrated these reactions with the apt skill learnt in the many commercials he has shot. The girl may despise the male, as embodied in this confectioner (echoes here, one guesses, of a Platonic distinction between the architect and the pastrycook), but where else is she to go? Where else is life to be found? Her revolt from male domination, from the role enjoined upon her by the ideology of bourgeois society, controlled as it is by men, can only be negative. It lacks political consciousness: she is unwilling to yield now, yet she falls for the young tycoon, in a later scene, who is hardly less 'candy-minded' than her first boy-friend. (In his first scene, he is seen choosing a *yard* of *bitter*mints for her.) Male domination tends, dialectically, to be even more domineering, in the face of the new female *prise de position*; the girl's very search for liberty leads her into humiliating bondage. She abandons 'love' as colonial people abandon 'loyalty', yet she is economically and socially dependent on the (male) 'neo-colonialists'. The tycoon introduces her to 'sophisticated, *liberated* people', as she calls them, who go to a brothel where they watch a 'slave scene' and later there is the suggestion, in a scene the censor is said to have cut, that the tycoon shows the girl his bed where there are 'funny straps' (I am quoting from an early script). What I am arguing is that unless female freedom has a politico-economic dimension, disappointment and brutality are always liable to be its ugly sisters. The film fails finally to make the positive requirements of liberation explicit and hence itself becomes, for all its bravura passages and its remarkable use (and I emphasize *use*) of Miss Lampard, propaganda for the very consumer society which it flirts with exposing. The elements of *de*liberation in the raising of issues which are then shelved makes the success of the film at once stylish and unmerited. It compares disappointingly in this respect with earlier work by the same director when he was kept on a firmer leash by either commercial or documentary exigence, or both.

Dotty Lampard's reactions may or may not have been rehearsed. The director, of course, claims that they were conceived, like the Princess's third marriage and fifth child, in rehearsal. 'I believe in improvisation only when it's carefully planned,' he tells a columnist. The writer, on the other hand, asserts that it was all there in the script, long before the director rehearsed anything except the press. Those on the floor at the time of shooting maintain that this fleeting, eternal glimpse of Eve with the apple to her lips was born of Dotty's embarrassment at being unable, under the pressure of a take, to repeat exactly what had been scripted and plotted. 'Despairing of professionalism, she resigned herself to being merely a genius,' the columnist concludes.

But there is more still to her famous scene. The young man's laughter lacerates her into brazenness. She undoes the southern bows on either side of her bikini bottom and throws it away, the baggage tag of a girl who needs no baggage. (We must not forget Victor England's missing suitcase; we shall see, in due course, the relevance of what it contains.) Dotty's symbolic impatience with pretence, indeed with virginity itself (the bikini is, according to Ms Stone, 'an externalized hymen'), is what makes her stand definitively for a new morality divorced entirely from what preceded her, alike in movies and in life. (A French magazine, which does not like the film at all, analyzes at length the tossing away of the bikini bottom as 'the existential repudiation of the hitherto essential'.)

Whether this act of reckless wit was foreseen or not, the director certainly kept his head: the camera continued to turn and Dotty was given her historic opportunity to take the can't out of cunt. Another French magazine, of a less philosophical nature, observes openly what the Anglo-Saxons could only whisper: '*Elle sourit avec son con.*' Even her smile, the more analytic article insists, has '*un niveau génital*'. Hugh Stone goes on to translate: '*It fattens but it does not curl, it invites but it does not promise, it solicits but it can never reassure.*' Female sexuality, once licensed, ceases to be either apologetic or indulgent. This point is highly suggestive when we think of what happens later in Victor England's story.

The scene ends with Dotty jutting her mouth provocatively at the young man. She is standing with her legs apart ('Like a boy!' Hugh Stone says). The young man puts his arms round her; desire and prudishness work together. The two are not even lovers yet. (What is more, the young man's parents are watching television in the next room: two comedians are in bed together, a family show.) Dotty has scandalously delivered to her boy friend the premature reality of all his dearest, dirtiest dreams. The modern girl need not wait to be robbed of her virginity; she can discard it like wrapping paper. ('*Voici le moment critique d'une révolution sans idéologie; la révolution de la chair féminine.*') The young man wants to kiss her mouth, but evading his lips, she breaks away from the bandaging bond of his embrace and turns, skittishly vindictive, and offers him her assets. (There is an echo here, it need hardly be said, of the moment when Billie-Mae turns back the flaps of her fur and shows Victor her round numbers. There is also a certain artfulness in the French quotation, for it reminds us that Victor puts his foot on a *chair* in the lobby of the hotel.)

To return to the seminal sequence: the camera now favours Dotty exclusively. According to Hugh Stone, the young man is effectively killed by Dotty's unambiguous invitation. The switch in sexual authority is manifest: it is henceforth no longer a question of 'Will she, won't she?' but of 'He will, won't he?' The male can no longer escape sexual challenge, and by the same token the risk of sexual failure, by relying on the double standard which requires of a woman that she accept sexual pleasure but never require it. If the male is symbolically killed at this point, it is because 'she won't wait' implies a castrating menace. The King's sceptre becomes less the emblem of his power than the fragile implement of his consort's satisfaction. Gynarchy threatens to re-establish itself: a soft sceptre and out he goes. Clytemnestra's clitoris is, so to say, back in the saddle.

The sequence ends with Dotty's eyes closing in tasteful but triumphant ecstasy. She has got what she came for. When she smiles now, it needs a man not to look away.

The whole of the rest of the picture is generally agreed to contain a new girl: 'impatient, impertinent, imperturbable, impudent, implacable'. Every shot of her, the director promises the columnist, has been planned to recall and echo that outrageous smile and that angling angle. More:

She seemed at every screening, even when the movie was playing a thousand simultaneous dates, to respond personally to the audience, winking in delighted and – people swore – impromptu connivance at the screams and whistles. It was as if a live performer had bluffed her buff way on to the screen. Dotty was shadow and substance, ubiquitous and unique: the qualities of a

Goddess were hers. But how long did Goddesses live? Alas, only forever.

Dotty gives desire a fresh, clean sheet and carnality the viceless, voiceless simplicity lost when the lease was up on Eden. Is love banished along with words?

'Love [Hugh Stone writes, and writes] is part of the rhetoric made obsolete by direct action. Courtship is a kind of lying rendered unnecessary when female desire trumps both calculation and convention. As soon as the woman takes the initiative, love becomes a price she need not and perhaps cannot exact.'

The irony turns out to be that all those scenes which the public believes to have been so infectiously dependent on what happened in the kitchen ('the post-cookery bits', Dotty calls them) were in fact shot before it. Life, one may infer, is montage: meaning is awarded not implicit. In the Dotty Lampard world, echo always comes first. There are a number of subtleties to be unravelled here.

What has happened to Dotty since her triumph?

She swore that she would never leave England. Her director made a similar declaration, before flying to America. She was happy as she was, she said, and she seemed it, the bitch. On every public appearance she was accompanied by her bloke. Each time she was announced as the winner of this award or that, and often it was both, she first clapped her hands to her mouth, as if she had forgotten to turn off the gas back in Battersea, and then flung her arms round his neck and hid her face from the vitriol of veneration.

When finally she goes up to the platform, '*as if to the scaffold*' (one thinks of Billie-Mae on the sidewalk outside the fur shop) and takes her rich medicine, it is the tall, bespectacled young man who gets her to pull her original Cinderella rags around her after-midnight middle and play the Princess the prints require. When the press press, she refuses to talk about marriage or whether, on rumours that she is pregnant, she has prams for the future. She will not be drawn to comment on the charms of the professional profiles who clamour to escort her to openings and clothings. She continues to go to men's outfitters and to live in the mansion flat where she and her bloke eat cheese and refuse to say it, at least for the photographic foe. When she declines to invent her memoirs though haunted by ghosts rattling their cheque-books, the papers announce that she is a spent farce. (Who but a phoney doesn't answer the phone?) She clings to her young man. She even says to someone that she is his property. (Echoing, of course, the use of 'property' as a term in show business: she prefers to give herself to him rather than to those who are so eager to buy and sell her.) Her director, plump with plums and modest with megalomania, comes back from America and announces, in the spirit of generous malice with which God granted free will to Man, that he has no immediate plans for her. He wouldn't like her to be beholden to him, he says. In any case before he goes behind a camera again, he's going to give the Opera House a Ring. 'And I don't think even Dotty thinks she's ready to sing yet.'

'He's done so much for me,' Dotty said, when they reported the direction the director was taking, 'I'm sure he's right. It'd be such a pity if he couldn't do anything without me.' She smiled a wounded smile and kicked a pair of ill-fitting, newly cobbled shoes through the open doors on to the green and chased after them as if they were clumsy kittens. She was hurt but relieved. She sent her director a telling telegram (ALL LOVE) and that evening she looked so dishy at the Sid Cohens' coincidental dinner that the director, observing that decapitation had not made her lose her head, sweated all night and had to have a male nurse. He called her after a dazed rest and refused to take the answering service for an answer. (Her flat had been flattered with an ex-directory line.) He contacted her in person later and his particular blend of con and tact so depressed her that, an hour after saying she would never make another movie, she called her agent and agreed terms for California.

The price of her signature – and whoever has got it, it seems that it cannot be Rex Keyes and Frank King, since they later deny her services to Victor England – is astronomical. 'It always is for bastards who won't do things for the money,' says someone in the club. The news of the deal is, however, a calming calamity for the knockers. Dotty may have had the last laugh, money-wise, but she has also consented to play the game the way her enemies have always liked it, by numbers. If the price bids fair to ruin the Studio, it proves that there is still a Studio to ruin.

Members of the club shook each other's hands just that much more firmly on the day the Trades betrayed the secret they all swore they knew already. Before a single frame had been shot or a single page of script junked, they told each other that the business was on the up. '*Sam* paid that much? You're sure it was Sam?' They stood an extra libatory minute at the non-splash urinals in their oyster-cloisters and shook their unbuttoned heads. It proved there was money around, that was what mattered: 'Sam Carnap? Jesus!' The Resurrection was back in the Creed. When the clouds lifted in California, the sun shone in London. Boom, there was money around. All at once, not just Dotty but everyone was talent; even weeds only needed a little water and they'd all come up roses. None knew how long the cash would last or quite where it came from, but when spring follows autumn, who wonders what winter is going to be like? People who had sworn never to make the same mistakes again rushed out and repeated them. Money gushed along the dry ditches and irrigated the saltiest fields.

Silent telephones that had been checked for faults a dozen times began to ring, and with people not engineers at the other end. To lunch was to launch: everything was going down the slipway. Even sinking ships were attracting the rats.

The good news spread through London: for a year or more, there was an r in every month. People had so much money Bob Pound had to make their new suits all pocket. Waiters took home more tips at night, and waitresses more than that. It was so hard to get a table, people found it quicker to open their own restaurants. Gamblers gambled at clubs that were the gambles of those who didn't gamble. Victor England contented himself, amid all the action, with a share in the Golden D, where small fortunes were lost only at the small tables. He made a fool of himself, of course, and went against all the best advice: in consequence he sold out at the top. The men who knew what was what stayed in and lost the lot.

Meanwhile, Dotty Lampard, without her bloke, has left for California.

Some time after Dotty's departure, Victor England is invited to 'drop out and see us here at the Studio'. Frank King, the young Turk ('Kemal Attaboy', Brute Andrews calls him) has recently been made Head of Production at Bowyer's Field. The old chief, Rex Keyes, is shooting Indians on his own production in Mexico. Why has he so abruptly delegated central authority to Frank? His hold on the Studio until this moment has been described tactfully as tyranny. Now, almost overnight, he appears to have been convinced by Frank King's handling of a proxy situation (a group of dissident shareholders is trying to take over the company) that Frank should be his one and only accredited representative on earth. As soon as Victor arrives at La Mission, there is a call from Bartholomew Heinz, Frank's associate:

*

'Victor, so nice. How are you?'

'I'm pretty good, Bart. How are you, Bart?'

'Victor, thank you, I'm well. Victor, Frank says to tell you he'll be back in town in the morning. He had to take the Lear down to Yucatan over a few things – '

'I heard Lear was there already, shooting a movie.'

'I heard that one too. In fact I just fired the guy who told it to me.'

'Only kidding,' Victor England said.

'His words exactly.'

'I haven't been hired yet, Bart.'

'Victor, I have to tell you: the first smartass I heard the story from was Rex himself. Victor, Frank sends you his very warmest personal regards. He's asked me to ask you whether you'd do something for him. Something he has no real right to ask.'

'I'll tell you something, Bart; nobody ever asks me to do anything else. Of course I will. Depends what.'

'Would you see a movie tonight?'

'I guess I could do that for Frank. Doesn't sound too demanding compared to some of the things people have had no right to ask me in the past. Any particular movie?'

'Victor, it's so nice to hear your voice.'

'You want me to lower it?'

'A very particular movie.'

'I see.'

'Victor, how is the hotel? Is Ramon looking after you?'

'He just got through washing my feet,' Victor England said. 'The hotel's fine.'

'I'll send a limousine for you. Would seven thirty be too soon?'

'Where's the screening?'

'The chauffeur will know.'

'Secret, huh? Tell him he can recognize me by my blindfold.'

'Victor, it's been too long.'

'Do I ever get to know what the movie is or do I have three guesses once it's over?'

'I think you'll understand everything once you see it,' Bartholomew Heinz said. 'And Frank'll call you in the morning, if you're going to be there.'

'That depends on the chauffeur.'

'He's going to want to hear your impressions.'

'I don't do impressions any more,' Victor England said, 'how about if I just hum to him?'

'Victor, so nice to hear you – '

'On second thoughts he can have my impressions. If I can have his Impressionists. Do I have myself a deal?'

'We want to see you very soon. We've got things we want to talk to you about. Seven thirty then.'

The limousine comes promptly. They drive down streets Victor remembers and go through a gate past all the silent stages of his early life until they reach a screening room on a distant lot, nowhere near the Studio run by Frank King. No one else is present except a sigh of ghosts, mostly writers.

The next morning, another limousine arrives at the hotel.

The back door opened and Victor saw that Frank King himself was the doorman, on the inside. Pepe del Fuego, his Chicano chauffeur, was too late round the trunk to do more than make sure the door fitted. The two men in the deep end of the car did not speak. Frank looked out of his low, fumed window, his smoking hand on the tasselled pigtail hanging from the door-jamb. Both men smiled, though not at each other and not at the same time. The car drifted in the hard stream.

Along the banks, mansions came and went as rapidly as Roman emperors in a bad year. One of them was on fire. Frank King did not break the glass over his silence. No one stopped to watch the fire. It was a No Stopping zone. The house was a house like any other: the foreign fun car was in the carport; the rocking horse, a brace in its teeth, nodded on the front porch; the sprinkler on the lawn flapped splayed wrists and threw rainbows first bounce towards the fence. The burning house was indistinguishable from its neighbours, except that it was also inextinguishable. (It belonged to a polysyllabic songwriter.) As they reached the freeway and Pepe pressed his window up, Frank King looked full at Victor for the first time.

'Well,' he said, 'you saw it.'

'Saw it?' Victor England said.

'Didn't the car come?'

'Oh the movie. Yes, I saw it.'

'What else is there to see?'

'And I don't understand a thing,' Victor England said.

'Nothing? Nothing? I know there are some rough edges, but *nothing* – that's a little tall.'

'About why you wanted me to see it.'

Frank King braced back his feet. Did he have cramp? He flexed his fingers. Was he going to play the piano? 'Victor, why do you think Rex made me Head of Production?'

'I heard the proxy fight – '

'Dissident shareholders,' Frank King said. 'Did you ever meet any major shareholder not on the Board who wasn't dissident? Jesus Christ, Victor, come on.'

'Sam has Dotty, doesn't he?'

'Sam? Sam *signed* her. Sam doesn't have a bean.'

'Frank, it's early in the morning. I'm tired.'

'Sam couldn't cut the mustard. I heard the news before anyone else. One thousandth of a second before. The Studio's holding him up. His name on that picture is the only thing that's his. And we have a lien on that.'

'You bought her contract?'

'Everything,' Frank King said. 'You name it, we bought it. We even hire Sam his truss today, I tell you.'

'Why the secrecy?'

'Do I have to tell you? Sam's running a crisis studio: that keeps costs down. If we'd taken over the picture, it'd put two hundred per cent on the budget. Who can afford that today?'

The old guard at the Studio gate salutes as the limousine goes creamily in on its whitewalled rubber hooves and then swings the barrier down behind the car, like a bribed executioner, late on his stroke.

Frank's office was originally occupied by the founder of the Studio, once a God and now a dirty word, a fate shared with all fallen Gods. The office was, we are reminded, refurnished and re-equipped from floor to sealing by Rex Keyes on the very same day the Old Fart was finally prised out. There is a story that when the Old Fart was in the Cedars of Lebanon and was asked what he wanted done with his body, he replied, 'I want to be cremated and I want my ashes thrown in that son-of-a-bitch's face.'

The Old Fart, in his day, was Kronos to Rex Keyes's Zeus. He was one of the pioneers. He founded his Studio and he made so much money he had to hire people to count it for him: 'My first and only mistake.' From the very beginning, his jaws dripped with the blood of his potential successors. He consumed all whom he had once called Son. None of the bright boys whose careers he sired ever survived his cannibal canniness. He watched his competitors hungrily and he gobbled up any young man who looked to threaten him. He brought them to Bowyer's Field and for a season or two he called them Son and gave them a lot of chances to make just one mistake.

The Old Fart could be evil to his enemies, but he was frightful to his friends. He was a God who would never, if he could avoid it, suffer anyone to sit on his right hand. He wanted it free to cut them down. To be hired by him was a terrible honour. 'Calvary without the Easter egg,' one of those writers said.

One day, soon after his latest boy genius had gone to cut the hay in a funny farm, the Old Fart asked the

89

young Rex Keyes to stop by Bowyer's Field sometime. All Hollywood's clocks were stopped for readjustment. Even in the thirties, they were usually slow.

The Board at Palisades tried to poleaxe Rex with promises. In their panic to retain him, they offered him ten per cent of everything that had a nought on it.

'What am I going to say to these people?' Rex said.

'I'll tell you exactly what to say to them.' And the Old Fart made the sound on which his nickname gave him the franchise. 'That's what you say to them.'

And so Rex Keyes went to Bowyer's Field. It took so long to straighten the legal details that the boy wonder had time to go right round the world before even the first agreement was in shape to be bounced against the wall. Once Rex had burned his oats at Palisades, the Old Fart was not above leaving him out on a limb to cool off. When he returned from his world trip, the documents were still held up on a technicality. He spent the next morning with a banker putting the rule over some vacant lots within spying distance of Bowyer's Field; a primed pryer took back the news that the stud was looking to build his own studio. Once he was sure the Old Fart had swallowed the hook, Rex picked up Dolores Montego and went round the world again, a little faster. The next time he hit Los Angeles, those damned would-you-believe-it lawyers had the papers ready for signature.

A decade later, in the very room where Victor and Frank hold their meeting, the Old Fart was invited to initial his own obituary. Rex Keyes became President of the Company.

The weakest member of the Board was sent in with the news that the Old Fart had been voted irreplaceable, and replaced. The Board had made him Honorary Chairman in Perpetuity.

'Perpetuity!' he shouted, 'How long is that going to last? You can't do this to me.'

But they could, and they did. Later he met some out-of-work people from Chicago, for whom he had some employment plans. But they had not brought their tools with them and nobody's nuts got tightened. The word was they wanted all the money before they started shooting. The Old Fart never made that kind of a deal.

A generation later, Rex Keyes transferred the keys of power in time to avoid a similar lock-out. 'I was Head of Production before Frank was born,' he told a lady columnist with syndicated sincerity, 'it's about time I had a promotion. I'm due.'

'The only despots who fall are crackpots,' she quipped for money. 'The smart ones just keep on moving up. What ladder worth a damn ever had a top rung?'

But how long can Rex's prophylactic withdrawal maintain his position? We shall see. Meanwhile:

'Well,' Frank said, sitting energetically at his desk, 'they screened you the new Dotty Lampard.'

'They sent a car,' Victor England said. 'What could I do?'

'You can say anything you like, Victor. You won't hurt me; you won't shock me; you might even help me.'

'Don't give me too much freedom,' Victor England said. 'I hate to have my neck the only thing that sticks out.'

'Good morning, Frank; good morning, Victor.' Bartholomew Heinz was the one man who came into Frank King's office without having to knock. He had to crawl, but he never had to knock.

'Morning, Bart, how goes it?'

'Excuse me, Victor, but just one thing I have to tell Frank. I just saw Shelly. They're two days ahead on *Bang Bang* – so there's something to tell Shap and company.'

'Shap,' Frank King said. 'I'd like to see that bum try to run a Studio.'

'Two minds with but a single thought,' Heinz said.

'God bless Shelly,' Frank King said. 'That girl must've come first time. That's what I call a pro! Bart, Victor screened the new Dotty Lampard.'

'You saw it,' Bartholomew Heinz said. 'And what did you think?'

'I've told him the whole position, the Studio's involvement. On the table. Out in the open. Victor knows as much as we know. So come on, Vic, shoot.'

'She looks sensational,' Victor England said.

'The sun comes up every morning,' Frank King said. 'Tell us something we don't know yet. It's a dog, right? Her first picture after she scoops the pool and it's a dog, right? You know her, don't you?'

'I love her. I wouldn't say I knew her.'

'I love her too. We all love her. It's never her fault. No one's criming the kid. Only we have a crisis on our hands and fooling ourselves isn't going to help.'

'Or only a little,' Victor England said. 'What is the crisis exactly?'

'I know a cool breeze when I meet one. Question is, how do we all avoid getting blown away? You still see George in London?'

'George? I see him.'

'Because how is he?'

'He's pretty good. He's fine.'

'Fuck him,' Frank King said. 'The money he took from this Studio he'd better be fine. Did I ever tell you that story? Look, Victor, I'm going to lay this thing on the line. Before we go into any detailed analysis, I'm willing even at this stage to shelve the whole picture. We have a contract situation to protect vis-à-vis Dotty and if we're one down, O.K. we've still got two to go. We made a mistake, we made a mistake. It's a piece of shit, it's a piece of shit. It was Sam's story and director before we ever came in on it. Victor, we're not going to forget what you're doing for us, believe me, no matter what. It just so happens I'm not about to send any piece of crap out that gate with our imprint on it. You know Rex's line:

"Don't dress a corpse for a dance or no one'll come to the next one." What percentage of the market is necrophile? Maybe we should do a survey. Meanwhile Rex always says only one thing to do with a cadaver – bury it, give it to the worms.'

'Then who do we give the worms to?' Bartholomew Heinz asked. 'The stockholders?'

'Fuck the stockholders, Barty.'

'Do I get to start with the pretty ones?'

'You start with letter A; you get paid, don't you? What I want to do is take a fresh, clean look at the material, starting from basics. Dotty's worth a whole lot more than our investment on one picture. Dotty's the future and the future is us. Sam can always carry the can. What else is an old goat for? Victor, believe me, you're only confirming something we all of us in this room know already. O.K., I respect your honesty; I respect your integrity; what's more, I agree with you. Leave the admin problems to us. I want your opinion as one of the greatest directors in the business. Can we save it or not? You're solid with us, no matter what you say. You want friends, you have your friends. You want finance, you have finance. Right down the line. So tell us the worst. No blindfold. No last cigarette. Shoot!'

'I liked it,' Victor England said.

There is a silence. Then the three men burst out laughing. But it is no trio: they do not laugh in harmony. Frank laughs first, as if at a piece of studied insolence; Bartholomew Heinz and Victor come in together, but Heinz's laughter has something of the hysteria of a man who has been unjustly acquitted. And Victor England? He laughs with the genial malice of a messenger whose unwanted good news has made nonsense of a tragedy.

'You liked it? Frank King said. 'You *liked* it?'

'I liked it.'

No one laughed. 'Victor,' Frank King said. 'Barty – '

Bartholomew Heinz was still laughing; no he wasn't. 'Let's not futz around here. If I let this picture out into the light of day and it dies in public, I follow it to the stake. And if I go, the Studio goes. Shap and his lunk-heads'll be in here like termites. Munch, munch. Last year's termites'll look like they were on a diet compared to Shap. You know how much of our money that bastard George took on the boat with him? He won't fly, you know that? Over ten million dollars. Dotty is our last Duchess, isn't that what you said, Barty?'

'One of 'em,' Heinz said.

'Who says they're two a penny? Not when one of 'em's Dotty Lampard, they're not. I'm sitting here because of that girl. I made a hot deal with Sam, right when the rest of the pack were kicking the door panels in. O.K., I'm a genius. Where everyone else keeps his nuts, I have the secret of the universe. Life's a fountain. I'm vice-president in charge of production. All I have to do is promise the Board I'm infallible, and wham – white smoke first time around. Pope Frank. What I cannot now afford is to be wrong in public. A loss I can shuffle away somewhere. What are accountants for? But a public run for a lame dog as big as the Ritz and where am I? Vice-president in charge of running for his life. So tell me the truth, Victor, willya? I'm not going to thank you for anything else. The house is on fire? Tell me. It's no big surprise. I thought I could smell smoke. Just so long as nobody catches me with a match in my hand.'

'What's the matter, Frank?' Victor England said. 'Can't you believe some news is good news any more?'

'Is anyone going to come and see it? You've been living in Europe. I don't want to know about art. I don't want to know about denouncing capitalism. Are people going to pay to see the thing? Dice or no dice?'

'Dotty's a beautiful girl,' Victor England said.

'O.K., she's a beautiful girl. But shall I tell you something? She should never have flashed her snatch first time around – '

'Frank – '

'She should never have flashed her snatch first time around. That is my considered opinion. I know what you're going to say. It made the picture a smash. That girl didn't need to do that kind of a thing.' He flicked the switch on his desk. 'Could we have some coffee in here? Cream and sugar? Cream and sugar for Mr England. Flash your snatch first time around and what do you do for an encore? Tell me something, how many pictures did the Princess make so far?'

'Oh Frank, that's ancient history.'

'Have you seen her grosses even today? Shall I tell you something? The public has no evidence that I've ever seen that that woman even has *nipples*. Victor, she's been in more than thirty pictures, and there is no cinematic evidence she even has nipples.'

'The Princess is something else – '

'O.K., you had a run-in together, we won't talk about her. All the same, the public still stands in line to see those things. And they don't even know if they've got knobs on 'em. *Because* they don't know. Don't let's knock 'em.'

'Knock 'em, they knock back,' Victor England said.

'I had a pair of her pants in my desk drawer for three weeks and that's no return on four million bucks, believe me. We all remember her. Jesus, Hullo pictures were bad enough but Goodbye pictures ... Well, from here on in we run a tight ship. So when I tell you, Victor, that I want you to come here and make pictures for us, at a price, at a price, Victor – '

'That's what they call me,' Victor England said.

'They call you a smart son of a so-and-so with a quarter of Murchison Canyon to prove it.'

'A fifth,' Victor England said.

'You could finance *us*. A fifth, do you really?'

'That's why I haven't made a picture recently. I've been picking the oranges.'

'I'm serious. When we give you a go-ahead, it's never

going to be because we don't know how to say no. We know how.'

'Why the threats, Frank?' Victor England said.

'Threats? Promises. By which I mean, if I say – and I do say – that we want you working out of this Studio, it's because that's what we want. No crap. When I say something like that, it's as good as a contract.'

'That's not what my lawyer says.'

'Unless Brute tries to screw us like he used to screw us in the old days. Morning, afternoon and night – '

'He doesn't come in much afternoons any more,' Victor England said.

'If he tries his old line on us again, he's going to have to go and marry another rich broad because he'll get no change this time around. You know he used to get nine air-fares for the Princess? In addition to her million; million-five one time. Nine air-fares. From *Malta*. She had a theoretical domiciliary arrangement for tax purposes, she lived in Malta. Brute said she had to have maximum mobility. Maximum mobility my ass. She was balling Sherman Knight the whole damned time, lives right round the corner from me. That broad never even knew where Malta was.'

'Brute's smart.'

'Brute is a crook. He's a crook. They killed the business, those guys.'

'What do you want me to do, Frank?'

'Victor, tell me something. You were and remain one of the greatest film editors this town has ever seen. Can you spare me one afternoon before you go winging home?'

'You're sending me home?'

'To Malta. Nine times. And we go take one more look at this thing together?'

'Do I bring my scissors?'

'Victor, if you did that – I don't know why in hell you should, but if you did that – '

'What would you do, Frank?'

'I'll tell you what I'd do. I'd bring the paste.'

'Frank, don't break my arm. I may need it. That's the one I thumb rides with.'

'Bart, you know something? This is the way people ought to work. This is the way they ought to work.'

'Behind the director's back?' Victor said.

'Behind the director's back? That sonofabitch won't even talk to me. He will not talk to me. He wants money to talk to me about something you'd have to pay people to take away. You ever hear of paying people to *deliver* garbage? Sonofabitch, not yet thirty years old, he wants money to sit down and talk. Brute Andrews! People like that kill an industry. They kill it.'

'Frank, save it,' Victor England said. 'We all – '

'Don't talk to me that way, Victor. I mean it.'

'Mr King, I have to go now,' Victor England said.

'O.K. O.K. I'm sorry. I apologize.'

'Victor, please,' Bartholomew Heinz said. 'Frank's tired – '

'Sure he is, but I never take shit until I've been paid,' Victor England said. 'The Directors' Guild wouldn't like it. I have to go.'

'Fuck the Directors' Guild,' Frank King said.

'Not starting with the letter A, I don't.'

The three of them laughed again, and Frank King and Bartholomew Heinz had time to hold Victor England in the room.

'Victor, I apologize, unconditionally, but one thing I am going to say. Help us on this one and believe me, Dotty Lampard's going to be one grateful girl or I'll know the reason why. You want to make a picture with her? You can make any picture you want. And Brute can draw up the contract. What more can I say?'

'Frank, I tell you: you're not that strapped.'

'We'll see,' Frank King said, 'when we go run the picture.'

During the course of this long and realistic scene Bartholomew

Heinz is presented as a yes-man but it now turns out that he is something more than that. He is one of those characters, not uncommon in downtown Byzantium, who has learned that he can give his intelligence full play only by seeming to embrace what controls and limits its use. He enjoys the discipline of an almost demeaning subservience. He resembles a court philosopher who is obliged both to flatter the Sovereign and to keep faith with the truth. Later that day, after Victor has been driven back to his hotel, Heinz calls and arranges that they have dinner. They meet at the restaurant:

'Victor, how are you?' It was only that morning that they had been in Frank King's office, but Heinz's tone allowed for the possibility that Victor England had undergone major surgery in the meanwhile. 'I hope you don't mind eating here.' They were in the best restaurant in town, but when was that good enough? 'I come here a lot when Carol has to go back East. At least I know I can get a table. Places are so crowded right now you have to wait to be thrown out. How are you, Gianno?'

'Very well, Mr Heinz, and you, sir? Good evening, Mr England, how nice to have you back with us again!'

'Gianno,' Victor England said.

'We'd like a nice quiet table, Gianno, away from the people. Victor, I'm so grateful to you. And I'm so happy things are working out on our project.'

'You spoke to Brute.'

'I spoke to Brute; who was brutal, of course. But I'm sure we can close this thing out on a realistic basis. Victor, I hope you know that not *only* because of what you're doing for us, but because of it too, we're going to give you the finest deal we can afford, only right now – '

'Are things that bad? I don't hear things are that bad.'

'Everyone's making deals but that's because they can't stand to hear the guns getting closer when they stop talking. You ever see a major bank on the march?

Soldier ants get out of the way. Angelo, we would like two Vodka Martinis straight up, without the olive. No one denies there's plenty of action in town. Maybe they've all come for the funeral, but you can't get a room between here and Malibu. I'll tell you something: Carol resold a house last week, three months and two coats of paint after she bought it – up thirty-one per cent. Thirty-one per cent. Why do we kill ourselves making motion pictures? Why?'

'Maybe she should be Head of Production.'

'Think I'm not working on it? Personally, Victor, I want to tell you, I remain optimistic. We have some fine product lined up. Quality is the name of the game today. Otherwise –' Bartholomew Heinz rehearsed suicide with a fish knife. 'But tell me, I want to know, how is my dear divine Fleur?'

'Beautiful,' Victor England said.

'I'll never forget what she did for Carol. Do I love that woman! You remember what she did for Carol?'

'I never knew she did anything for anybody,' Victor said.

'One of the great, great stories. Captain, will you please get somebody to come and take an order? You've met Brigid, haven't you?'

'Brigid,' Victor England said.

'Our divine Brigid? Sure you have. Chihuahua, Chihuahua, Chihuahua?'

'Your dog. Of course. Sure. We met. When did Fleur have anything to do with your dog?'

'She only saved her life on the Golden Gate Freeway. You don't remember? She only dived right into the traffic and grabbed her from under the wheels of a ten-ton truck. The total and definitive triumph of beauty over the military-industrial complex. The bravest thing I ever saw in my life. As far as Carol and I are concerned, anything Fleur wants, it's hers.'

'It is already,' Victor England said.

'I wonder where you were at the time.'

'I was under the wheels of a ten-ton producer.'

'Working for the Frog, of course you were.'

'Nobody ever dived in and pulled *me* out.'

'You heard about the Frog, I guess? Last thing I heard, he didn't even recognize Red Frances when she went to see him. I guess he really robbed you on that one, didn't he? How did Brute ever let you get into a thing like that? You did two pictures, didn't you? with Frog? He robbed you once and then he robbed you again.'

'If people hadn't robbed me,' Victor England said, 'I wouldn't be rich today. I came to this town with nothing. I've been robbed by everyone I ever worked with. Today I pay five-figure salaries to guys I never even see.'

'You're lucky. We see them. I wish you'd brought her with you,' Heinz said. 'Fleur. Carol and I truly dote on that girl. Gianno, come over here, will you? Tell me about these a minute, are they really all right? I don't want Mr England here to get sick now.'

'Mr Heinz, Mr Heinz, when did I ever give you a bad oyster?'

'You never did, Gianno, you never did. That's what makes you a dangerous man. Like I sometimes say to Frank, "Why pay a man who never laid an egg to come and lay his first one with us?" Take an oyster for granted, next thing you know you're damaging your bridgework on a pearl.'

'You have nothing to fear, Mr England.'

'If this is fear,' Victor England said. 'I hope it always tastes this good. Don't you like oysters, Bart?'

'I was brought up in New England, Victor. And after New England seafood, nothing else tastes quite the same. I tell Gianno it's the kosher in me, but it's really Cape Cod.'

'Bart,' Victor England said, 'why are we having dinner?'

'Victor, you're really an extraordinary character. You're two people – '

'Only for tax purposes,' Victor said.

'And I really like them both. You're absolutely right. I do have something I want to talk to you about.'

'Bart, I wouldn't really want it any other way.'

'It's this girl. Not Dotty.'

'The one Rex has in Mexico.'

'You heard.'

'I smelled.'

'Victor, understand me right: I'm not acting as anybody's emissary here tonight.'

'Sure you're not.'

'Nor am I about to give you a lesson on the rules of survival. You've been in the jungle a lot longer than I have, and with a lot more success. Would you believe friendship?'

'Chihuahua, Chihuahua, Chihuahua,' Victor England said. 'What's she like?'

'She's a very good-looking girl. Karen Smith.'

'What's the problem?'

'I'm going to lay it right on the line, Victor. A personal reaction but one that worries hell out of me. It's what she's doing to the old man.'

'Is there anything left she can do that hasn't been done already? He's tough. Don't worry about Rex.'

'I'm sorry, Victor, but this is something else. Frank has to fly down there in the Lear every time we have to have a decision. You can't get a response any other way.'

'Don't Heads of Production get to make decisions for themselves?'

'Oh come on, Victor: your left hand knows what your right hand's doing. Kings don't abdicate. No way. Rex runs the Studio, no one's kidding themselves. Except he won't do it. This girl has got him in a full Nelson; it's going to need more than Dick Tracy to get him out of this one and even if he does get out of it, we have problems.'

'You want me to have her in our picture, is that it, Bart?'

'The first of our pictures,' Heinz said. 'The first of our pictures. You know how our deal is shaping.'

'I thought we didn't make goodbye pictures any more. Or have things changed since this morning?'

'No one's said goodbye, maybe no one will. She's a talent in her own right, this girl.'

'Since when did that do anybody any good? You want her away from Rex, right?'

'Or I want Rex away from her,' Heinz said. 'The Studio has to be run. Decisions have to be made.'

'I was going to have Dotty.'

'When we have the right subject, she's yours. It's a promise. But she's not going to do you any good if Shap and his friends move in. These people aren't rubber stamps any more, any of them. When they stamp, you're liable to find there's a hole in the ground. We need Rex out from under. All of us.'

'First I'm recutting a picture for you, then I'm breaking the world's record for the snatch and press. What do I have to look forward to?'

'Brute and I are in a negotiation, Victor. I'm not asking you to rely on promises – '

'I did it once,' Victor England said. 'She's still getting the cheques.'

'I'm not asking anything like that. You know that. We're prepared to make some very solid commitments. We're making some very solid commitments.'

'Bart, I'm not about to shoot with a girl I don't want to shoot with.'

'This is a talented, beautiful girl,' Bartholomew Heinz said.

'They all are.'

'If you don't agree with that estimate, no one's going to force her on you; no one can, no one will. That's common ground.'

'And frequently fought over,' Victor England said.

'Victor, the truth is, we have to pump ship. Everything is fine. We're on schedule, we're on course. But we still have to pump ship. Or else.'

'Pump ship together or pump shit separately,' Victor

England said. 'I can always retire, Bart, and eat oranges.'

'They're better for you,' Heinz said.

'Sink my teeth into just one piece of fruit and I'm probably in breach of my alimony agreements. What's the girl's name again? Karen – '

'Smith. Victor, believe me – '

'And spoil something that means a lot to both of us? Heinzy, my wife saved your dog, I'll save the Studio. You'll still be more grateful to her than to me. Only let's not have it ruin our romance, O.K.?'

The two men laughed, and their laughter was a seal on their bargain, whatever it was. They might have been in a script conference where a laugh was the only proof that a scene was licked. They smiled at each other and a window seemed to open for them on green and happy sophomore days when they were simple buddies. Had they ever been simple? They had certainly never been buddies. They had not met until Bartholomew Heinz came West, on a train, to be Script Head of the Studio. Until then he had been a literary agent, with offices above a secondhand bookstore where clerks in striped pants wrapped purchases in brown paper, figured side inmost. He had been the first to read the manly manuscripts of writers who had since become the clients of people who no longer needed clients. His pensive pen had sieved early drafts of once proscribed and now prescribed reading. His marginal marks had been archly hived into archives by calm, collecting librarians. Who could believe that the movie executive was identical with the man who had suggested, in a sixteen-page letter now under glass, the cable-car confrontation in a novel said to be the key book of its decayed decade and whose fifty-one per cent Swiss-owned author lived behind locked steel shutters and weighed less than his weight in gold? Certainly Heinz himself could not.

The purpose of this long flashback begins to declare itself. One speaks of a flashback only as a locating device: it should now be clear that California Time is a sequence of presents. The Studio attempts to plan rationally, but it is attempting the impossible: to regularize the random, to order the simultaneous. California Time describes and exemplifies the paradox: reading, we see the author's past presented as our future; the pages not yet started by the reader have already been finished by the writer. The coming year which Bartholomew Heinz and Victor England are discussing has already been and gone. Men of power are eternally powerless, which is what makes their deliberations comic. Need we decide whether the temporal collapse which California Time conceives in aesthetic and literary form, is also a model of more general, metaphysical significance?

Let us return to the restaurant:

The mossy banks of the décor were printennial with flowers, but all of them were rootless; their stems were stiff with wire catheters and their spring would not last the week. As for the patrons, Angelo, the Maître d', assigned them to their tables with the vigilant calm of an officer, in a slow emergency, allocating places in the lifeboats. The restaurant had its mouth so full that even those with reservations felt privileged to have them honoured.

There was one ugly scene, however, when the son of a romantic producer, whose happy ending had left his offspring rich enough to mount the healthiest hell-raisings, dollar-for-doll, on the whole West Coast, arrived to claim an unregistered reservation for himself and his party, which included a recently uninterned international swindler, his mother, their child and a blonde professional woman, famous for her oral resuscitation. The young man snatched an old bottle full of new wine from its cradle and watered the candles at a table where a producer with a circulatory problem was entertaining two girls who claimed to be Romanoffs and who had taken a lot of trouble putting on their accents.

The swindler, who had become so short-sighted that even his closest associates could no longer see him clearly, bit a selection of fruit in a ribboned basket and then stubbed out a bunch of grapes in a gay cowboy's consommé. Angelo discovered a cancellation.

A little later, two actors were so affectionate towards an ageless agent that they tore her dress and dislodged one of her new breasts. At the same time Missy, the cigarette girl, who danced and sang a little, was kissed on the lips by a Star whose fourth (and second) husband had shot the man who came between him. Clients who had earlier been delighted to be seated grew testy when latecomers, with green grease palms, weighted the waiters in their favour. 'Their service is worse than mine,' said Babs Cologne to her tennis coach, who for twenty bucks an hour also supplied the balls. 'What do you expect?' he wanted to know, 'with half the waiters under the table looking for one of Maxine Liebermann's tits?' Babs leaned forward, to prove hers were where he could count them; she loved him to a fault. Only one old man remained, polished and unblinking, smiling and benign throughout the evening. Gianno went up to him, as checks were being served in padded silver boxes, and asked him, Judge, whether everything had been all right. He was dead and had to be helped home.

Bartholomew Heinz and Victor England finish their fight for the bill and go through the restaurant doing the honours and offers. The car is waiting in the parking-lot where Brute Andrews was once jumped by a producer whose wife was one of the few things he ever took lying down:

The story was Leo had had a few drinks and was having trouble keeping his courage down. Brute looked at the gun and then at Leo's face and said, 'You've gone green, why don't you shoot?' Leo threw up into the new convertible owned by a swimming star who had splashed out, while Brute held his gun for him. He didn't give it back until he had sold Leo an original screenplay, and a director to go with it.

It was, however, in this same parking-lot that a body would one day be found.

'Is there somewhere you'd care to go?' Bartholomew Heinz asked, when they were in the car. 'God forbid.'

'My sentiments exactly,' Victor England said. 'But thanks for leaving it open.'

'You know what we should do with her, don't you? Dotty. Get her into another picture. Fast. Before we do too much thinking; or she does. Leave her to worry, leave her to get lonesome, and what'll happen?'

They had halted by the tracks where trolley cars once ran on profitable lines to the Pacific.

'Lonesome?' Victor England said. 'That girl? Here? You know damn well what'll happen. You did elementary chemistry, didn't you? A College boy.'

'Try and get a date,' Bartholomew Heinz said. 'If that's what you think. Call her up. You or anyone else. She doesn't go anywhere. She's living with some stenographer in a tacky apartment house way out on Sunset someplace.'

'Give her time, Barty.'

'She still has the same boyfriend. In London, I mean. You try calling her up.'

'I'm a married man, Bart. I don't have the nickel.'

'She calls him every night, transatlantic, talks to him for hours. We're all married men. I don't know what she says, but we get the synopsis – in dollars and cents. Every night of the week.'

'Fly him over.'

'Think we haven't suggested it? He works. He has a job he won't quit. He has some ninety-dollar-a-week job he won't quit. He teaches psychologically deprived kids for ninety dollars a week.'

'He sounds like a real son-of-a-bitch,' Victor England said.

'Laugh,' Bartholomew Heinz said, shaking his head at the doorman as they drew up at Victor's hotel. 'Laugh, but these are the imponderables in this business. Why it has to be like no other business in the world. He's probably two-timing her with some paraplegic teenager. Victor, I'm sorry. What gets into us out here? I should never have said that. Regardless I should never have said it.'

'You have a lot of problems,' Victor England said.

'How is your daughter?'

'Forget it, Bart.'

'I'm ashamed of myself.'

'I guess she's alive. I get a bill now and again.'

'I'm going to go home and wash my mouth out.'

'Oh come on, Bart. I've been called a kike in my time. Being Bella's father's no surprise to me.'

'You know what Dotty needs,' Bartholomew Heinz said, 'that's somebody in the business. Who called you a kike?'

'A friend. Why somebody in the business? It never works, does it? What makes you think it's going to work for Dotty?'

'Who said anything about working? If she wants to be one of us, she should accept that. She has to decide what world she wants to be in. She's taking our money – '

'Luckily. What world do you want to be in, Heinzy?'

'Victor, I'm in the pack-and-wrap department. I put the string round the packages. I don't have to make those sorts of decisions.'

'You keep your finger on the knot O.K.,' Victor England said. 'Do you want to come in for a night-cap?'

'I have to go home. I have to go home. The guys who've tried to get into that girl's pants, you wouldn't believe: the cream. And she stays hooked on some ninety-bucks-a-week schoolteacher back in Battersea someplace. It's an insult to the industry, Victor! Rob Pascal: nuts about her! She won't even talk to him.'

'He talks now?'

'He's a little older. He has to. A few words. He's not so stupid, Rob. He's not necessarily so stupid. You know what the grosses were on *Flatfoot*? First three weeks in selected cities? Rob isn't so stupid.'

'I don't think Rob is stupid,' Victor England said. 'He can be very smart. I know.'

'Sure you do. I was forgetting.'

'That's O.K.,' Victor England said. 'I was remembering. And that was when he was twenty-two years old.'

'And she won't even give him the time of day.'

'He can always buy a policeman.'

'With twenty-five per cent of *Flatfoot*, he can buy himself a couple. What she needs to do first and foremost is work.'

'Do you have something for her?' Victor said, through the car window, while the toads pooped in the purple background.

'We've got guys out looking,' Heinz said. 'If you come up with anything, even if it's only a sniff, yell.'

'I'll yell,' Victor England said.

'And Frank said to tell you – '

'Something about a limousine?'

'Ten o'clock?' Heinz said.

'Your afternoons begin early out here,' Victor England said. 'I'll go sharpen my scissors.'

Victor and Frank King spend all the following day in the cutting-room, queuing at the movieola like kids on a pier, peering at what butlers have been seeing ever since keyholes came in. At first, Victor is cautious, even respectful of the work of the original director, whose name we still have not been told, but then, like a surgeon impatient of a patient's old scars, he begins to operate more freely. He and Frank King become closer and closer over the movieola. Anyone coming into the room might take them, if not for lovers, for safebreakers. The picture is sliced and spliced to the point where a kinsman watching the operation would have fainted away to see the size and range of the incisions. The two are up to their elbows in celluloid cells, but grins and winks and laughs of triumph begin to fill the hot room; a mere day or two later, they have cured most of the cutting-room flaws. The final joke comes when they paste the director's name back on to the front of the movie. All their work is below the collar. They have left the patient with the same face. The name is Peter Drakos.

How much later in time does the following scene take place? Is Victor back in California on another visit, or has he never left?

'Stay and take me to the opening,' she said.
  'I can't.'
  'Because I heard what you did.'
  'You weren't supposed to.'
  'I won't tell anybody.'
  'Tell everybody,' Victor England said. 'I love you.'
  'Oh,' she said, suddenly and unjustly accused.
  'You knew.'
  'I don't know anything.'
  'Did you think I edited the goddam picture for Peter's sake?'
  '*He* knows,' Dotty said. 'Is he supposed to?'
  'He won't tell anybody. There's one person who ain't never gonna tell.'
  She looked at him over the short candle and he was happy.
  'I hate him,' she said. 'I *hate* him.'
  'You've got yourselves a hit,' Victor England said. 'Did you hear about the cards in Portland, Oregon? Don't underestimate him.'
  'I don't underestimate him,' Dotty said. 'I hate him. I want to go back to London. Take me back to London. *Put me in your suitcase.*'

'I love you,' Victor England said. 'I love you. I love you.'

'Then at least stay and come to the opening. If you really loved me, you would.'

'If would and could were cousins,' Victor England said.

'I shouldn't have said that anyway. That was cheap. If you loved me, that stuff. That's cheap.'

'I do love you,' he said. 'To die.'

'I'm not worth it.'

'You're worth everything.'

'I'd like to run away. Run and run. I used to dream about it, you know, running. I wanted to be in the Olympic games. Never act. I was quite fast once.'

'Why did you stop?'

'Bum's too big,' she said, and tore off the best of her smiles to give him.

'So that's why you became a movie star, Miss Lampard.'

'That's why. I just couldn't get away.'

'Bullshit, baby.' It sounded like a promise.

'No,' she said. 'Swear.'

They sat like lovers, hand over handed over hand, and then she leaned forward and blew out the candle. Victor left money. They got up to go.

They reach the door and Dotty puts on a ratty dufflecoat with the lining loose in the sleeve. Victor wants to choke her with luxuries just so she can throw them away. He eats her with his eyes; he loves her. They are about to go into the uninhabited night when the door of the restaurant opens and in walks a fresh-faced boy, red-cheeked, tousle-haired, chewing a piece of gum, just the kind of white-toothed, carefree kid you could see any night of the week on television leaning out of a helicopter with a machine-gun busting Charlie's ass. He comes through the draught curtain right between Dotty and Victor.

'Aha, aha, *ahaaa*!' he said. 'So this is what's going on. This is the explanation why I can never get a date. Old man England, he just keeps rolling, he just keeps rolling along – '

'Good evening, Mr Pascal,' said Peppino, putting him effusively under arrest. 'How are you, sir?'

'Peppino, you've been concealing a material witness.'

'Goodnight, Robert,' said Victor.

'Not so fast,' Pascal said, 'not so fast.' He went close to Dotty. His chewing-gum was peppermint and vodka. 'Tell me something, lady. Am I ugly?'

She looked carefully at the face that laid them in more places than the aisles.

'Yes,' she said. 'Very.'

'I'm *what*? I'm *ugly*? I'm a movie star. I'm a goddam movie star. How can I be ugly?'

'They're all ugly,' Dotty Lampard said. She was crying. She took Victor England's arm and she was crying.

'Come back here. Not so fast. You come back here. Have you seen *Flatfoot*?'

'I haven't seen anything,' Dotty said, dry.

'I just happen to be the biggest thing in town. Rob Pascal, you heard of me. I'm the biggest thing in town. Are you in love with this old has-been? Victor, you're supposed to be a married man. You're not corrupting this kid, I hope, are you? Because we have legislation. I'm politically very aware, you know that? And we have legislation about that kind of a thing. Let me tell you something. I'm going to win the fucking Oscar. My psychiatrist has promised me. Have you seen the grosses, Vic? Listen, you're going to vote for me, I hope?'

'As soon as you run,' Victor England said.

Pascal put his arm round Victor's shoulders and leaned at Dotty. 'Victor and I are old friends. At least he's old and we're friends. Only kidding, Victor, only kidding, old pal. We've known a lot of people together, old Victor and me. We have a lot in common, ain't that right, old pal? We really love each other, don't we, Vic? All this stuff is really just a cover-up, isn't that right?' He put his arms round Victor's neck, looked him in the eye and kissed him full on the lips. Dotty turned away, holding the curtain like a ballerina bludgeoned with bouquets.

'Thanks, Rob,' Victor England said, 'but I've already eaten.'

'I want to know the secret. I want to know the secret. Who do you have to fuck around here to get her goddam telephone number?'

Why did it take so long to open the door and get out?

'Wait till I win that thing,' Rob flung after them. 'She'll answer the door to me then all right. Peppino might even give me a table without a reservation, huh, Peppino baby?'

He sits down on a bar stool and starts stabbing courtesy celery in the avocado dip. There is a girl with a man at the other end of the bar. Pretty soon, the man is giving him nasty looks.

Victor and Dotty sit in the parked car. In a bar down the street, the television is showing pictures of tornado damage.

'There's someone else, isn't there?' Victor England said.

'Still the same person,' she said.

'No,' he said. 'There's someone else.'

She leaned forward and gazed at him with a tenderness which, had she loved him, she might not have been able to manage.

'No,' she said. 'Swear.'

'I love you,' he said.

She cried then and threw herself into his arms and he knew it was hopeless.

Victor stays an extra day; it is hard finding his wife a present he can be sure she won't want. Then he flies out. His love for Dotty travels with him. His eyes and nose stream. He has loved her ever since he saw her first movie and didn't like her a bit. He reads a script where a couple are so crazy about each other they never want to see each other again.

*

Frank King calls Dotty about the Première. He would take her himself but he is about to part from his wife and the lawyers say careful. He asks Dotty is there anybody she wants to go with and, shrugging on the line, she replies 'I don't want to go at all.' He says in that case he will send a limousine.

'I'll walk,' she said.

'Walk?' he said. 'The hell you'll walk.'

'I'd like to walk,' she said. 'I'd prefer to walk.'

'How do I know you'll get there? Even if you ever start out, you're liable to get yourself picked up,' Frank King was wriggling in his chair, cocking his feet on the desk, twisting round on the lookout. 'You're liable to get yourself killed. Nobody walks in this town.'

'I walk all the time,' Dotty said. 'You meet people walking.'

'Nuts,' Frank King said. 'You meet nuts. You'll get yourself killed. You're too important to walk. I'll send a limousine. And you come in it. Dotty, you hear me?'

'All right,' the girl said, so quickly that he thought they had been cut off.

'Seven o'clock,' he said. 'And, Dotty, formal, O.K.?'

'Better send a dress then,' Dotty said. 'Sir.'

'He'll be there,' Frank King said. He was going to have to speak to the lawyer about putting in a clause about broads who wanted to walk. He was so agitated he had to call the secretaries in to untangle the telephone wires. He was really snarled up.

The limousine turns out to be a Maserati sports. The chauffeur wears a grey cap and grey ankle-length coat. He carries a package from wardrobe and a crown of thornless roses. She hates the dress in the fancy wrapping and goes through her flatmate's closet looking for something terrible enough to wear. Then she runs to the car where the chauffeur is waiting and asks him:

'How do I look?'

'You look fine to me, Miss Lampard,' he said.

'Oh well, never mind. I say, haven't I seen you some-where? I've seen you somewhere, haven't I?'

'Maybe in the movies,' the chauffeur said.

'Oh, are you an actor too?'

'No, I'm in the movies.'

'Really, what've you done?'

'I did a thing called *Flatfoot*,' he said. 'I don't know if you've heard of it.'

'Well, of all the dirty tricks!' Dotty said. 'What a filthy trick.'

'I thought it was kind of a clean trick. As tricks go. You'd better get in; we'll be late.'

'I suppose this is your car. Do we have to go in it?'

'It's quicker than piggy-back. Not so much fun, but quicker.'

'They said they were sending a limousine. I don't want you.'

'You have ten minutes to get to the theater. You drive, if you don't want me to. I'll trot along behind.'

'I can't drive,' Dotty said. 'Only don't expect a tip, that's all. Tips are out.'

So Rob Pascal finally gets to take her to the opening, but she refuses to speak to him. It is an unspeakable evening all round. Peter Drakos refuses to speak to Dotty. He has been recon-ciled to the Studio, as Victor England predicted. He forgives Frank King; he forgives Rex Keyes. He cannot forgive Dotty, who has had nothing to do with the saving surgery executed on the picture and who, once again, pulls in the public. Drakos, during the days that follow, gives interviews in which he disparages Dotty and asks laughingly how such a lousy actress can get such wonderful notices. 'I guess she must have had a good director,' he says, imitating the bastard he'll soon get to be. The Studio people have forgotten that they once regarded Drakos as an embarrassing hangover from Sam Carnap's involvement with the project. They take a whole page in the Trades to announce that they have secured his services for the future. They have very big plans for him.

*

Rob Pascal sends Dotty two dozen long-stem roses every day after the opening. Her tiny, tinny apartment in The Towers is crammed with them. She doesn't have enough vases. She gives bunches to hospitals. Her flatmate takes them to the office. She tries to turn them away. They are left to die on the doorstep. The second week begins. She hopes that they will now stop. Pascal sends four dozen a day. At the beginning of the third week, it is eight dozen. The smell of roses is suffocating. She calls Pascal.

'What's the idea? What'll make you quit this nonsense?'
    'See me,' he said.
    'Why should I?' she said.
    'I'm crazy about you,' he said. 'Didn't you get my flowers?'
    'Send any more and I'm going home,' she said. 'To England. I'm serious.'
    'England?' he said. 'Not *England*. I'll kill myself. *Victor* England? I'll kill myself.'
    'I don't like you,' she said. 'England my home country.'
    'Oh little old England,' he said.
    'I like Victor very much,' she said.
    'Did you hear I was going to win an Academy Award?'
    'Doesn't everyone?' she said.
    'For *Flatfoot*. Did you hear I was nominated?'
    'Your mother must be very happy for you.'
    'It's been nominated for five separate awards. I want you to be my date at the Presentation.'
    'Forget it,' Dotty said.
    'I hope you like the roses,' he said. 'Week after next, they'll be coming a dozen times a day.'

She goes with him to the Presentation. He wears a midnight-blue tux with a light-blue white-ruffed shirt and plum-coloured bow-tie.

'I figured you'd be against anything ostentatious,' he said.

'Christ, you're awful,' she said.

'I hope you're going to be nice to me,' he said.

'I said I'd come. I didn't say I'd be nice.'

'Don't you think that's kind of sneaky?' He smiled at the flesh wound, and she smiled back, for the first time. 'Anyway, after tonight I'm going to be in demand. I'm going to be wanted everywhere.'

'Oh good,' she said. 'I hope you go.'

He had been known to approach girls on the street, Rob Pascal the famous actor, and ask them whether they had ever been laid by a movie star. He got lucky quite often. He threw messages to girls from hotel balconies to come on up. And when they came, they came. There were those who shook their heads, but one or two of them walked slowly down the same street at the same time a day or two later and looked up, and didn't shake their heads second time around. Rob Pascal had been in a good few pictures and a few of them had been good. He had been to school down the street. He surfed before he surfaced in a beach pic or two and then he was taken up by an impressed Impresario from the East who thought he was an unspoiled kid. He *was* unspoiled: even being spoiled didn't spoil him. He rolled the dice, when nothing else was rolling, and knew to dodge when they were loaded. He stayed loose. He was California.

'I don't have a problem in the world,' he said. 'Except you don't like me. And that's a problem bigger than all the others put together. But if you're nice to me, I'll make sure you get all the hot pastrami you ever wanted.'

'I don't know what you're talking about.'

'I don't know what you're talking about,' he acted her. 'You know what I'm talking about. There are a lot of girls'd give a lot to be where you're going to be tonight.'

'I have tickets of my own,' she said. 'I don't need to go with you.'

'I can be very helpful in that direction,' he said. 'Ask around.'

'You've got a lot of teeth,' she said, 'for a baby.'

'Treat me like shit,' he said. 'Treat me like shit. Go ahead. It's your last chance.'

They reach the applauditorium. The architect has been given his headache and has solved the problem by building a latticed concrete straw hat with a parking lot on the brim. Rob looks in the car mirror and tousles his hair. He and Dotty go in, charm-in-arm, and down to the seats within a hope, step and a jump of the ramp to the stage where the Awards are to be dispensed. Rob stops to congratulate a couple of his rivals – one always plays the Winning Alcoholic With The Loser's Wit and the other is the Jew who is everybody's blue-eyed Goy – and he laughs and gives them testing punches to see if they're really hollow; they do the smileys and tell him he's got it in the brag.

Flatfoot wins a couple of minor awards, for breast photography and screamplay, and it looks as if, as expected, it's going to sweep the bored. Rob sits taller and taller. When *Flatfoot* wins a third award, he no longer confines himself to squeezing Dotty's thigh. He turns and kisses her, as if she's already agreed to a Mexican quickie. She almost slaps his face. She makes to get up, but he pulls her down, turning round to smile apologies on her over-excited behalf. She really hates him. When the five nominations for Best Actor are read, sections of the films in which the actors star are shown on the screen behind the stage. The star of *Flatfoot* gets the band-wagon's cheer. The other nominees agree that it is a four-gone conclusion: Rob looks like the only one in it. The envelope is passed to the Princess to open and read. The winner's name causes a gasp to go round the tierful audience.

For a second, and then for a second second, the company might never have heard of the household name who now stumbled to the stage. He stood shaking hands with the shaking hands of the Princess, both of them frowning at the piece of paper she had to show him before he would believe it.

'Ladies and gentlemen,' she said, 'I have been accused of not being able to act, but this is the first time since I was six years old anybody ever accused me of not being able to read!'

The Cowboy, who stood for Something We All Need Today More Than Ever, kicked shit for a moment, as he often had in dustier circumstances, and then he looked up and said, 'Well, all I can say is, folks: someone's sure as hell been *robbed*.'

There was a checking silence while a myriad of well-made faces looked in and out and then a grating, grateful laugh filled the bowl. Higher and higher the audience rode on the wave of laughter as it rose and rose. Then it broke and they were all wiping spray from their eyes. The Princess kissed the Cowboy who took the high-shouldered statuette and bit the bullet head, shrugged and went on pigeon toes and hawk heels towards the bigger time.

Victor England watches the ceremony on television in his wife's bedroom, and his. Fleur lies coldly in bed with a cold in the head. She is reading a letter from the man who looks after her investments, the only man she ever puts on her glasses for. Victor watches the programme with minute detachment, but only as the cowboy leaves the stage does he finally lean back. He takes no oh-boy joy in the look of triumphant mockery with which Dotty greets Rob Pascal's public puncture. He merely puts his hands behind his neck and sighs, but only for a second. For it only takes a second and Dotty is vindictive no longer.

… she was crying. She turned left and right, face and shoulders scalded with the malice that splashed on to her. And now he was laughing, Rob, laughing with the gaiety of degradation. The whooping gale tossed him, cock into cockle, on a sea of mockery. As the noise broke, she was shouting. He expected her derision and he was set to strike her; his hand was drawn back. Then he heard what she was shouting. She was shouting, 'I love you.'

His bravery shipped water. The hand that would have struck her went around her neck. He kissed her lips and her eyes and held her breasts as if he had never known girls had them before. She was more direct than he. In front of all those people, they were alone together. She loved him.

Victor England sees all this; his wife does not look up. Her mind is on the gold market. Victor leans forward and switches off the box.

'Who won?' Fleur asks.

'He did,' Victor replies.

Dotty and Rob go straight back to his hotel and from then on the suite-hearts are inseparable. After a couple of weeks, Dotty's flatmate arrives with a dump-truck full of roses: Rob has forgotten to cancel the order. He does so now, but on the first anniversary of their passion, about a month and a half later, a single red rose, culled from cuttings of precious metal and rubies by a silver myth in Mexico, is delivered, wrapped in florist's paper, to Dotty.

'It's beautiful,' she said. 'Only I don't want it.'

'I had it made!'

'You've got it made,' she said. 'I don't want any pension.'

'Pension? What do you mean pension?' He was wearing a judo robe and his hair was flat from the shower. 'Can't I ever give you anything?'

'No,' she said. 'That's exactly what I want. Nothing. Please. Now and forever.'

'It's yours,' he said. 'If you don't want it, give it away.'

She sent it to her ex-flatmate, who sold it to the store which had ordered it in the first place. Rob and Dotty saw it in the gilt-framed window when they went for a walk. It stayed there for a couple of weeks and then it withered and was withdrawn.

*

After his naked meeting with Dotty in the corridor, Victor England goes back to his suite. A suitcase has been put on the luggage stand. It closely resembles the one that he has lost, but he recognizes it at once for another apology. All the same he takes out his bunch of keys and tries the lock. The case opens.

There were terrible things inside.

He unpacks it carefully, first putting newspaper on the carpet. The blood on the clothes is dry. He frets it between his fingers and it crumbles, like clotted gravy. Can we be sure that it really is blood? There are hints that the contents of the case may be some sort of a joke. There is an elaborate shop right down the street where old children can show their young parents what they'd really like. This shop contains every handcuff, whip and gun love can possibly demand. There are uniforms for wounded soldiers, non-toxic blood, pasteurized pus and unthinking brains. Now the suitcase contains, among other things, bloodstained clothing and a small gun about right for shooting small people. It also contains some equipment which is not specified. Is a whip punningly included here? There is also a quite different style of contents: a simple gingham dress, a hair-band, a pair of sneakers, with Home on one and Run on the other, and some orange-topped socks. These things seem uncontaminated by the blood and stuff which mark the long dress, the panties and the strange magazine. There is also a roll of 8mm film. Having unpacked everything and found nothing to indicate to whom anything belongs, Victor repacks the case. He stands with his key out for several seconds, perhaps longer (the telephone has time to purl), and then he locks the case once again, thus somehow acknowledging it as his.

He no longer considered, as he had before he opened it, simply disowning it. He surveyed it keenly, resenting the wall that prevented him from making a complete circuit, intensely aware, intensely possessive, as if of all the things in the room – and his belongings were everywhere

– it was the one object from which he would not be parted.

The case is of a cheap make, blood-brown in colour (an echo here of the girl in the lobby, with her blood-brown ox-hide boots), and it remains odd that Victor should have a key that fits it. There is, one assumes, a sexual significance in finding that his key goes in all right after all. The case has a plumpness which testifies to its commonplace nature: its edges are swollen so that dexterous fingers can tickle what is inside. There are stains of no recognizable origin on the top, but the most curious thing about it seems to be that Victor England

... was inclined to listen to it; the sound of the telephone might have been coming from within. The suitcase throbbed, like a bomb, or something else with a casually murderous power, a heart for instance.

Is there a reference, in the allusion to the stains on the surface of the old suitcase, to the stain on the table made by Dr Jekyll? And does the mysterious power of the suitcase recall the power of the potion which the good doctor drank in order to become liberated into his dark self? Victor England goes and answers the telephone.

'Victor? It's Bart. How are you?'

  'Hi, Bart. How are you, Bart?'

  'I'm very well. So nice to hear you.'

  'They tell me Frank is out of town,' Victor England said.

  'Who told you that?'

  'I had a singing telegram. Out of tune.'

  'He'll be back. He'll be back very soon. We both want to see you. Out of tune! We want to see you very soon.'

  'That's what I'm here for.'

  'I'm glad to hear that, Victor.'

  'I read we were going to make a movie,' Victor England said.

'Is that right? Where did you see that?'

'In the contract Brute showed me.'

'Oh there. Sure. If only it was that simple, making a movie today! Tell me though, how is my dear, divine Fleur.'

'Well, I'll tell you, Bart; either she's asleep or she's working at it. Why isn't it that simple, Bart? Don't you think you'd better level with me on this?'

'Victor, that's exactly what we aim to do. If we don't level with you, who do we level with? That's just exactly precisely what we want to do.'

'That sounds like very close to wanting to, Bart.'

'Victor, we owe a lot to you. We don't deny it. We're not ducking it. Hell, we're proud of it! What you did for us. Victor, why not let's have dinner?'

'I have to see some people tonight, Bart. I promised. You know how it is with promises. We'd like to break them, but – '

'Victor, no one is going to break his word to you. No one.'

'Bart, you're the last person I'd accuse of doing anything like that. I can see your name right down there at the bottom of the list.'

'Victor, no one wants a happy ending on this more than I do.'

'Let's make one hell of a good motion picture, Bart. That's my idea of a happy ending. What's more it's the only kind that pays the bills.'

'You should see ours out here. Victor, we're old friends –'

'Too old,' Victor England said.

'Incidentally, just to prove we're not ducking out, I have a couple of points on the new script.'

'Bart, the script is a script I like.'

'I'm thinking of the girl.'

'Don't think I'm not,' Victor England said. 'You know who I want.'

'Her part,' Heinz said. 'Victor, you're tired. Go see

your friends. Get some sleep. Frank will be back maybe tomorrow and we can put all the pieces on the table and see how they fit together.'

'I hear Shap is in town.'

'Shap?' Bartholomew Heinz said. 'The old man took care of him good at the Meeting. Rex was back to his old self. He could have been a young man.'

'If it had been forty years ago.'

'You hear Sam Carnap is back?' Heinz said. 'All the old faces.'

'And all the old ass-holes. What's he doing? Running for dog-catcher?'

'Victor, until we meet, remember one thing: we're all on the same side in this thing. You have your deal. We intend to honour it. More I cannot say.'

'Bad as that, huh, Barty?' Victor England said.

After replacing the deceiver, Victor slumps on the bed. The slump in the industry is paralleled by his private posture. Are all the commitments which have crowned his earlier visits going to prove valueless in the present climate?

Is Victor England really planning to go out to dinner? He washes up and changes his clothes, but there is something unconvincing about his preparations. He might be compared to an actor who gets ready because his name is on the call-sheet but who has no belief that his lines will be lensed. When he cannot imagine anything more he can do to himself, he goes out into the corridor. He is about to walk to the elevator when

... it might have been some mistake in the stage directions, an error by a typist kept late, which turned him left instead of right. Once again, though he had spent all his speeches, he found himself approaching the double doors of Dotty Lampard's suite. He was conscious of a weakness in continuity: he had nothing new to offer. How could he be delivering himself once more to the same door without a thorned announcement or a rosy hope? His stomach told him, as it had told him when he accepted not a few assignments in the dear deadly days of the Studio's power, that he was in for something, if only a hit.

The tears could have been those of a newly-born adult. The voice of Rob Pascal proceeded over them, in maieutic commentary. Victor's heart rapped with rapture. The girl sounded desperate. Yet Rob lost neither his charm nor his calm: he might have been giving instructions to some third party, a penitent mother perhaps, concerning the docile doses to be administered if the patient was to be saved. Dotty's weeping pierced Victor England like Chinese needles, sweet and sour.

The girl's tears were not, after all, those of a baby. Her dreams were not nippled. Her sobs, as badly hidden as the egg at a spoilt child's Easter, carried a brazen note, to which the sound of her nose, blowing a tissue trumpet, added its stopped obbligato.

What most distresses Victor England is that, for all the dubbed blubs, she seems to be so uncomplaining. How he would like to be called upon to release her from her unhappiness ever after! Yet he remains unable to rejoice in the girl's rouge rage; Rob sounds too suavely in command. Is it merely that, as usual, Dotty's performance leaves something to be desired? Is she sincere but unconvincing, or is she in fact celebrating with sham pain? (We are reminded of Brute Andrews's gift.) After an orgasm, as after other meals, Rob's woman is always left to do the drying up.

Victor England, wearing his tux ego for a dinner to which he may or may not be on his way, is crouched winking at the door of Rob Pascal's suite, his eye keyhole-shaped, when the door is suddenly opened.

He went stamping into the room: an amateur butler who had miscounted the steps and forgotten the drinks. And the far-fetchedness of farce was maintained when, looking redly round, he saw that he was alone with

Dotty Lampard. Rob Pascal had passed so tidily through the door that not the smallest wake marked his departure. Only the last syllables of his voice were still there, like the lips of a departed diner on a flung napkin.

'It's me again,' Victor England said.

'Hullo, what's happened?' the girl said. Her face, un-diluted by tears, manifested a professional lack of surprise. 'Everything all right?'

'I spoke to Bart,' Victor England said. 'Everything's going to be fine. Rob not here?'

'He's working out,' the girl said. 'He works out on the roof when the sun's gone. He jogs.'

'Every night?'

'He says I should. Most nights. He says I should, but I don't like to. You wouldn't want a woman to jog, would you?'

'Are you going some place?' Victor England said.

'No. Oh, the suitcases!' Dotty said. 'They don't mean a thing. That's how we live.'

'When are you going to find something permanent?' Victor England said.

She smiled. He might have suggested she be in a musical, or something else she was somehow too clumsy, or too sincere, to do. Her mouth slid sideways, her eyes advertised forthcoming attractions and she looked young enough to be advised or abused. Her smile was like the ratty old duffle that she could now wear only to go marketing, but still suited her better than a thousand things she'd bought since just because she didn't want them. She blazed with a radiant greyness that she alone could contrive. When he saw it, Victor could believe that technicolor need never have been invented.

'If I can swing it,' Victor England said, 'we're going to do something together, and before too long too.'

'Can you swing it?' she said.

She was wearing a Judo robe, yellow-belted at the loose middle, and blue bedroom slippers with white

pom-poms on them. What rare animal had been crop-
ped to flatter those flat feet? Her head-girl's heels,
calloused by luxury, were visible when she dangled the
slippers. She drew her knees up to her chin, exercising in
her fashion. Victor England's eyes went to where the
robe had dropped from the unstitched seam between
her thighs. The old censor would never have allowed her
out, or in, like that.

Once more there is a hint that life and art are so close together
that it is a decision, rather than a natural distinction, which
determines whether we are to be criticised or punished. Is
Victor England's unblushing sight of the girl's squeezed purse
somehow authorized by professional familiarity with entrances
and exits or should a man not examine, uninvited, the tear
along that particular dotted line? It seems strange that having
held so long a conversation with Dotty when she was naked,
he should now, when she looks up and catches him at it, be
unable to withdraw his eyes without rasping a rash on that
fleshy monogram (is it an arch M or a pair of inverted V's?).

'Was there something else?' she asked.
  'Something else, Dotty?'
  'You wanted?'
  'There's always something else I want.'
  'Then why don't you ask?' She removed herself from
the blue sofa, an ungainly movement which might have
been demanded of an actress for some technical reason
– to match another shot perhaps. She sighed over an
open case and stirred the contents with a yellow foot
she had slipped from a slipper which stayed on the
carpet like a cute clue. 'What is it?'
  'Are you happy, Dotty?'
  'Of course,' she said. An oculist might have been
asking her if she could see the top line. 'Of course I am.'
  'What do you do here all the time?'
  'What do you do anywhere? We can have anything we
want.'

'They owe me a picture, they owe you a picture,' Victor England said. 'Fate, coincidence or plain good luck? Either way, it's too good to miss.'

'In which case they'll probably miss it,' she said.

'Not necessarily,' he said. 'Why do you think I'm here?'

'Don't you like the company?' she said.

Upstairs on the roof, Rob Pascal is chinning the bar, heaving pop eyes one storey higher than the architect planned, to look down at the electric beads on the flat chest of the city. The black cleaning man, in his ACME T-shirt, is also working out, with clubs. The two men are equals in the democracy of Narcissus. The cleaning man is also an actor, in fact, and once had the heavy privilege of swinging a left hook to within a convincing, wincing inch of Rob's ribs before biting the marked dust. As the two men rise and fall, the roof-top sign of the WEST COAST BANK also falls and rises, as if it too has to keep its pectorals in shape. Meanwhile, Victor England stands and looks at Dotty Lampard.

It was one of those scenes which writers could never write. They would complain that nothing happened. They would frost it with dialogue, like a birthday cake inscribed with the wrong name and stale a day too soon. They would want to specify the emotion, if it was emotion, which was displayed on Victor England's face, if it was displayed. They would want to know what was going on inside. How often did one have to tell them that movie characters had no insides? What did it mean when Victor England watched the slouching girl? What was in his eyes but the image of Dotty herself? If the old girls' scissors had sheared his life at that very moment, what could ever have been said of his intentions? What biopsy could establish that he was loving her as he had never loved anyone before or prove that she had so provoked him that murdering her too would have been a kind of Valentine? Victor watched the girl as she moved about the hired room, and that was all one could say of him, all that showed as the two of them lived in the shadow of the limbering Pascal who had jostled the sun from the roof.

'I love you, Dotty,' he said at last.

'I know,' she said. 'Thank you.'

'I have to go.'

'Where?'

'Nowhere, but I have to be there in half an hour. Can I see you again?'

'Here I am,' she said. It sounded like no in three syllables.

Later that evening, we find Victor England with a girl. It emerges very quickly that she is not Dotty and there is no serious intention to deceive us into thinking that he has sprung her, or himself. Yet there are suggestive similarities:

She was not a copy of the girl he loved; she was not a substitute either, though certainly she had taken Dotty's place. She lacked some of Dotty's refinements and, most refined of all, some of her vulgarity. She resembled one of those carbons which a writer took, if he was prudent, but to which he did not always transfer his second or his third thoughts. She was a fair copy that lacked the final touches. If she was less marked than the original from which she was derived, she also lacked most of its subtleties.

Presumably Victor has met this girl at the dinner party to which he says he has been invited.

… one of those parties in a house that wasn't ready yet, a house tacky with French polish, panelled with wood that here and there bulged like a brown boiled shirt, but which the hosts had got together, like an out-of-town set, only *just* not in time for their guests. They were a lovely couple, whoever they were, and quite the exception to the rule that people in the business couldn't be happy.

They were very happy people and they had a very happy family. They had children of all sizes and the best shapes. The older girl was working, she was eighteen, and the boy was a champion skier. The younger girl was gifted with textiles and planned working with the Indians in New Mexico and Benjamin was having tennis coaching from Chuck Mendoza, which said something for an eight-year-old.

There was a whole bunch of people supposed to be coming, so they would have a few drinks first. The nicest thing about the house actually was this room they were in now. The hosts fell in love with it the moment they saw it. Listen, a lot of things needed putting right. Mrs Eisenhower, the realtor's lady, had been ashamed even to show them the place. Somebody asked, hey, wasn't this the house where they found that actor after he had been cut in a thousand pieces or something? The silence said yes and was luckily lanced by the doorbell and a crowd of welcome welcomes and happiness to be there! The woman who had been too loud about the murdered actor tried again, pianissimo behind the piano, with a director whose work did well in Persia and places. It was true, he told her, pulling focus through a straight-up Martini without the olive, that a once romantically silent star had screamed his last in the Canadian pine library while a bunch of motorcycle kids tried new ways to make him talk. At first the director was blinking S.O.S. across the room to any woman who knew Morse, but pretty soon the golden cross between his questioner's best breasts got his casting vote and he warmed to his cruel task. He gave her the inside details about torture and mutilation amid the rare, red, rarely read books in the den where the old lion met his Daniels. The special effects soon had the gold cross between the woman's matching teeth and her thrilled thighs sighed together like lovers doomed to part.

The daughter of the house had joined the company in the living pit where there were big bowls of various dips and everybody was chipping in. The girl looked good in a dress her father had bought her to go to a party he didn't want her to go to and to which (he would have been furious to know) she was not actually going at all. Her father didn't like to be a drag about what she did but he was a little old-fashioned; he didn't want her murdered. Quite a lot of people around the room knew people who had been murdered – Gabe Stein's daughter had been murdered and so had that girl who used to be the secretary – cute too – in a soap opera, went out on channel 8 (or was it 13?) and so had the wife of one of the partners in the fastest growing agency on the Coast only she had sort of asked for it (everybody said) considering the pants she wore and the crowd she threw horseshoes with. Nearly everybody had been mugged or knew people who had or would have been if they hadn't had electric windows and security men to protect them from the police. The guest who had nothing to do with show business remembered an actor who now coached tennis in Estepona Spain (although he was incontestably the worst tennis-player in the crowd that used to play on the courts at Ramon Verdugo's old place) and he used to walk around at night with a knobkerri. A knobkerri. Right, a club in other words and when he got picked up by the police he said it was for self-defence. He was run out of town, not because of the armament and not because he was a pretty lousy actor (pretty *and* lousy) but because he sassed the Studios. He sassed the Studios one after another until he ran out. Even though it was wartime and he was the only non-faggot actor left in town, it was the kind of sass they wouldn't take, even from a stud with flat feet and in the best of 4F health. He had a problem with kikes: he didn't like them, and sooner or later they would be told about it in detail and in person and that was how he ran out of Studios. Now he was coaching tennis in Estepona Spain, a character who had to run round his backhand like he was trying to shake hands with it.

The majority of the guests were busy saying goodnight to their host's daughter, who was a lovely girl with braces on her teeth and wanted to be a trial lawyer. Her father was sure that she wouldn't mind if before she went he told their friends, many of whom he was meeting for the first time, exactly what happened to her in broad daylight a couple of days back, because it was unbelievable. She said, 'Oh daddy, *no*,' which was permission enough. Apparently she had been shopping in one of the best places down town (they certainly had the best ice-cream, Bar None) and when she went out to the parking-lot afterwards there was this guy, in broad daylight, and know what he did?

'He flashed it,' the girl said.

'He absolutely flashed it,' her father said. 'In broad daylight right outside the A1 supermarket. Opened his coat and guess what he said. He said, "I've got something I'd like to show you".'

'Isn't that what they always say?' said the only lady with more money than her hostess.

'How would you know that?' asked her husband, who used to be a producer and was now politically involved.

'What did you do, Candy?'

'Swung at him,' said the girl, 'with my foot.'

'This girl can touch the bar set at six foot eight and three quarters, she can swing up and touch that bar. She could really have damaged that guy's transmission, you know, if he hadn't split.'

'He split, did he?'

'Wouldn't you? But here's the spooky bit. You haven't heard the spooky bit. The spooky bit is, all the time they were talking he was shooting her.'

'He was *what*?'

'He was filming her. He was filming her. The whole time. He was shooting her.'

'With an erection?'

'I don't know about an erection. Did he have an erection, honey?'

131

'Sure he had an erection. Not a *full* erection, but sure he had an erection.'

'What do you mean, Candice, when you say not a full erection, dear?'

'She knows what a full erection is at this point. All the kids today know what a full erection is. They don't have the problems we had.'

'Speak for yourself, Seymour.'

'He was filming you at the same time? Did he have a *crew*? For Christ's sakes. Do flashers have crews today? Did he have *sound*?'

'Super 8; they all use super 8 today, these experimental film-makers. You can get some fantastic quality with that stuff. Hand-held. Who needs a crew?'

'Presumably this was some kind of a candid camera situation you'd gotten yourself in, honey, right?'

'Right. Give the kid some credit,' the girl's father said. 'At least he was trying to make a statement. He'd had this idea, probably self-financed ... you don't need finance to shoot super 8. You load up, you go out; you find something; you shoot.'

'I'm just glad I didn't freak out or anything. I mean I'd hate to think I couldn't adjust to a thing like that. I just swung at him and that was it. It all happened so quickly.'

'And you missed?'

'He dodged. Maybe I meant to miss. I wouldn't like to be responsible for gelding a guy.'

'I think that's very generous of you, Candice. I'd sure as hell want to geld him if I caught him doing anything like that to any daughter of mine.'

'Your *wife*, she'd have to look after herself, I suppose?'

'All he did was show me his gear.'

'And he kept right on shooting, even when he was dodging?'

'That was obviously the whole idea. It was wild. There wasn't too much I could do. I just kind of shrugged and turned away. I mean, he had me both ways, you know? Whatever I did. Gee, I really have to fly.'

'Right in the parking-lot of the A1 supermarket, would you believe it?'

'In broad daylight?'

'In broad daylight. That's our society today. That's the world our kids are supposed to grow up in.'

'That's the way they want it, that's the way it's got to be,' said the guest who had nothing to do with show business. 'The people who mugged that guy who specialized in second insurance, he needed fifteen thousand dollars worth of surgery and it turned out not one of them was over twelve years old. You know what they said at the trial? They said they only wanted to have fun. You know what else? The weapons they used, they'd bought every single one of them without exception at Junior City. Right around the corner. They sell Junior nukes in that place and there isn't a damn thing anybody can do about it.'

'When do we get to see the picture, do you think, honey?'

'Any day, because listen – I have to go but you still haven't heard the really wild part yet – '

'We haven't? My *God*.'

'A couple of days later I was in the supermarket again – '

'He sure gave you a taste for the place.'

'This ice-cream is something else, I tell you. Anyway, a guy comes up to me.'

'Not another one! Candice, you must have been the flavour of the month.'

'Wait a minute, guys, wait a minute because you've got to hear this.'

'And he brings out this piece of paper.'

'That sounds like a little bit of a comedown. A piece of paper?'

'Wait till you hear what it was. Because you know what it was? A release.'

'A *what*?'

'A release.'

'A release from what?' asked the wife of the man who would have gone a long way without her, even though she was a very sweet person.

'A release,' her host explained, 'a release. It's what you get people to sign when they've been in a crowd scene or something; it indemnifies you against any liability over intrusion into their privacy. A release. It's a formality. He wanted her to sign a release, so he could use the film he'd shot. Can you imagine?'

'What did you do?'

'Signed,' the girl said. 'Why not?'

'What did he give you? Didn't they give you anything?'

'What would they give me?'

'Isn't that kids today? What would they give you? They just might give you a hundred bucks. A hundred bucks, what's a hundred bucks to a kid today? I'll bet it didn't even occur to her to ask.'

'Why would I want their money?'

'You never say that about mine,' her father said.

'Daddy, be fair. I work,' the girl said. 'I have my own money. I certainly don't need theirs.'

'Now she's dating him,' her father said. 'His name's Gary; she's dating him.'

'*Dating* him?'

'The second one. Not the first one. Turns out the first one is only some kind of a friend, some nut he was doing a favour to; told him if he ever saw this girl, to ask her for a release. The first one has all kinds of problems apparently. He was a big hero in South-east Asia and it's made him very ashamed and stuff. He needs help and he isn't getting too much.'

'The Zulus always went into battle with erections,' the director said. 'They would line up and their king, Chaka for instance, would inspect their equipment. Anybody not standing up was liable to lose his credentials.'

'Seriously?'

'The Greeks too. The Spartans. Sure.'

'What do you know about the Spartans?'

'I know about the Spartans. We did a whole slew of commercials out there one time.'

'And you're going with this guy now, Candice? A nice girl going with a flasher?'

'Don't let's exaggerate: the friend of a flasher.'

'Sorry, everybody, but I really have to split now.'

'I don't care what time you come in –'

'Hear that, everybody? That's what I call a liberal father. I hope you're willing to testify when he denies he said it.'

'One condition. I want you to come and tell me you're in. I don't want to wake up, five in the morning, and have to get the car out and come looking.'

'I've been in the army eighteen years now, remember? When did I not respect curfew? Have a nice evening now, everybody.'

'You too, dear. What was the name of that ice-cream again?'

'Ice-cream? Bar None. You have to try it.'

'Bar None. I'm going to remember that. What a lovely girl! The A1, huh? What a darling girl really! How come a girl like that wants to be a trial lawyer?'

'Every time she goes out the door, I'm like this. If she forgets to tell me she's home and I wake up and see daylight, boy, I'm fit to be tied, I tell you. I guess it's a challenge.'

'They found a body in a heavy-duty sack at the bottom of the Canyon, two blocks down from our house, when was it? A week, ten days ago. I heard it on the news driving over to the Valley, a young guy went out to get a sandwich. They never catch anybody. You ever hear they caught anybody?'

'I keep money by the bed. I keep a hundred dollars by the bed. I have a fifty in every coat and every pair of pants I own and I keep a hundred, maybe a hundred and fifty bucks in the car dash. I don't want ever to be without something they can take. I regard it as insurance.

They want it, they can have it. Who wants to be brave and dead?'

'*Stupid* and dead. She's really a lovely girl,' said the guest who had nothing to do with show business. 'And when she gets those braces off her teeth – watch out!'

'Then I really start worrying,' her father said. 'Then I really start worrying. That's the moment. When those braces come off.'

'I think we have food on the table,' the hostess said, 'if anybody's ready to eat.'

'They have the most wonderful cook,' said the Canadian who proved that even Jews could be boring as hell. 'They have a cook my wife – we're split up now – really wanted to get a hold of. Chinese. But *mainland*, and brilliant. His name is Fu. Mr Fu. Isn't that the name of your cook, my dear, Fu?'

'It is, and hands off, Canuck. He's a genius. Steal my wife first. This guy is a genius with a skillet.'

'I bet you,' the director whispered to the woman who wanted to know more, later, 'it'll still be strawberry ice-cream for dessert.'

It was too, Bar None, Pekin-style.

Whether or not it is where Victor encounters the girl (is it something which in fact happens or only the *sort* of thing that happens?), the dinner-party ends early enough for Victor not to be thinking about bed just yet. He is next seen back at the hotel, coming out of the elevator with a black bag of the kind a doctor might carry when strictly off duty. He is said to feel better for having it. Does it perhaps contain the contract which requires the Studio to pay or play and which, because things like that never happen, just might be filched from his room? Or does it contain some evidence he is happier to hang under his hand? Evidence of what? One's mind goes to the blood-brown suitcase which has been delivered to his room. Is there a possibility that it is, after all, the one which he actually brought with him? The talk of murder at the dinner-table takes on a more menacing significance. Reconsider the following:

'I guess death is something we have to learn to live with today,' the Canadian said.

'That's good,' the host said, 'I like that, where did you get that?'

'Get it? It's home grown,' the Canadian said. 'I've thought about it basically with regard to a project I'm developing with independent finance – '

'Independent finance, that's what people have when they don't have any finance,' a latecoming lawyer dared to say.

'Death is not important today; it's kind of an irrelevance.'

'Not if you're the cadaver, my friend.'

'Come on now. Think it through. *Especially* if you're the cadaver. You're the cadaver, you're out of the race. You're in the pits. Literally. Who worries about the character who drops out? You're the cadaver, your problems are over. You can relax.'

'It goes back to the Greeks, doesn't it?' the director said.

'Sure it does. It goes back to the Greeks. How do you mean it goes back to the Greeks?'

'Blood-guilt,' the director said.

'Right. That's exactly what I mean. That's exactly what I mean. How does blood-guilt come into it?'

'I'll tell you,' the director said. 'I made a study of this one time for a project that was eventually junked. The writer fouled up. What happens in Greek tragedy is very simple. You get this change from a tribal society, where blood-guilt is an unalterable fact of life – kill somebody and somebody had to kill you – nothing personal – '

'Just like the Mafia. "No hard feelings, kid!" Remember? Jesus, what a wonderful performance. Wasn't that a wonderful performance? And what an ass-hole he turned out to be!'

' – to an ongoing, non-tribal economy. Now to achieve that there has to be a fundamental re-evaluation of the prevailing ethos. It figures: the state can't allow blood feuds to run riot through society; it puts all the priorities out. So what do you do?'

'Friend, if you don't know, I've got news for you: none of us knows.'

'He knows. He knows.'

'Society couldn't outlaw murder, so it outlawed revenge. It did better. It *nationalized* revenge. And to swing a thing like that, it had to promise to be just as merciless as the relatives of any victim could want. It killed in the name of justice, though, not in the name of retribution, as hitherto.'

'Were you ever going to be a lawyer?' the lawyer said.

'And once it started to do that, the principle of what *should* be done took the place of what *had* to be done, O.K.?'

'If you say so.'

'So over the years – '

'This guy's beginning to sound like a roller caption.'

'I happen to think this is the most interesting thing that anyone's talked about here this evening,' said the wife of the man who would have gone a long way without her, even though she was a very sweet person.

'Originally killing the killer had nothing to do with treatment or punishment in any way, shape or form; it was pure religious necessity. It got the ancestors off your back. The shades, right? Now with the decline of ancestor-worship, you get a change in attitude towards the killer. For a while, sure, the state went on hunting him, killing him; it went on appeasing the dead. But today where do the dead stand? The dead are dead. Why make waves? They don't come around much any more. But start trying to nail every single killer and you're liable to get into all kinds of trouble. So today we have two categories of people: people you can kill and people you can't kill. People we can afford to catch and people we maybe, for a whole variety of reasons, would just as soon not.'

'I make that four categories,' an accountant counted.

'You do the sums, my friend, but that's where we are today. You can't duck it. We all know guys who killed guys or fixed to have guys killed and what difference is there?'

'I don't know anybody like that.'

'You know me, don't you? I killed guys. And fixed to have them killed, once I was a little higher up. Once I made major.'

'Oh the war! The war was something else. The war doesn't count.'

'So forget the war. How many people are killed in automobile accidents every year, how many people are killed in *industrial* accidents, how many people are electrocuted or incinerated in their own homes? It's a question of percentages.'

'Were you ever in insurance? He talks like he was in insurance.'

'We don't destroy guilty automobiles; we don't blow up factories that kill people; maybe the Greeks would have –'

'Maybe that's why they never got any place.'

'My whole point. Murder is part of freedom. It's not nice; automobile accidents aren't nice, mining disasters aren't nice, but we are absolutely not about to destroy our whole society in order to eliminate killing. If it's one of the consequences of living the way we do that some people get killed, well that's the way we've elected it's going to be. De facto. Divorce and murder, what's the difference?'

'Now you've really made a jump. That's really a jump.'

'Think about it,' the Canadian said. 'Because is it, really?'

One recalls a scene in a Victor England film where all the dialogue of a party is played over the empty, ruined room in which the party has already taken place.

Victor comes out of the elevator, tripping on a trace of the Princess's laughter, and the girl is standing by the mirrored wall in which – has it been cheated there by a set-dresser with a taste for symbols? – can be seen the plant with the black, fleshy leaves. (The place of mirrors in Victor England's films has been discussed elsewhere.) We are clearly intended to make a connection between this girl and the one who was in the lobby when Victor arrived. It remains open, however, whether she has spent the earlier part of the evening with him, either alone or at the dinner-party. All we are told is

She came towards him like a frond detached from some driftwood which, for no obvious reason, obeys one current rather than another and, having been independent only for a moment, hurries to latch itself to a larger mass.

As she comes towards him, they are temporarily prevented from meeting by a wedding-party which flows from the *Sala de Bodas* and seethes, social sodium, on contact with the lobby. The flow of guests is so strong that the bride herself has, for a second (one thinks of a duel), to put her arms around the girl to avoid being knocked over.

They fought a smiling female fight against gravity, the girl and the woman bargaining for balance. In a thriller they would have been exchanging some plotted promise or tying a timely twist. As they separated, their eyes met in incurious intimacy, and then they had passed through each other and were on their ways.

The idea that they have passed through each other carries an allusion to another of Victor England's films, where much fun is had with the ghost of a first wife who excuses her untimely arrival through locked doors with the words, 'I was just passing through.' On another level, it could be held that, in order to trade identities, the women have taken advantage of one of those distracting collisions pickpockets engineer to mask deft theft. The girl has taken on something of the character of a bride. A sinister slant is added to this happy coupling by the revelation – on a bell-board calling her to the telephone – that the bride's name is Sanger, a literal transposition from *sangre* and surely an unveiled allusion to *Blood Wedding* (*Bodas de Sangre*). The theme of death is once again intruded. Who is going to die?

Is there any indication here of whether this is the first conversation between Victor England and the girl?

'Did you see what happened there? I almost didn't make it. I felt like I ought to know her. And who's the guy? Sanger? Who's Sanger? She's kind of beautiful.'

'What do you want to do?' Victor England said. 'You want to go out and eat something?'

'I'll always eat,' the girl said.

'I saw you before, didn't I? Here in the lobby this afternoon?'

'This is kind of wonderful, you know,' she said, 'for me. I'm not being obvious. I've heard a lot about you. I never thought you'd be so young.'

'I never thought I'd be so old,' Victor England said.

'Maybe a steak,' she said, 'I can always eat a steak. You're a legend with me!'

'Keep it dark,' Victor England said, 'will you?'

From this point onwards – and the notion of keeping it dark sets the tone – we begin to enter a kind of underworld, but it is the underworld of a city spread like a cosmetic on a desert; skin-deep is so far down no one can dig any further.

Victor and the girl are next seen face to face over a red check tablecloth, knock-kneed under it. They lean forward and count the cutlery as if beginning on some gauged game. Check makes one think of chess, with its time-clocks and its economic confusion of mating and death. (Cf. *Matar*, in Verdugo's language 'to kill'.)

They were in the dining-car of a train, the Superchef. They had been welcomed aboard by a red-capped captain who had never seen them before and was glad to see them again. He took their order on a long ticket and made transcontinental destinations out of their *filet* steak, double order of onions, two Pilsner, and a chef's salad. The windows of the coach were velvety with aerosolid steam. Beyond them, a sketchy heaven of prairie stars and wayside stations flared and faded. The waiter, with a ladder of dishes up his arm, came trucking towards them and he sure enough hadn't forgotten to scratch the starch from those baked potatoes. The pepper mill was right there, folks, and the beers were coming right up.

'You'd better tell me what it's all about,' Victor England said. 'You don't have to hold back. It's not as though we know each other.'

'I guess you've heard it all before. It's not exactly new.'

'You're new,' he said. 'We'll settle for that.'

'You're so *kind*,' she said. 'The one thing I never expected.'

'Tell me something. What were you doing before you got your big break?'

'Big break?'

'We're having dinner, aren't we?' Victor England said.

'Oh. *Oh.* Now you've made me blush. I was pretty slow back in there. You've made me blush!'

'Don't knock it,' Victor England said. 'There may be money in it. It's not easy finding a girl can blush today.'

'What have I done? I've done all kinds of things, things I wouldn't even want to tell you about.'

'Tell me about those,' he said.

'I've even been married,' she said.

'Married.'

'Sure,' she said. 'Does that throw you? And before that I was a drum majorette. I was a drum majorette for a couple of seasons. I studied tap and *gestalt* psychology.

I played a little tennis. I also experienced a religious conversion. That was how come I left home.'

'And since you got here?'

'I worked as a waitress. I did a little educational T.V.'

'Waitress?'

'Sure, I waited at table.'

'And how was that?'

'Tacky, it was kind of tacky. I caught a chill from the air-conditioning. Occupational hazard when you go topless, right.'

'Where was this, a bar?'

'Right. Sort of a bar. I danced a little. I had a few routines. Go-go.'

'And then what?'

'I quit.'

'What've you been doing since?'

'Not too much really. I've been looking around.'

'And saw me.'

'Right. Absolutely.' She was very pretty then.

'And how long has this been going on? Looking around?'

'Since yesterday. I quit yesterday. I figured I had to make the break.'

'Eat your steak,' Victor England said.

'I decided I really wanted to be in the movies. Is that silly?'

'You can see where it gets you,' Victor England said.

'I could fall in love with you,' she said. 'It's horrible.'

They leave the diner, after Victor has rubbed a hole in the steamy window ('To be sure it's our stop') and they step down into a new night, in the muddle of nowhere. There is, of course, no question of their having actually gone anywhere: the dining-coach rides on strictly brick wheels and the scenery of prairie skies and wayside halts is the city seen through sentimental glass. The girl carries a doggy bag with the scraps from their meal. They go to the edge of the yard in front of the diner. Across the street, a rackety motel promises 'P*easant Dreams'.

'I could use a few of those,' he said.

'Do you think I'm terrible?' she said. 'I'm not usually like this.'

'What are you?'

'You must think all kinds of things about me, but I promise you they're not true. Please kiss me some more.'

'Peasant dreams,' he said.

'You figure I'm pretty obvious, don't you? You figure I'm just about as obvious as a girl can be, right? Well, I'll tell you something. This isn't at all how I planned it, not at all. I planned it very, very differently.'

'You planned it, did you?'

'And now I'm going to pay for it.'

'That'll make a change,' he said.

'I planned I was going to be very quiet, very demure, home town girl, sort of chintzy, right? I was never going to tell you about waiting at table. I was humiliated. The chests on some of those girls! You know what they say? That's what happens if you scratch them.'

'Tell me something,' he said. 'Do you have a name?'

'Don't you have one of my cards?' she said. 'Here.'

'You have *cards*?' he said. '*Daisy*?'

'I had to call myself something. Station identification. Victor, let's go someplace. Please. I don't have anywhere of my own right now. I was rooming with some people but we had a spat and I split. What do you say we go over there? It's only across the street. Let's. You said you could do with some.'

'Some what?' Victor England said.

'Peasant dreams. I can make you happy; I know I can.'

'Don't threaten me now.'

The girl takes his hand and looks both ways before hauling him across the street.

*

'Hi, folks, what'll it be? One double?'

'It can count,' the girl said.

'Nobody parking the car, huh? That'll be forty bucks.'

'Forty *bucks*,' Victor England said.

'Flat rate,' the manager said. 'That's everything included. Water-bed, T.V., your first beverage, state and federal tax. And that's in advance, if you please, folks. Leave whenever you want to within a twenty-four-hour bracket. Anything you want ... '

No one brought luggage to P*easant Dreams.

Victor England must know what kind of a hotel he has entered. The promises in the lobby are scarcely ambiguous. The girl can hardly restrain herself from laughing – Dotty Lampard would call the place 'a bit of a giggle' – but Victor England watches his own image warily in the mirror.

'No one's going to recognize you,' the girl said.

The room was white. The bed was round as a drum.

'Modern dance,' Victor England said.

'Cute,' the girl said.

'Aren't you scared?' he said.

'Scared? Nothing happens in places like this. Anyone tries anything in a place like this, they blow his head off.'

'And what do they do to her?'

'Oh brother. Hey, you ever watch educational T.V.? Because this is educational T.V. Has to be: no commercials! See?'

'She looks a little like you,' Victor England said. 'The one on the right.'

'She does too.'

'Educational T.V.,' he said. 'Well, well, I'm learning something, aren't I?'

'I needed the bread,' she said. 'They were some people I roomed with for a while.'

'Boy eats girl,' Victor England said.

'That's Hubie. She's Louise. She wears glasses usually.

She doesn't normally look that way. She cut her hair, I don't know why. She had some hangup, maybe her old man would see her. She wanted to be sure and look her best.'

'How long does it take to make a thing like this?'

'How long? As long as it takes. The guys have problems sometimes.'

'And you have to help solve them, I guess?'

'There isn't a lot you can do. It's all in the mind. Once a guy loses it, it's not easy to get it back. You've got people waiting around and time's money, you know. They get impatient, you start apologizing. It's not easy to be a man at the best of times, I guess. Now she is terrific, this girl. Angie, this is a terrific girl.'

'The one with red hair.'

'Right. She dyes that as a matter of fact. Will you look what she's doing?'

'Is that you again?'

'You have excellent vision. She's a terrific person to have in the group. She has this gift for improvisation.'

'You need somebody like that,' Victor England said.

'Right, that's right, you do. *Ham!* Ham is in this. You have to see this guy. He is really funny. The guy with the dog. He is really funny. Deadpan, but the things he comes out with, you wouldn't believe. Isn't he something? You should see him eat.'

'Really?'

'Food. He has this fantastic capacity. He can put away six or seven twelve-ounce specials, with all the trimmings, with *all* the trimmings, in round fifteen, twenty minutes, oh and a couple of malteds thrown in, and they leave a lot in the shaker, you get almost two glasses out of every shaker and he can down the whole caboodle in twenty, twenty-five minutes. Does he have an appetite! An hour later, he's hungry again. Slim Jim, he calls himself. You hear he's going to be in on a gig, you feel completely different about it, right away, it's going to be a ball.'

'What do they give you to do a thing like this?'

'This is straight, you know, this one. You can see.'

'Sure can,' Victor England said.

'When it's straight they give you maybe fifty, maybe a hundred dollars. That's two, maybe three days, depending how it goes with the guys. They're the ones have the pressure on them, obviously.'

'Obviously.'

'You get some of these kids, they're completely inexperienced, they come along for nothing, for kicks, I guess they think it's going to be, and then comes the big moment, it doesn't. They get so *embarrassed*. And then someone in the crew'll maybe josh them, not really meaning anything, you know, but one guy couldn't stand it, he bust out crying. Ran out. He was destroyed, you know? Another one went ape and did I don't know how many dollars worth of damage. I don't know what ever happened to him. He had to split town because they have gorillas, you know, some of these people, the organized ones, they can really lay it on you if you break up their equipment. That's one thing really gets to them, you break up their lights and stuff. Will you look at her? Isn't she unbelievable? She is too much. Virginia.'

'Virginia,' Victor England said. 'I should have guessed.'

'I have a feeling she killed herself.'

'Killed herself? What is this, a golden oldie? When did you do this?'

'Two, three months ago? I needed the bread and, like I said, I was rooming with some of them. I was rooming with Virginia. She had this thing with death; it was on, it was off, it was on again. She never could make up her mind, but I think somebody told me she'd finally made the big trip.'

'The big trip.'

'Right. She used to discuss it with us. She had a very rational attitude. She was into Reason a lot. She was going with Slim for a while. Will you look at that? I don't know anybody else in the world can do that. I do that, I gag.'

'Did she get a bonus for that?'

'I certainly hope so. There was talk one time about getting representation. One of the politically orientated girls wanted us to get unionized because we were being really screwed by some of these characters. We really felt we were being screwed.'

'I can imagine,' Victor England said.

'Some of the girls got quite militant as a matter of fact and then ... a few things happened.'

'What happened?'

'A couple of people ended up in the desert.'

'The desert? What desert?'

'Maybe it was the hills.'

'I don't get it,' Victor England said. 'What do you mean, ended up?'

'Anyway, they didn't get to come back. Oh my God,' the girl said. '*Denise.* I don't believe it. I don't believe it.'

'Who took them to the desert?'

'This girl is something else. I guess David must have finally talked her into it. The glasses and everything. She's funny.'

'They dumped them in the desert? They just took them out and dumped them?'

'Maybe they broke their legs first. I don't know.'

'People really do those things?'

'All the time, don't they?'

'You could just be killed and ... '

'Who'd ever know? Right!' It might have been good news the way she grinned.

'Who are they, these people?'

'You don't ask. I don't tell. That way ... O.K.?' She shook her hair from its band. 'So now you know,' she said. 'That's the kind of thing I've been doing. How do you like that? Hey, you're not upset, are you? Are you upset? What's the matter? What did I do?'

'Will you marry me?' Victor England said.

And here the section ends. How the girl responds we are not told. Do they proceed to fake love on the round bed? Perhaps that is the only marriage which Victor England really proposes to the girl. Her belief that the movies they have been watching on the closed-circuit T.V. are educational is not so much naive (she surely knows exactly what they are) as symptomatic: all the discrete categories of life and art have been fudged. You can call things what you like. On this analogy, Victor's proposal can be as ironic as the girl's beliefs. How can one be sure? There follows one of those abrupt transpositions for which movies at least never apologize. If Victor and the girl have gone to sleep, or at least to bed, in a sordid motel devoted to love in its most commercial form, they wake to another world entirely.

They had the roof down on the convertible and the wind-machine back-combed their hair and gave them high foreheads. The words came in capitals from their mouths; they might have been parents prompting a slow reader. Their eyes did the listening and watched the words blow like tumbleweed across the flat countryside beyond the Freeway. Above their heads, jets stitched last-minute cotton-wool to the blue ceiling.

The girl was wearing a *gingham dress* and a pair of *white Oxfords*. Her hair was fastened with a *red ribbon*. When she smiled, Victor almost expected braces on her teeth. Her arms were pollen-yellow when the sun glanced at them. A pointed path of gold went down the back of her dress. Her eyes had filched the best of the sky; her teeth were as white as an advertiser's lie.

Somehow this drive, also in an open car, does not quite recapture the rapture of the journey undertaken with Billie-Mae. This time, there is no intrusive third person in the car with them and the auspices seem more genial, but the wind is not the only disconcerting omen. They have not long turned off the Freeway when they meet a roadblock. Some highway patrolmen, armed with shotguns, flag them down with orange-heeled batons.

'Stay in your car, folks, just stay in your car.'
  'I'm not getting out,' Victor said.
  'What's going on?' The girl took the easy line.
  'We have kind of an on-going Mayday situation out here right now.'
  'Mayday?'
  'We have a lion loose in the county.'
  'A real live lion? Wow. How do you like that?'
  'We don't like it too well.'
  'How did that get to happen?' Victor asked.
  'This circus. I guess they gave him a key.'
  'He was probably twenty-one,' the girl said.
  'And where is he now? Do you have an indication?'
  'Someplace hereabouts we think. So just don't get out of your car. Maybe with a drophead you should even turn back – '
  'I have some machinery here, officer,' Victor said, 'if I can just find it, it'll put our hat on for us.'
  'O.K., but if you see anything suspicious – '
  'What would you like us to do?'
  'Try not to put your head in its mouth.'
  'We'll try and remember,' Victor England said.
  'He was real nice,' the girl said, when they had driven another block or two. 'Imagine a lion! Wild!'

They arrive at 'Fun State':

It was the cleanest state in the Union and that was saying something they were not afraid to say. They sold passports at the gate, visas for every kind of fun above the waist. The girl skipped in her gingham dress; she was the happiest thing in the whole happy place. She put out her hand for Victor, because this was what she had always dreamed about; it was so *clean*.

*

They are given 'Fun Names' which they are obliged to pin on their breasts. The girl is 'Bella' and Victor is 'Dude'; the staff of 'Fun State' are thus able to call them personally, like old friends. The staff also have names, printed on big buttons with 'Have Fun' on them. There is no end to the pleasures.

Victor was in a stetson by now and the girl – Daisy, Bella, whatever her name was – she was wearing a poke bonnet and carried a basket of dentist's sweet dreams.

'Am I having myself a time!' she said. 'I'm so happy I could die.'

They passed a bandstand where a New Orleans band were pumping up their brass balloons in the face of a wind that turned their music over more quickly than they could play it. A single man, wearing a black stetson and gun-belt, eased himself from the lattice-work surrounding the stand and ambled after Victor and the girl like a gambler hoping to poach somebody's luck.

The girl wants to do everything. They go on roller-coasters; they are whirled champions on the Carousel; they slide down mats round an upright version of that 'old Leaning Power of Teaser'; they get horsed up on a stagecoach going to Tombstone; have themselves waffles in the saloon (can she eat, this girl!) and Indians come and shoot arrows into the woodwork right over their heads – 'How do they *do* that without killing anybody?' – until the cavalry come with coffee and brown betty. After that, it's off to the ghost town. They go up rackety old stairs in the dust-gusting hotel and suddenly one of the steps gives way and, oh my goodness, they're falling and falling and *screaming* and they find themselves way down in the cellar someplace and, of course, it's all planned and safe as safe and they're couched in rubber blocks, along with a few other characters who have dropped in at the same time.

A man in a black stetson helped the girl to her feet.

'Upsadaisy,' he said. 'You all right?'

'Yes,' said the girl. '*Yes.*'

151

'Nobody wants you to get hurt now.'
'I'm fine. *Please*. I'm fine.'
'O.K.?' Victor England said, when he found her.
'I came down with a bump.'
'You're cold.'
'No. No, I'm not.'
'Who was that character?'
'Who was who? Nobody was anybody.'

It is difficult to be sure whether the girl is genuinely uncon-
cerned about the man in black or whether she is hiding her
fears. Victor seems more overtly anxious. Is it on her behalf or
his own? He stands uneasily with her, his eyes searching the
crowd, while a Cartoon Favourite, in a lion's unity suit, takes
their picture with a Polaroid. A few minutes later:

**He looked up sharply in the Tennessee Pancake Parlour.
His eyes quizzed the margin of the mirror for a face that
he might have seen before. The face was gone before he
knew it, but he turned around sharply at the Guate-
malan Gewgaw stand, where the girl was being tempted
by a snakeskin belt, and caught the wind leering at him.**

He thrusts the girl into the ghost train with a lack of tenderness
which contrasts with his earlier indulgence.

Now something remarkable, almost inexplicable, seems to
happen in the tunnel: when they come up the ghostly ramp
and return to unshared shadows, Victor's companion is
suddenly seen to be a different girl. She may be wearing the
same button, but can this be Bella? She walks with bowed
shoulders. Her legs are now less brown than jaundiced and
they are roped with cold veins; her ankles are swollen; she
doesn't even want to shake hands with Mr Hi There! (who
goes around on stilts) and she sits down with a bump on a
hobbyhorse bench. She puts her elbows on her knees and
shuts her head in a finger cage like she never wants to come
out. Has she had too many panicky pancakes? Has the cream

whipped her? Or are we being confronted with a time collapse and has the honeymoon in the tunnel already brought
about a bout of mourning sickness? 'I feel like death,' she says.

Victor returns to the hotel alone. Frank King is sitting in the
lobby.

'I hoped I'd catch you,' he said.
  'You're back,' Victor England said.
  'Everyone says so. Can we go someplace we can talk?'
  'How are you, Frank?'
  'Alive,' Frank said, 'and kicking. Kicking like hell.'
  'That doesn't sound too good.'
  'It's good for you, Victor. It's not good for the people
I've been kicking. This has been one hell of a fight, but
I finally won out. I finally got you your deal.'
  'I have my deal, Frank.'
  'I have a horse,' Frank King said, 'in stables down the
Coast, but try getting it to run. We're off and running
with the project, Victor, that's what I stopped by to tell
you.'
  'Great,' Victor England said, 'why do we have to go
up to the Suite?'
  'It's not as simple as that,' Frank King said.
  'Let's go up to the Suite,' Victor England said.

Frank King's face is creased with his trying triumph. He has
been smiling at too many things that aren't jokes. As he and
Victor stand in the elevator, his eyes cannot keep still, but go
up and down the closed doors like a painter's brush.

'I don't ever want to go through this week again,' he said
when Victor England had closed the louvres and banished the warm wince from the room. 'One battle of
Waterloo is enough. They tried to put the finger on Bart,
did you hear about that?'
  'They did?'
  'I guess you heard about that.'

'Just this minute,' Victor England said. 'Can I pour you something?'

'Was I mad! But everything is going to be fine from now on. They tried to nail Bart for something Rex initiated, carried out and thoroughly balled up. Victor, I hate to say this, you know what I feel about Rex, but he's senile today, you know that?'

'I haven't seen him today,' Victor England said. 'You want some seltz and lemon? I'm having a seltz and lemon.'

'Give me one of those,' Frank King said. 'Did you hear Andreshka and I are splitting up? Because Andreshka and I are splitting up. I guess you heard about our daughter. She never got over it.'

'I heard she was studying modern dance in New York.'

'Sure, with both feet in the air. I don't know what's true and what isn't. Somebody told us they'd heard she was in New York. I don't know. She could be in Des Moines. I heard she was in Tijuana.'

'What was she doing in Tijuana?'

'Maybe she was kidnapped; maybe she was cutting the grass; we never found out. The telephone today, who can rely on even getting a ransom demand?'

'I was waiting by the phone all day yesterday,' Victor England said.

'Andreshka's not really her mother, of course. You have a daughter, don't you, Victor?'

'That's what it says on the bills,' Victor England said.

'It wasn't the kid going so much that got to Andreshka. They were too close in age to be close. They never related. Put a little Beefeater in that, will you? A couple of fingers. It makes me sore. I don't blame her exactly. But it makes me sore. What does a man work for? We have a fine home. You've been by our house. You were by the night of the assassination, weren't you? Sure you were. We had dinner.'

'Andreshka is a sensational cook.'

'I haven't been home too much lately. Do you blame a

woman, today, Victor? She has everything she wants, but what kind of a life is that?'

'Didn't we have spare ribs?' Victor England said.

'Scotch salmon – we had that with the new potatoes and the peas. So she wants to walk away. She wants to walk away and I sure as hell don't aim to stop her. She figures, Natalya can do it, she can do it. If I ever find time to catch up with her, I'll maybe bust her head in, but that's something else again. I have a sister married to a guy was a professional killer until he retired. They farm. She gave him a box of hand-grenades for his last birthday and he went out and blew up a couple of dozen shorthorn cattle. Everybody needs something of their own, right? The way she figures it, I'm married to the goddam studio, not her. I'm fucking the studio and who says she's wrong? We've had ourselves every kind of problem there is out at the Field this last little while: Rex senile, Shap riding herd on the shareholders. It's been quite a time; thank God we finally won out, but ... '

'Who's behind Shap exactly?'

'She wants to have something of her own,' Frank King said, 'let her, right? Behind Shap? A lot of macaroni, if you ask me, but try proving it. Who cares? They can all go take a powder. She has a great figure, she works out, she skis, she waterskis, she does Royal Canadian Air Force exercises. She keeps her body in first-class condition. Know what she's considering quite actively? She's considering being a hooker, strictly for a limited period. I think she could really make it.'

'A hooker,' Victor England said, 'is she really? Is that tax exempt?'

'She's talking to some of our accountants about that. There's a case going through the courts right now. She's taking advice. Secondary rights are something else, of course; those you do have to pay on. Memoirs; stuff like that. Recipe books. But you can always spread it. I think she might make a big success out of it. She was in land-scape gardening for a while and she made quite a success out of that. Didn't she do the Princess's garden one time?'

'Not while I was paying the bills,' Victor England said. 'We had Capability Brown.'

'Shall I tell you something funny? I might even be a client myself. We have contract cleaners. We have these people come and clean the pool. Who wants house staff today? Someone always around; it's an intrusion. You knew Barbara didn't you?'

'Barbara.'

'Handled the top end of the market. Still does, for a few select clients. Andreshka got to talking with her the other week. You know what she clears... even today, with Wall Street in its present state? She has a turnover bigger than Nate'n'Al's.'

'Is that right?'

'And no plant. No overhead. She manages her whole operation on out-calls. Does she have a story to tell, one day, Barbara! Brute could get her a million dollars if she wanted to publish her story.'

'And two million if she didn't,' Victor England said. 'How about our movie?'

'It's a rational development. Why let's be ugly about it? It's a service. Can you go in exactly six weeks from now?'

Victor England looked at his watch. 'What time do you have?' he said.

'Bart has a couple of points on the script,' Frank King said. 'Nothing intelligent compromise can't settle. Victor, you remember that girl Bart talked to you about?'

'Frank, you remember when we fixed the Drakos picture, what you said about Dotty?'

'There's a talented guy, Peter, Jesus,' Frank King said. 'I'm glad that turned out the way it did. Remember? I'll never forget it. How important is the girl, how important really is the girl? The way you have her scripted at the moment, she's a victim. Is a victim worth what you're going to have to budget Dotty for, in today's market? Think about it, Victor; it needs to be thought about. May I have a couple of fingers more of that Beefeater? I haven't eaten in two days. There's a difference between selling you somebody – there's a difference between that and sincerely recommending somebody we all think is right. I think this girl is right. O.K., she doesn't have a name yet. Did Dotty have a name when she made her first picture? I say, kill Dotty halfway through your picture and you kill the picture at the same time. Do you believe in visceral reactions? Because this is something visceral with me. The people won't forgive you.'

'She can be a victim. Do you know how she lives?'

'It'll kill your picture, Victor. I'm not talking about which end Rob Pascal stubs his cigar. I'm talking about our movie.'

'Yours and who else's?'

'Victor, Victor, Victor.'

'We're off and running in different directions, Frank.'

'Horseshit, Vic.'

'Has Dotty been warned off the script by any chance?'

'Warned off the script? How can you say a thing like that? Ask her yourself; she lives right next door. Victor, let me ask you something: would you be prepared to come in and talk to the Board after the meeting tomorrow if necessary?'

'If necessary to what and to whom?'

'You're the kind of a man the Board respects, a man with a track record no one can argue with. I'd like us all to have a talk, all of us together, right out in the open.'

'That's not a place I like to be, Frank, not without my lawyer.'

'I just want them to realize that it's men like you'll put the Studio back where it belongs. Forget lawyers. Victor, you know what I think of Rex. You know what Rex has done for this industry.'

'And I know what this industry has done for Rex.'

'It's a two-way street – '

'And he's been down it both ways, more often than not at the same time – '

'Check. Rex *is* the business. No one can ever take that away from him. I'll tell you what's on my mind – '

'Who was it wanted to fire Bart?' Victor England said.

'Victor, I think Rex's position in the Studio needs to be recognized officially. I want to organize a tribute to him. I want him to have that position for life. I want a situation whereby his experience and knowledge – because who has his kind of knowledge today? – can be at the disposal of the Studio forever, but in a way that doesn't keep him under the hammer. He's a great man, but a young man he is not. He can still behave like one – Thursday afternoons, Tuesday mornings – he can still have some great days, half-days anyway, but he should not, at his age, any more have to bear the burden of all the crap that goes with heading up a major Studio in today's world. He should be free of that. Frankly, that's what the Board intended when I was made Head of Production, only Rex couldn't see it that way. I'll tell you something: he's basically insecure. Rex Keyes is an insecure man. I spent a weekend down at Playa Moriscos recently. They have quite a set-up down there. This was after Andreshka broke it to me. I was playing around with deep meditation for a while in there and that's when it hit me: Rex is a frightened, insecure guy. Why didn't anyone see it before? He needs help. He needs reassurance. I think he should be President For Life. I aim to propose to the Board that we have a Committee, not just drawn from the executives – who ever gave a shit about what a row of studio executives thought? – a Committee of honour of people who've known Rex and worked with him and know what a fantastic character he is. I want to make him a presentation that no one'll ever forget, a public mark of the industry's esteem and affection!' Frank King smiled.

'Do you really hate him that much?' Victor England said.

A girl's body is discovered on the beach the following morning.

Some young guys went coasting for an early wave. An old man in a rubber skull-cap, skin warped over re-signed bones, was already out stirring the grey water. The big waves were deep breathing off-shore. The old man's footsteps had stitched the hem of the sea; he had passed below where the young guys stumbled on the girl. The old man was a refugee. He swam every morn-ing, dewlapped arms slavered with high effort, before the sun turned on the key light. He seemed forever to be measuring the length of some accurate despair, a European man less drowning than exercising his sor-rows. The young men called to him, 'Hey, sir, hey, *sir*,' but he crawled on. 'She's beautiful,' the young men said, trite as truth. Her body was blonder than the sand. The politeness with which they surrounded her was the only sign that she was not alive. They gathered around her, the four young men, and she was so fresh, so clean of corruption, that their bets on her being dead were hedged with desire. She was the unbruised fruit of a dream none of them could quite wake up to.

The girl's body is carried up the scraped scarp of the beach, where a black man in a headline hat has already driven a yellow Beachmaster tracking smoothness between the sea and the immobile swings which hang chained for pleasure in front of the trash cans and the dead lifeguard's cabin.

They laid her on a stretcher dressed with a sheet, prone caryatid, a pillow for a capital. The ambulance men conceded, with their careful carriage, that her condition was serious, but their peaceful pace carried a hopeless hope that treatment might yet retrieve their beautiful burden from the bad accident of death. At first the four young men followed the stretcher across the beach. Their generous vanity believed that their desire could do her the favour Jesus did Lazarus. They did not complete the course across the banded, crisping sand. The desire which had ironed the creases from their denims declined. They fell further and further behind. Their eyes wavered. A memory of the future, of all that they had never needed to know, clouded their blue charm and pinched wrinkles around eye and mouth. They ran back towards their abandoned surf boards.

The ambulance, on its way to the morgue, is ensnarled in a traffic jam. The unknown girl acquires a motorcade of morning mourners, unconscious of the death to which their funereal pace gives a hooting tribute. In this same traffic jam, on his way to the Board meeting, is Frank King, pacing up and down in his limousine.

Only now do we hear of the murder of Drakos's girl. Drakos has not, so far as we know, been in California at all during this time. The murder is of a brutality which reminds Lieutenant McLeish why he is paid. It is not only Drakos's girl who has been assaulted, but his house too, the fruit, in considerable part, of his ten per cent of a hundred per cent of the profits of the film which Victor England made snipshape. The girl on the beach is, so far as the young boys' reaction indicates, unmarked by violence; there is no evidence that she has been murdered. (There is no law to stop a young girl dying.) Yet there is something almost farcical in the rash of death which now occurs. This departure from the usual economics of story-telling is not a casual lapse. One does not learn of the deaths of three young girls within so short a space because the author is unaware of the implausibility. Has it not been said that the end of an aesthetic is the end of a world?

When someone says, on hearing of the deaths, 'That kind of thing doesn't happen,' he offers a clue about why one of the endings of the story is acceptable and at the same time says something metaphysical: he tries to reject facts – for we have no reason to believe that the girls are not all blonde, all beautiful and all dead – because they are ridiculous. What do they render laughable? The moat which surrounds the slaked acres of delivered lawn and weeded mead where people unlike Drakos put a roof over their money enables the inhabitants to maintain a beleaguered belief in a world where nice things happen only to nice people and ugly to ugly. The inhabitants of 'The Heights' have their own private police-force. They boast that no one has ever been burglarized within the white walls of the precinct where even the patrol cars are white-walled. Their insurance rates thus remain reassuringly low; the murder in the Drakos house is doubly horrifying because it is the first undeniable instance when something incredible has taken place within the pearly purlieus. Bodies have, it is secretly confessed, been discovered in 'The Heights' before: we have heard what happened in the house where the dinner-party took place, but that was way in the past; besides, it was a special taste which led to the silent star's loud end. At first it is put about that the girl killed herself. Suicide does not affect insurance rates. Then when the anatomical problems involved in cutting oneself into pieces prove beyond explanation, all allege that her body was brought to the house from somewhere else. What finally brings home the horror is what whoever it was did to the house. 'Who'll ever be able to live there again?' one of the 'welcome ladies' wonders.

Drakos flies in.

He wore dark glasses and a darker suit. The suit pants were flared at the knee. His face was yellow and without definition. Had he not had time to put the bones in? He fought his way to the Studio car someone had been kind and cunning enough to send for him. The press pressed. When he had nothing to say, men with heavy things on their shoulders bent the knee to shoot him, in self-defence, through the window. The presence of Lieutenant McLeish licensed accusing assumptions that Drakos knew more about the death than was going to be good for him. Shock at what had taken place on Kensington and Summit yielded to wise whispers. Drakos was rich and he had already had one wife and child who had died in Europe: a fire which still smoked. Drakos had never belonged to the sea and the sun. His tenniscourt was unscorched by drives; his pool undented by dives. His movies were always full of the kind of gags that kept an audience uneasily silent once the lights had gone up. He wrote his own scripts and it was neat to think that the death of the girl he loved had been an original of his. True, he seemed to have foundered on a grief which was genuine, but no one had ever seen him desolate before; he had no record of sincerity. How could he suddenly do it so well unless he'd been rehearsing?

At first no one had been able to understand how such a thing could happen. Within a few hours, it was not only reasonable but even inevitable. A beautiful girl butchered, a house trashed, a garden modernized with obscenities, what else was new? Drakos's parents had been murdered, his wife and child had died in an oven of another kind, he had escaped to fame and fortune which, in some unAmerican way, he had not coveted and hence not deserved. By the time Drakos was home, he was a pariah. So what if the evidence of his innocence would have furnished the commonest criminal with an alibi? Maybe the mysterious techniques he handled so slyly and so arrogantly in his films were at his disposal in life itself. Could not such a man easily be in two places at once?

By the time Drakos arrives at the murder house, a crowd of neighbours has gathered across the street. The car cannot go up the drive, because they haven't finished checking it for tyre-marks. Drakos gets out, before McLeish can play the tactful shepherd, and stands in the road.

'My neighbours,' Drakos said, framing up on the peeping people. 'Nice-looking, don't you think?'

162

'Very.'

'They cost me a quarter of a million bucks. They ought to look nice.'

'Do you think we could go inside now, sir?'

But Drakos was inspecting the faces of the extras who lived next door. They began to shuffle and think of things they should maybe go and do.

'I was in New York,' Drakos said, going real close. 'O.K.? I was in New York. I was casting a blonde. You guessed that, right? And you were here. You were here and you none of you heard a thing. You none of you saw a thing. Nothing, right? You were home, you were the good guys and you didn't see, you didn't hear, you didn't nothing.' They had to stand there. 'Nazis,' he said.

He walked back to McLeish. Had he finished? Not quite. He turned again to the cowed crowd and there was a see-you-next-time smile on his face. 'Have a nice day now,' he said.

He and McLeish measured the long walk up the drive to the front door. The photographers were in a bunch on the dab-free porch.

'I want to see her,' he said. 'Where is she?'

McLeish pointed to the house and they started on up. They were under fire from the photographers. Drakos stared at them for a moment and then, abruptly, he began to dance. He was a successful candidate and he danced. He joined his hands together, the champion doing his bitter bit, and hung them high in the air. He grabbed McLeish's hand and held it sincerely, with a winner's wink. The photographers looked at each other and saved their bulbs and Drakos and McLeish passed them and went into the house where bloody hands had left rouged weals on all the whiteness.

Drakos can be read, in different equations, as victim (the bereaved) and as villain (if the girl hadn't been quantified by him, she would still be alive). What is the answer? What answer is wanted? Drakos certainly finds himself socially ostracized, but only among the ostriches of 'The Heights'. People up there do not make him the offer of bed and boredom which is usually extended to those who have lost a loathed one. He goes to the borrowed beach-house where funny people meet to smoke stuff. Drakos hits out at the straights and narrows with an interview so full of abuse, accusation and anger that it incites them to believe even more strongly that he is behind the death of the lovely girl who, it is now forgotten, gave the 'Welcome Lady' the unwelcome side of the mat when she came to enrol her in the community. The word goes round 'The Heights' that the people who killed Drakos's girl are habitués of the beach house and that terrible things have been going on there.

What scandalizes 'The Heights' above all is the rumour that a blow-up of the girl, naked, is projected on the wall of the beach-house and that Drakos has been playing around with holography. Is some kind of electronic resurrection being attempted? Now it is below this very house that the young guys find the dead (though not necessarily murdered) girl who is also blonde and who excites the four young men, *as if she wore a staple in her navel*.

Is the girl on the beach perhaps not flesh and blood at all? The investigations which follow her supposed death have a singular imprecision. The response of the four young men to her body is one of sexual excitement, but it is an excitement which could as well be prompted by art-work as by flesh. The staple which attaches the gate-fold to the body of a best-selling magazine is more than a certificate of desirability; it is also a licence to imagine what games one will. There is thus a certain ambiguity about the nature of the body on the beach. The four ambulance men carry it as if its owner might still have a use for it. Drakos's attitude to the murder of his girl (here there cannot be much doubt about a real death) scandalizes 'The Heights' because he does not treat her as if she were properly dead. He gives his angry interview to a freak paper called *Talking Head*. His funeral oration shares space, on its continuation pages, with a blow-by-blow account of how three people can make it together.

' ... I don't really know what she was like. It wasn't important to me what she was like. I don't know what else she did. I don't think it was any of my business. I don't care what she did, as long as she didn't sit around thinking about me. I don't want people to think about me. I don't know who I am and I don't know who she was. I don't even know if it was always the same girl I came home to all the time. Who knows that kind of thing? She looked like she was the same girl; that was good enough for me. You want me to talk about her? What do you want me to tell you? What kind of a cook she was? She couldn't cook. What books she liked? We had a bunch of books, people are always sending me books. I guess she read a few of them. We had a bunch of records. She played all kinds of stuff. Let's say she liked Bartok, O.K.? She was a Bartok buff. I was with her, when I was with her, because I liked to screw her, O.K.? I loved her because she was clean and white and I made her dirty, O.K.? I don't flatter myself. She had me because she was in my movies; because I'm rich and I make movies. You think it hurts me to realize that? It doesn't. It gives me more pleasure than anything I can possibly think of. I took one of your beautiful California girls and I did everything to her you can think of and a few things you can't. I'm a bastard. My parents weren't strong enough to look after me. They were losers, O.K.? They went up the chimney. Do you think I respect them for that? I don't. They loved me, sure they loved me. What else did they know? They were nice people. I don't like nice people. You want to know, was she nice? Will I ever forget her? I hope so. I said, I hope so. I don't like memories. I don't want to have memories. Will I find someone else? Sure I'll find someone else. Sooner the better. Will I ever make another movie? Sure I'll make another movie. Sooner the better. You want to cut my head off? Go ahead. I can't stop you. Would I care if every house in The Heights was trashed like mine was? Why should I care? Those people, will you explain to me why I should care if they go up the chimney? They want me to cry. Well, I cried. I cried when I thought of all the holes in that girl I'd never get to screw again. One thing I despise: respect. What do I like about girls? I like the holes in them. A girl to me is like a piece of soft sculpture, O.K.? Something you own so you can handle it. That's the only sense in having it around, to get your fingers into it, to get your prick into it, your tongue into it, anything you've got into it, O.K.? Was I happy? I was happy. I was a fool. I was happy. I was getting old. You're right: look at it that way and I'm younger now she's dead. Isn't the world younger every time a lot of people get killed? Death makes people young again. All you have to do is survive. That's all that matters. Why do you think they put deaths in the papers? They're the good news, that's why. If I'd been in the house, what would I have done? I'd have maybe killed whoever it was; maybe I'd have run like hell. You think I know? I don't. What was she like? Great ass. What does talking about a girl mean? What is there to say? She photographed good, O.K.? She screwed good, O.K.? Finish. You what? You think it's what? You think, I'm sorry, you think some people might think it was irreverent having her on the wall like I do. Shall I tell you something? The night I came down here, the night I was down here after I left those bastards on the hill, I did everything on one of those pictures. I shat, I spat, I pissed, I jerked off. I did everything on that picture I could get out of myself. I cried, sure. I fucked holes in the damn thing. People say what? Sure they do, because they killed her. Because they hate me? I don't know if they hate me. Maybe you're right, maybe they hate me. Why not? I haven't done anything to them. Can you think of a better reason? I ought to be dead, that's the point. Something went wrong somewhere. Who loved

Banquo? Banquo. In Shakespeare. Who loved him? Macbeth. Let's quote him for bad luck, O.K.? Bastard coming to the feast. I like bad luck. They wish I'd been killed and she was still alive. That's why they say I killed her, O.K.? Because I should've been dead, not her. When people like me get killed no one feels threatened. They feel better. Sure they do. I'm the devil; I frighten them. I should. I should. They've given me my character. Sure, they have. *They clipped me out of the papers.* I'll survive, and the more I survive, the more they'll be after me. Who gets hunted more than a survivor? People hate survivors. Of course they do. They haunt them. The dead never haunted anybody. The dead are dead. When I die, I hope I shan't ever be remembered. I don't care a damn about being remembered. Art? Same thing. I make movies because it gives me something to do. Money? I used to steal. Now I get interest. What do you do when you're alone in the world? What belongs to anyone when there's only one person in the world? I was alone. I didn't respect anything. Now? Not much, friend, not much. Myself? Who's that? Is this me? Or am I only pretending? Do *you* know?'

The refusal of Drakos to concern himself about art encourages a critic to say that he is the most considerable artist working in film; such a statement dates the critic no less than it classifies Drakos. Criticism, like judgment of all kinds, lags further and further behind events. Thus the inability of Lieutenant McLeish, despite his talents as a detective, even to decide what 'kind of a thing we're dealing with here', is a failure not of one (intelligent) individual but of the system in which he operates, or which operates him. The bewilderment of the Studio over what the people want is equally noticeable at police headquarters. The top cop shakes his head at the public just as executives do.

'People want crime more than they want detection,' McLeish said. 'Look at the figures. More and more crime, less and less detection. If we want to be on the winning side, we should maybe go with the mob.'

'The mob? I wish it was the mob. I can get a line to the mob. They have people I can talk to. You should see the art some of those guys have in their living-rooms. But these people? Half the time you don't know if they're people or not. How can you tell who's who? Fingerprints. Fingerprinting germs! We play doctors, we play cops, but we're into a second generation situation already; we're getting to a bunch of people who've never been officially born, never officially die. It's a new race, McLeish. Anyone recognize this girl yet?'

'Sure; she's been recognized everywhere.'

'Anybody know who she was?'

'No.'

Victor England, meanwhile, is waiting in his suite for the Studio to call.

He had waited for calls before. Like everyone else, he had once believed that early success was lasting success. Like everyone else, it had taken long waits for return calls that were not returned before he found that only other people's success was uninterrupted. He had learned to ride the broken promises; he had never, for the sake of a dram of drama, stumbled, drunk at ten in the morning, through a rising tide of secretaries and assistants to argue the toss with an executive who had heads and tales of his own. Victor England did not gamble at the public tables; he cashed what was left of his chips and kept his piece, even when the wheel was crooked and the croupiers smirked at his cowardice. His mildness accumulated, over the years, a rich interest. Though he never shouted or waved his fists, Victor England created a sort of uneasiness in those who thought to do him down. Powerful men were unwilling to lose him. He packed no punch, but nor did he ever look to be hurt. He won more than he lost. He was regarded as a good man to have in your corner, even if he had cornered you in it.

Victor made himself busy in the suite during the morning of the Board meeting at Bowyer's Field. The silence of the telephone was maybe an aspect of all his activity (a bad director would constantly have cut back to it), but Victor England kept his eyes on the plenty of other scripts which Brute Andrews, who knew the game, had sent round by black hand.

Victor England has calls from Brute Andrews and from his lawyer. He looks a busy man. Some people call who want to make a different kind of a thriller which is also a love story. 'That's the same kind I'm always being asked to do,' he tells Brute. At last the right phone rings.

'Victor? Victor, it's Bart.'

'Bart! How are you?'

'Victor, you've been waiting a long time; I'm sorry. We've had ourselves a morning out here.'

'And an afternoon and another morning,' Victor England said.

'There've been a lot of decisions. A lot of decisions. More than you can imagine.'

'I can imagine,' Victor England said.

'Victor, I'm on my way in the car right now. Would it be possible for you to meet me outside your hotel in a couple of minutes? I'd so appreciate that.'

The car is a blue station-wagon with a black driver. The driver is wearing a green suit and green glasses which mirror Victor England as he comes through the yielding doors from the lobby. Victor wears a suit and carries a thin briefcase. He passes three men standing with Ramon Verdugo, is greeted 'Mr England, how are you today, sir?' by the driver he has never seen before and gets into the station-wagon to find Bartholomew Heinz agreeing with a white telephone.

*

'Good morning, Victor, how are you?' Heinz said, after putting the phone back in its walnut box. 'Another beautiful day.'

'What's wrong with it?' Victor said.

They watched the palm trees, the tall ones and the short ones, and the green driver went easy, easy at the intersections.

'Does Frank want me on out at the Studio now, is that where we're going?'

'Frank,' Bartholomew Heinz said, and it was time for his Havana.

'He wanted me to talk to the Board, or have they heard enough talk in the last couple of days? I could always do a little mime.'

'Frank's been having a few problems,' Heinz said. 'You hear about his wife? You hear about Andreshka?'

'Depends what,' Victor England said.

'The house burned down.'

'Andreshka?'

'Inside. The mortician needed a vacuum cleaner. We were in the meeting. No calls. Not even God. We finish, he gets the news. For a capper. Can you imagine?'

'I rely on my writers for imagination,' Victor England said. 'But how do you like that?'

'And you heard about Drakos, I suppose? His girl?'

'That was yesterday,' Victor England said. 'So how was Rex when the big one came up?'

'It's been blood in the palms, Victor, today, all the way. The toughest decision any of us ever took.' Bartholomew Heinz showed Victor where the nails of his clenched fists had scored the flesh. 'Crucifixion time.'

'How about the wound in your side, Bart?' Victor England said. 'Do you have one of those to show me? It's no dice without. My middle name is Thomas.'

'How often do you see a Rex Keyes in tears?'

'But when a man has to go, he has to go, right?'

'That's how the board figured it, but this was always

going to be something else. This was a gut thing, Victor. Here were two men closer than most fathers and sons are today. That isn't the kind of collision you just get up and walk away from. Listen, don't think for a minute Frank isn't going to be taken very good care of, because he most certainly is. No question about that in any-body's mind whatsoever.'

'Rex,' Victor England said.

'Pardon me?'

'Is going to be taken very good care of. You said Frank.'

'Frank I said and Frank is right,' Bartholomew Heinz said.

The car is now driving down a boulevard which goes through an old studio lot. The acreage has been reconstructed and now contains a large shopping plaza, an international hotel and some high-rise office blocks with heavenly hamburgers in the basement. The station-wagon is stationary by some lights when suddenly, from high up, they hear shots. Heinz and Victor lean forward. A man with a rifle is sitting on top of a rotating totem advertising pizza. He is firing down into the shopping precinct where his targets are slow on the cue to run in all directions. The window of a supermarket with 'Come Right In' caves right in. There are not many people in the target area and a sort of depopulated panic develops as new arrivals, pushing grocery carts, realize that there is an ongoing massacre situation.

'Bart, give me a ladder here, will you? Who did what, and to whom exactly? Just a plot outline, huh?'

'Victor, here's a guy's taken a beating – I'm talking strictly about work-load now – you'd better pull in to the side, Winston, because they seem to be shooting a scene – the way Frank's worked over the last couple of years, even Superman would have plumped for a rocker in the shade for a while – you know something, that's pretty damned realistic what's happening out there! Can you see where they have the camera? I don't see where they have the camera. And now this thing with Andreshka – '

'Well, I'll be a sonofabitch,' Victor England said.

'You will if you want to survive,' Heinz said.

The two of them sit in the still car. The man on the sign is sighting up and firing through the supermarket window. He manages quite a few spectacular reductions. In the plaza, wounded people crawl and haul themselves across to the insurance building. No one much comes out to assess their claims. It takes a long time for the police to get into the picture, but now they arrive with their telescopic toys and bite pieces out of the advertisement. When at last the gunman falls out of the leaning tower of Pizza, it can be seen that he is a cop in uniform.

'Without a parachute,' Victor England said, 'that ground has to be pretty damned hard.'

'How do they do that?' Heinz said. 'They must have let a section of foam rubber in there. I guess that's what they did.'

'He still isn't going to be in too much shape for the re-take,' Victor England said. 'But you still haven't told me: who's the new Head of Production?'

'Victor, you may not believe this – '

'Bart, forget about Thomas, I'm a very credulous man.'

'They've asked me, just to tide things over. And provisionally I've accepted.'

'Provisional congratulations, Bart. You finally made it over the title.'

'Don't think I'm not sick as hell about it. I am.'

'Sure you are, Bart. I know you'd never have taken the job unless Frank had begged you to go ahead.'

'Wouldn't you know it? What a guy though. I still damned near turned it down, you know, Victor. Some days I really wish I'd never left New York.'

'But this wasn't one of them, right?'

172

'Frank was fantastic. What a guy, I tell you! I really told them, you know, how much he'd done for the company. I really laid it on them.'

'You would, Bart. That's the kind you are. Where in hell are we going?'

'The airport,' Heinz said. 'Rex hopes you won't mind. He asked me to explain to you.'

'And what is the explanation?'

'That is,' Heinz said.

'Head of Production, huh, Barty?'

So now we know. The plot against Rex Keyes has backfired. For Frank King the last straw has turned out to be the short one. And we have also discovered, almost casually, the identity of the third beautiful dead girl. It is Frank King's wife: 'She's given her last barbecue,' is how the word goes round. However, the official reaction on 'The Heights' is ostentatiously different from that to the death in Drakos's house. The Studio is prompt to make treachery tactful (inverting a phrase used when Victor England first sees the girl in the lobby), and Frank is said to have asked for leave of absence as a result of what happened, or at least was discovered, *after* he had in fact been fired. The inversion of cause and effect has gone a stage further: effects are now the only real causes. A gloss on this dislocation is provided by a scene that takes place in the hospital where the policeman who has done the shooting in the shopping plaza is being repaired. He has, amazingly, survived the direct flight down from his nest. He is visited in his soft cell in the hospital by Lieutenant McLeish (a very responsible as well as a very busy officer):

'Well, Forrest, how are you doing now?'

'No complaints, Lieutenant,' came the bandaged statement. 'But Lieutenant, there's one thing I'd like to ask you.'

'Ask,' McLeish said.

'Don't let them cover this thing up. Don't let them do a snow job on it.'

'Cover what up?'

'Because he was there. He was there.'

'He was?'

'Would you expect an experienced officer to open fire for nothing, Lieutenant?'

'Who was?'

'You know me, Lieutenant.'

'I know you.'

'They were hiding him. They were shielding him. How long are we going to go on taking this kind of crap?'

'I don't know, Forrest. Could you be a little more specific?'

'They're all accessories. Every single one of them without exception. It's getting to be them or us, Lieutenant. Those people are criminals, people who shield criminals are criminals themselves. Lieutenant, I had to fire. I had no choice in the matter. Would I fire for no sufficient reason? They've shielded those bastards for long enough. I wasn't going to have them make a mockery of the law any longer. I had to let go when I had identified a definite and recognizable target. I'm a patient man, Lieutenant, but the time comes –'

'Sure it does.'

'Not firing would be a dereliction of duty. So no snow job, O.K.?'

'Leave it with me.'

'And I couldn't live with that.'

'You get some rest now.'

Victor England and Bartholomew Heinz arrive at a private airport. A black aeroplane, as cheaply disguised as a Rolls-Royce with California plates, is waiting on the back burner. The station-wagon drives through a hiked barrier and up to the starway at the front of the aeroplane.

'Whose plane is this?' Victor said. 'I hope you have the Board's O.K. on this. This is the sort of thing a group of dissident shareholders could make sound pretty waste-ful in today's conditions.'

'Victor, you're just the thing we all need after a morn-ing like we had this morning. Come on in and meet people,' Heinz said.

It was so shady in the interior of the aeroplane that Victor England had to frown before he could count the heads in the tail. They were grouped round a black table and rested against black velvet seats.

'This must have been a nice place before it got burnt out,' Victor England said.

'England, you son-of-a-bitch, come down here and have a drink.'

'Well, Rex,' Victor England said, 'nice piece of tail you've got here.'

'I want you to meet some associates of mine,' Rex Keyes said, 'in particular J. Harvey Shap. Harvey, if you don't know who Victor England is, you might as well go check the tyres.'

'I sure do,' Shap said. He offered a warm hand to Victor; his white face had not yet taken delivery of an expression. 'This is a moment I've been waiting for.'

'And somebody I think you know.'

Victor saw blue against the black. 'Noodle oo, England,' Bradley Biddle said. 'It's been a long time. You ever manage to get that taxi?'

'I walked,' Victor England said. 'That's why it's been so long. Do you have a wine-gum with you, or are you serving lunch?'

'Both,' Bradley Biddle said. 'If you like Chinese.'

'With Roquefort dressing,' Victor England said.

'You'll have heard of this morning's events.'

'Yes,' Victor England said. 'Bart filled me in.'

'Franco, tell them they can start,' Harvey Shap said. 'That was Franco.'

'Tragic,' Rex Keyes said.

'Yes, and his wife too,' Victor England said.

'She was a charming and talented girl,' Rex Keyes

said, 'believe me. I know that from personal experience. Victor, you've heard the news, I'm sure.'

'I've heard some news,' Victor England said.

'Dotty and Rob.'

'Have left town? Somehow I don't think that wins a prize, does it?'

'Married,' Rex Keyes said.

'When did this happen?'

'Today. In London.'

'Has today happened in London? I thought it didn't get to go until the noon flight.'

'That's tomorrow,' Franco said, coming back.

'Mr England and I will handle the dialogue, Mr Franco,' Rex Keyes said. 'They wanted privacy.'

'Well, today's sure going to be a day for anniversaries.'

'All kinds,' Rex Keyes said. 'How's Fleur?'

'Fleur? Just the same as always. Not a mark on her.'

'She's lucky,' Rex Keyes said. 'Victor, we've discussed a number of things this morning. Including you and the Studio.'

'Did I get equal air time?'

'We want you connected with the Studio for a long time to come,' Shap said. 'In fact we're counting on it.'

'Do they have to start the engines to heat the sweet and sour?' Victor England said.

'As a matter of fact,' Bartholomew Heinz said, 'this is a heist. We were hoping you wouldn't notice till dessert.'

'I'll bet it's strawberry ice-cream,' Victor England said. 'Bar None, am I right?'

'Mr England,' Shap said, 'we are all at one in being admirers of your work.' His voice swallowed German ancestors. 'Mr Heinz has told you, I think, of how we see the future.'

'I hear you abandoned the crystal ball,' Victor England said. 'But what's going to replace it?'

'Our first steps must be in the nature of emergency treatment,' Shap said. 'Before the situation gets to be terminal.'

'Victor, we've been losing too damned much money,' Rex Keyes said.

'The Studio has been haemorrhaging for the last two years,' Shap said. 'Only nobody was willing to admit it. They kept saying it was ketchup. No one can afford to go on losing blood that fast.'

'We can't even afford to go on losing ketchup that fast,' Heinz said.

'It's thicker than water,' Victor said, 'but why are you telling me all this? And why are we flying wherever we're flying? I don't have my dramamine; I don't have my passport; I'm liable to forget who I am and on top of everything I just might throw up. Now what the hell's the big idea? Because let's get to it.'

'I understand your impatience and I respect it,' Shap said. 'It is our position that certain officers of the Studio have been guilty of – shall we say? – irregularities. That is why the shareholders have insisted on a rearrangement, a *fundamental* rearrangement of the Board. I gave instructions, immediate on my appointment, for a thorough inspection of the books. If this process turns out as I believe and fear it will, very serious charges may well follow.'

'Where are we going?' Victor England said. 'And when will we be back? And not necessarily in that order.'

'The purpose of our flight is above all to avoid publicity. Up here, we're just ourselves. No telephones, no reporters. I thought in view of the private tragedy which, I understand, occurred earlier today – '

'Frank,' Bartholomew Heinz said.

'It would be more tactful to be out of the way of the media. Believe me, what happened distresses me very much. If I thought the present investigation could be dropped without compromising my obligations, I'd be strongly inclined to drop it.'

'Investigation?'

'Mr England, certain directors, as I was indicating just now, have been guilty of practices which leave the company in a position from which certain consequences seem inevitably to flow. If I failed to take cognizance of that position, I would myself be guilty of criminal negligence. Franco's made that very clear, didn't you Franco, from the legal standpoint?'

'Oh, are you a lawyer?' Victor England said. 'I thought you were one of my admirers.'

'I'm that too, sir, believe me. I have a whole raft of questions I'd be very obligated if you were to answer for me. For instance, you remember the dance routine in the elephant house in *Unless It's Love*, was that a process shot in there? Because – '

'No, one of the elephants came to us with the idea,' Victor said. 'He remembered he had a brother who could Charleston and we winged it from there.'

'And when she comes home from her night job at the cigarette factory – and walks up the path and sees him writing his novel and – '

'A contract signed by a delinquent executive might be challenged,' Shap said. 'It might even be negated, isn't that right, Franco?'

' – realizes his sight has been restored and he's finally kicked the sauce and there's nothing left between him and a *Reader's Digest* condensation with all that entails, was that one shot or two?'

'Negated?' Victor England said.

'I'm sorry to say yes, it is possible,' Franco said, 'under certain circumstances. Particularly if it could be shown that there had been irregular payments or privileges. What a sequence though! Pure golden age!'

'Which is why I thought you ought to have the full picture, Mr England,' Shap said.

'I ought to get up and walk out of that door,' Victor England said.

'It's fifteen thousand feet to the ground,' Rex Keyes said.

'That's why I didn't go yet. I'm a thinking man.'

'Victor,' Bartholomew Heinz said, 'fundamentally nothing's changed. Nothing.'

'That's what I figured,' Victor said.

Bartholomew Heinz's promise that nothing has changed confirms, like all political denials, that everything has: Shap and his associates are clearly in complete control. Why have Heinz and the senile Rex Keyes been retained at all? Their continued presence reassures the movie community that Shap and his entourage intend to respect the creative echelon; furthermore, the two men have information which the Shapshooters will find it easier to extract from colleagues than from enemies. The threat to everyone connected with the old management remains obvious. What good can Victor England's contract be to him if Shap establishes that Frank King deceived both the shareholders and the auditors over a substantial period of time? All the deals signed by Frank will become suspect and, possibly, voidable. There is the further suggestion that there have been improper kickbacks. Even if Victor's contract were to prove untainted, it might take years of litigation. How does Victor react during the heated eating which now takes place?

He was neither surprised nor annoyed. He had said his lines. He had given Shap and Heinz and even old Keyes the pleasure of playing him for the hooked shark which, perhaps, he was. He had seen Studio chiefs come and go; he had come and gone himself. People always said things were going to be different; how else could they stay the same? Frank King had wanted to renegotiate and finally he was going to get his way, only not his way. It seemed right that they should be in the air, burning fuel to get to wherever they were going, only for the sake of going back again. Victor knew he was being murdered and he knew they were going to get away with it. The funny thing was: it didn't hurt. It was almost a pleasure, like pleasure was.

It comes out during the meal that Sam Carnap, the old thief, is going to produce Peter Drakos's next picture. The murder of Drakos's girl is still unsolved, but the police are sure to come up with somebody, like the Studio always does. The irony is that the battle-plan has almost certainly been conceived by Frank King, the only man finally to be defeated by it.

'Victor, Dotty's going to do Peter's picture,' Bartholomew Heinz said.

'I thought she was getting married.'

'With Rob,' Heinz said. 'She and Rob are both doing it. The chemistry has to be right.'

'And the biology,' Victor England said. 'Never underestimate the biology. When was all this arranged?'

'The girl got killed, we had to find somebody in a hurry. Dotty was free. They're doing the whole thing in Europe.'

'She was never right for you,' Rex Keyes said. 'You need a victim. That girl's never a victim.'

'So everybody keeps telling me,' Victor England said.

'Kill her a third of the way in and you lose your audience. They'll never forgive you.'

'So everybody keeps telling me,' Victor England said.

'Now a kid like Drakos's girl. She would have done perfectly. Only she had to go and get killed before she even had a script. Victor, this is the logical way for everybody. This way everybody's happy.'

'So everybody keeps telling me.'

Victor England has reached a strange frontier. With Petrine pettishness, he three times repeats the trivial formula which, at the very moment when everyone is relaxing, presages breakdown. Has he perhaps seen it coming all along?

He knew actors who performed with every sign of confidence, who might not have been acting at all, so easy were they with their lines and their moves, and yet they would say that they had known, from the very beginning, the exact point where they would dry. They had seen it, like the shadow of a chasm on the horizon. No other actor ever had an inkling of their darkening apprehension. The actor dried when everyone was sure that he had never been in more fluent form.

Victor England has kept his patience for days, months, possibly for years. Yet all along he has feared that this dark moment was coming when his contract, for all the nuts and bolts tightened by Brute Andrews, would somehow, with a Cheshire smile, vanish into thin air. (Baldness as a symptom of the loss of creative and personal power is mentioned in the scene with the Chicano barber who is learning Latin.)

What now follows lends California Time an idiosyncratic and hallucinatory dimension. How much of it is true? After this triple refusal (an image relevant also to horse-jumping, which recalls Frank King), Victor closes his eyes, a little dead, and listens to the incidental drilling of the jets. Bartholomew Heinz asks, is he all right? 'I hope you haven't eaten anything.' Is there a sinister element in the speed (and ambiguity) of Heinz's concern? It was Heinz who was so worried, in Gianno's restaurant, lest Victor be given a bad oyster. Would it be the first time that an innocent episode prefigured a guilty one? Victor admits, mortified, that he doesn't feel too good. He is immediately shown every kind of sympathy in tablet form. He goes and sits in a row of empty seats, all upholstered in black, and tries to close his eyes to what is happening. Does he have some fear that they have not finished with him yet? Has he been drugged? Someone gives him a satin band to put across his eyes.

'What about my last cigarette?' he said.
   'Do you smoke, Mr England?'
   'Only when they put a match to me,' Victor England heard himself say.
   'You want a cigarette?'
   'Why do I only get the things I make jokes about?' Victor England asked Victor England. 'Where are we going?'

'How are you feeling? Is that better? Does that help the sickness?'

'What did you give me?'

'A little draught, nothing more. Mr Biddle had it with him. To help settle you.'

'Draught? I don't want any draughts, and I'm not settling anything without Brute. Brute was coming to meet me.'

'He went to the Studio. You misdirected him.'

'I'm sick. I need Doctor Kolesnick. Doctor Kolesnick knows what I need.'

'I'm glad you feel a little better. Try to sleep.'

'Sleep,' Victor England's voice said. 'Maybe I am sleeping. I can't move. Why can't I move?'

'I fastened your belt, that's all. We don't want you falling out. Try and get some sleep, sir.'

'Yeah. If I close my eyes, maybe you'll go away.'

'I guess I'll just sit here quietly.'

'What's the matter, pal, run out of questions?'

'Oh no, sir. If you feel up to it. For instance, you remember the girl? The girl – in the flashback – was she really an angel or did he just think she was?'

'Girl?' Victor England listened to himself say, 'What girl? There've been a lot of girls. They were all angels. It was in their contracts. I never had any other kind.'

Now once again, there is an abrupt transition. Is it an hallucination? If so, how does Victor England know that the investigating officer's name is McLeish? Has the scene with McLeish been taken out of sequence? Or is it imaginary? How do we recognize the imaginary? One of the standard assumptions about what is imagined is that it has no consequences in the real world. 'One may insult a man in a dream, but he's not offended when one meets him next day,' is how a textbook on psychology deals with the problem. How reliable is this notion? Is the following a dream?

'What happened to her, Victor?'

'I never saw her again.'

'Maybe there was a reason for that.'

'I fixed to. She never showed.'

'Maybe there was a reason for *that*.'

'I wanted to marry her.'

'We have you down married already.'

'I loved her. She said she loved me. I dropped her at her agent's. I never saw her again.'

'She has no agent. No agent in this city ever heard of her.'

'Are you saying she's dead? Is that what you're saying, Lieutenant?'

'You're doing the talking. We're just a couple of good listeners, Basilio and me, that's all we are.'

'Because is there a body? If there's a body, I want to see it.'

'That's the kind of thing you like to see, is it? I didn't say there was a body. You're the first person to mention anything about a body. What do you say you tell us exactly what happened and we quit horsing around here?'

'I don't know what happened. Nothing happened.'

'She was wearing your dress. You don't deny that, do you? Quit that sniggering, Basilio, or turn in your badge. I don't take that from anybody, even you. Well, Victor? Was she, wasn't she?'

'If you have any evidence –'

'Evidence? Then you admit there's a crime.'

'I gave a girl a dress, I admit that. If that's a crime. I gave her a few things. If it's the same girl we're talking about –'

'You gave her a few things.'

'I said so.'

'Including maybe a hit in the head.'

'Basilio, I'll take care of this, if you please. What did you do it with, Victor? What weapon?'

'I'm sick. I need a doctor. I'm sick.'

'You go on this way, you're going to need a priest. Now wise up. Start talking.'

'I loved her.'

'Forget all that. You pick her up. Some kid from no-where as far as you're concerned. You take her to dinner – we know about that – you take her to a hotel – what happens then?'

'I didn't do anything to her, nothing.'

'She says to do anything you want to do, right? And then what happened? Now let's hear it. Basilio and me, we have wives we'd like to go home to, right, Basilio?'

'That's right, Lieutenant.'

'I left her at her agent's.'

'Victor, let me ask you something. Does the name Barbara mean anything to you?'

'Barbara.'

'Does that name mean anything to you?'

'This is a frame-up. You know it is. It's a frame-up.'

'We just do this for the money, Victor. We don't know anything. If I told you she was one of Barbara's girls, what would that mean to you?'

'This is a frame-up.'

'Oh? How come? When we don't even have a crime yet. In your estimation I understood we didn't even have a crime yet.'

'I took her to dinner.'

'And you made quite a meal of her, didn't you? I mean, that was really some meal.'

'Tell me what I'm supposed to have done.'

'You're supposed to have behaved yourself like a kind, generous man, but you didn't exactly do that, did you? One thing Miss Barbara really does not like and that's people knocking off her girls. She's quite particular about that, as a matter of fact.'

'I want to speak to my lawyer. You have no business keeping me here. None.'

'You're wrong. That is our business. That's just exactly what our business is. Tell us about the beach-house.'

'What beach-house?'

'Let's go back to the girl. Now don't say what girl. Basilio's liable to go ape.'

'How do you explain the film, buster?'

'What film?'

'He's giving us the runaround, Lieutenant –'

'Basilio – BASILIO!'

'I don't like for people to do that.'

'Easy now, easy. Don't freak out on me, Basilio. We don't want any repetitions of what happened with that Martinez guy. I'll never forget his mother at the coroner's office. She didn't even recognize him. Now steady down, O.K.? You go start to run the film for us and I'm sure Mr England will soon appreciate what we're concerned about. You'll try and help us, won't you, Victor?'

'I don't know –'

'You go start to run the film, Basilio. Basilio's crazy about movies. Now Victor, this you're going to have to admire, because we have really a talented girl here. Watch closely because maybe you could use her one day. Or maybe you already have. Just give us your reactions, O.K.?'

'What is this film? I never made any film –'

'I guess you could say it's kind of a love story. Wouldn't you say it was a love story, Basilio?'

'Will you look at that girl? Beautiful, Jesus!'

'She certainly is. Don't you think she is, Victor? Majoring in psychology. An understanding, beautiful girl. Neat figure too. Doesn't she have a neat figure, though? She works with the doctor. You were talking about a doctor, Victor. Look at that, she works in a doctor's office. How about that girl, Victor? Recognize her? Now here comes the first patient. Here comes the first patient. She's going to take care of him. Look at that, she's really going to lay herself out for him. If that isn't intensive care, what is? The way she's getting down to it. What dedication! And what art, though, isn't that right, Basilio?'

'I never saw art like that before, Lieutenant.'

'I'm not surprised you're proud of this, Victor. You excelled yourself here. You know, I'll bet you something, I'll bet that girl plays a hell of a good saxophone. Look at that fingering, Victor. Can she blow! A guy could really be happy with a girl like that, psychology major with a talent for the saxophone. A guy could be really set up for life with a girl like that. Don't you figure that, Basilio?'

'Sure, for life. Why not?'

'Because how about that girl, Victor?'

What is happening here? Victor England is being interrogated by two men. One of them is Lieutenant McLeish whom we have met before, the other is called Basilio. He seems to be a surrogate for Franco; both have Italian names, both are film fawns and both are capable of bruiser's brutality. In some sense, clearly, the frame-up in the police-station – where Victor is being 'taken for a ride' – mirrors, if distortedly, the scene in the aeroplane where, once again, legal processes are being employed in order to hustle and humiliate him.

What is this film Victor England is accused of owning, perhaps of having made? It is almost certainly one of the 'educational' movies he and the girl saw on closed-circuit T.V. in P*easant Dreams. We are in a doctor's office (supposedly a psychiatrist). The girl is his nurse. There is also a male assistant. Between them they take care of the clients, who are of a standard kind. The second is a young girl, brought by her mother. The two 'therapists' are asked to prepare her for marriage. This sequence follows a standard scenario. But there follows a middle-aged man (he does not look much older than thirty).

DOCTOR: Well, let's take a look, shall we?
PATIENT: Look at what.
DOCTOR: You.
PATIENT: Oh I couldn't possibly.
DOCTOR: You have problems relating to your own body?
PATIENT: No. None. Never.

DOCTOR: Hercules, show this gentleman the door. This is a serious institution. We don't take no shit.

PATIENT: Doctor, please. You've got to help me.

DOCTOR: In that case, cooperate.

PATIENT: Be patient with me.

DOCTOR: You've got it wrong. You've got to be patient with me. Right, Herc?

MALE ASSISTANT: Right, doctor.

DOCTOR: So now let's take a look. We're all professional people here. We none of us get any pleasure out of anything we do. Right, Herc?

MALE ASSISTANT: Right, doctor.

PATIENT: What about her?

DOCTOR: Miss Ariadne? Miss Ariadne is a trained nurse. The human body is no more than a piece of fallible software as far as she's concerned.

PATIENT: How much is this going to cost?

DOCTOR: I knew we'd find a common language.

PATIENT: Am I going to need shock treatment?

DOCTOR: You'll get a hell of a shock, I promise you that. After taxes, you're going to have a hard time making ends meet.

PATIENT: A hard time?

DOCTOR: That's what we're here for. If we can't give you a hard time, we're wasting ours, right, Herc?

MALE ASSISTANT: Right, Doc.

DOCTOR: Now come on. We don't have all night. At least we have, but I doubt your credit'd stand it.

PATIENT: How long do I get for what?

DOCTOR: We start the clock when you come in. Everything is automated and computerized.

PATIENT: Just so's I'm not getting ripped off.

DOCTOR: You'll go out of here with everything you came in with except your money.

PATIENT: I feel better already.

DOCTOR: I'll be the judge of that. Leave that kind of thing to qualified medical personnel. You don't want to go out of here with cancer, do you?

PATIENT: Cancer? But –

DOCTOR: Because if you want major surgery, you're going the right way about it. I have an operating theatre right through that door. Smart talk me and I can have you on that table inside half an hour. I advise you to play ball, my friend.

PATIENT: I came here for help. Is there really a danger – ?

DOCTOR: Just behave yourself and nobody has to have anything they don't want. Monkey around and I'll have Herc throw the book at you. He used to be a National League pitcher –

PATIENT: This seems most irregular –

DOCTOR: Does your wife know you're here today?

PATIENT: I didn't want to worry her –

DOCTOR: Cooperate and she never has to. Any more of your horseshit and we'll pass the word.

PATIENT: I'll cooperate.

DOCTOR: Mr *Hosannah*? What kind of a name is that?

PATIENT: We were Finklesteins but my father was converted. He saw the light.

DOCTOR: That's enough about your super-ego. Get your goddam clothes off. We got work to do.

PATIENT: Do I have to, in front of other people?

DOCTOR: Miss Ariadne is not other people. She's a fully trained and qualified psychiatric assistant, and if that doesn't impress you, get a load of those jugs. How can you keep her waiting? Time is money, Mr Fink. Don't give us the runaround.

PATIENT: Hosannah. Hosannah.

DOCTOR: Never mind the ecstasy. Get 'em off. Or have you got something to hide? Quit crapping around or I might just give you a terminal diagnosis. A guy can go quickly today. There are a lot of rich widows in this town. People don't ask where people went, once they go. Time is money, Fink.

PATIENT: I'll do anything. I want to live.

DOCTOR: Then get your wraps off. Give me your credit card ... I'll take care of that. Now this is a very simple test.

I want you to do just what Herc – my assistant is doing.

PATIENT: That looks very irregular.

DOCTOR: Wanna bet? They do it all the time.

PATIENT: I never met a doctor like you before.

DOCTOR: They don't all have my overheads. I never met a Fink like you. What do you think of that?

PATIENT: Hosannah.

DOCTOR: I knew you'd see it our way. Now get on the couch.

PATIENT: But she's there. Is there room for me?

DOCTOR: I could have your lungs out and in that waste-basket just like that and there isn't a damn thing you could do about it. Herc, get me a premed. here.

PATIENT: I'll do it, I'll do it. It just looks kinda crowded.

DOCTOR: You'll fit in somehow. Miss Ariadne, how is that for you?

PATIENT: I'm afraid I'm sticking into her.

DOCTOR: Can you feel anything, Miss Ariadne?

FEMALE ASSISTANT: No problem, doctor.

DOCTOR: Miss Ariadne is a dedicated therapist. Behave just as though she wasn't there.

FEMALE ASSISTANT: Why, Mr Hosannah!

DOCTOR: Fink.

FEMALE ASSISTANT: You go your way and I'll go mine. Hos-ANNAH!

DOCTOR: Miss Ariadne, remember the code. Remember the hypocritic oath.

MALE ASSISTANT: Hippocratic, doctor.

DOCTOR: Keep out of this or I'll have you back on that goddam funny farm so fast. Miss Ariadne, what's your reading? How's the mercury?

FEMALE ASSISTANT: Way up and rising, doctor. Eight point three.

DOCTOR: Good girl. This is the only therapist on the Coast with a calibrated cunt. You're a lucky man, Fink.

PATIENT: Hos-ANNAH!

MALE ASSISTANT: I think he's been fully motivated, doctor. Sounds like he's peaking.

189

DOCTOR: He's got what he came for. Give me that credit card. Mr Fink that's the end of treatment for today –

PATIENT: Go away. Leave me alone.

DOCTOR: Herc, quick – get him off –

PATIENT: I love you. I love you.

DOCTOR: The straitjacket.

PATIENT: You're beautiful.

DOCTOR: This is an outrage.

PATIENT: I love this woman. Leave us alone.

DOCTOR: Miss Ariadne, you'd better wash up.

PATIENT: I love her and she loves me.

DOCTOR: This is an infringement of medical propriety. I may have to have you struck off the list of reliable patients, Fink. I'll torpedo your credit, you maniac.

PATIENT: Tell them what you told me.

FEMALE ASSISTANT: Hosannah.

PATIENT: Miss Ariadne has agreed to be my wife.

DOCTOR: Give me that syringe, Herc. We've got a full Mayday situation on our hands. I'm here to help you, Fink. Think of me as your friend.

PATIENT: You're nothing but a cheap quack.

DOCTOR: He's on a high. We've got to bring him down.

PATIENT: We hope to honeymoon in Mexico and Guatemala. Where's my nearest travel-agent?

DOCTOR: Miss Ariadne, tell him the truth. Quickly.

PATIENT: She loves me.

DOCTOR: How many treatments have you administered today? Miss Ariadne, answer me –

PATIENT: This time it's different. I'm going to remove her from your clutches forever.

DOCTOR: Remember your oath.

PATIENT: She loves me.

DOCTOR: Your hour is up, Fink. In fact, you're way over. Get out of here. Take your goddam Mastercharge and beat it. Don't ever come near Santa Barbara again or I'll have you run out on a rail. Love is a word I will not tolerate on these premises. Do you want me to lose my licence? We pride ourselves on observing clinical standards. You've breached all known canons. How about if I called your wife?

PATIENT: Call her. Screw her, for all I care. Miss Ariadne, will you marry me?

DOCTOR: Hercules, get that cheap hooker out of here before he goes bananas. And him with her. The pair of them.

MALE ASSISTANT: You've really done it this time, smart ass.

DOCTOR: Don't smart ass me.

MALE ASSISTANT: Wait till I tell the boys.

DOCTOR: Herc, you wouldn't.

MALE ASSISTANT: Try me.

DOCTOR: Now you're talking, sweetheart.

PATIENT: Miss Ariadne. Miss Ariadne. Where's she gone? What've you done with her? I love her. I love her.

DOCTOR: Love her? What do I care? I love Hercules. Look at it from my angle. Am I getting a fair crack of the whip? I'm not really a doctor. I only do this so I can be near him. Oh, Herc, Herc, I *love* you.

MALE ASSISTANT: That's all I've been waiting for, *Doctor* –

DOCTOR: Oh Herc, I can't wait. I can't wait.

MALE ASSISTANT: This is a raid. Don't anybody move. I'm a law-enforcement officer. Drop your weapons.

DOCTOR: If you're a dick, where's your badge?

MALE ASSISTANT: Up my ass. The only safe place.

DOCTOR: That's what you think, sweetheart.

MALE ASSISTANT: I said drop your weapons, or it'll go hard with you.

DOCTOR: It's hard with me now, that's why I can't drop it.

MALE ASSISTANT: You wouldn't want rape among the charges, would you now? How would that look on your sheet?

DOCTOR: My mother worked nights to put me through medical school and now this. Herc, I swear it was only a momentary lapse. I've admired you for so long.

MALE ASSISTANT: I have a job to do and I mean to do it.

You're going over the hill –

PATIENT: Down the river.

MALE ASSISTANT: One thing gets me up to here, and that's deviation, in any shape or form.

PATIENT: What have you done with my girl? I love her. I love her.

MALE ASSISTANT: Beat it, John, or somebody might just think Miss Ariadne's disappearance had something to do with you. Put this down in your diary as your lucky day and don't show your ass around here again. O.K.?

When Victor England opens his eyes, the jet has landed. They are in the middle of a desert. Stiff prongs of vegetation rise, ribbed and green and pointed as uncircumcized epigrams. Heat hammers the black plane. Victor looks out of the fumed window and sees a quartet of mechanicals carrying something away from under the rear doors. When he twists for a better view, he finds Bartholomew Heinz smiling down at him.

'Well, Victor, feeling better?'

'I'm not sure,' Victor England said. 'What's happening?'

'Everything's going to be fine,' Heinz said.

'What are they doing out there?'

'They've had a little technical trouble, but everything's going to be fine. You had yourself a little sleep in there. *Pleasant dreams?*'

'I don't know,' Victor England said.

Heinz came and sat beside him and pointed his knees inwards, for confidences. 'Victor,' he said, 'I have to tell you: these are remarkable people. They run a remarkable operation.'

'Which people are these now?'

'Mr Shap and his associates. These are remarkable people. I was leery for a while back there. I was wrong. These are people who can do things. People who want to do things.'

'Are they burying something?' Victor England said.

'The past,' Bartholomew Heinz said. 'They look to the future. I guess you feel you've had a rough ride.'

'What are we doing here in the desert, Bart?'

Bartholomew Heinz frowned. He might have changed his name and here was Victor failing to honour his new handle. 'I have to tell you something, Victor, that may hurt a little. Frank was giving you the runaround.'

'I don't think so.'

'Victor, if I don't know about the ins and outs of that particular situation, no one does. He gave you the runaround. How come Peter Drakos turns out to be directing your picture?'

'My picture? What's that supposed to mean?'

'Sure it's your picture. He has Dotty; he has Rob; he has the financial appropriation. He has your picture.'

'Drakos has the financial appropriation, what's that supposed to mean? Sounds like that story about the bank, they had a robbery, lost a hundred thousand dollars and it turned out it was your hundred thousand, Mrs Finklestein. I have a contract, Bart. That's one thing of mine Peter Drakos doesn't have. That's one thing that isn't going to go away. They're digging a hole. Why are they digging a hole?'

'Victor, I don't think you should even look out of the window. Just looking makes you hot. I told you: these people think of everything. Put yourself in their hands, you have no more problems.'

'How's the dog, Bart?'

'Dog?'

'Bow-wow,' Victor England said. 'The chihuahua?'

'Oh listen, Victor, that's a long story. It started to bite. We had to let it go.'

'How do you tell when a chihuahua bites? And where do you let them go to?'

'They can set up infections,' Heinz said. 'We went into it with a veterinarian.'

'A veteran aryan,' Victor England said, 'did you really? It *is* getting hot in here.'

'They're nearly through,' Heinz said. 'Victor, we want you on board with us, because this company is really going places from here on in. We want you on board with us when we go.'

'I dreamed I killed a girl,' Victor England said.

'We're taking care of that right now. We're taking care of that whole thing.'

Any experienced dreamer is familiar with waking from one dream only to find himself in another. When Victor England says, 'I dreamed I killed a girl,' it is his first open assertion of guilt. Is he asking for absolution or for a smiling shrug? Either way, Heinz's practical reply is unnerving. It suggests that the corpse the mechanicals are burying – they certainly seem to be a burial detail in some sense – is Victor's. Is there really a dead girl? Heinz counsels Victor not to look out of the window. There is no close-up, therefore, of a dead body, no establishing shot. But need there be? The dead now merely vanish; like the living, they lack substance. Why, after all, should we accord a cadaver a more solid existence than a live person? The odd remark at the end of the dinner-party conversation, when death and divorce are somehow equated, (with the teasing 'Think about it' for an *envoi*) begins now to take on a normative force. Death is the divorce, traditionally, between body and soul. It used to be an inexorable, a decisive event, but now there is a blurring. The body of Drakos's girl, it will be recalled, has been conveniently sectioned. A passage in dubious taste – it shares the kind of brutal levity to be found in Drakos's own films – demonstrates how different death is today. This time the scene is a legitimate doctor's surgery.

'This is a good day for us,' the doctor said. 'It's not every day we get spare parts to specifications as good as these. We're going to be able to make a lot of people very happy today. Here you have a case where there is going to be virtually no wastage of any kind. Someone who can't see is going to see, someone who can't pump ship is going to be able to pump ship. Sheldon, you know what

I think about death today? I think it's something we can do business with. It's a second chance. I'll tell you something, I sometimes think a medical man can apportion resources ecology-wise more intelligently than God can. Does that sound arrogant?'

'Not on a man with your record, sir.'

'Well, let's saddle up, shall we?'

'Only one thing seems like kind of a pity, sir.'

'And what's that?'

'Nothing we can do with her tits.'

'Give it time, Sheldon. Maybe one day we can lick that one too; we licked kidneys, didn't we? One day we'll lick tits.'

Termination is no longer the end. Nothing nightmarish or criminal is involved in this; the doctor's views are widely published, readably digested, under the rubric 'You're Dying – Now For the Good News'. The corpse which the doctor recycles stands for each of the three deaths supposedly discovered on the morning when Shap and his associates take over the running of Bowyer's Field. (Itself, of course, the name of a landing-strip where, in the early days of flight, 'quite a lot of funny things went in and out': cf. 'flyting', the origin of the cult of the quick comeback.) It is significant how little chance there now is to protest against the cannibalizing of a body which is booked to make a lot of people happy. The time available for the routines of mourning, post-mortem and detection has shrunk almost to invisibility. The reason may be said to be less sinister than pragmatic, but what is more sinister than that? The consequence is that no one can ask questions any more. The nationalization of death has given way to the next stage: commercialization. Morals retreat in the face of what the people want, just as aesthetics have. The contract on which Victor relies has been cut to pieces. According to Heinz, who here echoes the surgeon, it has had to be recycled in a form 'we can all live with'.

There remains the puzzle of the girl. Enough emphasis has been placed on the relationship of Victor England with *Dr*

Jekyll and Mr Hyde for California Time to be read (one is mindful here of Victor's reputation as an editor) as a re-cut version of an old, older story. Hugh Stone's synopsis (in her collection *Didn't They Once Make A Movie?*) runs as follows:

A famous director is married to a woman whom he hates, but with whom he lives a rigorously correct life. He goes to California in order to finalize arrangements for making a new film. When he first arrives, his contract is not questioned. He is respectfully received. True, there is a crisis at the Studio, but it is about to be resolved and in any case it has nothing to do with him. All he must do is wait. The wait is longer than he expects and longer than he has interests or resources to cope with. Luckily, he bumps into a girl. She declares her ambitious purpose so frankly that he is able to find it innocently charming. Because he has time on his hands, he becomes involved with her. A romance develops, entirely divorced from his normal, formal life. The protocol of studio politics enjoins a politeness which turns his relationship with the management into a parody of *bourgeois* marriage. Personal affection hides a businesslike concern with money and property. With the girl, all is different: there is nothing on paper (the lawyer's medium) to connect him with her. At first he seems to patronize her, then to fall in love. But love brings out in him less the tender passion traditionally repressed by the shifts and calculations of business than a murderous violence. Cruelty, not love, is the expression of his romantic self. Yet it is not a question merely of a split personality, one half of which is murderous. Killing is the consummate form of possession. The cannibal eats his victim; the director shoots his. Once he has finished shooting (once the victim is in the can!), he can resume his normal life without a scent or sentiment of guilt.

Now, according to Hugh Stone, the missing suitcase stands for

Victor's subconscious, which turns up to embarrass him (we shall see that there is a further twist in store here), and she seems to think that it is explanation enough to say that 'Victor's is a life without a cellar'; he has nowhere to hide his unwanted secrets. But what evidence is there that the girl whom he takes to P*easant Dreams is a mere figment without fig-leaves? Could she not just as plausibly be a creature of the Studio's story department? *In that case*, she would be far from a gratuitous flourish. And how much more pertinent would be the 'bang' that has robbed Pleasant of its 'l'! (To speak of a blown fuse only adds to the suggestiveness.) The visit to Fun State now also falls into place. Far from being a mere piece of confected set-dressing, the clean city becomes, with its passports and its *vis-à-visas*, an image of California itself. The escaped lion, which turns into a cartoon figure, stands for the diminished power of the studio *King*. Without his circus, one might argue, he becomes a mere figure of fun. The Fun State incident encapsules Victor's whole story, in miniature. The cartoon lion shakes hands with the girl, congratulating her on 'delivering' Victor. That there is a more sinister element, incarnate in the man with the black stetson, may or may not be the studio's responsibility. At any rate, we are now in a position much more thoroughly to understand the bitter end of Heinz's conversation with Victor England:

'The past is the past, Victor. Let's bury it. Frank did a lot of things we don't go along with,' Bartholomew Heinz said. 'From here on in, we intend to do business in a rational, open-handed way. Nothing up our sleeves.'

'Not even arms?' Victor England said.

'How well did you know him, Victor? Because, wow, did we find some weird things in his files. You'd be amazed, some of the stuff we found in there.'

'This guy Franco, he reminds me of somebody.'

'I never knew anybody knew more about a film-maker than that guy knows about you,' Bartholomew Heinz said.

'Where have I seen that face?'

'He has a brilliant mind,' Bartholomew Heinz said. 'Nothing escapes him. I mean nothing.'

'That's where Shap gets his money, I guess,' Victor England said.

'I don't follow you, Victor.'

'But you know where to find people who do, right?'

'He has a mind like a razor,' Bartholomew Heinz said. 'Everybody gets a prize, that's Mr Shap's slogan.'

'As long as they play ball,' Victor England said.

'Why play anything else?' Heinz said. 'You know, Victor, if there's one thing I've learned to hate, result of all this business, it's the media. Once they get a hold of something, they're like a dog with a long nose. Sniff, sniff, sniff. The media can bury you even when you're not dead and I'm sorry to say that's the kind of funeral nobody ever gets to forget.'

'How do the media come into all this?'

'Victor, I most sincerely hope they never do. That's how I came to raise them. Who wants to be crucified because of a little ketchup on his clothes?'

Can an innuendo be much clearer? McLeish is clearly just as much a weapon of the Studio bosses as the cops who raise and lower the barrier when limousines come into the lot. He is said once to have done a couple of good turns for Rex and always gets taken care of at Christmas, whenever he says Christmas is coming. The Studio sometimes passes evidence to McLeish, especially when the travel department can't get people out of town any other way, and Bartholomew Heinz's allusion to ketchup could scarcely be more pointed. If Heinz gives McLeish the word, Victor England is liable to face the media tipped off for one of their smirch-and-destroy operations. Frank King's secret files, which so shock Heinz that he's sure never to give anyone except himself access to them, contain body blows for any celebrity who has ever had any kind of a tail between his legs. Victor England has no choice but to come to heel.

*

He and the Studio were going to come to terms, the Studio's terms. What were they burying out there under the unsaved light? It hardly mattered any more, did it? Who needed to be Midas? If Victor would never bite on the golden fruit, maybe it was just as well: that kind of stuff never did anybody's bridgework any good. He had been sapped, the sap, despite all the fine print with which Brute's people had infibulated the sharper clauses. And yet he smiled, and not like a boxer who sheds his shield and grins with painfully red teeth, no, he smiled because so much trouble had been taken to do him down. They had sent him roses and roses, the pricks. Whose body were they burying out there under the unsaved light? They were not burying his, were they? Because here he was being sweet-talked, and who sweet-talks the dead? Was he weak not to resist? He could not resist. They were strong, and from their strength he could always draw sweetness. He smiled because he was happy. The Studio had forced itself on him; he was being screwed. Wasn't that something? O.K., it was an up-and-down business. If you were one of the lucky ones, it was; and he was. He recognized his reflection, like an old flame, in the window and flirted with it.

Victor has caught sight of the ghost of his other self. The fumed ochre of the aeroplane window is an unsilvered mirror in which the ghost of his ghost can play the snub-nosed urchin. At this point, a hand heavier than a royal accolade knights Victor on the shoulder.

'How are you feeling now, sir?'
    'Have they nearly finished?'
    'They look like they should have. I think they should have, don't you, Mr England?'
    'Where are we exactly?'
    'That's a nice point. That's a very nice point. One thing's for sure: we're two days march from the nearest clock.'

'Let's hope we can get this thing off the ground again.'

'I don't want to pressure you at this time, Mr England, but it would be a big help to me if we could initial a few things before we get airborne. How would it be if we went through a couple of points?'

'Two days from the nearest clock,' Victor England said. 'Maybe we should have brought a policeman.'

'I don't think we're going to need any policemen,' Franco said. 'Mr England, before I make with the paper, may I say personally how much I look forward to all the pictures you're going to make for the Studio from here on in? Not, of course, that I have any influence on the creative side, I'm just a fan around here, but –'

'Sure you are,' Victor England said, 'I can feel the breeze.'

'You should write your own scripts, Mr England. I always felt you were let down by your writers. When I retire, I think maybe I'll attempt a critical appreciation of your contribution to the movies. Let's just take a look at what has to be done here.'

'You're getting away with murder,' Victor England said.

'These changes are basically minimal. Just a few sets of initials and we have no more problems. I don't call a few sets of initials much of a murder, do you, sir?'

'You know what the man always says in the first draft, don't you? What if I refuse?'

'It's hot out there.' The heavy hand drew a heavy handkerchief from a slot in Franco's suit and polished the white lintel above his unfired eyes. 'I'd hate to have to find my own way home. A guy could miss a turning. Fall asleep in the wrong bed and you might just wake up with a cactus for company. They grow at night, those things. You sleep; they don't.'

'Not the kind of a picnic anybody without a change of shoes and a hump like a camel would want to be left behind after,' Victor England said.

'Not that anything remotely like that is going to happen,' Franco said.

'You just thought you'd mention it in sort of fine print, right?' Victor England said. 'I guess it's the legal background. You did say legal, didn't you?'

'Nasty things can happen, no matter how careful you are. I've heard of miscounts, people who weren't missed till weeks later, sometimes not even then.'

'Hell yes,' Victor England said. 'And a guy can easily be miscounted after he's had his skull lightly fractured and he's been dumped out of a fast-moving plane. It's not that unusual today. In fact I hear it's even quite common on Sunday School outings.'

'How goes it, Victor? Is he twisting your arm?'

'He's a funny guy,' Victor England said. 'First he gives me the anaesthetic, then he twists.'

'I guess they've about finished,' Heinz said. 'They seem to be on their way back. Some location, don't you think, Victor?'

'Nowhere much to go in the evenings,' Victor England said.

'And one more set of initials here. And then a signature right here,' Franco said. 'And we're back in business.'

'Better lettuce than no lunch at all, England,' Bradley Biddle was leaning over the back of the seats in front. He pushed up a California wine-gum with his ribbed thumbnail and held it out to Victor England. 'That's a song my mother taught me.'

The jet is airborne again. Victor England accepts a glass of cold comfort, but he is already recovering his strength, a man less hurt by the operation than the incision suggests. He is used to being overcharged; what matters is staying alive.

It was lucky he had pockets to turn out; there was sure to be dust from some old talent in one of them. Talent was always the best insurance. Someone would always want you again for what you had done before. To get him for less than they had promised struck them as a victory. Let it be so: being somebody's trophy meant you always had a case. What if he had to live on only twice what a prime minister made? The simple life had its attractions, so long as they didn't include simplicity. He relaxed in his black, velvety seat and sipped the beaded beaker. The poison was just the way he liked it.

Shap comes along and offers Victor a cigar. He refuses and the banker stands there in the aisle, counting clouds. He bends down suddenly and frowns out of the window.

Had he seen somebody he once knew marooned in the nimbus, thumbing a ride? He smiled and applied his cigar to the place in his face.

'Mr England, may I sit down for a minute?'

'Just bend the knees,' Victor England said.

Shap took late delivery of a smile. 'Can I tell you something? There's a picture you made years ago, that picture is like the Bible as far as I'm concerned.'

Victor England started to hum.

'That's the one. I guess I'm not the first person said that to you.'

' "Unless it's love – Throw it away/Blow it away/Like an old, old glove – Unless it's love – " '

'That's what we want to get back to,' Shap said. 'Those are the standards we have to get back to. And then that dance. Talent! Real talent! You remember, when they get up in that little Italian restaurant and dance?'

'Sure I remember,' Victor England said. 'They had a licence from the macaronis. It was framed and hanging on the wall behind the two-shot of the proprietor smiling at his wife. She was the one with the moustache.'

'Magic,' Shap said. 'One thing I hate, violence. I'd like "Unless It's Love" to be the marching song of the Studio.'

'It's a good marching song,' Victor England said, 'if you like marching in circles.'

'Discipline, control, craftsmanship. Those are the qualities that made great movies, those are the qualities that made "Unless It's Love". Qualities, Mr England, that I associate with you personally. That's why I'm so glad we have you aboard.'

'The desert's no fun this time of the year,' Victor England said.

'You think I'm flattering you,' Shap said. 'About your movie. I'm not. I owe you a lot.'

'The Studio owns it outright,' Victor England said. 'You don't owe me a cent.'

Shap leaned out into the aisle, a motorcyclist about to veer sharply to his left, and put up a finger. Victor England had never before heard 'Unless It's Love' arranged for a thousand strings. Shap conducted; Victor England wished that he had brought his dramamine.

Bartholomew Heinz rides back in the limousine with Victor. It is a powerful black limousine this time, with a black, powerful chauffeur frowning under a piqued cap.

'Victor, I hope you'll bear with us taking you in the plane like that. It seemed logical.'

'It's not so much where I get screwed,' Victor England said, 'as the kicks when I'm down.'

'Read some of those clauses carefully, Victor, will you do that much for me? Because I believe in the end this could be a better deal for all of us. The days of everything up front are gone forever. That's not the way we can any of us do business any more, but there's liable to be a whole lot more for everybody in the long run.'

'I hate the long run, Barty,' Victor England said.

'What counts is, we're in business. There's still a ways to go before everything's running smoothly again, but it won't be too long before it all shakes down.'

'I feel kind of shaken down already, Bart.'

'It takes a whiles to get used to it out here again, Victor. Jet-lag, Jesus! Give it time. I'm sure you'll find you've made the right decision. I recognize there's an element of where-did-everybody-go, but balance that against the fact that you have a reorganized Studio behind you, a Studio in better shape now than it's been in in, oh, years. We've been stumbling, Victor. We've had our ups, but they haven't matched our downs. Now we have the muscle we need. And without muscle, what are you? You can't function.'

'What's going to happen to Frank?' Victor England said.

The limousine had stopped to let some senior citizens get half way across the boulevard towards the concrete bench, courtesy of a kosher mortician, on which they could spend some twilit hours. Heinz's head turned towards Victor England in the same slow rotation as a plastic hamburger, with all the trimmings, atop a creaking pole in the parking-lot behind some vandalized vending machines.

'Everybody's going to get prizes, Victor,' Heinz said. 'There's going to be no nastiness. None. From now on, only nice things are going to happen. You have my word on that.'

The limousine moved forward again. Victor England's fingers came up from the hairy groin of the upholstery with a folded find. He did not need to look at it; his fingertips could read initials.

'What about all these suits everybody was bringing?'

'We'll hang them in the closet. Keep the creases in them. Mr Shap is not a vindictive man.'

'What about you, Barty?'

'Me? What have I got to be vindictive about? Nobody's done me any harm.'

'That's right,' Victor England said. 'Think you can handle it?'

'I have a lot of fine friends, Victor. You'll pull me through. And I've always got Rex, I'm glad to say. We don't intend to lose access to Rex. In fact, I'm putting up a plan to the Board I think they'll find they can live with, a plan to make Rex President For Life.'

'President For Life, huh? That's a pretty smart idea.'

'It makes sense. He's not a young man today.'

'A very honourable and a very practical idea,' Victor England said.

'I think it is, Victor.'

'This is my stop,' Victor England said. 'How neat that things have worked out so nicely!'

'Who wants nastiness?' Bartholomew Heinz said. 'We have to live with each other.'

He offered Victor his hand on that and Victor took it and turned it palm up.

'All better now?' he said. Heinz laughed. What else does a man do when he's forgotten the joke?

When Victor England looks down to confirm what his other fingers have told him, he sees that he is holding a packet of old flames with F.K. on the metallized cover. He opens the flap. Three or four matches have been used. As he stands there, an ambulance drives in, whooping, under the side awning of the hotel. He strikes a match, turns it between licked fingers till it is all consumed, and then drops it on the monogrammed (RV) mat under his feet. He goes into the lobby and across towards the elevators. The clerk calls to him from the desk.

'Mr England?'

'Yes?' Victor England did not promise to be the man the clerk wanted.

'I thought you'd checked out, sir.'

'Did I?' Victor England said. 'I didn't think I did.'

'I have you on my list, sir, to that effect.' The clerk turned the relevant paper towards Victor.

'As a matter of fact,' Victor said, 'I still have the key in my pocket. I shouldn't really. It's not good for my posture. What's the matter? Did I say something?'

'It's nothing, sir. A personal matter. I have an allergy problem. It passes.'

'What causes it? Did they run any tests?'

'I'm sure you have better things to do than worry about a clerk who has an allergy and an error in his listings.'

'I have a certain repository of specialized knowledge,' Victor England said.

'Oh, you do? Well, I seem to have these symptoms – inflammation of the mucous membrane, a tendency to lacrimosity, whenever I hear of the death of somebody in my personal framework of acquaintance. It's totally irrational; that's what makes it so difficult to control.'

'Somebody died?' Victor England said.

'I probably need to get a shot. That'll probably take care of it.'

'Who died?'

'I'm afraid it looks very much like Mr Verdugo, sir.'

'Ramon? Not too many people look like him.'

'It sounds pretty bad, sir.'

'How did it happen?'

'We had some unpleasantness in the Bonne Auberge this noon, sir. Maybe it was only some kind of a publicity stunt. But Mr Verdugo was markedly upset.'

'Unpleasantness?'

'I didn't see it entirely clearly myself personally, but a couple came into the hotel and walked right into the restaurant, sir, and insisted on being seated.'

'They had no reservation?'

'They had a reservation, sir. A reservation had been made, but –'

'What was the problem?'

'The lady was completely nude, sir.'

'Nude?'

'She had no clothes on whatsoever.'

'What age was this lady?'

'She was young. Very young. She looked entirely delightful although personally I'm gay myself.'

'And this upset Mr Verdugo?'

'That wasn't the thing, sir. It was the gentleman.'

'Didn't he have any clothes on either?'

'Oh he had clothes on all right, sir. But he wasn't wearing a tie.'

'No tie?'

'And he refused absolutely to put one on. Mr Verdugo offered him a tie and he completely and absolutely refused to put it on. He just stood there and he laughed.'

'Who was this girl?'

'I guess she was some kind of a blonde. She behaved with perfect propriety, I have to give her that. No gripes in that department whatsoever. It was the gentleman. He had this really vicious expression.'

'Did he strike Mr Verdugo?'

'He was just abusive. Very abusive. Yelling all kinds of stuff. He kept saying it was the end of the line so far as Mr Verdugo was concerned. I can't explain, sir, just how horrible he made it sound. He was dark, sir, and ugly. Ugly and kind of pretty at the same time. He had eyes – eyes like they'd seen everything. Maybe I'm just being emotional. Sir, this is not one of our keys.'

'I beg your pardon?'

'This key, sir, you were carrying. It's not one of ours. This comes from some kind of a motel – '

'Give me that,' Victor England said. 'I guess I picked it up on the set someplace.'

'And then after lunch, everyone was very sympathetic to Mr Verdugo, but he sort of couldn't buy that they were on his side. They all came and shook his hand and he kept saying "goodbye, goodbye" and then he went up to his room and I guess he collapsed.'

'Who found him?'

'He dialled the Bell Captain.'

'The Bell Captain? Why the Bell Captain?'

'I guess he figured he was the person responsible for bringing things downstairs, sir.'

'Who was this character, that's what I'd like to know?
This – '

'We have some photographs, sir, if you think you'd
recognize him.'

The clerk, who continued to be convulsed by shrugging sobs he did his best to sneeze away, opened a
drawer and took a string-fastened beige envelope
marked DO NOT BEND from under a police automatic
and handed it up to Victor England. 'He said just terrible
things to Mr Verdugo,' the clerk said. 'He didn't just
laugh. He said terrible things. Right in front of everybody.'

The face of the man is familiar to Victor England. The girl, in
her double-breasted birthday suit, is blonde and has come
straight from the beauty parlour. The man's insolence contrasts with her model manners. She might be showing off a
style dependent on such neat needlework that only a cute
couturier could hope to get away with it.

It wasn't an outfit any old body could wear. Victor
England concentrated on the man. Surely it was Franco;
if not *the* Franco, then *a* Franco. He had dark, lustrous
eyes like loaded one-spot dice. No one else was going to
win in his book. The terrible things he had said to
Ramon Verdugo were there on his pretty, ugly face, like
the slogans on athletes who advertise cheap products
with graceful movements. Those eyes boasted of money
and of there being more, much more, where that came
from. They were the eyes of a hard man who had a
harder brother. There was humour in them too, a
humour that was almost innocent. The devil had eyes
like those; he had knowledge of human weakness, he
traded in human fear, but he was neither weak, nor
fearful, nor human himself. He was untroubled by the
taint he could recognize just as a doctor reads without
alarm the death sentence written between the lines on a
face. He was innocent, this man with the mask of the

family pulled down over the charred child he had been, because he had never known innocence and he brought Ramon Verdugo the gift of death. Verdugo had recognized the bad news in his ungroomed intrusion; he had overreached himself, and he knew it, and this carrier vulture served him notice and served him right. There remained the girl. She was innocent too. She looked at the photographer through the glass of an aquarium in which she swam, cold and alone, mouth saying ah for the crumbs that were sprinkled, con man's confetti, on the trembling deck of her tank. She rippled and fed behind the pane of her world, wide-eyed and unblinking, a vegetarian shark, sabre-toothed on salad.

Ramon Verdugo, the old devil, has cleaned his house and, unable to maintain effective dominion, has in turn been cleared out by seven new devils. (Franco is one of seven brothers, or the Francos *are* seven brothers, it is not entirely clear which.) The old parable has been re-cast and, although in public domain, re-written. The message remains; the new devils are taking over.

Victor goes upstairs. He passes his own door and continues towards where we first saw Dotty. The doors of other suites are open. A fresh breeze blows through them. Dotty's door is open too. He goes in. There is a pile of sheets, used snow, under the sideboard. On the coffee table in a stem-stall is a single rose, its spent petals repeated in the mirrored surface.

The television is switched on. Dotty's famous film is being shown; we have come to the seminal scene in the kitchen. As Dotty shucks her bikini bottom and begins a new era that is already old, there is a movement in the bedroom of the suite. 'Someone there? Dotty?' The orchestra of Victor's hopes saw on the strings of his heart. A trailer in the bedroom mirror: it must be her! A duster wipes; the image is gone and the chambermaid steps through with an armful of soiled dreams under her chin. Her name is Darlene.

*

'Hi, you looking for somebody?'

'I already found her,' Victor England said.

'They all gone left town.'

'I think I left myself,' Victor England said.

'I like to have the video on while I work. I don't care what it is. Anything to help the time go. You ever see that one? First time I caught up with it.'

Victor England took a petal from the table and raised it to his lips, the velvet shell of a fugitive oyster.

On the roof, the house flag of La Mission is being lowered to half mast by a black man in an ACME T-shirt.

Everything in Victor England's suite is as he left it. How curious that the clerk should have accused him of checking out! The windowed fruit and the bowed bottles are as they were when he arrived. He lies down on the bed and closes his eyes. When he opens them, we hear once again that he might have been asleep for as long as a minute, or only for a day or two. The memory of the last few days, *if they existed*, are bleached out like part of some fancy credit sequence that finally gets junked.

The trick is as insolent as that of the macaroni cheesing into the Bonne Auberge. ('Cheesing' is a nautical term: a wire cheeses into a bollard or other obstacle.) Before our eyes the whole text is being revised, the meaning of an event cancelled like an unwanted booking. (In a later scene, a new maître d' crosses out a client's name, before his eyes, and denies it was ever there.) Victor England ought to be collapsing under the force of the hard arts practised against him, but instead he disdains to 'print' or register them. To be a director, it has been said, is a neurosis not a profession (the words are those of a writer cheated into bitchy riches); a director can select what he wants from life and edit it into 'the real' (or the reel). What we are witnessing throughout California Time is an explosion of conventional expectation, an assault on the proprieties both in life and (the same thing?) in art. It may be that Victor England is a murderer or the victim of 'murder', but the issue becomes insignificant. Death has dwindled into an event which happens to others; something so trivial that to lament it must be passed off as an allergy. Bodies are disposed of by private agencies; no record exists of their provenance or their destination. *There isn't time.* Death, crime and guilt have all been eliminated as points of departure for the investigation of the human condition. The city without a centre has spawned a morality without a structure.

Victor England has survived because he does not learn and is not altered – the very negation of the morality by which the novel has been made metaphysically respectable, that of trial by circumstance. The maze which has been constructed to bait and abet him serves neither to contain nor to flummox. How much has really happened to Victor England of all the events with which his name has been connected? It may be that he has dreamed them all. It may be that they never took place, or that he misunderstood them, as he has been accused, by Hugh Stone, of misunderstanding his own films. (We may recall the agents discussing the value of a man coming back from the dead.) All that one can say is that they have a certain status. They have been paid for, the definitive Californian justification.

Victor England's defeat left him with – what else, after all? – the character of a victor. He searched his unlined face for the furrows of failure, but buoyant boyishness was the fruit of his years and his tears. He had done well. The red carbuncle flashed; it was a message from Brute. Everything was fine. Who cared what happened at Canossa anyway? Victor dressed in the clothes in which he had arrived. The creases were still in the pants; the stitches had endured the hemming and the whoring. He wore a white shirt and a knitted black tie, like a Morris-man of the 'fifties. It was a sort of modesty in him, the vanity of a man with a secret, even if it was only the secret of what he did with his money.

He did not turn left. That Dotty Lampard, whom he loved, had lived a few doors down the primrose path was now forgotten. Victor England strode to the elevator. He would have brought Eurydice easily out of Hades, for he was never tempted to look back. Once distant from the dominion of Dis, however, and free to live together forever, he would almost certainly have divorced her.

He is waiting for the elevator when a man comes out of the service door carrying a suitcase. It is immediately evident that the case is the one lost at the airport, even though

... the flowers with which it was printed were in need of water; it had the appearance of a tribute left overnight in a hot cemetery. The man who carried it made it heavier than its size warranted. He had a malign halo of black hair above his shining beige face. The striped apron might have been tied on to him by a running wardrobe-mistress as she bundled an understudy on to a deserted stage. He carried the case as if he had never had time to rehearse the scene. It was at once an humiliation and a laugh that he should have to do such work.

'You found it,' Victor England said.

'It came. You're Mr England?'

'We had a lot of trouble,' Victor England said.

'If this is it, the trouble's over,' the man said. 'It was downstairs.'

'What do I owe you?'

The man put down the case and was burdened only by his empty hands. He took a deep breath of the desert air. 'Not a thing,' he said.

'What's the news of Mr Verdugo?' Victor England said.

'Verdugo? He croaked,' the man said. 'Dead on arrival. They gave him treatment in the ambulance; he was dead when they got him there. I guess he was too old.'

'Here,' Victor England said it with money.

'It had your name on it,' the man said, counting without looking down. *His fingers were his tellers.* 'At his age a guy shouldn't have enemies.'

'Enemies? What enemies did Mr Verdugo have?

'Ramon? A hotel can't afford to be exclusive today, that's my analysis. I think most experts would agree. He thought he could run an exclusive place, but today – '

'That's all changing,' Victor England said.

'A guy's got a dollar, he's got a right. We don't live in a world it pays to make waves, that's my analysis. Morals are changing.'

'I guess that has to be true,' Victor England said.

'Girls go down on guys at their first date today. That's a whole new ball-game in the last year or two. You ever hear of that a few years back? Even between husbands and wives.'

'Thanks for the bag,' Victor England said.

'No problem. From now on anything you want, any hour of the day or night, you have the money to pay for it, it's yours. In my view that's the way things have to be. It's the logical development. My name is Vincente. Any problem, don't hesitate.'

'Thank you, Vincente,' Victor England said.

'Let me give you an instance, if I'm not taking too much of your time. I got a brother's in the police department. Would you like me to take the case into the room for you? No problem. No problem at all. I have a pretty big family; I guess I'm lucky. How about you, sir?'

'No,' Victor England said.

'Shall I tell you something I've discovered, result of my brother Basilio? A cop likes to do a favour. Don't get me wrong. It's not a question of winking at a misdemeanour. It's a question of feeling the public appreciates you, the public isn't afraid to come to you. That's my analysis anyway. So listen, if you have any kind of a problem – and I'm not talking about a parking-ticket, you know what I mean – call him up. If you have something you can't handle alone. He's a big tough cop to look at, Basilio, but he wouldn't harm a baby. Not unless it was coming out of a burning liquor shop at three in the morning, with a gun in each hand. Then he might just detain it for questioning. He's a good man to know. Now what about the case?'

'I'll take care of it,' Victor England said.

'No problem,' Vincente said. 'Would you like one of my brother's cards? Let me give you one of his cards. Why not? You never know, Mr England. In this country no one is above the law. *Just in case*. Because how can it hurt?'

The Orphic myth is lightly glossed here. Victor England has successfully escaped from the lower regions, with their dark dangers and desires. He is restored to the kingdom of everyday. The messenger with his case, whose contents we shall examine in a moment, wears the livery of death. Not only does he have a dark halo, he also is a brother to those other fraternal fixers, Franco and Basilio. 'Vincente' suggests a man in the course of a conquest; the brotherhood is taking over the Verdugo empire, while his body is still cool. The order given to Orpheus that he should not look back was, if obeyed, to give him back a beloved wife. Here a change is worked in the myth: Victor has been framed, it may be, for a killing. (Or the killing may itself be 'framed', part of a scenario, as one critic suggests, which is forming itself in Victor's mind and which, in due course, after the writers have done each other's stuff, can become the basis of his next success.) What is required of Victor, whatever the circumstances, is that he keep going forward. He must not look too closely at the shifts by which power has been wrestled into new hands, both at the Studio and here in La Mission. He must refrain from reflection. If he will, the forces which have destroyed others will protect him. Like Orpheus, he must not look back: to remember the past is always to question the present. The past is always more attractive than the present, it is better furnished. But Victor England proves willing, after all, to be an oblivious Orpheus and he will never lose his head. He knows when to stop singing. To sing is, of course, in criminal parlance to give evidence.

Victor could have no clearer warning on that score than the one contained, literally, in the case which has just been delivered to him.

It weighed next to nothing. No wonder it needed both hands. He lifted the lid on the blackness it contained *as if it were what he had always wanted*. The roots of the flowers on the outside of the case were ashes within. It was a conjurer's box that Vincente had brought, and here was the clinching trick: Basilio's card, which had been offered to Victor England by the elevator, had passed through the flat flowers of the lid and lay, white on carbon black, in the very centre of the ashes.

Victor closes the case and posts Basilio's card in his top pocket. The ashes seem to promise Victor that he will have no further trouble from the police. Will the murder now be hushed up, wished on to someone else or simply buried? Was it all a charade? Or was the girl a pro – and has her dirty washing been incinerated in earnest of the game's end? Victor makes no effort to get rid of the case. Can it then contain anything that is still incriminating? Hugh Stone might take the view that he arrived in California with the ashes, that they are the vestiges of his old life (old flames!) and that the case is proof of his intention, from the very beginning, however recently that may be, to quit London and to come to sweet, onerous terms with California. The suitcase thus becomes the portmanteau promise of a new life and a portable pot for the ashes of the old.

Victor goes down to the lobby in the elevator in which a celebrity-hunting canine could still sniff a vestige of the Princess's sweet meat.

There was a girl sitting there, near a large potted plant, with black, fleshy leaves. She wore a long cotton dress and blood-brown ox-hide boots. It was either the same girl whom he had not dared or cared to approach when he first arrived, or else an identical one.

*

There are, however, differences. She does not wear mirrored glasses and she comes towards him, practising a smile.

'Mr England?' she said. 'I'm Karen.'
  'You're here,' he said, 'and nobody told me.'
  'I just got here.'
  'Well, this time just don't go away,' Victor England said.

The love-story which follows requires no elaborate rehearsal:

The script was not original, but it had charm. The ease with which the two of them played their parts accorded it a freshness which proved how old it was. Victor England was amusing and he was wise and, without it disturbing his ease or his wit, he was a little bruised. She could touch him first with fingers that were at once tender and almost impersonal. They asked him not what he wanted, but *where it hurt.* He treasured such fingers and inspected them through the monocle of an inquiring chirologist. The script did not call for the two of them to do anything out of the way. There were no eccentric locations, no straining for defects. The quality of the dialogue, which assumed a common knowledge not of subjects but of styles, was without jokes that might fall flat or solemnity that might grow wearisome. There was a levity, during the drinks and the meal (ordered from a French-born Captain, ex-Foreign Legion, with a képi on his American accent), a prey-let-me-help-you-courtliness derived from the early reels of thrillers with a hitch in the proceedings, when the menace had yet to declare itself. The curtained restaurant, with a looped tie still in the drawer, appeared as it had always been. It was a petty state, the Bonne Auberge that evening, where the régime had changed and the foreign colony mistook for deference the measuring eyes of those who were planning to expropriate them.

The girl was beautiful; her appearance alone justified close-ups of amused and well-turned conversation. Who knew how many writers had been used before it was decided to settle for the stylish, yet accessible witticisms the two of them agreed to exchange? If this was sophistication, as the pianist and the candles and the price of the wine corks insisted, then it was of a kind that made no one uncomfortable. It required neither knowledge nor understanding. The girl's eyes, gorgeous with opportunity, made intelligence a matter only of make-up. Victor's generosity was the sole proof of his vintage taste. They watched each other while the champagne was poured and the girl sipped the bubbling air between them. She shared the humour in Victor's expression, an expression that already seemed to be turning off the light so that he could see her more clearly. How could she guess that he was smiling to think that they were drinking champagne when a much better case of the stuff stood unopened upstairs and would go home, at the end of his stay, with the valet?

'Here's to it,' Victor said, when the lights were right, 'whatever it is.'

They think of going to a movie, but there is a line around the block. Surely Victor could show them his badge? It turns out that both of them have actually seen the picture already. Each has at first refrained from saying so in the belief that the other really wants to see it. There is now between them the bond of two people who have not shared an experience. Victor drives down towards the ocean and they finish up parked below the villa where, blind under bright lights, some young people are making educational T.V. They watch the ocean from which invaders have never come. They are in her car, whatever car it is, one that she has earned from a line of work she doesn't care to do any more. No doubt she is referring to being cast as Miss Available for the hero with the hot gun in his pocket who only comes by when he wants to borrow her razor, but one is clearly meant to recall the girl who made the big decision to foreg o going topless. The dialogue between Victor and Karen grows a little more serious, as if life were obliging art.

The radio was on, low. Somebody's concert orchestra did violined violence to their ears. They walked down to the breakwater where starfish had cast themselves on the dumped rocks. It was there that he told her about his daughter, about her tormented body, every joint disjointed, every feature defeated, as if nature had racked her for a secret she never possessed, the child of a woman so renowned for her beauty that admiration kept a twenty-four-hour guard on her life, the prisoner of fame, fettered by flawlessness. One night during her pregnancy, the mother woke and yelled out to Victor that the foetus was not only kicking, but crying as well. He greeted her absurd anguish with *the smile of a clinician with something to hide*, he was kind to her, but with a kindness that secretly welcomed her fears like traitors with an interesting proposition. He had never dared to frighten her himself; now he left secret food for the fear he swore was imaginary. When the baby was born and the womb was seen to have been the child's soft cross, he saw himself as the accomplice of its crucifixion. He told the silent girl of this as if it were somehow humorous; a light touch was needed if such uncommercial material were not to prove too much of a downer.

'It had all the wrinkles its mother never had.'

'Wrinkles?'

'It was creased like a badly pressed flower. She hadn't given it an inch of her beauty. Not a jot, not a tittle. She kept all her beauty for herself. She had to. It was in her contract. The baby was everything she feared, Karen. The baby was Nine pounds of bad news, old age by special delivery.'

'And she hated it, right?'

'She loved it.'

Karen aged around the eyes, imagining that.

'She loved it. She wanted to keep it, to raise it herself. I was the one wanted to send it back. Not her.'

'Send it back?'

'I'm keeping it light, Karen. We don't want to lose the people, do we? She loved it.'

'And what happened?'

'Rex Keyes had a picture he wanted us to do. She didn't want to make it. She didn't want to make anything. He had me over to his office. It was up to me. I had to get her to do the picture or else – or else – suspension, court action, cancellation – Rex could press a button and California had the coldest climate in the hemisphere. The baby had to leave town. No problem. Rex always had people working for him could take care of a little thing like a baby that got in the way. That's nothing new in this town. There's always somebody around can dig a hole where nobody's going to look for it.'

'What did they do? They didn't – ?'

'Nothing nasty. They found a place. One of those places money can buy. The best. The best. The night Bella went – the Princess had some Italian – she chose the name already before the kid was born – that night the Princess went round the house and she broke every mirror in the place.'

'And you went ahead and made the picture.'

'Rex said to. And when Rex said to – that's what you did. I loved her then more than – I loved her to die, Karen, the weeks we were making that goddam movie. She never looked at me, the whole sixteen weeks. She never looked at me.'

'You were one of her mirrors,' Karen said.

In due course, Victor proceeds to tell her, the Princess woke crying for alimony. Rex takes care of that too. The child grows up alone in the limited company of others similarly afflicted with deformities and parents who can pay for them. Neither Victor nor the Princess forgets her. In some respects, she is all they can remember. But now the Princess is increasingly terrified and burdened by her own beauty. She plays night-watchman to herself, and needs a bottle on her rounds in the small hours. Victor makes one happy picture after another. He has seen enough of what hurts. He sends cars to take the girl wherever she wants to go and does not get to hear that most times she sits in the back with the dark glass all round her and eats candy, a senile teenager.

'One night,' Victor England said, 'one night she fixed for the car to come back. I didn't know anything about it. I was shooting on *Dime A Dance Girl* – '

'I loved it,' Karen said. 'It was in one of my courses. Weren't they fantastic together?'

'Bella used to go down to the beach sometimes with the rest of the zoo. She called it the zoo. She had to crawl to get to the water. Gravity was too strong for her. It got her down. All those muscle-beach bodies stretched out on the sand, she used to crawl through them like a soldier in a minefield. A minefield with no bangs. I just thought of that. Maybe I shouldn't.'

'Could she swim then?'

'Could she swim? She had gills. She loved to swim. Water was the best crutch she ever had. So one night she had the car come back for her. She told the people at the institution she was going to a party. Her birthday. It wasn't her birthday, Karen, so help me, but that's what she told them. She had the driver bring her to the beach. She crawled down the sand and into the ocean. Midnight. Cinderella went home.'

Karen put her arm through Victor's and held it to her.

'Man crawled out of here just a few million years ago, remember? You weren't here, but you remember. It was in the papers.'

Karen nodded; she was dry-crying.

'She went back. The driver waited. She never came out. But I'll tell you something, because it would be nice if there was one more neat little detail, don't you think it would, Karen? A grace note. So here's the grace note. The next morning they found a body on the shore. Right down here at the water's edge. Flawless. They said it was her. They said it had my name on it. I said no. I said it couldn't be. She'd washed my name right off, doing what she did. I wasn't about to take any credit. A beautiful body. Unmarked. Perfect. How could that be anything to do with me?'

She put her arms round his neck and kissed him. He held her make-up against his shoulder and nodded where she couldn't see, looking across the ocean for the invaders who wouldn't show.

It is the following, or a following, day. Karen is dressed in her long cotton dress and blood-brown ox-hide boots. They are driving up a steep road leading out of one of the canyons. On either side, propped on the steep slopes, are houses as stilted as the dinner parties where flowers float in the finger-bowls and the ladies wear long dresses and have known each other ever since they married their first money. Once again the car is a drop-head. If you open your mouth, your dialogue is liable to blow away. Karen has a script on her knee which she holds down with both hands.

'It doesn't bother you being a victim?' Victor England said.

'I've been killed before,' the girl said. 'When you're starting out, it happens all the time. I last longer in this script than I ever did before.'

'How about the way it gets done? Do you have any feelings on that?'

'The way they do it does seem kind of ordinary, I have to admit.'

'I think so too. I have the writers working on that one right now.'

'Wanna bet?' she said, taking long hair out of her mouth and pressing it on to the top of her head.

'The shellfish of the business,' Victor said, 'writers.

Sewage with pearls in them. You're beautiful. I'm so glad you're going to do it.'

'Are you? Truly?'

'Would I be marrying you if I didn't think it was good for my career?'

'I thought you'd hate me,' she said. 'Like it says in the script – '

'I'm having them look at that scene. I only like my corn on the cob.'

She breathed out and leaned her forehead on his shoulder.

Victor turns the car off the road and up a driveway through some shrubberies. A signboard advertises OPEN HOUSE. The name of the realtor is Harry Amoureux. The house has been freshly painted; the gardens have arrived only minutes before Victor and the girl. There isn't a scratch on the new bushes.

Drakos is wearing a leather coat, very long and with lapels wide enough to carry a ballerina's bouquet for a buttonhole. He has Moroccan slippers on his cold feet. Pictures of his girl lie, face up, on the marble coffee-table in front of the mesh screen behind which firedogs crouch in a sooty kennel. Victor and the girl, we now realize, have come to the house where the murder took place.

Drakos spreads his arms as Karen steps through the glass doors from the patio. She runs up to him and he kisses her, over the eyes of the photographs on the marble slab. Victor stays, tactful (the adjective has been used before), by the pool. He stares at the image of himself tethered, head down, in the depths of the water. He looks up to see Karen and Drakos mouthing inaudible dialogue (the kind nobody pays a writer for) and standing hand in hand like old enemies; he touches his pocket for his cheque-book. Mr Amoureux is going to love this. Victor glances once more at his image in the pool and then walks towards the glass doors of the living-room; his image remains, feet up in the water, like a jilted Narcissus.

'What are you leaving, Peter?'

'Everything,' Drakos said, 'right down to the thermidor and Philippinos. Everything. I don't have time not to be generous.'

'Oh Victor,' the girl called from the view that was really something, 'this you have to see.'

'Do I give Dotty your love?' Drakos said.

'She has it,' Victor said.

'I never saw anything so beautiful,' Karen said.

Drakos said, 'Shit, I forgot. You know what they're showing on the Z channel? We missed it.'

He presses the extra button and they are just in time to see the prospector turn away from the mining company's concession and ride up slowly towards the setting sun. As he passes some shade in the American night, a girl rides forward in a here-I-ambush. They embrace, once down here and then again for the folks on the other side of the hill and then they plunge over the precipice of a golden future.

'I'll leave you with that thought,' Drakos said. 'Now you'll have to excuse me. Europe is getting impatient. Karen, Victor, if there's anything, just call the Welcome Lady. Believe me, you're welcome. Bless you, my children. Bless you, one and all.'

How much later was it that Victor and Karen sat with clinking drinks by the unwarming flames of the gas logs with the whole evening, an untouched loaf, in front of them and, moved by the loneliness they had agreed to share like a legacy, looked into each other's ice? How easily they had fitted into Drakos's shucked shell, hermits that did not crab! Of course they would make some changes. The girl would bring all the things she had picked up, inexpensively, from all over the place; and Victor the things he too had picked up, expensively. They would fill the house with hopes as fresh as the spring water that was delivered by Nebuchadnezzar twice a week. She would play the victim, above the title, in his movie and prove it was all make-believe by coming to the Première on his arm, Victor's long white darling in her long white gloves.

'I love you,' he said, 'whoever you are.'

Through the glass doors they could see the underwater lights keeping Narcissus warm.

'Oh Victor,' she said, 'can we really be happy?'

'Well,' he said, 'we can try.'

It was the way all unhappiness began.

EVELYN WAUGH

Also by Philip Eade

Sylvia, Queen of the Headhunters
Young Prince Philip

EVELYN WAUGH

A Life Revisited

PHILIP EADE

WEIDENFELD & NICOLSON

First published in Great Britain in 2016
by Weidenfeld & Nicolson
an imprint of The Orion Publishing Group Ltd
Carmelite House, 50 Victoria Embankment
London EC4Y 0DZ

An Hachette UK Company

1 3 5 7 9 10 8 6 4 2

A CIP catalogue record for this book is
available from the British Library.

ISBN (Hardback) 978 0 297 86920 7
ISBN (Export Trade Paperback) 978 0 297 60948 3
ISBN (eBook) 978 0 297 86921 4

Typeset by Input Data Services Ltd, Bridgwater, Somerset

Printed and bound by CPI Group (UK) Ltd, Croydon, CR0 4YY

MIX
Paper from
responsible sources
FSC® C104740

www.orionbooks.co.uk

For Rita

Contents

List of Illustrations

All photographs are courtesy of Alexander Waugh unless otherwise stated. While every effort has been made to trace or contact all copyright holders, the publishers would be pleased to rectify at the earliest opportunity any errors or omissions brought to their attention.

FIRST PLATE SECTION

The Waughs, 1890
The Brute out shooting, *c.* 1890
Midsomer Norton
The Rabans, *c.* 1892
Kate and Arthur Waugh with their bicycles (Boston University)
Posing after their engagement
Alec, Arthur and Evelyn, *c.* 1906
Evelyn with his nanny at 11 Hillfield Road
Kate, Arthur, Evelyn , Alec and poodle at Midsomer Norton, 1904
Alec, Kate and Arthur in the garden at Underhill, 1909
The Pistol Troop, *c.* 1910
Evelyn, aged eight
Evelyn and Cecil Beaton at Heath Mount
Alec, Evelyn, Kate and poodle, 1912
Lancing school photograph (Lancing College)
Evelyn at Lancing, 1921
At Oxford, 1923
As a teacher at Aston Clinton, 1926
Richard Pares in the Alps with Cyril Connolly (Deirdre Levi)
Alastair Graham (Duncan Fallowell)
Alastair Graham nude (The Waugh Estate and the British Library)

At Captain Hance's riding academy (Private collection)
Madresfield (Historic England and Bridgeman Images)
Evelyn with Arthur after winning the Hawthornden Prize, 1936
With Penelope Betjeman and her horse at Faringdon House (Private
 collection)

THIRD PLATE SECTION

Laura Waugh, late 1930s
Pixton Park
Laura and Evelyn's wedding, 1936
Piers Court
Three photographs at Piers Court
Evelyn in military uniform, 1940
Bob Laycock, photographed by Yousuf Karsh (Camera Press and Martha
 Mlinaric)
Evelyn with Randolph Churchill in Croatia
Anna May Wong, Evelyn, Sir Charles Mendl and Laura
Waugh family and staff, late 1940s
Evelyn and Laura returning to Plymouth in the Île *de France*
Evelyn in his study (Mark Gerson and Bridgeman Images)
With his family and two Italian servants, 1959 (Mark Gerson and
 National Portrait Gallery, London)
At the entrance of Combe Florey (Camera Press and Mark Gerson)
With James, Laura and gardener
With Margaret in the Caribbean
At Margaret's wedding, 1962
Interviewed by John Freeman for *Face to Face*, June 1960
The Waughs, *c.* 1965

Family Tree

William Herbert
1696–1757

1st Earl of Carnarvon
(inherited Highclere from uncle)

2nd Earl of Carnarvon

3rd Earl of Carnarvon

Lady Evelyn Stanhope   m. (1)   Henry Herbert,   m. (2)   Elisabeth Howard
(daughter of 6th Earl   4th Earl of Carnarvon   (daughter of Henry
of Chesterfield)   1831–90   Howard of Greystoke
                                                                                                  Castle)

George   Lady   Lady   Lady
Herbert,   Winifred   Margaret   Victoria
5th Earl of   Herbert   Herbert   Herbert
Carnarvon   1864–1933   1870–1958   1874–1957
1866–1923   'The Baroness'   m. George   'I thought we'd
Discoverer of   m. (2)   Duckworth   heard the last of
Tutankhamen   Herbert Gardner   that young man'
                         1st and last Lord
                         Burghclere
                         1846–1921

                                                          Aubrey Herbert m. Mary
                                                              1880–1923 | Vesey
                                                          'The Man who was
                                                              Greenmantle'

Juliet   Mary
b. 1892   b. 1896
m. Alexander   m. (1) 2nd Lord Hollenden   Auberon b. 1922 —
Russell   m. (2) Alan Hillgarth
                                                                Gabriel b. 1911 —
                                                                m. Alexander Dru

Alathea b. 1893   Evelyn b. 1903   Bridget b. 1914 —
m. Geoffrey Fry   'Shevelyn'   m. Edward Grant
1st and last Baronet   m. (1) EVELYN WAUGH m. (2) Laura b. 1916 —
                              m. (2) John Heygate
                              m. (3) Ronald Nightingale

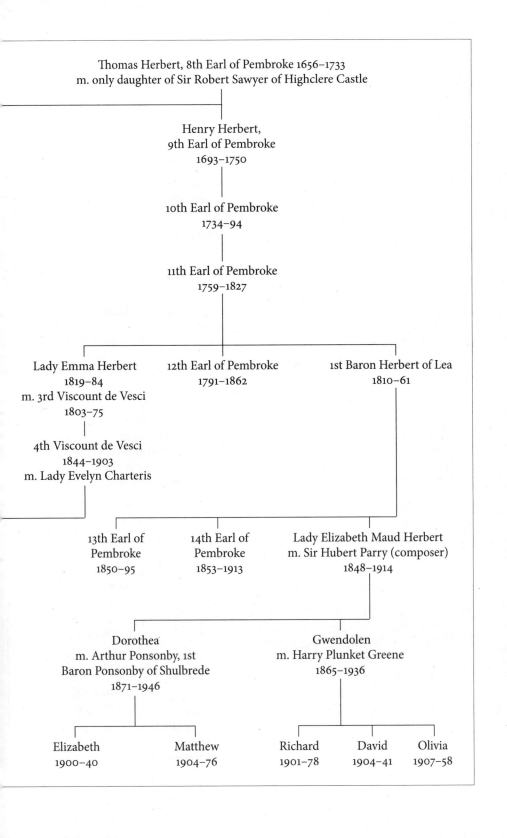

Thomas Herbert, 8th Earl of Pembroke 1656–1733
m. only daughter of Sir Robert Sawyer of Highclere Castle

Henry Herbert,
9th Earl of Pembroke
1693–1750

10th Earl of Pembroke
1734–94

11th Earl of Pembroke
1759–1827

Lady Emma Herbert
1819–84
m. 3rd Viscount de Vesci
1803–75

12th Earl of Pembroke
1791–1862

1st Baron Herbert of Lea
1810–61

4th Viscount de Vesci
1844–1903
m. Lady Evelyn Charteris

13th Earl of
Pembroke
1850–95

14th Earl of
Pembroke
1853–1913

Lady Elizabeth Maud Herbert
m. Sir Hubert Parry (composer)
1848–1914

Dorothea
m. Arthur Ponsonby, 1st
Baron Ponsonby of Shulbrede
1871–1946

Gwendolen
m. Harry Plunket Greene
1865–1936

Elizabeth
1900–40

Matthew
1904–76

Richard
1901–78

David
1904–41

Olivia
1907–58

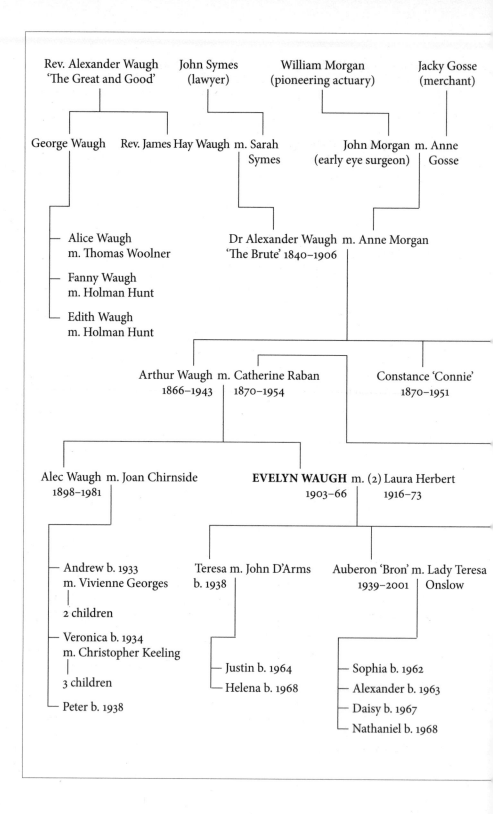

Rev. Alexander Waugh 'The Great and Good'

John Symes (lawyer)

William Morgan (pioneering actuary)

Jacky Gosse (merchant)

George Waugh

Rev. James Hay Waugh m. Sarah Symes

John Morgan (early eye surgeon) m. Anne Gosse

Alice Waugh
m. Thomas Woolner

Fanny Waugh
m. Holman Hunt

Edith Waugh
m. Holman Hunt

Dr Alexander Waugh m. Anne Morgan
'The Brute' 1840–1906

Arthur Waugh m. Catherine Raban
1866–1943   1870–1954

Constance 'Connie'
1870–1951

Alec Waugh m. Joan Chirnside
1898–1981

EVELYN WAUGH m. (2) Laura Herbert
1903–66   1916–73

Andrew b. 1933
m. Vivienne Georges

2 children

Veronica b. 1934
m. Christopher Keeling

3 children

Peter b. 1938

Teresa m. John D'Arms
b. 1938

Justin b. 1964
Helena b. 1968

Auberon 'Bron' m. Lady Teresa
1939–2001   Onslow

Sophia b. 1962
Alexander b. 1963
Daisy b. 1967
Nathaniel b. 1968

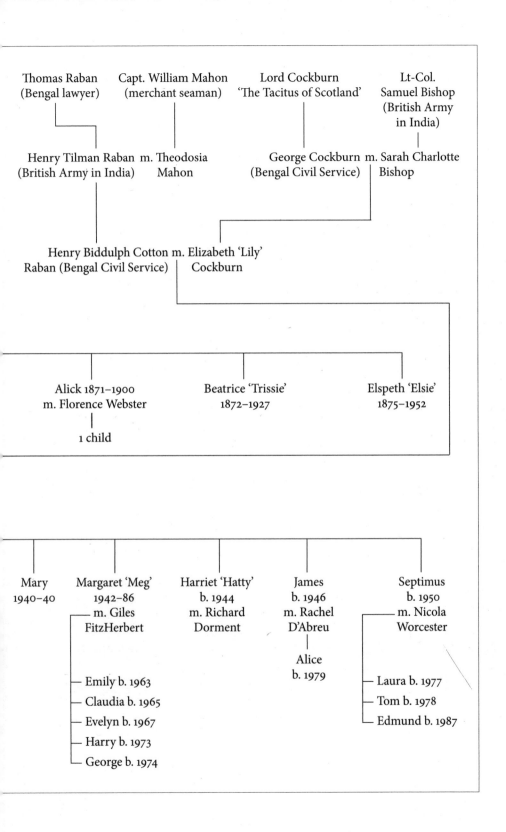

Thomas Raban
(Bengal lawyer)

Capt. William Mahon
(merchant seaman)

Lord Cockburn
'The Tacitus of Scotland'

Lt-Col.
Samuel Bishop
(British Army
in India)

Henry Tilman Raban m. Theodosia
(British Army in India)   Mahon

George Cockburn m. Sarah Charlotte
(Bengal Civil Service) | Bishop

Henry Biddulph Cotton m. Elizabeth 'Lily'
Raban (Bengal Civil Service) | Cockburn

Alick 1871–1900
m. Florence Webster

1 child

Beatrice 'Trissie'
1872–1927

Elspeth 'Elsie'
1875–1952

Mary
1940–40

Margaret 'Meg'
1942–86
— m. Giles
FitzHerbert

— Emily b. 1963

— Claudia b. 1965

— Evelyn b. 1967

— Harry b. 1973

— George b. 1974

Harriet 'Hatty'
b. 1944
m. Richard
Dorment

James
b. 1946
m. Rachel
D'Abreu

Alice
b. 1979

Septimus
b. 1950
— m. Nicola
Worcester

— Laura b. 1977

— Tom b. 1978

— Edmund b. 1987

Preface

In one of the funniest scenes in Evelyn Waugh's novel *Brideshead Revisited*, Charles Ryder's father pretends to suppose that his son's very English friend, Jorkins, is an American.

> 'Good evening, good evening. So nice of you to come all this way.'
>> 'Oh it wasn't far,' said Jorkins, who lived in Sussex Square.
>> 'Science annihilates distance,' said my father disconcertingly. 'You are over here on business?'

Mr Ryder never makes his misapprehension explicit enough to give Jorkins the opportunity of correcting him but he is careful to explain any peculiarly English terms that come up in conversation, 'translating pounds into dollars,' as Waugh writes, 'and courteously deferring to him with such phrases as "Of course, by *your* standards . . ."; "All this must seem very parochial to Mr Jorkins"; "In the vast spaces to which *you* are accustomed . . ."'

Evelyn Waugh played similar games in real life. When a young American fan named Paul Moor wrote to him out of the blue in 1949, he was amazed to be invited by return to stay at Waugh's home in Gloucestershire. Moor later described to Martin Stannard his reception by Waugh's butler and, almost immediately, being confronted by his 'idol', who was wearing a dinner jacket and greeted him with a show of astonishment: 'But I thought you'd be black! . . . What a disappointment! My wife and I had both counted on dining out for months to come on our story of the great, hulking American coon who came to spend the weekend.' Dazed by his host's exaggerated absence of taste, Moor never realised that Waugh was making a joke about his surname.

Later at dinner, when the butler went to fill Moor's wine glass, Waugh waved towards a jug on the sideboard, declaring, 'I'm sure you'd prefer iced water,' as though that was all Americans liked to drink. When Moor bravely declined, Waugh exclaimed, 'But we've gone to so much trouble!' Soon he was off again: 'At breakfast tomorrow I expect you'll want Popsy Toasties or something like that, won't you?' The teasing went on throughout Moor's three-day visit and yet the baffled innocent came away with the impression that his host was 'an essentially kind man'.

A brilliant and extraordinarily clear writer, Evelyn Waugh could hardly have been easier to understand and enjoy on the page; yet the peculiar traits of his character were often harder to fathom, inclined as he was to fantasy, comic elaboration and mischievous disguise. If the imaginative flourishes in his letters were intended to entertain the recipients, the eccentric and sometimes frightening façades he adopted in person were more often designed as defences against the boredom and despair of everyday life.

Moor was right about Waugh's kindness and one only has to read his novels to find the deep humanity behind the forbidding front. One of his more sympathetic American obituarists accurately described him as 'a man of charity, personal generosity and above all understanding', however it is also true that he rarely went out of his way to advertise the benevolent side of his nature. 'I know you have a great heart,' his close friend Diana Cooper wrote to him, 'but you hate to put it on your sleeve – rightly up to a point – but rather than sometimes letting it fly there, by its own dear volition, you pin a grinning stinking mask on the site.'

*　*　*

This is not a 'critical' biography in the sense that it does not seek to reassess Evelyn Waugh's achievements as a writer, but aims to paint a fresh portrait of the man by revisiting key episodes throughout his life and focusing on his most meaningful relationships. Drawing on a wide variety of sources – published and unpublished – it also seeks to re-examine and rebalance some of the distortions and misconceptions that have come to surround this famously complex and much mythologised character.

My biggest thank you is to Alexander Waugh, who suggested the idea of a new biography to mark the half-centenary of his grandfather's death and gave me unfettered access to his archive which has supplied a great deal of the unpublished material in the book. In the course of researching his own richly entertaining *Fathers and Sons: The Autobiography of a Family* (2005) and more recently as editor-in-chief of the first *Complete Works of Evelyn Waugh* (Oxford University Press; the first of forty-three volumes is due in 2017), he has assembled the most comprehensive Waugh study archive in the world, comprising original manuscripts, rare transcripts, photographs, rare editions, memorabilia, professional records and copies of the vast majority of the existing primary and secondary material.

Among the numerous unpublished letters that cast fresh light on Evelyn Waugh's life there are more than eighty written to Teresa 'Baby' Jungman, with whom he fell hopelessly in love in the 1930s, and who he later claimed formed the basis for every character – male and female – in his masterpiece *A Handful of Dust*. These letters have long been regarded as the holy grail of Waugh biography and while charting the course of this unrequited affair they show a deeply romantic and tender side to his character that counters the popularly-held view of his heartlessness.

No less significant is the brief unpublished memoir written by Evelyn Waugh's first wife, Evelyn Gardner, describing the short-lived marriage that is thought to have unleashed a bitter and capricious side to his character and propelled him towards the Roman Catholic Church.

Evelyn Nightingale, as she became by her third marriage, has had a harsh press and was understandably wary of Waugh's biographers, declining most requests for interviews. She was however forthcoming with Michael Davie, editor of *The Diaries of Evelyn Waugh* (1976), who interviewed her and corresponded with her regularly. In her 1994 obituary in *The Independent* he described her as 'a much more substantial person as well as a much nicer one than the propaganda spread by Waugh's circle had led me to expect'. After his own death in 2005, Davie's extensive collection of Evelyn Waugh papers (including his interview transcripts and copious correspondence with Evelyn Nightingale) were acquired by Alexander Waugh. These records constitute another significant cache of untapped primary sources in his archive.

In the course of editing Evelyn Waugh's diaries Davie had undertaken intensive background research, interviewing several key figures in Waugh's circle besides his first wife, in several cases shortly before they died. Some of them Davie had sought out; others contacted him to correct false impressions – or, as they believed, the outrageous fictions – in the diaries as they first appeared in *The Observer Magazine*. His interviewees included Sir John Heygate, for whom Evelyn Gardner had deserted Waugh, who died shortly after meeting him. Alastair Graham, Evelyn Waugh's intimate Oxford friend, who had become a recluse on the west coast of Wales, was another of those who did not co-operate with any other Waugh biographer to the same extent again, although a few years before Graham's death in 1982 the writer Duncan Fallowell chanced to discover him in a New Quay pub, which began a quest entertainingly related in Fallowell's book *How to Disappear: A Memoir for Misfits* (2011).

Alexander Waugh's archive also holds a significant collection of materials donated by Selina Hastings, derived from researches in the 1980s for her own outstanding biography, published in 1994. I am profoundly grateful to her for the resulting access to her numerous interview transcripts and for her great generosity in volunteering several additional stories that she had omitted from her book.

Another part of Waugh's life which the discovery of 'new' material renders ripe for revision is his army career in the Second World War. Here I owe a large debt to Professor Donat Gallagher, who for decades has been scouring military archives across the world for evidence to challenge many of the entrenched myths surrounding Waugh's military service – including Antony Beevor's widely adopted thesis concerning the supposed wrongdoing of Waugh and his commanding officer, Robert Laycock, during the Allied evacuation from Crete in 1941.

I am also grateful to Bob Laycock's son Ben and daughters Emma Temple and Martha Mlinaric for their help with my own research into this complex cause célèbre and for allowing me to quote from their father's unpublished memoir which sets out his version of events on the fateful night in question. I am equally indebted to Richard Mead, whose full and fascinating biography of Laycock – making full use of the memoir – is due to be published in the autumn; he could not have been more open-handed in sharing information and insights.

This book owes a considerable amount to the various scholars, editors, biographers, critics, filmmakers and bloggers who have done so much over the years to illuminate Evelyn Waugh's life and work. In addition to those already mentioned I am greatly indebted to the work of Mark Amory, Martin Stannard, the late Christopher Sykes, Robert Murray Davis, Artemis Cooper, Ann Pasternak Slater, Nicholas Shakespeare, the late John

Howard Wilson, Douglas Lane Patey, Charlotte Mosley, Paula Byrne and Duncan McLaren – whose various books are listed in the bibliography.

For access to various primary sources relating to Evelyn Waugh I am grateful to the Bodleian Library, Oxford; Boston University Libraries; Brasenose College, Oxford; the British Library; Christ Church, Oxford; Columbia University, New York; Georgetown University, Washington D. C.; the Harry Ransom Center, University of Texas, Austin; Hertford College, Oxford; the Huntington Library, San Marino, California; the Imperial War Museum, London; the Liddell Hart Centre, London; the National Archives, Kew; and the New York Public Library. I have sought to obtain permission from all relevant copyright holders and greatly regret it if I have inadvertently missed anyone; any omissions can be rectified in future editions.

I am enormously grateful as ever to my agent Caroline Dawnay and her assistant Sophie Scard; to the endlessly helpful staff of the London Library, where much of this book was written; to Mrs Drue Heinz for a very comfortable and productive four-week fellowship at Hawthornden Castle; and to my preternaturally patient publishers, Alan Samson at Weidenfeld & Nicolson in the UK and John Sterling at Holt in the US. Many thanks too to everyone else who worked on the book at Weidenfeld – Simon Wright, Lucinda McNeile, Leanne Oliver, Elizabeth Allen, Helen Ewing, Craig Fraser and Hannah Cox; and also to Linden Lawson for her excellent copy-editing; Kate Murray-Browne for her painstaking proof-reading; and to Christopher Phipps for compiling yet another model index.

Grateful thanks also to the estate of Harold Acton (c/o Artellus Ltd, London), Johnny Acton, the Dowager Countess of Avon, Theo Barclay, Matthew Bell, David Belton, Caroline Blakiston, Rachel Blakiston, Michael Bloch, Tessa Boase, Nina Campbell, Raymond Carr, Matthew Connolly, Barbara Cooke, Richard Davenport-Hines, Maria Dawson, Jill and Tommy Eade, Jo Eade, Duncan Fallowell, Hugo de Ferranti, Claudia FitzHerbert, Giles FitzHerbert, the late John Freeman, Derek Granger, Robert Gray, Jasmine Guinness, Nicky Haslam, Lord Head, Bevis Hillier, James Holland-Hibbert, Kate Hubbard, Luke Ingram, Kathryn Ireland, Paul Johnson, Rosanna Kelly, David Landau, Jeremy Lewis, Imogen Lycett Green, Euan and Fiona McAlpine, Patrick and Belinda Macaskie, Giles Milton, Harry Mount, Rosalind Morrison, Benedict Nightingale,

Michael Olizar, James Owen, Thomas Pakenham, Henrietta Phipps, Saffron Rainey, Alex Renton, Hamish Robinson, Jonathan Ross, Charlotte Scott, Nicola Shulman, Christopher Silvester, Rick Stroud, Michael Sissons, Charles Sturridge, Christopher Simon Sykes, Inigo Thomas, Blanche Vaughan, Rupert Walters, Eliza Waugh, Hatty Waugh, James Waugh, Septimus Waugh, Teresa Waugh, A. N. Wilson, Sebastian Yorke and Sofka Zinovieff. And finally, my love and most profound thanks to my wife Rita and daughter Margot.

1

....

Second Son

In *A Little Learning*, the autobiography published two years before he died, Evelyn Waugh maintained that his childhood memories were suffused with 'an even glow of pure happiness'.[1] This was possibly designed to thwart what he called the 'psychological speculations' and 'naive curiosity' of nosy interviewers and biographers, who seemed to be always 'eager to disinter some hidden disaster or sorrow'.[2] In any event, there is plenty of contrary evidence that from an early age he occasionally felt both alienated and unloved, excluded above all from the extraordinarily gooey bond between his father, the publisher and critic Arthur Waugh, and his elder brother Alec – the 'popular novelist' as Evelyn later disparaged him. Nothing approaching an equivalent relationship existed between the father and his more exceptional younger son, who remembered that 'at the height of the day's pleasure his [father's] key would turn in the front door and his voice would rise from the hall: "Kay! Where's my wife?"'.[3] The arrival of this intruder would mark the end of his mother's company for the day and confine him to the nursery. 'The latch-key which admitted him imprisoned me. He always made a visit to the nursery and always sought to be amusing there, but I would sooner have done without him.'[4]

Alec remained very obviously his father's favourite throughout Evelyn's childhood. 'Daddy loves Alec more than me,' Evelyn once said to his mother. 'So do you love me more than Alec?' 'No,' she tactfully replied. 'I love you both the same.' 'In which case,' concluded Evelyn, 'I am lacking in love.'[5] 'I was not rejected or misprized,' he later told his friend and biographer Christopher Sykes, 'but Alec was their firstling and their darling lamb.'[6]

When Alec returned home from school for the holidays, a notice would be hung over the face of the grandfather clock in the hall, declaring 'Welcome Home to the Heir of Underhill!' – eventually prompting Evelyn to ask his father: 'When Alec has the house and all that's in it, what will be left for me?'[7]

Underhill was the house that Arthur had built for his family at North End, Hampstead, in 1907, when Evelyn was four. Its construction was paid for by a small inheritance from Arthur's father, Dr Alexander Waugh (1840–1906), an exceptionally gifted country doctor who had won all the major student prizes at Bristol and Barts and invented Waugh's Long Fine Dissecting Forceps – still used by obstetricians today. Publicly jovial and popular with his patients in Somerset, Dr Waugh nonetheless came to be known by his family as 'the Brute'[8] because of his tyrannical behaviour at home. Geneticists might wonder whether certain of his foibles explain the more demonic traits of his grandson Evelyn, who was only three when he died.

Barely a hint of the doctor's less wholesome characteristics found their way into his son Arthur's cloying memoir *One Man's Road*, however family tradition has it that when the word 'sadist' was first explained to him, Arthur responded: 'Ah yes, I believe that is what my father must have been.'[9] Subsequent Waugh memoirists, notably Evelyn and his grandson Alexander Waugh, have been less reticent, hence we learn that Arthur's rowdier younger brother Alick* was regularly thrashed by his father while timid Arthur was deliberately frightened – ostensibly to toughen him up – by being sent downstairs to kiss his father's gun-case in the dark (the Brute was mad about shooting but Arthur, although a good shot, was never keen), or violently swung on five-bar gates, or mounted on a rocking-horse while it reared on its back rockers, or left on high branches for hours on end and then surprised by the blast of his father's shotgun just behind him.[10] After a bad day, Dr Waugh was apt to lash out at the drawing-room ornaments with a poker, or fly into a ludicrously disproportionate rage, as when he came home to find his family using his sacred whist cards to play snap.[11]

---

* Alick left home as soon as he could, enrolling as a naval cadet at the age of twelve in 1883. Six years later he married a Tasmanian girl, Florence Webster, and brought her back to Midsomer Norton, where their son Eric was born in 1900. Later that year Alick died from malaria, whereupon the Brute promptly evicted his widow and child from the house he had lent them, ordered them to pay Alick's funeral expenses and other outstanding bills and packed them back off to Hobart.

Despite the ordeals of his childhood, Arthur made no mention of these explosions in his autobiography, partly, it seems, out of some residual filial piety and partly out of deference to his sisters, who despite being badly bullied themselves remained curiously loyal to their father's memory. He merely recorded that 'the great lesson of our childhood was undoubtedly discipline . . . day after day, week after week, discipline, discipline and discipline'.[12]

Evelyn, though, already knew all about the Brute from his mother, who hated her father-in-law with a passion after witnessing his tantrum over the game of snap and eagerly disseminated many of the least flattering stories about him. Later in life Evelyn would entertain his own children with cartoons depicting the Brute's misdeeds and, as his grandson Alexander records, 'the arresting images he produced – snorting nostrils, flaming devil's eyes, lascivious mouth and snapping black-dog teeth – never failed to set their imaginations aflame'.[13]

Arthur grew up asthmatic – a condition often associated with 'nerves' – and a worrier. His mother Annie, a talented watercolourist, was a great worrier too; as her grandson Alec recalled, she was 'infinitely apprehensive . . . her imagination pictured dangers everywhere'.[14] Yet however watchful, she could not escape her husband's extraordinary and unpredictable cruelty. Evelyn recorded how one day when his grandmother was sitting opposite his grandfather in a carriage and a wasp settled on her forehead, he 'leant forward and with the ivory top of his cane carefully crushed it there, so that she was stung'.[15]

The Brute derived his nickname partly from stories such as this, and partly to distinguish him from his grandfather, known in the Waugh family as 'Alexander the Great and Good'.[16] Born in 1754 at East Gordon in Berwickshire, where the Waughs had been yeoman farmers for several generations, this Alexander Waugh was ordained a minister of the Secession Church of Scotland before moving south to London – thereby anglicising the family – where he became one of the most celebrated Nonconformist preachers of his day, a vigorous campaigner for the abolition of slavery and founder of the London Missionary Society. His popularity was never more evident than during the remarkable scenes at his funeral in 1827, when his horse-drawn hearse was followed from Trafalgar Square to Bunhill Fields cemetery by more than fifty carriages and a vast crowd of people stretching over half a mile – according to Arthur Waugh 'one of

3

the longest processions that had ever attended a private citizen through the streets of London to his last resting-place'.[17]

Alexander the Great and Good had ten children, among them Evelyn's great-grandfather James, who with his brother George used his inheritance (they each inherited £30,000 from their mother's brother, John Neill, who had made a fortune trading corn during the Peninsular War) to establish a smart chemist's in Regent Street, with exclusive rights to import the mineral waters of Vichy, Seltzer, Marienbad and Kissingen. Still more lucratively, they invented Waugh's Curry Powder – which is still made today – Waugh's Lavender Spike, an ointment for aches and pains, and Waugh's Family Antibilious Pills, which Queen Victoria was known to favour as a palliative.[18] After experiencing a religious calling, James eventually sold his share to George, who further acquired a large house in Kensington, a country villa at Leatherhead and blocks of property in and around Regent Street. Of George's eight beautiful daughters, Alice married the Pre-Raphaelite sculptor and poet Thomas Woolner, and Fanny married his friend Holman Hunt. Ten years after Fanny died in childbirth, Holman Hunt flouted convention and the law as it then stood to marry her younger sister Edith. Evelyn rarely spoke about his heredity but he often expressed fascination with his connections with the Pre-Raphaelites,[19] which helped inspire the choice of subject for his first book, a biography of Dante Gabriel Rossetti.

James meanwhile became an Anglican clergyman and at his own expense built a large vicarage at Cerne Abbas in Dorset, which he later bequeathed to the parish when the Marquess of Bath offered him the living of Corsley in Somerset – near to where most of Evelyn's other forebears had by then somehow converged. There the Rev. James Waugh, a tall, striking figure with a long white beard, 'lived well in mid-Victorian style,' Evelyn recorded, 'with long, abundant meals and an ample installation of servants and horses'. His theatricality would be inherited by subsequent Waugh generations, however his apparent joylessness and high regard for his own dignity and reputation[20] were such that his less reverential descendant Auberon deemed him 'mildly ridiculous'.[21] By Evelyn's reckoning he was fundamentally benevolent, but the same could scarcely be said for his son Alexander.

* * *

Born in 1840, Alexander 'the Brute' Waugh was sent to Radley, where he excelled at almost everything – academic, sporting and theatrical. His subsequent successes as a medical student promised a glittering career in London, however the lure of country life with its endless possibilities for shooting and fishing took him instead to the then remote village of Midsomer Norton, near Bath, where at the age of twenty-four and already sporting fashionable Dundreary whiskers he set up as a GP. He remained there for the rest of his life, tending to patients as far afield as his dog-cart would carry him – including Downside Abbey and school, whose monks later recalled him as always smartly turned out, 'with a button-hole and a jolly word of greeting'.[22] He married Annie Morgan, descended from an ancient but impoverished family of Welsh gentry, 'unambiguously armigerous' according to Evelyn,[23] and granddaughter of William Morgan (1750–1833), the clever, club-footed and acerbic associate of Thomas Paine who later earned a small fortune as a pioneering actuary to the Equitable Life Assurance Company. Annie's father, John Morgan, one of the earliest eye surgeons, died when she was six, and she was brought up by her mother Anne, one of the Gosse family of fundamental Christian Plymouth Brethren movingly if unreliably portrayed by her cousin Edmund Gosse in his classic memoir, *Father and Son* (1907).* Years later Evelyn's grandmother would recall 'with a recurring shiver, the sound of Philip Henry Gosse's [Edmund's father] knock at the door, his austere appearance at the portal, and his solemn but confident question, as he unwound an interminable worsted scarf from his neck: "Well, Cousin Anne, still looking daily for the coming of dear Lord Jesus?"'[24]

Annie doubtless saw marriage as a way of escaping the oppressive solemnity of her childhood, however she quickly found herself bound by a new set of constraints, her well-being according to Evelyn 'entirely subject to [her new husband's] will and his moods'.[25] While pregnant with their first child, Evelyn's father Arthur, she became terrified lest his

---

* In *A Little Learning*, Evelyn Waugh writes that one of his great-great-grandfathers was Thomas Gosse, an itinerant portrait painter. In fact he descends from Thomas's youngest brother John (Jacky) Gosse, who prospered as a merchant in Newfoundland before returning to Poole around 1820. Jacky Gosse's daughter Anne (Evelyn's great-grandmother) was thus first cousin of the naturalist Philip Henry Gosse (Thomas Gosse's son), chief protagonist of his son Edmund's memoir *Father and Son*. And Edmund Gosse was second cousin of Evelyn's grandmother Annie Waugh (née Morgan). See Ann Thwaite, *Glimpses of the Wonderful: The Life of Philip Henry Gosse* (Faber & Faber, 2002).

arrival interfere with her husband's first day of partridge-shooting. To the relief of everyone, he was born a week before the start of the season, on 24 August 1866.[26] After Arthur came his ill-fated younger brother Alick and three girls, Connie, Trissie and Elsie, who were never properly educated and were regularly reduced to tears by their father's outbursts. It is possible that they were all put off men for life and Evelyn later hazarded that 'so far as there can be any certainty in a question which so often reveals surprising anomalies, I can assert that my aunts were maidens'.[27] Though not without suitors, none of them married, Evelyn later explaining that within 'the stratified society of North Somerset they were part of a very thin layer, superior to farmers and tradesmen, inferior to the county families'.[28] After their parents died, the sisters all stayed on at the family home at Midsomer Norton, where Evelyn spent many of his childhood summer holidays, about two months a year. Save for decay, the house had hardly changed since his father's childhood and Evelyn relished its dark hidden corners and assorted interesting smells. Behind the creeper-clad façade lay a rambling interior in which the only bathroom featured a stuffed monkey that had, improbably, died of sunstroke after being brought to England from Africa by a great-uncle. Its grinning teeth were all that could be seen when the room filled with steam. Other curiosities included a collection of fossils in the library that the local coalminers used to bring Evelyn's grandfather, and a glass phial of 'white blood' that he had morbidly preserved from a patient dying of acute anaemia. Evelyn would always be fascinated by the macabre, and when the last of his aunts died in 1952 and he came to oversee the disposal of their property he 'sought vainly for this delight of my childhood'.[29]

For Evelyn the house at Midsomer Norton 'captivated my imagination as my true home never did'. As a boy he explained his preference to his parents on the basis that 'people had died there' – a pointed contrast to the sterile newness of Underhill where he grew up.[30] 'The bric-a-brac in the cabinets, the Sheffield plate, the portraits by nameless artists quickened my childish aesthetic appetite as keenly as would have done any world-famous collection and the narrow corridors stretched before me like ancient galleries. I am sure I loved my aunts' house because I was instinctively drawn to the ethos I now recognise as mid-Victorian; not, as perhaps psychologists would claim, that I now relish things of that period because they remind me of my aunts.'[31]

For Arthur, childhood at Midsomer Norton had held less happy memories. He recalled being 'perpetually haunted by vague apprehensions, fermented by the mysterious talk of the younger servants' – favoured topics included the brutal murder of a local cripple and the wicked activities of a cross-dressing highwayman.[32] Aged eight he was sent to board at a 'dame-school' in Bath, from where he wrote plaintively to his mother: 'Dear Muz, I will try to be a dutiful son and put cold cream on my lips at night.'[33] He later went to Sherborne, where he was teased for being swotty and unathletic. The nightly expeditions to kiss his father's gun-case had failed to arouse any enthusiasm for field sports and the only interests they ultimately shared were amateur theatricals and cricket, which Arthur adored despite being regularly outplayed by his sisters – he eventually scraped into the Sherborne second eleven.[34] To the added disappointment of his father, he showed no desire to enter the medical profession, and instead began to incline towards a literary career, editing the school magazine and winning the Senior Poetry Prize. At New College, Oxford he managed only a double Third in Mods and Greats[35] but won the prestigious Newdigate Prize (past winners of which included John Ruskin, Matthew Arnold and Oscar Wilde) for his poem on 'Gordon in Africa'. A great surprise to everybody, this triumph laid the foundations of what was to be a remarkable literary dynasty, Arthur's descendants having since produced some 180 books between them.[36]

By now resigned to his son's calling, the Brute told Arthur that he had 'nearly cried with joy' when he heard the news. 'You have made us very very happy and it is such a good thing for you in connection with any literary career you may take up & I am so glad because you have had disappointments and have borne them so nobly and now you have gained this great distinction – & one I know you will prize . . . God bless you my own darling son & make your career worthy of your best endeavours & then I know it will be a glorious one.'[37] If subsequently irked by the 'self-satisfied atmosphere of puffed success' surrounding Arthur, the Brute affected equal magnanimity when he learned about Arthur's third-class degree: 'Do you imagine that I look upon my sons as machines for the gratification of my self-esteem? You did your best and that is more than enough.'[38]

After he came down from Oxford, Annie Waugh sent her son's prize-winning poem to her cousin Edmund Gosse, the family's only literary contact, hoping he might open doors. Edwardian England's pre-eminent man of letters, whom Evelyn later shuddered to recall as the worst of the 'numerous, patronising literary elders who frequented our table',[39] Gosse began asking his young cousin to his Sunday literary soirées, where a star-struck Arthur met the likes of Henry James, Thomas Hardy, Bram Stoker, J. M. Barrie, Arnold Bennett and others. He also introduced him to Wolcott Balestier, the dazzling if slightly shambolic American publisher who had recently arrived from New York to woo English authors on behalf of John W. Lovell & Co.*

Balestier asked Arthur to come and work for him but then died suddenly of typhoid in 1891 while on a business trip to Germany, whereupon Arthur found himself placed in sole charge of Lovell's London office. Shortly afterwards, he began writing what turned out to be a very timely first biography of Alfred Tennyson, his idol, which Heinemann managed to publish eight days after the poet died in October 1892. The reviews were glowing – 'Mr Waugh's discriminating judgments have evidently cost time and thought,' said *The Times*, 'and proceed from a critical faculty of no mean order'[40] – and the book soon ran to six editions. It might well have made the twenty-six-year-old Arthur financially independent from his father at last, however in February 1893 Lovell's went bankrupt in New York and Arthur nobly took it upon himself to divert all his book royalties to his staff in lieu of their unpaid salaries. His personal sacrifice was all the greater since he now had to postpone his planned marriage to the girl he had been assiduously courting since his final year at Sherborne.

* * *

Arthur had met Catherine Raban (generally known as Kate, or to Arthur simply as K) eight years previously when her family moved into a village near Midsomer Norton. He remembered one day reading in the library window and seeing their dog-cart hurtling up the drive behind a high-stepping chestnut, the elder brother driving, Kate 'in a tam-o'-shanter cap and long, flowing locks, the apparition, as it seemed to me, of one of the jolliest-looking girls I had ever seen'.[41]

---

* Balestier was followed by his sister Carrie, who came to keep house for him in Kensington but shortly became the 'hated' wife of Rudyard Kipling, the most famous of her brother's new recruits.

Kate Raban had been born in India, where her father served as a magistrate. According to Evelyn, Henry Raban* was regarded with a mixture of admiration and bemusement for his 'familiarity with all the insalubrious purlieus' of his postings, and he eventually succumbed to one of the endemic diseases when Kate was just a year old.

Evelyn thus knew neither of his grandfathers, however the sketch of Henry Raban in his autobiography includes the haunting story of how as a little boy he had been removed from his teenage mother after she remarried and converted to Roman Catholicism (thereby becoming the only Roman Catholic beside Evelyn in the lower branches of Evelyn's family tree), to be looked after by his aunts. Years later they found a rosary that the boy had hidden and slept with as a memento of his lost mother.[42]

Kate's mother was Elizabeth 'Lily' Cockburn, granddaughter of the famous Scots judge Lord Cockburn (1779–1854)[†] whose *Memorials of His Time* is easily the best-written book by any of Evelyn's ancestors. Evelyn professed no particular pride in this illustrious predecessor, once telling a friend that he would have far sooner have been descended from a 'useless Lord', by which he meant a hereditary peer, than from one 'ennobled for practical reasons'.[43] For all his much talked-about snobbery, Evelyn never made any attempt to aggrandise his own antecedents and his position as a member of the hardworking, professional middle classes. He was in fact descended from plenty of useless lords, however he was never an especially diligent genealogist and seems to have been entirely unaware of his various historic links to the nobility via Lord Cockburn and his wife Elizabeth Macdowall, who between them descended from several of Scotland's oldest and grandest aristocratic families. Henry Cockburn could count John of Gaunt and King Edward III among his forebears, as well as the Earls of Buchan, Erroll, Huntly, Marischal and Morton, while Elizabeth descended from the Earls of Calendar, Gowrie, Linlithgow and

---

* Henry Charles Biddulph Cotton Raban, born 1837, son of Henry Tilman Raban (born 1799) and Theodosia Mahon (born 1821).

† A friend of Walter Scott and other Edinburgh luminaries at a time when the city was 'the Athens of the North', Henry Cockburn was an engaging figure whose 'rather melancholy eyes, when roused by energy or wit, sparked like a hawk's'. A dash of eccentricity manifested itself in his attire that 'set the graces of fashionable dress at defiance. His hat was always the worst and his shoes, constructed after a cherished pattern of his own, the clumsiest in Edinburgh.' (See *Edinburgh Review*, January 1857.)

Southesk, the first Marquess of Montrose, the first Duke of Lennox and, further back, King Henry I.

* * *

After Henry Raban's death, Lily had married a Raban cousin of his, an army chaplain in India with whom she had two more children. At an early age Kate and her sister were sent to England to be looked after by two maiden great-aunts and a bachelor great-uncle just outside Bristol. According to Evelyn, Kate was 'entirely happy' at their house, 'the Priory' in the village of Shirehampton, and 'all her life she looked back on that elderly *ménage* as the ideal of home'[44] – an unconscious echo of his own feelings towards his aunts' house at Midsomer Norton. The chaotic houses Kate's family lived in during her adolescence fell far short of this paragon, her stepfather having retired his Indian army chaplaincy to fill short-term vacancies at various West Country churches without a regular vicar.

By the time the Rabans came to live near Midsomer Norton Kate was fifteen, Arthur eighteen and about to start his last term at Sherborne. Smitten at first sight, he began asking her to tennis, picnics and dancing, and as he coyly recorded they soon became 'something more than friends'.[45] The Rabans were far from bookish – when Kate's half-brother Basset first saw Arthur's library, he cried: 'All these books! And not one a feller could read!'[46] – but Kate read everything that Arthur lent her and in later life read a book a fortnight, 'always a good one', according to Evelyn.[47] She did not much like writing letters and, in the estimation of her great-grandson Alexander, though 'shrewd and prudent' she was 'not particularly bright'.[48] However her calm and reticent nature proved an excellent foil for Arthur's nervous insecurity and impulsive, garrulous theatricality. Their courtship progressed over the next eight years, after which their parents raised no objections to their getting married.[49]

In a typically intimate letter to his elder son Alec, Arthur later confided that 'when I became engaged to your mother, I was able to tell her that I had never had anything to do with any woman in the world. And the chief reason why I had that inestimable gift to give her (for man's innocence is the finest of all marriage gifts) was largely that as a boy I broke myself early of the habit which is worrying you.'[50] The habit he referred to was masturbation, or 'self-abuse' as he called it.

Yet Arthur evidently found it a struggle to rein himself in. In July 1893 he wrote to Kate: 'I long for you so much, but after being away from you for so long, I can't promise I should be good. So for the sake of your peace of mind, Old Chum, it's just as well we can't meet . . . don't long for me to come to you for you know I am a brute and it's better for you that I stay away.'[51] Their great-grandson Alexander deduces from their long engagement that Kate was reluctant to commit, perhaps disconcerted by Arthur's 'immodest and demonstrative gropings'.[52] However they were eventually married by her stepfather in October 1893, by which time Arthur had gone some way towards repairing his battered income with freelance literary journalism. After honeymooning at the spa town of Malvern in Worcestershire they began married life in West Hampstead, in a small flat above a dairy off the tree-lined Finchley Road. This was then much closer to the open fields than it soon became and was chosen partly because Kate would have far preferred to live in the country. They also hoped that, being higher than smoky central London, the fresh air would be good for Arthur's asthma.

In the five years before their first son was born, Kate relished her role as homemaker. Having been surrounded by servants in India, her mother was a lousy housekeeper and to Kate's mind lived in a state of continual, avoidable discomfort. Kate decided that her best strategy in any given domestic situation was to think what her mother would do – and then do the opposite.[53] Evelyn later remembered his mother as 'always busy with her hands, sewing, making jam, bathing and clipping her poodle . . . and with hammer and screwdriver hanging shelves and building rabbit hutches from packing cases'.[54]

Arthur, meanwhile, concentrated on his career, attending Gosse's Sunday literary gatherings, reviewing books and writing for newspapers and journals. His essays included an appeal for 'Reticence in Literature', published in the first issue of *The Yellow Book*, an avant-garde magazine in which Arthur's piece was hailed by the stuffier *Academy* as 'sane and manly' unlike the rest of the 'worthless, silly' articles. According to Arthur, the essay had an 'immediate, recuperative and permanent influence on my chances of getting literary work', and by the time he came to write his memoirs almost forty years later he had reviewed some 6,000 books.[55] His anxious temperament did not suit the fluctuating fortunes of a freelance, however, and in 1896 he took a job as literary adviser to the board of Kegan Paul, Tennyson's former publishers, in Charing Cross Road, with a salary of £600 a year,[56] while writing reviews when he returned home each evening.

By this time, intending to start a family, he and Kate had moved to 11 Hillfield Road, a Victorian terraced house not far west of their old flat, backing onto a narrow back garden with a lawn, borders, an apple tree and a willow, and a patch where Kate could grow vegetables. The sound of owls at night added to the rural illusion. They had no telephone or electric light but lived comfortably enough, waited on at table by their maid Agnes in a cap and apron,[57] with a man coming two days a week to do the heavier work in the garden. When they returned from holidays, a bare-footed porter would follow their horse-drawn cab all the way from Paddington in order to earn a shilling by carrying down their luggage.[58]

Their street was a cul-de-sac, which made it ideal for learning to ride the bicycles they had bought as part of the cycling craze sparked by the recent development of the 'safety' bicycle, whose inflatable rubber tyres made it far more comfortable than the previous boneshakers and pennyfarthings. Arthur could draw additional reassurance from George Bernard Shaw's pronouncement that bicycling was 'a capital thing for a literary man!'[59] and he and Kate were soon going off on long bike rides to explore the lanes of Buckinghamshire, pursued by their poodle Marquis,* Arthur in tweed jacket and plus-fours, Kate in long skirt and balloon sleeves.

These expeditions continued for several years until Kate fell pregnant with their first child. He was born on 8 July 1898 and christened Alexander, though this was later shortened to Alec, in memory of Arthur's brother Alick, who died in 1900.[60] An indulged child from the start, Alec was given the sunniest room in the house for his nursery, with a south-facing bow window from which the Surrey hills could be glimpsed on a clear day. Almost all his earliest memories revolved around his father, his mother and nurse barely featuring.[61] At five o'clock each day, when Arthur arrived home from work, Alec awaited him with his sketchbook and demanded he draw elaborate gory scenes from history or literature or spectacular disasters that might befall the Waugh household.

---

* Marquis was the first of a succession of spirited poodles owned by the Waughs. Terence Greenidge recalled one of his successors in the 1920s, Beau, having 'an extraordinary habit of eating papers' which he thought appropriate to a publisher's dog.

After Arthur became managing director of the publishers Chapman &
Hall in 1902, he would get home slightly later but still found time to read
poetry to his son, who loved the sound of it even if he rarely understood
what it meant: 'Noble words,' young Alec would murmur when Arthur
had finished. 'Noble words.'[62] Arthur also taught Alec to love cricket,
and when he was five he gave him a cricket bat and they began playing
single-wicket matches on the lawn. When Arthur announced Evelyn's
birth that autumn, Alec's immediate reaction was, 'Oh good, now we'll
have a wicket keeper.' It proved to be a vain hope, cricket being one of the
chief annoyances of Evelyn's early life, the netting over his cot constantly
pounded during his elder brother's endless indoor Test matches.[63] Alec
admitted that any attempts on his part to teach his little brother its joys
only served to reinforce his 'permanent repugnance for the game'.[64]

Evelyn was born at 10.30 on the evening of 28 October 1903, quite suddenly, so Kate recorded in her diary, before the doctor could get there.
Despite the speed of the birth, she had lost a lot of blood and needed
extensive stitching. For the next few weeks she remained frail, suffering
painful headaches and post-natal depression – possibly deepened by the
fact that she and Arthur had both been hoping for a girl. She stayed in bed
until at least the middle of December, when a wheelchair was brought to
the house so that a maid could push her up and down the road outside,[65]
and she was only just beginning to regain her strength by the time of
Evelyn's christening early in the new year.

On 7 January 1904, at St Augustine's Church in Kilburn, he was christened Arthur Evelyn St John. In later years he grew to dislike both Evelyn,
by which he was always known, largely because of the confusion it gave
rise as to his sex,* and St John, which he thought gave him an air of absurd
affectation.[66]

Unlike Alec, Evelyn remembered very little about his father from his
infancy beyond the sound of his coughing and the smell of his pipe to-
bacco mingled with the menthol preparation he burned for his asthma.

---

* Chosen 'on a whim' by his mother, so he recorded, perhaps as consolation for not having
had a daughter, the name was usefully distinctive for his future career as a writer, however
his arrival in Abyssinia in 1935 was awaited by an Italian press officer 'in a high state of
amorous excitement' holding a bouquet of red roses. 'The trousered and unshaven figure
which finally greeted him must have been a hideous blow, but with true Roman courtesy he
betrayed nothing . . . and it was only some days later, when we had become more intimate,
that he admitted his broken hopes.' *Waugh in Abyssinia* (1936) p. 164.

Although Arthur continued coming to the nursery each evening after work, Evelyn saw his appearance as an unwanted interruption in the day's fun. Of far more interest to him were his mother and his young nurse, Lucy Hodges, the daughter of a Somerset smallholder who had come to look after Alec but formed a far stronger bond with his younger brother. Evelyn remembered Lucy with great affection and her influence could be detected in his early interest in religion – she read the Bible all the way through every six months – in his scrupulous truthfulness (when he wasn't indulging in fantasy) as an adult and in the fact that the nurses in his fiction seemed to be the only characters to escape parody.

*　*　*

In the autumn of 1906, when Evelyn turned three, his only surviving grandfather, the bad-tempered Alexander Waugh, died from pneumonia after falling ill while out shooting. Evelyn's grandmother did not long survive him, dying fifteen months later. Between them they left enough money – the remnants of John Neill's Peninsular War corn-trading fortune plus income from a coal mine on one of the Morgans' Welsh properties – to enable Evelyn's aunts to remain living quite comfortably at Midsomer Norton, while Arthur decided to use his legacy to build a new house.

The family had long since outgrown their home on Hillfield Road, where Alec's non-stop cricket was getting on everyone's nerves, and one day early in 1907 Arthur set off with Kate to explore the area being developed two miles away, just beyond Hampstead Heath, on what was then the north-western edge of London. From the top of the Heath they came down the steep wooded cutting to the village of North End, passing the bow-fronted Old Bull & Bush pub – soon to feature in Florrie Forde's popular music-hall song – and the carriage entrance of North End Manor, one of the principal houses in what was then still a relatively rural community. Next to this was a small paddock where a character called Gypsy Joe kept his pony and trap and where, with characteristic impulsiveness, Arthur decided he would build his house.

2

....

The Sadism of Youth

The chosen plot for their new home was on the North End Road, then still a quiet, dusty lane with low white rails bordering its grassy footpaths, bypassed to the east and west by trunk routes for carters and coachmen. Within a year it would get a lot busier with the opening of the Tube line from Charing Cross to Golders Green, which set in motion a frenetic burst of housebuilding that quickly engulfed the dairy farms and market gardens to the north.

The terminus of the new line was at the junction of Golders Green Road and Finchley Road, a quarter of a mile downhill from where the Waughs built their house. A postcard of this crossroads from 1904 shows a lonely farmstead surrounded by open fields with a wooden signpost pointing to London, Finchley and Hendon[1] – 'such a place,' wrote Evelyn, 'as where "The Woman in White" was encountered'.[2] By the middle of 1907, though, estate agents' pavilions had begun to appear in the fields and by 1914 the entire area had been built over. Evelyn later pronounced his father 'the first of its spoliators'[3] and he spent much of his childhood living beside a vast, sprawling building site.

Nowadays a publisher of Arthur's standing would have to spend well over ten times his salary for an equivalent London house, however in 1907 it cost Arthur barely what he earned in a year to build his new home – 'little more than £1,000' by Evelyn's reckoning.[4] By the standards of those days it was a very ordinary suburban villa, a typical middle-class professional's home, although for a time it had the distinction of being the only new house in the village and its relative isolation made it look far more desirable than it now appears, next to a drive-in car wash.

Arthur involved himself in every aspect of the plans, stepping out all the rooms and stipulating sufficient windows to make it light and airy, although the effect was offset by his penchant for gloomy interior oak panelling, wainscoting and floorboards. The finished house – which Arthur named Underhill after the leafy lane where he and Kate had trysted at Midsomer Norton – was no architectural gem and Evelyn later deemed his father's sentimental attachment to its actual structure 'slightly absurd'. The only two times he could remember being beaten by him was when he had done 'wilful injuries to its fabric; once by paring the corners of a chimney-piece with a new knife, once by excavating a tunnel through a boot-cupboard into the foundations where, until detected, I was able to crawl about under the floor joists'.[5]

Arthur's devotion to his new home was intense, however, particularly since his asthma and slight deafness made him increasingly reluctant to go out in the evening. He was almost certainly the only person in North End at that time who went to work in London, but when he got back home each evening he retreated to his 'book-room' to dash off book reviews for *The Daily Telegraph* (his reviews were written, so Evelyn recorded, 'as he did everything, at deleterious speed'),[6] poems and other writings.

Several evenings a week in the same room after dinner he would read aloud from his literary favourites. Sometimes he also read the popular plays of his youth, 'stepping about the room,' as Evelyn recalled in *A Little Learning,* 'and portraying the characters as he had seen them on the stage'. Evelyn described how Arthur held his family rapt 'with precision of tone, authority and variety that I have heard excelled only by Sir John Gielgud'.[7] 'In these recitations of English prose and verse,' Evelyn wrote, 'the incomparable variety of English vocabulary, the cadences and rhythms of the language, saturated my young mind, so that I never thought of English Literature as a school subject, as matter for analysis and historical arrangement, but as a source of natural joy.'[8] However, as an adolescent Evelyn was frequently embarrassed by these readings and was scathing of them in his diary, describing one of Arthur's typical performances as 'a good lecture but incorrigibly theatrical as usual'. The diary was later bound and left on the shelves at Underhill and after Arthur nosily read what Evelyn had written, he never read aloud again. Alec later begged Michael Davie to omit these references from Evelyn's published diaries, arguing that it was not what he would have wanted.[9]

* * *

French windows led out from the book-room to the garden and to the north Arthur could gaze out across bucolic meadows until they too were sold to developers and houses sprouted up beside them. Kate had a small sitting room directly above on the first floor where Evelyn sometimes sat with her and the boys had a day nursery alongside, to which Arthur eventually added a balcony overlooking the garden. Their night nursery was on the floor above facing the road and the large Victorian villa opposite where the thirty-one-year-old ballerina Anna Pavlova came to live in 1912 in wooded seclusion until her once extensive grounds were built over too. There was one spare bedroom, which was often occupied by some guest or relation from the country,[10] and a solitary bathroom, although the resulting inconvenience, compounded by the fact that it doubled as Arthur's dressing room, was not unusual for a house of its kind at the time.

For Evelyn and his mother, neither of whom were especially enthusiastic city dwellers, the chief attraction of Underhill was the garden where Kate happily spent hours potting, planting, weeding and dead-heading while Evelyn drew countless complaints by climbing over the wall into the neighbouring North End Manor's kitchen garden in search of lost balls. In his autobiography he portrayed the complainant, a maiden lady, as 'an aged misanthrope',[11] however he scarcely went out of his way to endear himself to her. On one occasion he led his friend Mac Fleming into her garden and began lopping cabbages off their stalks, shouting, 'Here we come, the Cabbage Chopping Clan!'[12]

When the manor house eventually came to be sold, Arthur took the precaution of buying this bit of ground, after which it became for Evelyn 'the only part of my home to fascinate me' on account of its tall jungle of weeds and the dark steps leading down to a derelict furnace-house. 'This cellar and this wilderness I took as my special province, thus early falling victim to the common English confusion of the antiquated with the sublime, which has remained with me; all my life I have sought dark and musty seclusions, like an animal preparing to whelp.'[13]

On his frequent childhood visits to his aunts' house at Midsomer Norton, Evelyn thus relished 'the still airs of gas and oil and mould and fruit', the fact that some rooms smelled 'like a neglected church, others like a populous bazaar'. He would always remember their fierce cockatoo with its peculiarly pungent tray and the smell of leather and horses in the stables, even though the coachman had long since decommissioned the old brougham and kept only a solitary pony and trap, making up his hours by cleaning boots and pottering about the garden. To Evelyn's young eyes, the Midsomer Norton household 'belonged to another age which I instinctively, even then, recognized as superior to my own'.[14]

* * *

Almost as soon as they had moved into Underhill, Alec was sent away to board at Fernden, a prep school in Surrey, creating yet more distance between the brothers: the few postcards that he sent to Evelyn from there tended to begin 'Dear It'. Meanwhile Kate began to give four-year-old Evelyn his first lessons at home, shared with a local girl called Stella, the red-headed daughter of their friend Ernest Rhys, the Welsh poet and founder of the *Everyman's Library*. Stella found Kate Waugh 'a dear – everybody was very fond of her' and Evelyn 'so self-reliant, cocky, outgoing and enthusiastic'. He was also 'stronger and more clever than I was, but he did not rub this in'.[15]

But Evelyn's most constant companion at this time was his nurse Lucy, with whom he regularly went shopping in Hampstead, where he was ex-cited less by the merchandise than by 'the dexterity of the shop-keepers . . . with butter-hands weights and scales, shovels and canisters, paper and string . . . I delighted in watching things being well done'.[16] Three times a year they would also go to Hampstead Fair, where Evelyn exulted in the jostling crowds with their 'pentecostal exuberance which communicated nothing but goodwill', the monkeys capering on hand organs and, once again, the smells – 'orange peel, sweat, beer, coconut, trampled grass, horses'.[17] According to Evelyn's autobiography, written some sixty years later, Lucy entirely reciprocated his love for her and was 'never cross or neglectful',[18] however Stella Rhys recalled Lucy once telling them both off and Evelyn countering that she had 'no business to speak to us like that' because 'we're of a much better class she is!'.[19]

It was on one of his regular outings with Lucy that Evelyn came across three children playing on a mound of clay and was invited to join them. They were Jean, Philippa and Maxwell ('Mac') Fleming, who lived on the former farm that was now the estate office of the new Hampstead

Garden Suburb. Their father (Edward Vandermere Fleming) worked at the War Office and to Evelyn's fascination kept a revolver for his family's protection and an Airedale watch-dog called Warder. The Flemings soon became Evelyn's regular holiday playmates and the first of the surrogate families that he adopted during his early life, compensating for what he saw as the shortcomings of his own family and his rather isolated place within it.

Infected by Mr Fleming's defence measures as well as the prevailing unease in the years shortly before the First World War, the children convinced themselves that a German invasion was imminent and set about fortifying the clay heap, storing provisions in anticipation of a siege and preparing poison soup for the enemy. Quickly having established himself as leader of their little band, Evelyn dubbed them 'The Pistol Troop' and rallied them each morning from the field by their house with the cry of 'Hoik! Oy-oik!', his right arm bent across his chest in salute.[20] They agreed a strict code of laws and various initiation tests, such as walking bare-legged through stinging nettles, climbing tall trees and signing their names in blood. Never having been mollycoddled or discouraged by warnings of physical danger,[21] Evelyn was a fearless participant in all these rituals, displaying the same bravery that he would later show when swimming in the sea, which he preferred 'toppingly rough', and as a commando during the Second World War.*

His physical courage and combative nature meant that he liked nothing better than a good fight and relished the regular skirmishes with other 'roaming bands who attempted to enter our fort, whom we repelled with fists, clay-balls and sticks,' he recalled. One regular adversary called Felix aroused particular indignation among the Pistol Troopers by enlisting the support of a far larger band of 'gutter children', as Evelyn contemptuously recorded in his diary at the time. At the height of hostilities, Felix 'came again at a fierce charge but a voley of clay pelits combined with a stick charge drove him back again'. Felix charged once more, repelled this time by a 'smashing blow in the face' from Philippa, 'our best fighter' (she was awarded a medal for bravery that night); and again, now beaten

---

* Arthur Waugh was also curiously brave. He insisted on having all his teeth drawn without gas, refused to take cover from air raids and when warned one night – falsely as it transpired – that there was an intruder in the garden, he strode about it alone with a walking stick calling: 'Come out you ruffian, I can see you.' (*A Little Learning*, p. 67.)

back by 'such a blow in the ribs', delivered by Evelyn to one of Felix's recruits, 'that he fell flat on his face'.[22] Despite his evident satisfaction at this, Evelyn maintained that the conflicts were rarely started by the Pistol Troopers, who as Evelyn later admitted were a self-righteous lot, forever going on about honour, and in any case they needed to save their strength for the Prussian Guard.[23]

*   *   *

In September 1910, just short of his seventh birthday, Evelyn donned green tweed knickerbockers for his first day at Heath Mount School, twenty minutes' walk away up in Hampstead. The idea had been for him to spend two terms there before following his brother to Fernden, an alarming prospect given Alec's reports about his despotic headmaster, who bade Alec 'finish up!' after he had disgorged his revolting sago pudding, dipped his fingers in 'brown bitter liquid' when he bit his nails and appeared in his bad dreams long after he had left the school.[24] In the event, Kate's wish to keep her younger son at home* combined with Evelyn's evident happiness at Heath Mount meant that he stayed there for six years.

A month after Evelyn's arrival, the headmaster, J. S. Granville Grenfell, told Kate he was 'very pleased indeed with your young man. He is a smart boy, decidedly so, and promises extremely well. I do not know who has been teaching him, but he is better prepared than any boy of his age I have had for a long time. You will I am sure get an excellent report of his work and conduct generally at the end of term.'[25]

'Granny' Grenfell had been a few years senior to Arthur at Sherborne and was by then a forty-six-year-old widower. An admiral's son, he had a naval air with his tall, slim figure, neat, pointy beard and tight-buttoned serge suit, his demeanour alternating 'wrath [with] explosions of bluff geniality, in a way which might be supposed to derive from the quarter deck', as Evelyn recalled.[26] Already strongly attracted to fantasy, Evelyn was particularly intrigued by furtive talk among the boys of his wife's 'death-chamber' somewhere in his lodgings, which he was rumoured to

---

* According to Alec, she also thought that at that age at least Evelyn had 'too gentle a nature' for the Spartan discipline of Fernden (Alec Waugh, *My Brother Evelyn*, p. 168).

have locked and never re-entered and which Evelyn liked to imagine as 'Miss Havisham's bridal room, heavy with dust, festooned in cobwebs and rotting picturesquely'.[27]

Each morning began with roll-call and prayers in the gym, a sentry boy yelling *Cave!* at the approach of the headmaster and the room falling silent as he leaped up the steps and entered with a lusty 'Good morning, gentlemen!' Like Dr Fagan's charges in *Decline and Fall*, the boys chorused 'Good morning, sir!' in reply.

Saturdays were more nerve-wracking, when the headmaster drew everyone's attention to the boys who had done well that week and then publicly denounced those who had not: 'What is this I find? *Fletcher*. Fletcher has been idle. Stand out, Fletcher . . . We had better understand each other, young man . . . Any idling, Fletcher, and' – banging his fist hard on the table – 'I'll be down on you like a ton of bricks!' Only later did Evelyn realise that Grenfell's fury was mostly feigned and in any case he never suffered it in its fiercest form as he did well in his lessons and was one of the headmaster's favourites.

Evelyn usually walked to school with Arthur on his way to Chapman & Hall. He remembered these morning walks as the first time he really got to know his father and enjoy his company.[28] Still, Evelyn considered his office 'a offely dull plase',[29] as he recorded in his earliest surviving diary entry shortly before his eighth birthday, and was ashamed of Arthur's 'sedentary and cerebral occupations'. He would have 'better respected a soldier or a sailor like my uncles, or a man with some constructive hobby such as carpentry, a handyman; a man, even, who shaved with a cut-throat razor'. He always saw his father as rather 'old, indeed as decrepit', although he had been only thirty-seven when he was born.[30]

In his first year at school, Evelyn had lessons with a governess until 12.30, when the youngest boys were collected by their nannies. From his second year he stayed until 'middle-day dinner' and was taught by masters whom he recalled stoically as 'mild enough'. None of them were married and they included one who chalked his ruler to ensure consistency of aim when carrying out a multiple beating[31] and another who slobbered over his favourites[32] and bade troublemakers bend over a footstool while he kicked their backsides – he was eventually dismissed for pinching boys' bottoms.[33] 'Some liked little boys too little and some too much,' reflected the adult Evelyn. 'According to their tastes they mildly mauled us in the

English scholastic way, fondling us in a manner just short of indecency, smacking us and pulling our hair in a manner well short of cruelty.'[34]

Cruelty was more likely to come from other boys – not least Evelyn. In 1912, the pretty and transparently timid eight-year-old Cecil Beaton arrived at Heath Mount. Beaton later recalled elevenses in the asphalt playground on his first day when 'suddenly, out of nowhere, the bullies arrived'. Their leader was 'half the size of the others' and ran at full tilt towards Beaton before abruptly stopping just in front of him with a 'wild, diabolical stare'. Standing on his toes, the boy deliberately moved his face closer to Beaton's, 'ever closer until the eyes converged into one enormous Cyclops nightmare'.[35] Several times, according to Beaton, the boy withdrew and thrust himself forward, and then 'stood baring his teeth at me'. In an earlier version of the same story they were black pitted teeth. 'By the time the physical onslaught began, fright had mercifully made me only half conscious.'

Beaton's vivid account of his terrifying introduction to Evelyn Waugh was written almost fifty years after the event. The next year he told the interviewer John Freeman on the television programme *Face to Face*: 'Evelyn Waugh is my enemy. We dislike each other intensely. He thinks I'm a nasty piece of goods, and, oh brother! do I feel the same way about him.'[36] Given their long-standing mutual loathing, it is conceivable that Beaton exaggerated his playground reminiscences. However Evelyn refuted none of them when he reviewed Beaton's book in *The Spectator* in 1961, confessing 'with shame' that 'the spectacle of his [Beaton's] long eyelashes wet with tears was one to provoke the sadism of youth', and that far from it having been an isolated incident, as the photographer suggested, 'the bullying of little Beaton' had been repeated many times. The flimsy excuse for all this, Evelyn recalled, was that 'he was reputed to enjoy his music lessons and hold in sentimental regard the lady who taught him. I am sure he was innocent of these charges.'[37]

The persecution also included greeting Beaton with a loud 'Hullo Cecil!'. The boys generally called each other by their surnames and Evelyn explained to his friend Stella Rhys that it was an 'awful score to a chap to find out his Christian name!'.[38] He and his accomplices also bent Beaton's arms back and stuck pins into him. Evelyn recalled that the harassment stopped only when 'my companion in this abomination and I were caught out and soundly beaten for it by a master'.[39]

Evelyn's cruel streak remained evident throughout his life. Clues to it might lie in the more diabolical characteristics of his paternal grandfather, however if a tendency towards sadism was passed down from grandfather to grandson, it happened without them ever meeting each other. More likely Evelyn's propensity was prompted by the circumstances of his upbringing.

There appears little doubt that at this age he felt entirely loved by his mother, who oversaw his homework each evening and listened to his prayers at bedtime. Their closeness was evidenced by the secret code in which he finished his notes to her: 'Evoggles Goggles Moggles' for 'Evelyn Loves Mother'. If threatened with discipline by his father or Alec – who was given limited powers in this regard when he was eight – Evelyn would throw himself into the back of his mother's high-backed chair in the dining room and shout 'Sanctuary, sanctuary!' Everyone understood that he could not be touched there.[40]

His sense of love and security underpinned the self-confidence and sunny nature for which he was known as a boy – albeit with the occasional fits of 'life weariness and despair' that his friend Stella Rhys noticed. However at the same time he had inherited Arthur's emotionalism, which probably explains why he was later so scathing of this trait in his father, and Alec recalled that as a small boy he was apt to dissolve into tears at the slightest provocation.

Meanwhile, there was plenty of reason for Evelyn to feel left out by his father's blatant favouritism towards his elder brother.[41] In spite of their morning walks to school, Arthur was never entirely at ease with his younger son, and Evelyn could hardly fail to notice that he preferred Alec: in the school holidays they would disappear for long walks arm in arm over the Heath, or to cricket matches or the cinema. Years later, in 1933, Arthur wrote to Alec's elder son on his christening: 'The three great things in my life have been my Mother, my Wife, & my son – your father. Nothing else has mattered much to me but their love.'[42] It was as if Evelyn had never existed.

Alec subsequently admitted that he had 'remained an only child to all practical purposes right through my childhood, my brother Evelyn being in those early days no more than an encumbrance in a corner'.[43] From an early age Evelyn would have been conscious that his elder brother saw him as such. The few surviving postcards that Alec sent to Evelyn from

Fernden were occasionally affectionate, asking 'How is your thumb?' or 'Has your cold quite gone? I hope it has.'[44] However Alec later conceded that he had possibly been 'not very kind' to Evelyn when they were young and that he could 'still visualize the occasion when my mother lectured me on this point'. He confessed that as an indulged child he had grown up with a superiority complex, confident that he was 'going to make a considerable mark in the world', while 'Evelyn may well have felt himself relegated to a second place'.

In all the circumstances Alec ventured that Evelyn might have felt 'challenged to assert himself'[45] – which is presumably what he was attempting with the unfortunate Cecil Beaton in the playground, free at last from the yoke of his father and elder brother. Alec went on to observe that in spite of his later fearsome reputation, Evelyn had 'a very tender heart' as a young boy. 'The toughness was superimposed, in self-defence. Beneath it he was highly vulnerable.'[46]

Evelyn's short stature was possibly a contributory factor in this regard, rendering him more anxious to make his presence felt and thus more aggressive and domineering. He also had to contend with his effeminate name, although he later claimed to have successfully countered derision at school by reference to Field-Marshal Sir Evelyn Wood, who had won a VC during the Indian Mutiny and later commanded the army which defeated the Zulus.[*]

*   *   *

Looking back half a century later, Evelyn recalled that he had been 'happy enough' at Heath Mount but that the school was 'merely an interruption of the hobbies and affections of home'.[47] His school career was itself interrupted in the summer of 1912 when he fell ill with acute appendicitis and required an operation at home on the kitchen table. An appendectomy was then far riskier than it is today and not long previously the King's

---

[*] Leaving aside his gallantry and splendidly mustachioed appearance, Wood was perhaps not the ultimate embodiment of manliness. He was also known for his hypochondria, his vanity – it was said that he had his medal ribbons edged with a black border to accentuate their effect – and for being comically accident-prone, once managing to get his nose smashed by a giraffe that he tried to ride at a private zoo in India. See the *Oxford Dictionary of National Biography*.

surgeon had watched his own daughter die during the same procedure. Eight-year-old Evelyn was thus not told the diagnosis and later recalled a strange man appearing at his bedside inviting him to 'smell this delicious scent', before being put to sleep with chloroform. When he came round after the operation* he felt sick and found his legs strapped to the bed to protect his stitches. His next three nights were successively 'bad', 'good' and 'splendid', so Kate recorded in her diary,[48] but it wasn't until three weeks later that he was able to get out of bed, by which time the strapping had left him so weak that he could barely walk.[49]

To cure his lameness Kate took him off to stay on the Thames estuary near Southend, where they paddled on the mudflats and a nurse came regularly with an electric battery to massage Evelyn's feet and ankles. After three weeks of this regime they returned home but Evelyn's feet had still not recovered, so in late August back they went.[50]

This time Kate left Evelyn there on his own and for the next month he was billeted in a girls' boarding school which had long since been deserted for the summer holidays. His only companion was a little girl named Daffodil whose father was away serving in India and who was punished for wetting her bed by having her hands bandaged for a day. Never having been separated from his family before, Evelyn felt utterly abandoned. The only bright spot was the appearance three times a week of the cheerful masseuse, Nurse Talbot, who after several weeks of seeing how miserable Evelyn was suggested to Kate and Arthur that he lodge with her family instead, which he did for the next five weeks. Her husband was an old soldier who became merry with drink most evenings, singing songs and showering Evelyn with praise. Their daughter Muriel was slightly older than Evelyn and, as he recalled from time to time, she obligingly 'exposed her private parts to me, and I mine to her'.[51] So content was he in this Dickensian household that he forgot to write home, prompting a pious letter from Arthur deploring his ingratitude – which Evelyn later recalled moved him 'not to penitence, but intense resentment'.[52] When he did eventually return home, Kate decided that he should do lessons with the Fleming children under a governess rather than go back to school for the autumn term. Mrs Fleming was for some time under the impression that

---

* This was Evelyn's second operation, the first having been when he was circumcised as a baby.

he was an only child. 'Oh but he isn't,' one of her children corrected her. 'He has a brother at school whom he hates.'[53]

An agreeable consequence of this extended convalescence was extra time spent with the Pistol Troop, which that year began producing a magazine that was typed by Arthur's secretary and bound in full morocco, the first issue beginning with Evelyn's short story 'Multa Pecunia'. Arthur later conceded that while Evelyn had been inclined to take the routine of school 'in a sort of negligent stride' – in stark contrast to Alec – away from school he 'displayed at the earliest age a precocious capacity for organising'.[54] Besides the Pistol Troop and its magazine, he arranged shadow plays and theatricals in the nursery, writing the plays, making the costumes and scenery and directing the Fleming children who were themselves promising actors.[55] More unusually, around this time Evelyn also proved himself 'an irrepressible advocate of female suffrage' according to Arthur. While visiting Boscastle he placarded the harbour with signs he had made demanding the vote for women, and during a garden party at Underhill, when half the guests disappeared from the lawn, they were found crowded into the boys' playroom upstairs listening to an impassioned address by Evelyn on the 'imperative necessity' of the franchise being extended before the next general election.[56]

As a boy Evelyn was rarely lost for something to do. His father remembered him as 'bubbling with ideas'.[57] He spent much of his time either rearranging the nursery furniture and pictures or drawing and painting, committing vivid images to his diary – including a gory picture of his appendix operation in which he is held down by his mother as the surgeon gleefully waves scissors and a knife in the air while a man (possibly Arthur) hammers a chisel into his groin. Battle scenes were another favourite subject, in styles derived from various magazines and comic books, as were inscriptions copied at the British Museum.

He produced illustrated stories, also modelled on comics such as *Chums* and *The Boy's Friend* rather than the classics that Arthur was constantly trying to press on him. He was an intermittent diarist, often in verse, and an eclectic collector – 'coins, stamps, fossils, butterflies, beetles, seaweed, wild flowers, "curiosities" generally'.[58] He possessed a microscope and an air gun, and aged twelve went through a chemistry phase 'when with a spirit lamp and test tubes and assorted bottles, I conducted entirely unregulated and rather dangerous "experiments" in a garden shed'.[59] An obsession with conjuring meanwhile took him often to a shop near Leicester Square, where the staff of expert conjurors soon tired of performing illusions at his request. 'I must have proved [equally] tedious to the audiences I was constantly attempting to mystify,' he later wrote, 'particularly as I composed a facetious patter in imitation of the professionals I sometimes saw at children's parties.'[60]

His imagination and enthusiasm were quickly and broadly aroused, and so when his mother read him an article called 'How to Join the Navy', he promptly resolved to become a 'Merry Jack tar'. 'If I should be a sailor bold / I'd stand up on the deck / I'd lock my prisoners in the hold / And make their ship a wreck'.[61]

Such imaginings were common enough among boys of his age – although his seem to have been more inventive than most. More striking was the interest he began to take in Anglo-Catholicism when he was eleven.[62] At first religion was 'a hobby like the birds' eggs and model trains of my schoolfellows,' he recalled, the appeal 'part hereditary and part aesthetic'.[63] When he went to stay with his aunts at Midsomer Norton he relished the frequent churchgoing and especially Sunday evensong.[64] The High Church curate there taught him to serve at the altar and Evelyn recalled revelling 'in my nearness to the sacred symbols and in the bright early-morning stillness and in the sense of intimacy with what was being enacted'.[65] Back at Underhill, Evelyn began to worry his mother by drawing angels rather than soldiers, and at the age of twelve he made a shrine by his bed with candlesticks and incense and white plaster statues of saints bought from a religious emporium in Golders Green.[66]

As a small boy he had gone with Lucy to the Low Church matins in the village and he later accompanied his parents and Alec to the newly consecrated St Jude's in Hampstead Garden Suburb. One of Lutyens's finest churches, the building was designed to dominate surrounding houses with its tall, pointed spire and sweeping, barn-like roofs;[67] however a far bigger draw for Arthur was the hammy vicar Basil Bourchier, a cousin of the actor-manager Arthur Bourchier and himself an incorrigible performer in the pulpit. Evelyn would later portray him without embellishment in *Charles Ryder's Schooldays* as 'the very remarkable freak named Father Wimperis' who drew great congregations to his church in a northern suburb and 'alternately fluted and boomed from the pulpit, wrestled with the reading-stand and summoned the country to industrial peace. At the end he performed a little ceremony of his own invention, advancing to the church steps in cope and biretta with what proved to be a huge salt cellar in his hands. "My people," he said simply, scattering salt before him, "you are the salt of the earth.'"[68]

Bourchier's own sung Eucharist was full of incense and the same improvised ritual with the salt. During the actual Communion a large electric red cross was switched on over the altar.[69] His vestments were more than conventionally ornate and his sermons, according to Evelyn, 'dramatic, topical, irrational and quite without theological content'. Arthur maintained they would have served perfectly well as leading articles in the *Daily Mail* and thanks to his friendship with its proprietor, Lord Northcliffe, Bourchier's pronouncements often did appear in that paper, variously demanding the lash for men who attacked women and fines for people who coughed in church, inveighing against vivisection and any clothes that entailed suffering to animals. People flocked from all over London to attend his services.

In his autobiography Evelyn deemed Bourchier 'a totally preposterous parson',[70] however according to his teacher at Heath Mount, Aubrey Ensor, this was a case of him 'taking an after look', whereas as a boy he 'took St Jude's and the Rev. Basil very seriously'. Ensor recalled going to see the medieval morality play *Everyman*, with Bourchier playing the Voice of God (and forgetting some of the Almighty's lines) and Evelyn walking in front of him carrying a large open prayer book.[71] Perhaps because of Evelyn's subsequent loss of faith, the role of St Jude's and Bourchier in his early religious formation has often been understated, not least by Evelyn himself; yet even he conceded that, in spite of the vicar's histrionics, he gained 'some glimpse of higher mysteries' during his services.[72] In any event, Evelyn was confirmed at St Jude's by the Bishop of Willesden on 29 June 1916 and the next week received instruction from Bourchier before his first Communion.[73]

Evelyn's precocious holiness put him at variance with the rest of the family, especially Alec, who 'accepted religion without belief' and saw his confirmation as 'something to be taken in my stride ... the next thing on the list'.[74] Arthur, meanwhile, had undergone a spell of Darwinian doubts in the 1890s but was passing through an Anglo-Catholic phase by the time of Evelyn's birth. After they moved to Underhill, at Evelyn's request Arthur led the family and servants in prayers before breakfast but stopped in 1914, saying it was 'no longer any good'.[75] He served as a sides-man for many years at St Jude's and apparently adhered to the Christian moral code, yet Evelyn doubted whether he had 'a genuine intellectual conviction about any element of his creed'. Arthur seems to have been far more interested in the theatricality of Bourchier's services than in any of the doctrines the vicar purported to teach there, and he was equally entertained by the various goings-on among members of the congre-gation – at another church he attended previously he particularly enjoyed the story of a solicitor of his acquaintance who had allowed himself to be caned by the curate as a means of showing penitence.

Even if the adult Evelyn later came to question the depth of Arthur's theological thinking, as a boy his interest in religion almost certainly helped him to feel closer to his father. For Arthur's fiftieth birthday in 1916 he wrote him a poem, 'The World to Come', describing a soul's journey to heaven, in the metre of Hiawatha. Evelyn later dismissed it as a 'deplor-able' and 'shameful' effort, although at the time he was proud enough to have it bound in leather. Arthur was proud of it too, describing it to his friend Kenneth McMaster his 'most wonderful' present. 'Not bad for a twelve-year-old,' he crowed.[76]

Evelyn's religion brought him into occasional conflict with his other-wise doting mother. One Lent, Kate told him that he should be on his guard against his 'besetting sin', his 'quick and unkind tongue'. He seemed at first to accept this but then rejoined: 'You know, Mother, what is your besetting sin?' 'No, Evelyn,' she replied, 'what is it?' 'A lack of faith in Catholic doctrine.' Recounting the incident afterwards to Alec, Kate admitted: 'And of course, he was completely right. I do lack faith.'[77]

She was thus all the more alarmed when, around the age of twelve, Evelyn announced that he wanted to become a clergyman and 'began to recite long devotions from a pious book'. As a young girl she had grown distinctly disenchanted with her stepfather's clerical life and the last thing she wanted was for her son to follow the same path. From then on, she decided it might be best if she declined to hear Evelyn's evening prayers.[78]

3

....

Serving Lord Kitchener

Although he was happy enough at Heath Mount, Evelyn was still due to go and board at Fernden in 1914 in order to prepare him for public school two years later. However the outbreak of the First World War that July caused *The Daily Telegraph* to dispense with all its freelance book reviewers and Arthur promptly lost half his income. Besides 'saving every penny against the winter & giving up at once our nice parlourmaid',[1] as he wrote to a friend, Arthur decided that it would now be quite out of the question to pay for boarding school for Evelyn and he wrote to Grenfell to warn him that even Heath Mount's fees might prove beyond him. According to Evelyn the headmaster replied that if necessary he would keep the boy on for free; another master* recalled that Grenfell discreetly sent a bill without a total – allowing Arthur to fill in whatever sum he saw fit before signing his cheque.[2] Afterwards Arthur solemnly told Evelyn that he was now 'honour bound to be an exemplary pupil' – an exhortation that Evelyn did not remember having yielded to.[3] In any event, Arthur's fears of financial disaster proved exaggerated and he never had to take advantage of Grenfell's generosity.

Evelyn was excited by the outbreak of war and when the family took the train down to Midsomer Norton that August he eagerly counted the signal boxes and sentries guarding the mainline bridges. 'I followed the retreat from Mons to the Marne,' he later recalled, 'and drew countless pictures of German cavalry plunging among English infantry with much blood and gunpowder about.'[4] The Pistol Troop had disbanded before seeing any of their longed-for action, but he and the Fleming children

---

* Aubrey Ensor; see pp. 28, 32.

did their bit by selling empty jam jars for the Red Cross and cut up lino-leum to sole slippers for wounded soldiers. Their Christmas show, a series of topical sketches performed before a crowded house in the Underhill nursery, raised 3/6 for the Belgian Relief Fund.[5] The next summer, 1915, Mr Fleming arranged for Mac and Evelyn to work as messengers at the War Office, sitting 'in a smoky den inhabited by an old soldier' while waiting to take files from one room to another. Evelyn, then eleven, was determined to 'serve Lord Kitchener', as he recalled, but though he often passed his door he was 'never summoned to his presence'. He was nonetheless thrilled by the whole experience.[6] At Underhill nights were occasionally enlivened for Evelyn by the Zeppelin alarm going off, whereupon he would be 'brought down from bed and regaled with an uncovenanted picnic'. Evelyn felt no sense of danger, which was in any case fairly remote in that part of London – no bombs fell within a mile of them. On summer nights, however, they would sometimes see 'the thin silver rod of the enemy caught in the converging search-lights' and 'on one splendid occasion' he saw a German plane brought down, 'sinking very slowly in brilliant flame', and hurried out to join those who were cheering by the roadside.[7]

At school Evelyn raised more war funds by 'making boats, Zeppelins, etc' and 'selling 'em to other chaps', as he recorded in his diary.[8] He joined the Boy Scouts and raised a Heath Mount patrol in one of the local troops, parading on Saturday afternoons in the basement of a shop and marching to the Heath to play various war games. However their activities seemed distinctly dull compared with those of the Pistol Troop. More invigorat-ing were the many fights he continued to pick at school and describe in his diary. When a boy called Fletcher accused Evelyn of being a 'silly old thing' and, behind his back, of being small and a fool, Evelyn declared his intention to 'slay him'. Spotting him outside the school changing room, he 'called him and jumped at him and knocked him down and immediately he said he had never called me a fool'.[9]

Another outlet for his pugnaciousness was afforded by the wave of anti-German feeling then sweeping the country, as a result of which anyone or anything vaguely Teutonic – dachshunds included – was liable to come under attack. Quickly infected by this hysteria, Evelyn described a game of footer in the autumn term of 1914 as 'grand' apart from the poor posi-tional play of a boy called Pappenheimer – 'I suppose it comes from being a subject of that miserable German nation,' he wrote in his diary.[10] Long before the royal family changed its name from Saxe-Coburg-Gotha to Windsor, several boys turned up at Heath Mount with names suddenly anglicised – one called 'Kaiser' reappeared less conspicuously as 'Kingsley'. Evelyn's claim that 'we did nothing to persecute them' is as hard to believe as it is to verify,[11] but in any event the next year he recorded that he and Pappenheimer had decided to settle their quarrels 'with the gloves'.[12]

The enlistment of several masters prompted tearful send-offs at morning prayers during which Evelyn noted that 'there were many chaps who hid behind each other so as not to be caught blubbing'.[13] Among their replacements, the handsome and theatrically inclined Aubrey Ensor made the most favourable impression on him. Alec later maintained that Ensor saw his time at Heath Mount merely as 'a prelude to a substantial career as a dramatist'[14] – an ambition he scarcely realised although he did write and direct a handful of plays and revues on the London stage from the 1920s through the 1940s, occasionally impressing critics with his ear for dialogue and 'neat pen for character sketch'.[15] 'Man' (as Evelyn called him) Ensor's greatest talents lay in the classroom, however, where he was an animated and inspiring teacher, apt to dance around the room while crooning the popular songs of the day.[16] By contrast, Ensor complained that all the headmaster really cared about was the Common Entrance exams, and thus he was forever being told to 'stick to facts' rather than do anything so exotic as to 'try to interest the boys in their work'.[17]

A distant cousin by marriage through the Cockburns, Ensor soon made friends with the whole Waugh family and was often at Underhill. He particularly liked Kate – who was by then nursing hospitalised soldiers in Highgate – 'a lovely person with a quick glint of humour in her eyes'. Evelyn may have inherited the glint, yet Ensor noticed that 'neither of the boys seemed to have reproduced the warmth that lay behind her slight Scots reserve'.[18] He clearly detected something worth nurturing, however, and although Evelyn did not mention him by name in his autobiography, Alec later identified Ensor as a key formative influence in his brother's artistic development, responsible for broadening his horizons and 'opening windows on new landscapes', and in particular for introducing Evelyn to Saki Munro, whose short stories he would always admire. Ensor was a little taken aback when the eleven-year-old boy remarked, 'Terrible man, my father. He likes Kipling.'[19]

As their rapport grew, Evelyn confided to Ensor how whenever he wanted the day off school he would wiggle the end of the thermometer with his tongue to obtain a temperature. And he shocked him by his persecution of a wretched master known to the boys as Uncle Water Rat, and his defiance of the headmaster's request for clemency whenever a master 'more than normally unsuitable was engaged'.[20] Evelyn and Ensor's friendship survived long after both had left the school, and years later, when Ensor was working as stage manager at the Everyman Theatre in Hampstead, he would contrive to get Evelyn tickets for matinees as close to the stage as possible. However he was po-faced when Evelyn sent him scurrilous postcards about the other Heath Mount masters,* and when he received a bundle of caricatures he admitted that he 'felt it better to get rid of them'.[21] Ensor was further reminded of Evelyn's belligerence at the final matinee of an Old Vic season. The only available seats were in a box and Evelyn seemed so to resent the other people in it that he kept referring to Ensor's recent chickenpox. He only stopped when Lilian Baylis entered the box in mortar and gown, which rendered Evelyn speechless.[22]

Despite their ups and downs, they were still sufficiently in touch by the time Evelyn wrote *A Little Learning* for him to send Ensor an uncorrected proof copy, which Ensor annotated, even though he was very friendly with Evelyn's arch enemy Cecil Beaton, to whom Ensor sent samples from his vast collection of theatrical postcards to help Beaton with his work as a costume designer in Hollywood in the 1960s. Evelyn and Beaton had several other friends in common at Heath Mount, including their fellow theatre fan Dudley Brown, Evelyn's regular accomplice in persecuting vulnerable masters and 'business manager' of his private detective agency, Messrs Wuffles[†] and Co.[23] The son of a prosperous surgeon who lived at one of Hampstead's smarter addresses, the Mount, Brown was a

---

* Ensor recalled: 'In the holidays the following conversation took place:

    Me: "Evelyn if you send me another postcard like that I will send a copy to your Head Master and one to your father."

    Evelyn: "Man, you wouldn't do that."

    Me: "Send me another p.c. and see."

    I did not get another.'

† One of Evelyn's nicknames, although he did not permit its universal use, recording in his diary one day: 'Rostail entered [the boot room] and squatting temptingly on the edge of a basin proceeded to call me "Wuffles". I informed him that unless he refrain from using my names in a corrupted form I would have to chastise him. He, knowing he was larger than me, continued with the name whereupon I fulfilled my promise one hundredfold.' (Easter Term, 1916; *EWD*, pp. 8–9.)

good deal richer and more sophisticated than Evelyn and gave him an early taste for the high life. Evelyn was particularly impressed by the fact that while playing football Brown was attended by a nanny 'to refresh him at half time with lemon squash from a thermos flask'. He later greatly disappointed Evelyn, however, by asking him to lunch followed by a matinee and then casually announcing when Evelyn eagerly arrived at his house that there was really nothing good on that he had not already seen.[24] Besides keeping an album of theatre programmes, Brown seemed to know an awful lot about the private lives of actresses and was revered by the other boys for his extensive knowledge of sex. Beaton remembered Brown whispering that children were produced by the man 'mixing his "stuff" with the woman's',[25] and Evelyn, though prudishly shocked when Brown taught him a scatological limerick, recalled being equally fascinated by his theories of reproduction – albeit not the sexual act itself, which he seems to have remained determinedly ignorant of despite the stripping sessions with Muriel Talbot. Whether or not Evelyn succeeded in his reciprocal attempts to interest his friend in Anglo-Catholicism is not clear. In any event, the adult Brown was ultimately drawn to the low life, which he took to 'like a duck to a pond' according to Beaton, and at the age of twenty-two he committed suicide by throwing himself from a window in the rue Jacob in Paris.[26] According to Evelyn the property belonged to 'a notorious pederast and drug dealer'.[27]

Another close friend of Evelyn's at Heath Mount was Ernest Hooper, with whom Evelyn edited (and illustrated) an alternative to the official school magazine. 'By George when the term begins things will hum,' Evelyn told his diary just after New Year 1916. 'I think it's my last so I'm going to raise hell. Our first shell to smash the ramparts of convention is *The Cynic*, the most gorgeous paper out.'[28] Subtitled 'Cynical without being cheaply so. Piquant in moderation. Racy in Excess', the paper was typed and duplicated by Arthur's secretary and in its editorial volunteered 'helpful' observations about the masters' efforts in the rival publication, predicting loftily that 'when they have had a little more experience [they] will be able to produce quite a presentable little paper'. One of these masters, Mr Hynchcliffe, forbade them from selling *The Cynic*, but as Evelyn gleefully recorded they nevertheless sold out of the first issue, covering their printing costs and leaving half a crown over for their war fund.[29] Four more issues followed over the next few months, providing further evidence of the impulses propelling Evelyn towards an eventual literary career – which at that stage largely involved poking fun at masters and fellow pupils, chief among them the unfortunate Cecil Beaton. (The adult Evelyn dismissed it as 'flippant rather than cynical' and conceded that 'the few jokes that are intelligible seem very feeble'.[30])

Despite these various endeavours, it was clear to Evelyn that his father was never going to be as interested in them as he was in the activities of his elder brother Alec, whose exploits at Sherborne (since 1911) Arthur had followed with an eagerness bordering on obsession, awaiting his letters, as Alexander Waugh puts it, 'in the palpitating manner of a teenage paramour'.[31] To his friend Kenneth McMaster Arthur admitted that he had 'built my earthly hopes on him, and one must have something to keep one's ambition young and fresh'. 'Alec's career has, no doubt, in consequence grown too large in my imagination. But I do want to see him doing some of the things that I have had to give up hope of doing.'[32]

Arthur was thrilled when Alec won the school's senior poetry prize, just as he had done, but he derived far greater satisfaction from his sporting successes, Arthur's own shameful inadequacies as a games player having been compounded by a weak chest and poor eyesight. Seizing the opportunity now to relive his inglorious Sherborne career through that of his more athletic and gregarious son, Arthur took about with him a copy of the school roll, annotated with Alec's latest achievements, and with the names of those masters and boys that Alec liked underlined.

These characters and their various peculiarities soon became as familiar to Evelyn as the boys at Heath Mount,[33] and the conspicuous celebration at Underhill of everyone and everything to do with Alec only intensified his feeling of being left out. Indeed at the time he claimed to have felt more than merely excluded; he also felt despised, or so he told Mrs Fleming when in 1914, aged eleven, he went round to her house wearing a bowler hat. 'It belonged to my father first,' he explained. 'Then it descended to Alec: now to me. In fact it has come down to me from generation to generation of them that hate me.' When he was told this, Arthur deemed it yet another demonstration of Evelyn's 'sharp tongue', and his irritation was magnified by Mrs Fleming 'cordially' adding that he had never been a good father to Evelyn, who she said was afraid of him and at his worst in his presence. 'Cheery news!!' wrote Arthur when he reported all this to Alec.

The extraordinary bond between Arthur and Alec was demonstrated the same year when Alec's housemaster told Arthur that his son was worried about masturbating too much – his passions inflamed, so Alec later recorded, by a novel containing nothing racier than 'two luscious descriptions of embraces upon a sofa'.* 'My Own Dear Boy,' wrote Arthur. 'I know from experience that there is nothing that eats into and corrodes the soul more than a secret. Now that you know that *I* know, you can feel there are two of us to fight this trouble – two of us absolutely as one.' Continuing in similar vein for several pages, he warned Alec that persistent 'self-abuse' would lead to 'weakness both of body and mind . . . paralysis and softening of the brain' and the risk of his fathering 'feeble and rickety children' – if indeed he was capable of having any at all. 'Say it is Saturday night and the idea attacks you,' Arthur suggested. 'Put it from you at once. Think of cricket or the day's game, of the probable team next week.' As to his reading, Alec should avoid Swinburne, 'who was a victim of self-abuse (as I once told you)' and therefore 'not a very wholesome companion'. 'Nothing inflames the mind like a lascivious picture or a suggestive line of poetry. Try to concentrate on more manly poets and give as much of your mind as you like to games, out of school. You won't get your firsts [colours] unless your body is in subjection. Train the body, by this perpetual effort of putting off temptation, to be the handmaid of the soul, and not its cruel mistress.' He reassured him that 'in all your efforts, your struggles, your failures, your beginnings again, in all that makes life one perpetual battlefield, you have at any rate one fellow soldier by your side; one who has fought all your battles before you and knows every inch of the way'.[34]

Arthur's infatuation with his elder son did not go unnoticed by Alec's headmaster, who accused him of spoiling the boy and making him self-centred. At Chapman & Hall the staff would enquire, slightly tongue-in-cheek, 'And how is Master Alec this morning, sir?'

Arthur's paternal devotion was accompanied by a newfound love for Sherborne, far exceeding any feelings he had had for the place as an unhappy schoolboy. 'More [often] than was wise,' Arthur later admitted, he would catch the train down to Sherborne on Friday evenings after work and install himself for the weekend at the Digby Hotel (later converted into a schoolhouse), entertaining Alec and his friends, watching the

---

* The novel was *Joseph in Jeopardy* by Frank Danby (Methuen, 1912).

school matches on Saturday afternoon and attending chapel on Sunday morning.[35] Kate often went with him and her surviving letters suggest that she became almost as obsessed as Arthur was with the school career of their eldest son.[36] When Alec won his cricket colours in 1915, Kate wrote to him: 'A thousand congratulations! It is almost too good to be true. How we longed to see you wearing that blue and gold ribbon, and now you will do so . . . I am <u>so</u> happy.'[37]

Having listened to the rest of his family going on about what a wonderful time Alec was having at Sherborne, Evelyn was naturally keen to go there too, and one evening in October 1916 he said to his father: 'Oh, look here, Hooper is going to Sherborne in the summer term. Can't you buck up & do some articles in the Fortnightly so as to be able to afford to send me also?' As Arthur told Alec: 'Seeing that I had had an assessment that morning for £142 income-tax to be paid in January, with more to follow in July: & had worked just on 8 hours at my desk – reviewing a book on Germany & the East & making notes for my next <u>Book of the Week</u> – <u>The Soul of Russia</u> & reading Mais* as well, & was dead tired, I felt this insult was about the last straw!'[38]

However, it was not Arthur's annoyance or money worries that stood in the way of Evelyn following his brother to Sherborne but rather a scandal (about which Evelyn claimed to know nothing until he read Alec's account years later)[39] concerning Alec's romantic entanglements with several younger boys at the school – and the novel he subsequently wrote about his experiences, *The Loom of Youth*.

In the throes of one of these affairs, in early 1915, Alec had written to a friend: 'I shall never get tired of kissing Davies† – he is a darling. As he now works in his study in hall, I see an awful lot of him. But he is leaving this term, *O lacrymarum fons*, it will be very lonely without him.'[40] Sometime later he reflected: 'These loves are great passions while they last. They are mad and short and burn themselves with their own fire. I doubt that I shall ever feel again the same ecstasy that I knew three years ago

---

* S. P. B. Mais (1885–1975) was Alec Waugh's inspirational English teacher at Sherborne and featured as 'Ferrers' in *The Loom of Youth*, whose writing and publication he did much to assist. Mais was a prolific author himself, eventually notching up 200 books, and a well-known early broadcaster, his astonishing work rate fuelled by bipolar disorder that went undiagnosed until he was almost eighty. Late in life he was reduced to asking Alex to help him out with bills, pointedly reminding him that he was 'NOT the author of *The Loom of Youth*'.
† William Wookey Northam Davies, known at Sherborne as Davies mi because he had an elder brother at the school.

when I discovered I was in love with Simonds . . . The love of boy for boy is in my mind one of the most beautiful things in life.'[41] The affair with Davies continued well into the summer of 1915 and although Alec claimed to have been devoted exclusively to him, a few weeks before the end of term he was caught in some unspecified but evidently compromising situation with another boy, Mervyn Renton. The headmaster wrote to Arthur, sparing him the 'exact particulars' of what they had been doing but telling him that Alec could not now come back to Sherborne for his final year. Shattered by this letter, Arthur urged Alec to keep the circumstances of his disgrace 'sacredly to yourself. It is the first time to my knowledge that such a thing has happened to a Waugh. I want no one to know of it, except the Chief [the Sherborne headmaster], Mother, you and I. It is enough that we should have to bear it.'[42]

Needless to say, Arthur glossed over all this in his autobiography, yet at the time, far from straining their relations, Alec's humiliation seemed to bring father and son even closer than they had been before. 'Dear Boy,' wrote Arthur, 'I am sure there is some spiritual relation between you and me which transcends the merely material world.' In a subsequent letter, after it emerged that Alec had been shunned by many of the masters and boys, Arthur wrote to him: 'The nails that pierce the hands of the Son are still driven through the hands of the Father also.'

Kate, too, now seemed to worship Alec even more than before. When he ended his Sherborne career in triumph by playing a match-winning innings in the final of the house cricket cup, she could barely contain herself. 'Happy, Happy, Happy! Hurrah! Hurrah! Hurrah! It was some beating that! & your 77, some score that! I am so awfully pleased at your winning that Cup. I nearly went mad with joy . . . My joy is unspeakable. I did want you to finish up like that and you've been and done it!! Thank you ever so much Ally boy for the pride and pleasure you have given me. May you always play the game where ever you are and always come out strong in an emergency.'[43]

When Alec left Sherborne, he was destined for officers' training and ultimately the trenches – whose obvious dangers were soon brought cruelly home to the Waughs by the death of Kate's younger brother, Basset Raban, who was killed when a shell burst in the mouth of the dugout where he had been conferring with his staff. Conscious that his life too might soon be cut short, Alec somehow found time that winter to write a novel, *The*

Loom of Youth. Beginning it just after Christmas 1915, he completed it in a remarkable seven and a half weeks, getting up at 4.30 each morning and returning to his manuscript at night after the day's parades, and then posting each finished section to Arthur.

Halfway through, Arthur pronounced himself 'astonished at the skill which your narrative shows' yet he doubted the wisdom of its publication, given that it was so obviously autobiographical and contained candid descriptions of Alec's contemporaries and masters at Sherborne and references to schoolboy homosexuality which were then considered shocking. Arthur feared that the book would 'make enemies everywhere' and 'neither you or I could ever go to Sherborne again, and all idea of sending Evelyn would be at an end'.[44]

When Alec nevertheless secured a publisher, in January 1917, Arthur applauded his son's 'great achievement' of having a novel accepted at eighteen but admitted he was 'filled with conflicting emotions'. 'Of course this means the end of Evelyn as a Shirburnian,' he wrote. 'I don't know what to do next, but after you have actually got an agreement I shall write to Chief, & perhaps he will advise me. I feel rather lost for the moment: but I must remind myself that I have always been very uncertain about the advisability of Evelyn going to Sherborne, and I shall hope and trust that we may come to a wise decision which will make for the good of us all.'[45]

As publication of *The Loom* loomed that spring, Arthur arranged to have lunch with the Chief at which, according to his autobiography, they agreed that he would have to find an alternative school for Evelyn. Overriding Kate's preference for sending him to a London school such as Westminster or St Paul's, Arthur chose Lancing in Sussex, 'a small public school of ecclesiastical temper on the South Downs' as Evelyn later rendered it in *Decline and Fall*.

As so often with Arthur, the decision was reached with 'a minimum of deliberation', so Evelyn recalled, his tone betraying resentment at his father's snap choice. Arthur could claim no family connections with the school and had never even visited it. However he thought Lancing's High Church tradition would be ideally suited to his self-proclaimed 'church-loving' boy' who, by his own account, aspired to become a parson.[46] Arthur reckoned that the organised liturgical duties entailed by Lancing's twice-daily compulsory chapel services would afford the 'best test' of his religious conviction.[47]

4

A Lesser Place than Eton

Arthur had started at Sherborne in the summer term so knew perfectly well how difficult it was to go to a new school in the middle of the academic year. Yet his customary impatience to get the job done meant that he set his younger son on precisely the same path – one that Evelyn later reflected resulted in the 'bitter, avoidable loneliness of my first terms at Lancing'.[1] Evelyn was taken there for the first time on a dull and damp morning in May, travelling by train from London to Shoreham on the south coast and then by taxi the last mile up to a cluster of austere flint buildings set on a bleak spur of the South Downs, looking out over the grey English Channel. He later claimed to have parted from his father 'without a pang', excited to be embarking on a new phase of his life;[2] an alternative indication of how he saw his plight at the time was the black border of chains he drew around the relevant page of his pocket calendar.

Founded in 1848, Lancing was the first of the schools built by the Tractarian clergyman Nathaniel Woodard, who had set himself the task of establishing a group of public schools to provide a sound Church of England education for what he saw as the country's neglected middle classes. Each school was rather crudely graded to reflect the peculiarities of the British class system, with the idea that the richer schools would help to subsidise the poorer ones.

Woodard conceived Lancing as the richest and most socially elevated of them all, intended in his mind to cater for the sons of impoverished noblemen as well as those of clergy and other gentry of limited means. Hurstpierpoint, another of Woodard's earlier foundations, was aimed more at the sons of tradesmen, farmers and clerks, while Ardingly was supposedly for smaller farmers, mechanics and shopkeepers.

Lancing was certainly impressive to look at. Though still unfinished, its magnificent chapel was already the fourth tallest ecclesiastical structure in England and to Evelyn's mind the most spectacular post-Reformation church in the country – it was known locally as the Cathedral of the Downs. Furthermore, the school's fixture list boasted matches against Eton, Winchester and Westminster, and its old boys were eligible for the newly founded Public School's Club, evidence that the older schools were beginning to regard it as one of their own.[3]

However, it was still far from comfortable, one of Evelyn's contemporaries recalling that the boys 'slept in stone dormitories with the windows open, a minimum of bed-clothes, and then a cold-bath when we got up at 6.30'.[4] And it had never achieved the social cachet that its founder envisaged. The school roll hardly abounded with sons of the nobility and Evelyn clearly felt that Lancing did not measure up to Sherborne, either socially or academically. His sense of its inferiority was reinforced not only by the endless talk at home about Sherborne but also, rather unhelpfully, by the Lancing headmaster, the Rev. Henry Bowlby, who, as Evelyn recalled, 'never dissembled the opinion, to which we all assented, that Lancing was a less important place than Eton'.[5]

A former contemporary of Arthur's at Oxford, Bowlby had been a scholar at Charterhouse and worked as a housemaster at Eton before arriving at Lancing in 1909. Evelyn's friend Roger Fulford rated Bowlby 'a great Headmaster',[6] and it is true that before the war he had carried out an impressive series of changes, additions and improvements, completing the building of the college, doubling the number of boys and firmly establishing Lancing in the second rank of English public schools. Moreover, his reputation as a successful housemaster at Eton meant that quite a lot of second sons who might otherwise have gone to Eton came to his house at Lancing instead.

By the time Evelyn arrived at Lancing, however, Bowlby had become a rather remote figure. According to the school historian he was by then 'a tired and sick man', worn down by the anxieties of running the school during a war in which his own sons were fighting as well as so many of his old pupils.[7] His wife, meanwhile, was a 'kind, silly woman', Evelyn recalled, 'with a peculiar proclivity for gaffes'.[8] Once, when passing the photographs hung in the chapel of old boys who had been killed in action, she remarked: 'Oh, isn't it nice to see a second row go up!'[9]

Evelyn's descriptions of the headmaster in his autobiography are not especially generous, recording for example that he had got his hurdling Blue at Oxford 'in a bad year' – whereas in fact he had hurdled for Oxford four years in succession and was president of the Oxford Union Athletic Club.[10] Though Bowlby now walked with a limp, he was still tall, lean and 'distinctly handsome,' Evelyn conceded, 'except when the keen winds of the place caught and encrimsoned his narrow nose'. According to Evelyn, his headmaster had more interest in becoming a bishop, like his father, than in schoolmastering, but his ambitions had been thwarted due to his having 'made himself rather ridiculous [at Eton] by his courtship of the more illustrious fathers and by flirtations with the prettier mothers and sisters'.[11]

A possibly greater obstacle was Bowlby's widely-reported acquittal years later, in 1929, while Canon of Chichester, on a charge of molesting four small girls on a train, after, by his own account, feeling their bare legs and 'asking them if they were cold'.[12] While the trial was being reported in the newspapers, one of Evelyn's old school friends came to lunch at Under-hill and was in the middle of denouncing their former headmaster when Arthur suddenly interjected: 'There, but for the grace of God, goes Arthur Waugh!'[13] This puzzling – and to Evelyn possibly rather embarrassing – remark was presumably Arthur's way of candidly acknowledging that he too felt vulnerable to temptation at times. Two years previously he had confessed to a clergyman friend that a 'dark-eyed, curly-headed, dainty, smiling little fairy of about 23 *fair springs*' had been massaging his 'hinder parts' to treat his rheumatism. After asking him to remove his trousers, the girl 'waved her delicate fingers mystically & began taking the most reprehensible liberties with my body . . . It was the deepest enchantment I have ever undergone, but my conscience has tortured me ever since.'[14]*

At Lancing, meanwhile, Evelyn had been placed in Bowlby's house, Head's, which was considered the most prestigious in the school. Occasionally the headmaster hobbled round the dormitories addressing dutiful small talk to his charges.† The day-to-day running of the house

---

* Arthur's masseuse was Mollie Udale-Smith. Later in life, after divorcing Sir Ian Aber-cromby, 10th Bart, she lived on Tenerife, where the local paper, described her as 'a liberal and eccentric Englishwoman who changed her husband as she did her shirt'.
† Waiting for a bath one evening, sixteen-year-old Evelyn endured 'seven solid minutes of Head's conversation. He is a bore, though rather an old dear, I'm beginning to think.' (27 September 1919; *EWD*, p. 21.)

was left to the house tutor, Dick Harris, a warm-hearted young man who was especially kind to new boys and, as Evelyn remembered, 'entirely' responsible for 'such vestiges of happiness' that he experienced during his first term.[15] Otherwise it was a painfully lonely time during which the only boy in Head's with whom he was permitted to associate was the other 'new man', Roger Fulford, with whom he was obliged to sit at the 'new man's table', pointedly ignored by the rest of the boys in the House Room.

For their first three weeks, another junior boy was assigned to instruct them in Lancing's strange rules and rituals: who was permitted to walk on which plot of grass; who could link arms with whom; when boys could put their hands in their trouser pockets (in their second year – though with the jacket raised, not drawn back); and so on.

On the third Sunday of term, new boys were required to stand on a table and sing a song. Arthur had suggested 'My wife's gone to the country, hurrah! hurrah!', which Evelyn performed well enough to spare him the usual pelting with books and money boxes.[16] However, in general he was not well liked, and in his first two terms he tended to be written off as an 'awful little tick'.[17] His first experience of the Ascension Day holiday was particularly miserable, when the whole school dispersed but Evelyn found that he had no friends to go with and so spent the day wandering about the empty school grounds alone. 'Evelyn is a misfit, I'm afraid,' Alec wrote to a friend at the time. '[He] hates Lancing. He shouldn't. A boy ought to like his school.'[18]

Evelyn's friend Fulford later recalled that he was 'too independent, too prone to notice oddities and comment on them'[19] – none of which qualities was welcomed in a new boy. Evelyn felt the hostility towards him all the more acutely because, as he recalled, previously he had met 'only people who seemed disposed to like me'. 'Experience has taught me that not everyone takes to me at first sight (or on closer acquaintance),' he wrote, 'but I am still mildly surprised by rebuffs, such is the confidence which a happy childhood founds.'[20]

His isolation at Lancing was exacerbated by his fastidiousness. He was especially revolted by Lancing's doorless, open-drained latrines, 'the Groves', where most boys went in pairs after breakfast but which Evelyn elected to visit alone during school hours at the cost of writing twenty-five lines. He was similarly repelled by the shared tepid, muddy baths after games ('Clubs') and the abysmal wartime food, as a result of which he experienced real hunger for the first time in his life.

His refusal to help less clever boys with their prep on the grounds that it was dishonest won him no friends, nor did his general abrasiveness: 'Poor Evelyn has been getting into trouble at school again and all through that unwise tongue of his,' Kate told Alec. 'Perhaps some day he will learn.'[21] His letters from Arthur were flung towards him by the head of the House Room with a contemptuous sigh – 'Another one for Waugh!' – eventually prompting Evelyn to ask Arthur to write less often, even though the letters were a great solace to him.[22] Lancing's respect for religion meant that he was rarely ridiculed for kneeling, in defiance of convention, at the *incarnatus* in the Creed at Holy Communion, however his habit of remaining 'plunged in prayer' by his bedside long after everyone else had finished was considered strange.

His conspicuous eccentricities suggest a desire to set himself apart from the other boys. Yet he later maintained that this was not always the case. 'I did not admire the other boys,' he wrote in his autobiography. 'I did not want to be like them. But in contradiction, I wanted to be one of them. I had no aspirations to excel, still less to lead; I simply longed to remain myself and yet be accepted as one of this distasteful mob.'[23]

Sunday afternoons were especially desolate, with the House Room out of bounds for two hours and the boys despatched to the Downs in their straw hats and black coats. 'I often found myself walking alone or obliged to make a rendezvous with some equally unpopular boy in another House.'[24] He sought refuge from his loneliness in the classroom, the school library, where he could only go on Sunday evenings until he was awarded his 'library privileges', and in chapel. Services were held every morning and evening and three times on Sunday, when the names of old boys killed in action that week were read out, a sombre ritual that became especially affecting for Evelyn after Alec was posted to the Western Front that summer.

The first summer holidays could not come soon enough as far as Evelyn was concerned and as they approached he eagerly marked off the days in the calendar he kept in his pocket. But just as the boys' trunks appeared in the dormitories and he was on the point of going home, he caught mumps and was told that he had to spend the first two weeks of the holidays in the school sanatorium – an injunction that came as 'an insupportable blow', he recalled.[25]

More homesick now than ever, he spent his quarantine reading a copy of *The Loom of Youth*, which he refused to let his fellow invalids see.[26] By the time he was eventually allowed back to Underhill, his parents were far more preoccupied with the welfare of Alec, who was on the point of being sent to France (in late July) – and then straight into the Battle of Passchendaele, where three out of seven of the line officers in his company would be killed.

While that battle was still raging, glowing reviews of *The Loom of Youth* appeared in the press and it quickly became a bestseller, as talked about as *Tom Brown's School Days* had been sixty years previously. Arthur was delighted by its success yet dismayed that the book was seen as an attack on his old school. Alec wrote from the trenches denying this but the school magazine declined to print his letter. When Alec in turn refused to resign from the Old Boys' Society, his name was summarily removed from the school roll, whereupon Arthur felt he had no choice but to 'stand by my son, and follow him into exile'.[27] Evelyn, meanwhile, was sent to Midsomer Norton to stay with his aunts, who found him 'greatly improved' after his first term at public school. 'He couldn't be nicer,' wrote Aunt Connie, 'so pleasant and ready to do anything we want him to do and pleased with any little joy we try to arrange. I don't think he is nearly so satirical as he used to be. We are all very happy together.'

After a miserably cold and wet autumn term back at Lancing, during which Evelyn begged Arthur to remove him, the next holidays he arrived home to find a new member of the household, Barbara Jacobs, to whom Alec had become engaged after an intermittent two-year courtship. She was the daughter of Arthur's friend W. W. Jacobs, the famously grumpy humorist and author of *The Monkey's Paw*, who was said to have earned more than any other English writer of the time except Rudyard Kipling. Barbara was staying with the Waughs while attending a course of lectures at Bedford College in Regent's Park, and although she was nearly three years older than Evelyn they took to each other immediately. Over the next two years she and her family would replace the Flemings as Evelyn's favourite holiday companions, and he went often to their home at Berkhamsted, where Barbara's brother attended the school of which Graham Greene's father was headmaster.

Evelyn's most vivid memories of Berkhamsted were of the games the children used to play in the Jacobses' galleried music room, during which he and Barbara's younger sister Luned would seek each other out 'grapple, and, while the younger players squealed in the excitement of arrest and escape, would silently cling and roll together. We maintained a pretence of conflict. There was no kissing, merely rapturous minutes of close embrace. No mention of our intimacy was ever made between us. But after the game, when the lights came on, we would exchange glances of complicity and it was always either she or I who proposed "the dark game".'[28] Their attachment did not go unnoticed by Alec, who in January 1919 told his friend Hugh Mackintosh that 'Evelyn has become quite amorous, I regret to say. [He] loves Barbara's sister, a comely wench, and at odd periods of the day they are observed holding hands.'[29]

The attraction to Barbara meanwhile was purely platonic – or so Evelyn maintained. He was intrigued by her upbringing and rebellious and agnostic beliefs which were so different to his. 'Until I met her, maiden-aunts and Anglican clergy had been in the ascendant; in Barbara I met the new age. I did not surrender to it without reserve, but I was stimulated by the encounter.'[30]

She was equally entranced by her new young friend and years later remembered him as 'a perfectly darling boy, the nicest youngster you can imagine'.[31] They spent entire days exploring London together randomly by bus, or, to Arthur's dismay, daubing the walls of the old nursery – which Evelyn had redesignated 'the studio' – with their experiments in Cubism. Her enthusiasms rubbed off to the extent that Evelyn pretended to be a socialist at various times over the next few years[32] and his form master cautioned him against approving 'merely those things that are ultra-modern'.[33] However Arthur discerned that his son was 'not yet so wedded to what is new that you seem likely to despise what is old. You may copy the Cubist in your living room, but an Old Master hangs above your bed.'[34]

Evelyn's next school holidays were once again overshadowed by the family's fears for Alec, who was reported missing after straying behind enemy lines during the 1918 German spring offensive. Arthur's anxiety this time was mixed with irritation at Evelyn and Barbara's apparent indifference. 'Their loud laughter rings through the house,' he wrote to Jean Fleming. 'I sit alone and think of the other boy, lonely, cold, hungry, even if he is alive; and I wonder *what* their hearts are made of.'[35] Arthur spent ten fretful days replying to letters of sympathy before he eventually received a telegram from the Red Cross at Geneva to say that Alec was being held as a prisoner of war.

* * *

Evelyn had been miserable at Lancing during wartime, however life there perked up considerably after the Armistice of 11 November 1918. Alec was home by Christmas and Evelyn recalled that holiday as 'the most joyous of my life'.[36] Back at school, food was at last plentiful and the tuck shop, which in wartime had stocked only occasional oatcakes and tired bits of fruit, now brimmed with such long-forgotten delicacies as buns and chocolates and walnut whips.[37]

The House Room's eight most senior boys, 'the Settle',* vied with one another to throw the finest tea party, with piles of crumpets, cakes, pastries and in summer strawberries and cream. Those with private studies ('pits') procured the odd pot of caviar and *foie gras* from London, and various varieties of China tea from a shop in Piccadilly, brewing them 'as nicely as a circle of maiden ladies,' Evelyn recalled, and 'discoursing on their qualities as later we were to talk of wine'.[38]

Socially, Evelyn had also begun to feel more assured. Within Head's House he had grown steadily more respected and even feared for his strong will and determined independence. By the age of fifteen, he and Roger Fulford and Rupert Fremlin[†] fancied themselves leaders of the self-styled 'Bolshies', a group of boys Evelyn later maintained were benevolent towards their juniors but hunted 'as a small pack to bring down our equals and immediate superiors'.[39] He and his friends 'practically controlled the founts of popularity,' Evelyn recalled, 'and capriciously stopped or let them flow'.

Victims of their persecution included one Desmond O'Connor,

---

* So named because among their privileges was to be allowed to sit on the settle by the fire in the House Room.

† Waugh described Fremlin as 'a delightful mercurial fellow, whose father we wrongly believed to have a been eaten by a tiger'. His alternations of exuberance and depression were known as 'Fremlin's states'. He was later with Evelyn at Oxford, but died young of black-water fever, a complication of malaria, in Nigeria (*A Little Learning*, p. 125 and *Mallowan's Memoirs*, p. 27).

nicknamed 'Dungy', who had unwisely antagonised Evelyn when Alec went missing by suggesting that he had deserted or was a traitor. When O'Connor was promoted above Evelyn and his cronies onto the house 'Settle' and as head of the dormitory, they 'exercised every ingenuity' to humiliate him. As an adult the wretched Dungy apparently shot himself while in India – as Evelyn recorded with neither relish nor remorse.[40]

Another casualty was Emlyn Bevan, later a prosperous City man and fellow of Evelyn's at White's but known at Lancing for obvious reasons as 'Buttocks'. Evelyn recalled how he and Fulford composed a song which 'celebrated his large posterior, his gluttony, his affectation for shaving before he need'.[41] Cruel as the jibes often were, Evelyn did at least admit that 'in all these nasty manoeuvres there lay the hidden fear that I myself might at any moment fall from favour and become, as I had been in my first year, the object of contempt'.[42]

The Bolshies also directed mockery at their new house tutor, E. B. 'Gordo' Gordon, who replaced the popular Dick Harris in September 1919. To begin with the rheumatic Gordo appeared duplicitous and sneaky, prowling about the house unheard in his gym shoes, for which he was dubbed 'Pussy-foot' and 'Super-spy'.[43] Yet Evelyn soon realised that he was essentially a good sort who moreover helped foster his artistic interests.

Evelyn was at that time particularly passionate about lettering and illumination, recently inspired by having visited with his parents the Arts and Crafts community at Ditchling and met the famous calligrapher Edward Johnston. The great scribe had shown him how to cut a turkey quill and demonstrated his 'foundational' hand, taking the fourteen-year-old boy's breath away with the sweep and precision of his strokes, which as Evelyn later remembered were 'as virile as a bullfighter's'.[44]

In 1919, aged sixteen, Evelyn won the Lancing art prize (judged by the architect Detmar Blow) for an illuminated collect, and one teatime after a characteristically unsuccessful boxing match Gordo summoned him to his study so that he could show his prize prayer to another local scribe called Francis Crease. Evelyn had noticed this peculiar-looking man on Sundays in the school chapel, 'an incongruously elegant figure in the side aisle' who would sit through most of the service in meditation and then, after the sermon, suddenly wrap his cape around him and disappear onto the Downs.[45] Dressed foppishly in soft tweeds and a silk shirt and cravat, the man had 'a pink and white complexion often found in nuns', a high-pitched voice and a 'delicate, almost mincing' gait.

Evelyn maintained that Mr Crease was 'without immoral proclivities', although he conceded that he 'showed a distinct interest in the better-looking boys'.[46] With his ginger hair, big ears and bright, staring eyes it is debatable whether the young Evelyn came within that category. In any event Crease went into raptures about Evelyn's border decoration, declaring it far better than anything he could hope to do. He also said he thought the script shamefully unworthy of it and offered to teach him how it should be done.

So with the permission of his house tutor one afternoon in January 1920 Evelyn walked over to Crease's 'cloister', an isolated farm four miles away across the Downs at Lychpole. On this first visit he lost his way in the mist and on his second he was caught in a heavy hailstorm and arrived sopping-wet. 'Crease met me at the door and led me to his bedroom where he lent me dry socks, trousers and shoes,' Evelyn's diary records, although he tactfully omitted such details in his letter the same day to his father, whom he reassured that besides being 'rather effeminate, rather affected', Crease was 'very refined and artistic, well bred and charming . . . the truest dilettante I have ever seen'.[47]

Though never especially keen on Crease's elaborate Celtic-style script or decorations, Evelyn quickly fell under his spell, confiding to his diary within a few months that 'I owe anything at Lancing worth remembering to him'.[48] He later admitted to having enjoyed the actual lessons far less than the 'hot scones, [handleless] Crown Derby cups and conversation' that followed.

Crease was reticent about his past but hinted vaguely that he had previously been attached to an Anglican fraternity and once held a distinguished academic post at Corpus, Oxford – although Evelyn later thought it more likely that Crease had come to know the university through his friendship with a rich American fellow there. He did not name the American in his autobiography,[49] but Evelyn may have been referring to the flamboyant art and pornography collector Edward Perry ('Ned') Warren, an extremely wealthy Bostonian who ran an all-male establishment at nearby Lewes House, wrote A *Defence of Uranian Love*, which has been described as 'the premier pederastic apologia in the language',[50] and would have a pervasive influence on Evelyn's generation of English aesthetes at Oxford in the 1920s.

The extent to which Crease followed his friend's credo is hard to ascertain at this distance, but most other Lancing housemasters warned their boys against going to visit him. There is no evidence that he ever behaved improperly towards his new pupil, however, and so intensely did Evelyn enjoy the visits that Thursday soon became his favourite day of the week. 'It is such a relief to get into refined surroundings, if only for an afternoon,' he recorded at the time.[51] Sometimes Crease would accompany him halfway on the walk back to school, 'I eagerly questioning him about architecture or aesthetics or Limoges or Maiolica,' recalled Evelyn, 'he trying to turn me to the beauty of the evening and the downs'.[52]

Crease's letters to Evelyn that spring term reveal a growing familiarity, one of them telling him that 'I can be as direct as you sometimes & you don't like it so much in others as in yourself – but it is good for you. You want a Friend who is a thorn in the flesh not an Echo!'[53] Their rapport did not go unnoticed by Gordo and in March 1920 Evelyn recorded that his house tutor had become 'very jealous of Crease's influence' and had 'been subtly trying to put me off him'. More awkwardly, Dick Harris subsequently forbade Evelyn's friend Dudley Carew from going over to tea with Crease, apparently on the basis that he had 'heard scandal of him'. Evelyn evidently passed the whispers on to Crease, who shrieked that he would send his landlord to the headmaster to vouch for his innocence.[54]

As if to demonstrate his own devotion, meanwhile, Evelyn had invited Crease to stay at Underhill for ten days during the Easter holidays – never having asked any of his Lancing contemporaries home – an invitation that was then repeated in a letter from Kate Waugh. Crease felt distinctly apprehensive at the prospect, the more so having read Arthur's description of the visits to Underhill of the ill-fated young poet Ian Mackenzie, a friend of Alec's at Sandhurst who had stayed there several times before dying of pneumonia on Armistice Day. Arthur described how their first evening had been spent 'under the red lamps by the book-room fire, taking down one book after another, and each reading favourite passages in turn'. Even more alarming to the pathologically shy and reclusive Crease was Arthur's recollection of how Mackenzie liked to start the day by singing and how 'we made him roar with laughter at the breakfast-table as we imitated the strains that accompanied the process of his dressing'.[55]

Before Crease could be persuaded to come, Evelyn had to reassure him that his family was nothing like as hearty as Arthur had made out, and also that his father would cover all his expenses. When eventually he did come, Crease spent much of each day in his bed and at other times cowered in the book-room with his hands over his eyes.[56] It was evidently more enjoyable than he had feared, however, and proved to be the first of several visits.

Most significantly as far as Evelyn's development was concerned, Crease's first visit to Underhill changed the way he saw his father, the scribe having perceptively observed that he thought Arthur Waugh 'charming, entirely charming, and acting all the time' – an assessment with which Evelyn's mother agreed. 'My eyes were opened,' wrote Evelyn, 'and I saw him, whom I had grown up to accept in complete simplicity, as he must always have appeared to others.'[57] From that moment on, his attitude to Arthur would grow progressively more dismissive.

What Arthur made of Crease is unclear – he doesn't get a mention in his autobiography *One Man's Road* – although after Alec's troubles at Sherborne he may have been a little apprehensive about the relationship between this old-maidish man and his younger son, as much as he was offended by Evelyn's observation that until he met Mr Crease, he had 'lived among philistines'.[58] In any event, Arthur treated their guest 'kindly if somewhat derisively', so Evelyn recalled.[59] Kate was far more indulgent and continued asking Crease to Underhill for years to come, even after his arrest on a charge of sexual misconduct – a case of mistaken identity according to Evelyn.

Evelyn's attachment to Crease grew during the summer term of 1920 to the extent that his going away for a month in May made Evelyn 'very depressed and unhappy ... he is the only real friend I have here. I do believe that I am getting homesick again after three years.'[60] In his mentor's absence, Evelyn continued going over to Lychpole to practise his illuminated script, and one afternoon he broke the blade of one of his quill-cutting knives. He thought little of it at the time but Crease was far more annoyed than he had expected and wrote to tell him that the knife was very old and quite irreplaceable. In any case, it was in a drawer and Evelyn had no right to be using it at all; he had betrayed his trust. The next post brought another letter from Crease apologising for sounding so cross and their sessions resumed as before when he came back. But their friendship was never the same again.

Crease went away again that October, this time for nine months, and when he returned in July 1921 Evelyn recorded in his diary: 'The spell is broken. His influence has quite gone. I see just a rather silly perhaps casually interesting little man.'[61] As Evelyn later recalled, he had already transferred his allegiance to 'the more forceful and flamboyant' figure of J. F. Roxburgh, an outgoing and agnostic man of the world, in many ways the exact opposite of the monastic aesthete Crease.[62]

5

....

Watertight Compartments

Later renowned as the first headmaster of Stowe and universally known by his initials 'J. F.', John Fergusson Roxburgh was a brilliant classicist who had taken a First at Cambridge and been recruited to the Lancing teaching staff before the war to boost the school's academic standing. Tall and slightly stooped, he cut a dash with his flamboyant wardrobe – the boys counted fourteen suits – and the various idiosyncratic mannerisms he had cultivated as an undergraduate. With his sonorous voice and precise diction he was especially effective at inspiring the boys to read poetry and plays. His popularity was boosted by his religious scepticism and his liberal approach to discipline. His biographer recounts how one boy who was returning with a 'cricket-bag stuffed with bottles of beer and cider for an end-of-term party had the misfortune to be offered a lift by J. F. who heaved the bag into his car. He said nothing as the bottles clinked but when he dropped him off handed him a packet of fifty cigarettes and said, "Perhaps these will come in useful."'[1]

When Roxburgh came back to Lancing after the war (during which he had been recommended for an MC and his younger brother was killed) Evelyn quickly became a devotee, delighting in his sarcastic asides about the headmaster's 'profound classical witticisms', as Roxburgh described them, and finding his French lessons 'really a joy. It is almost worth doing the wretched subject.'[2] 'Every hour in his form room was exhilarating,' Evelyn later recalled.[3] Just as the younger and more reclusive Evelyn had been drawn to the hermit-like Crease, the more convivial Roxburgh now appealed to his growing gregariousness.

It was in Roxburgh's modern play-reading society in October 1920 that he first studied George Bernard Shaw's *Candida*,[4] which gave him further unflattering insight into the character of his father. Evelyn evidently associated Arthur with the Rev. James Mavor Morell, the sermonising husband of the play's heroine. The next April, Evelyn recorded in his diary: 'Father has been ineffably silly the whole holidays. The extraordinary thing is that the more I see through my father, the more I appreciate Mother. She has been like Candida and went to Father, whom she must have despised, because he needed her most. I always think I am discovering some new trait in his character and find that she knew it long ago.'[5]

Meanwhile Evelyn so revered Roxburgh that for a time he even adopted his way of speaking as if he had a hot potato in his mouth.[6] More permanently influential were his stipulations on the precise use of grammar and his hatred of clichés. Besides the French lessons, Evelyn had Roxburgh for 'general' subjects in the Upper Sixth from September 1920, studying anything that caught the master's fancy. Each week the boys wrote 250 words on a chosen subject, which Roxburgh would then read and hand back with verbal comments of praise or debate or, more disconcertingly, no comment at all – a sure sign that the piece had bored him rigid. For Evelyn, most disparaging of all was the remark, 'Excellent journalism, my dear fellow,' which he interpreted as 'trite in thought, colloquial in expression and aiming for effect by smartness and overstatement'.[7]

Evelyn never doubted that Roxburgh was homosexual: 'Most good schoolmasters are,' he reasoned. 'How else could they endure their work?' In his autobiography he professed to think it unlikely that Roxburgh would have given his desires 'physical release' with his pupils, yet shortly before leaving Lancing he had recorded in his diary how Tom Driberg had entered Roxburgh's darkened room one day and found him in a chair with a boy called MacDonald, looking very embarrassed.[8]* But Evelyn was not Roxburgh's type. 'I was small and quite pretty in a cherubic way. His tastes were more classical than rococo.'[9] Roxburgh's particular favourite was his head of house, Eddie Capel Cure, a 'golden-haired Hyancinthus' to whom J. F. gave a motorcycle which the boy soon crashed, ruining his handsome looks.† With Evelyn, meanwhile, Roxburgh merely discerned 'potentialities worth cultivating'.[10]

---

* Driberg was never an especially reliable witness, however he later vehemently denied this particular story (Francis Wheen, *Tom Driberg*, pp. 28–9).
† W. E. Capel Cure later modelled his career on Roxburgh, becoming a master at Stowe after graduating from Cambridge and J. F.'s closest personal confidant. Like J. F. he remained a bachelor. He died of cancer in 1953. See Annan, *Roxburgh of Stowe*, pp. 50, 196–7.

Evelyn's ambitions at this time were more obviously directed towards a career as a draughtsman than as a writer. However, as Roxburgh noticed, for someone of his age he was exceptionally well read and discerning about literature, and he had by no means ruled out the idea of following in the Waugh family literary tradition. In the autumn term of 1920 he made his first proper stab at a novel, the transparently autobiographical 'study of a man with two characters by his brother'.[11]

In the surviving ten-page fragment, the hero Peter Audley is at public school in Sussex in 1918 and contemplating the possibility of going off to the trenches the next year: 'He had learnt much of what it was like over there from his brother, but Ralf saw everything so abstractedly and with such imperturbable cynicism. Peter flattered himself that he was far more sensitive and temperamental. He was sure that he would not be able to stand it.'[12] However, Peter clearly admires Ralf's 'awfully clever' idea of living his life in 'watertight compartments'[13] – recalling a suggestion of Alec's that Evelyn seemed to see as a means of giving the freest possible rein to the Jekyll and Hyde sides of his own character.

The war was by then a fading memory for Alec. Bored at Chapman & Hall and wretched in his marriage, he was also suffering a crisis of confidence in his writing career. So when his seventeen-year-old brother – a year younger than Alec had been when he wrote *The Loom of Youth* – breezed home for the Christmas holidays announcing that he had started a novel, Alec naturally appeared 'apprehensive of a rival',[14] as Evelyn noted in his diary, his unease deepened by Evelyn's choice of subject. Although Evelyn thought his novel 'fairly good' and 'pretty sure' to get published, his family's disapproval combined with 'my own innate sloth' soon caused him to abandon it – though not before he had written a revealing dedication to himself, bemoaning the lot of an aspiring writer brought up in such an entirely literary family:

Many of your relatives and most of your father's friends are more or less directly interested in paper and print. Ever since you first left the nursery for meals with your parents downstairs, the conversation, to which you were an insatiable listener, has been of books, their writers and producers; ever since, as a sleepy but triumphantly emancipated school boy, you were allowed to sit up with your elders in the 'bookroom' after dinner, you have heard little but discussion about books . . .

By the end of March 1921 Roxburgh was sufficiently impressed by Evelyn to ask him to tea in his small study, an honour only accorded to a select few. 'How delightful,' declared Roxburgh when Evelyn arrived. 'We have nothing to do until chapel but eat eclairs and talk about poetry.'[15] Six months later, following the publication of the first issue of the school magazine under Evelyn's editorship, J. F. wrote to tell him: 'If you use what the Gods have given you, you will do as much as anyone I know to shape the course of your generation.'[16]

Roxburgh's tribute to Evelyn followed a string of accolades in his final year at Lancing, during which he became editor of the Lancing magazine and president of the debating society, and won both the poetry and English literature prizes. After the literature prize in June he wrote blithely to Arthur: 'I've got the Scarlyn, all right . . . I am a little cheered. Of course it is no testament to my brain – there was no serious competition – but I think it shows a certain capacity for work.'[17] He was also offered house captaincy in the spring of 1921 as a way of curbing his ongoing campaign of ridiculing the school Corps.[18] His choice was to either accept or leave the school. Knowing how much it would mean to his father (whom, despite all his scornful thoughts, Evelyn was still keen to please) and that it was a precondition of the other positions he wanted, he reluctantly accepted.[19]

But his new responsibility made him feel miserably lonely and disloyal to those who had looked to him for leadership in their troublemaking. He dreaded being thought of as self-important, officious or patronising, and his gloom was compounded by his loss of religious faith. He took to going for long walks after lights-out with with another senior boy called James Hill, during which they consoled each other about the 'loneliness of leadership' and talked about suicide, Evelyn going so far as to compose 'last letters' in which he admitted his deep fear of failure: 'I know I have something in me,' he wrote to his friend Dudley Carew, 'but I am desperately afraid it may never come to anything.'[20]

Just as he was about to embark on one such excursion a frantic letter arrived from Arthur, who had somehow heard about his nocturnal visits to the seashore. 'It is years since we have heard anything that has so distressed us,' wrote Arthur. 'That you, a House Captain, in the confidence of your leaders, should play such a rotten & contemptible game. It is unworthy of the name of Waugh, and doubly unworthy of yourself, of whom I have always been so proud . . . When Alec told me this sort of thing was going on at Sherborne, I asked him for his word of honour that he would never do it . . . I appeal to you to send me by the first post your honourable assurance that never again will you break bounds, never go out at night, never do anything so fatuously foolish to endanger your whole future.'[21] Still ignorant of the circumstances surrounding Alec's earlier expulsion from Sherborne, Evelyn thought the letter 'unconvincingly rhetorical', a product of his father's habitual theatricality which made him wince. But he wrote in his diary: 'I am at least glad he has taken a strong line about something at last.'[22]

Arthur admired even if he did not much like the play that Evelyn had written that term called *Conversion*, a satire of public-school life in three burlesques: 'As maiden aunts think it is'; 'As modern authors say it is', a skit on *The Loom of Youth*; and 'As we all know it is'. In the final act Evelyn's hero is blackmailed out of his troublemaking in chapel just as Evelyn had recently been persuaded out of ragging the Corps. 'Now look here,' says the prefect, 'we shall be needing another House Captain next term and I shall recommend you . . . Now, will you be sensible?'[23] 'Congratulations on your wit and cynicism,' Arthur wrote after he had read it. 'With such promise I feel you are bound to come off at Oxford. You have at 17 what we laboured to get, and couldn't, at 23. Go on and prosper and my heart goes with you.'[24] After it had been performed to great applause before the whole school, Roxburgh told Evelyn the epilogue showed 'a touch of genius'.[25]

*   *   *

Among Evelyn's contemporaries, his friend Roger Fulford later recalled his 'immense, uncanny power over his schoolfellows'.[26] Another boy, Christopher Chamberlin, thought him 'the first subversive person I've met who was obviously thinking for himself'.[27] However, Max Mallowan, the future archaeologist husband of Agatha Christie and one of Evelyn's main intellectual rivals while at Lancing (after beating Evelyn in his Roman history essay, Mallowan crowed to his parents, 'That is a triumph!'),[28] recalled that he was 'popular among the boys for he was amusing and always ready to lead us into mischief, but he had a way of getting others into trouble and himself invariably escaping. He was courageous and witty and

clever but was also an exhibitionist with a cruel nature that cared nothing about humiliating his companions as long as he could expose them
to ridicule.'[29] But just as Evelyn admitted to hiding the fear that he might
at any moment suddenly fall from favour, his truculent and domineering
demeanour did not preclude the occasional influence of other boys. One
who made a significant impact on him was the future politician Hugh
Molson, who later recalled that he and Evelyn had been 'close friends
without really liking each other',[30] while Evelyn ultimately deemed
Molson 'a pompous ass'.[31] However, when Molson had first arrived at
Lancing in October 1919, sixteen-year-old Evelyn thought him 'amazing'
and 'undoubtedly clever', with 'the true aristocrat's capacity for being
perfectly at home in anyone's company'.[32]

If not quite aristocratic, the amazing Molson was the scion of a prosperous Canadian brewing family who now lived near Lancing at Goring
Hall, which Hugh's father, a Unionist MP, rented from the Bowes-Lyons.
Though born in Montreal, Major Molson had been educated at public
school in England and was scarcely distinguishable from the local gentry,
listing his recreations in *Who's Who* as 'shooting, motoring, golf'. Evelyn
paid several visits to the Molsons at Goring, designed by Charles Barry
and frequented for a time by the young Lady Elizabeth Bowes-Lyon, the
future Queen and later Queen Mother. It seems likely that this was his
first experience of staying in a large English country house and he noted
approvingly how comfortably the Molsons lived and that dinner was 'excellent and beautifully served'.[33]

Molson went equally often to the more modest Underhill, where Arthur
Waugh struck him as 'a caricature of a Victorian' with a rhetorical, sentimental, canting way of speaking. The adolescent Evelyn, meanwhile,
'couldn't bear it, or him,' noted Molson, 'and made no bones about expressing it at table or in the presence of his parent'. This was all rather
embarrassing for Molson, especially given Arthur's tendency to appeal
to him for sympathy and wonder aloud what he had done to deserve this
treatment from his son.[34]

Evidence of what Evelyn later saw as Molson's self-importance came
soon after his arrival at Lancing, when he edged Evelyn into one of the
bays in the school library and confided that he had written a book on education which he meant to publish.[35] The same term, when asked whether
he was interested in politics, Molson replied 'preternaturally so' – thus

acquiring the nickname 'Preters', which stuck for the rest of his Lancing career.

Destined to follow his father into politics and at one time touted as a future leader of the Conservative Party, at school Molson espoused a curious combination of socialism, atheism, pacifism and hedonism.[36] Among his other precocious endeavours was a series of essays, some of which he pressed on Arthur Waugh for criticism, others he persuaded periodicals to publish. Evelyn deplored his friend's long-winded prose,[37] yet the mere fact of publication served as an important spur. After Molson boasted to him that he had had an article accepted, Evelyn told his diary: 'I must try and write one next holidays.'[38]

Another activity in which Molson led the way was drinking. Before he had taken to alcohol in earnest himself, Evelyn marvelled at his friend's consumption during a drive out from school on Ascension Day, 1921. Molson had borrowed a car and at lunch in Chichester managed to get through: 'a neat whisky, a whisky and water, a gin and bitters, two whisky sodas, two liqueurs, a double whisky almost neat, two bottles of cider, two glasses of port, one neat whisky'. On the drive back he was 'a trifle risky' and 'drove round and round the market cross shouting to passers-by that we were looking for the alms houses'.[39]

Evelyn did not approve of all of Molson's excesses. In February 1921 he recorded after a morning's walk together: 'He is very much all over himself as he has just stolen more cocaine from the doctor. I see myself having a fairly hectic time with him . . .'[40] And after they spent a reading fortnight together in preparation for their Oxford scholarship exams, he primly dissuaded his friend from letting off steam with a night of 'whoring' – not that Evelyn would prove completely averse to such recreations in his later bachelor life.

Back in 1919, it was also Molson who had come up with the idea of a cultural society for the Upper Fifths, frustrated with not being allowed to air his important views at the school debating society. He recruited Evelyn and Fulford and together they founded the Dilettanti Society (the name suggested by Evelyn) for poetry readings, art lectures and political debate. Applicants poured in, among them Tom Driberg, the future journalist and Labour MP who recalled an unsettling interview in which Evelyn strode up to him one day in Great School and barked: 'Who's your favourite artist?' According to Driberg's biographer, he was so 'flustered by the unblinking stare of Waugh's eyes' that he 'suddenly forgot every artist who ever lived. Eventually, in a panic, he managed to pluck a random name from some distant recess of his brain – "Sir John Lavery". It was a ridiculous reply. But, to his surprise, he was elected forthwith.'[41] Another boy who said that his favourite painter was Landseer was promptly rejected.[42]

A bespectacled scholar eighteen months Evelyn's junior, Driberg would become a lifelong friend and credited Evelyn with providing much of the literary and artistic stimulus during his time at Lancing. Like Evelyn, he was very unpopular at the school to begin with, alienating other boys with his showy intelligence and unashamed aestheticism, his extravagant High Church religiosity and his camp renditions of Roxburgh's fruity diction. Despite his hatred of Driberg's politics, which by the age of fifteen veered towards Communism, Evelyn soon warmed to him, particularly after both became sacristans in the school chapel, serving at the Eucharist and changing the altar frontal.

It was to Driberg that Evelyn eventually confided that he had lost his faith, a bombshell delivered in the summer of 1921 in the midst of arranging the altar for the Sunday service. According to Evelyn, Driberg said that if he no longer believed in God, he had no business handling the altar cloth.[43] Driberg's slightly different memory of the incident was that he had rebuked Evelyn for not hanging the altar cloth straight, to which Evelyn retorted: 'Nonsense! If it's good enough for me it's good enough for God!' – a remark that Driberg later deemed 'mildly blasphemous [but] not a proclamation of atheism'.[44]

In his diary, Evelyn recorded that he had been an atheist for the past two terms without the courage to admit it to himself. He felt sure it was only a phase, however, and the only thing that really worried him was the possibility that it might cut him off from a devout boy named John Longe, whom he liked better than any other Lancing contemporary at the time. 'If I thought it would I would believe anything,' he wrote. 'He has been one of the few things that make school worthwhile.'[45]

In later life Driberg was a famously reckless homosexual* and while

---

* Driberg (later Lord Bradwell) was the first person in public life to be described as a homosexual in a *Times* obituary. His entry in the *Oxford Dictionary of National Biography* records that as an adult he 'had a consuming passion for fellating handsome, lean, intelligent working-class toughs . . . his sexual prowling never abated'.

at Lancing he wore make-up during the holidays and in term-time harboured several unrequited crushes. He more or less controlled himself until his last year, however, when as deputy head of school he made unwelcome advances to a boy in his dormitory.[46] Perhaps keen to welcome his friend to the fold, Driberg maintained that the schoolboy Evelyn, too, had had similar inclinations but that he repressed them. 'I certainly never heard of him as a practising homosexual until later, at Oxford,' Driberg wrote. He saw Evelyn's subsequent marriages and outspoken intolerance of homosexuality as a 'suppression of his true nature' and ventured that the pressure of denying his bisexuality may even have helped precipitate the eventual mental breakdown related in *The Ordeal of Gilbert Pinfold*.[47] Despite subjecting some of the characters in his fiction to archly homophobic contempt, Evelyn admitted in his autobiography to having been 'susceptible to the prettiness of some fifteen-year-olds' (in 1920 he gave 'library privileges' to a boy called Lowther 'just because he is pretty')[48] yet maintained that he 'never fell victim to the grand passions which inflamed and tortured most of my friends'.[49] In his last year at Lancing he wrote disapprovingly in his diary of 'keennesses' and congratulated himself for suppressing such emotions, preferring to act as censorious confidant to his more besotted friends.

Evelyn's reserve may have partly reflected his immaturity and prudishness – references to sex in his diaries tended to be couched in terms such as 'filth', 'lust' and 'depravity'. But in any case he was less restrained with girls and at the age of fifteen he appeared to be keen on several. Besides the 'comely wench' Luned Jacobs, who admitted to having adored Evelyn,[50] Alec discerned him to be 'somewhat enamoured' of Hugh's sister Moira and 'a little affected' towards Philla Fleming – he wrote home before the holidays urging his parents to arrange some theatricals and 'choose a play in which I kiss her passionately'.[51]

Philla, though, was a waning flame, as in due course would be poor Luned. In the autumn of 1919 Evelyn wrote brutally in his diary: 'I trust she [Luned] realizes the ridiculous affair is at an end' and 'if she does open the subject again I think I shall have to snub her. She is really not worth it.'[52] Evidently he had second thoughts and the next Christmas holidays they again held hands and frolicked by the fire. Evelyn hazarded at the time that she 'would have let me kiss her had I wanted to', and later that year it did develop into a fully fledged kissing romance. However, in

January 1921 he wrote to her telling her that it was finally over.[53] Luned responded with a pathetic letter: 'What a fool is a fond wench,' wrote Evelyn in his diary – a line from *The Beggar's Opera* which he saw six times that year. Nevertheless, she later recalled his letter ending their affair as 'the kindest' and acknowledged that in any case she was 'too young [and] a boy of Evelyn's age was not going to be tied down to a little schoolgirl'. Besides 'he was streets ahead of me intellectually'.[54]

Evelyn's attraction to Luned had dwindled that summer ('She has coarsened out a lot')[55] and he had found himself drawn to others, among them the 'divine' Betty Bulleid, whom he met with his aunts at Midsomer Norton, 'sweetly pretty,' he recorded, 'much better than Luned'.[56] More recently he had fallen for the 'remarkably pretty'[57] Ursula Kendall, daughter of an Old Etonian headmaster friend of Arthur's in Hampstead, 'beautiful and gracious and womanly,' seventeen-year-old Evelyn wrote wistfully in his diary, 'but I am afraid that others, better than I, have seen this too'.[58] A flirtation followed – at any rate a friend later described Ursula as an 'old love of Evelyn's'[59] – however after accompanying her to one or two dances that spring he discovered that Ursula was madly in love with a slightly older boy, a likeable but as Evelyn saw it 'quite brainless and slow' Old Wykehamist called Bobby Shaw. Around the same time, he also took a shine to the more boyish-looking Joan Laking, sister of the rakish Sir Francis Laking, Bt, but she turned out to be a lesbian.

Joan Laking was a first cousin of Dudley Carew, Evelyn's slavish disciple at Lancing, a fellow habitué of the school library and co-founder of the Dilettanti, of which Evelyn was the elected chairman, Carew the secretary. Their friendship had developed along similarly unequal lines, with Evelyn the condescending master, Carew the doting pupil: 'If only I can hold his affection I shall be alright,' Carew anxiously told his diary.[60]

Like Evelyn, Carew was an aspiring writer and he later published a couple of novels – 'justly forgotten' as one Waugh scholar brutally puts it – before joining *The Times*. Virtually everything he wrote at Lancing he passed to Evelyn for criticism. When in June 1920 Carew sent a poem that began: 'You have broken all my idols / Given me fresh creeds to keep', Evelyn reflected that it was 'rather embarrassing to have so large an influence which works out in such a bad poem'.[61]

Carew later accepted Evelyn's description of him as a 'natural hero-worshipper', yet he saw himself as Evelyn's Boswell and hung on his every word. He is often seen as a risible figure, and certainly his conversations with Michael Davie while he was editing Evelyn's diaries suggest a rather pathetic character: 'Oh Evelyn, dear, Oh . . . He was so wonderful, and he makes himself out so dreadful . . . He was perfection as a boy.' But to give Carew his due, he was among the first to recognise Evelyn's extraordinary talent. 'Oh but he's great,' he wrote in 1921. 'I have got unwavering faith in his genius.' Accordingly he kept every scrap that Evelyn wrote to him, all of which he ultimately sold to the University of Texas in a rage after reading Evelyn's unkind portrayal of their friendship in *A Little Learning*. Carew contended that what had latterly damned him in Evelyn's eyes was not so much his obsequiousness – he claimed unconvincingly that he 'always stood up to him'[62] – as the fact that he had introduced Evelyn to his disastrous first wife, having earlier become too close for comfort to Evelyn's parents.

Carew was a frequent visitor to Underhill and his diary affords revealing glimpses of the Waugh household just as Evelyn was about to become an adult. In August 1921, he recorded that the normally jovial Alec was 'an extraordinary chilling and repressing influence. Directly he comes in Arthur stops making jokes. Evelyn stops being clever, I stop talking and only Mrs W is left undisturbed. He has gimlet eyes, a baleful glare . . .'[63] unbeknown to Carew, Alec was wretchedly unhappy at the time, hating his job reading 'tenth-rate' manuscripts at Chapman & Hall[64] and even more miserable in his marriage with Barbara, whom he had wed under pressure from her parents in July 1919.

At first the couple had lived at Underhill, before eventually building a wooden bungalow on a small plot at Ditchling bought with Alec's earnings from *The Loom of Youth*.[65] Throughout this time the marriage remained unconsummated, however, a situation for which Alec gallantly claimed full responsibility, attributing their difficulties to his ignorance of 'the physiology of sex' and of 'the amount of tact and skilful patience that is required to initiate an inexperienced girl'.[66] Alec and Barbara eventually separated in January 1922 and a year later divorced. Alec's humiliation was completed by the judge who, struggling to grasp his explanation as to what had gone wrong, peered over his spectacles and said: 'I think I understand, young man, you couldn't get it in.'[67] The non-consummation became the subject of endless ribald speculation in the Waugh family, Evelyn's son Auberon suggesting 'a malfunction of erectile tissue due to invisible emanations from a silver cup inscribed from W. W. Jacobs, which was kept, for some unclear reason, next to the newly-weds' bed'.[68] There also lurked a suspicion that Alec, despite his subsequent reputation as a compulsive womaniser, remained essentially homosexual. One of his sons recalled him in old age sitting outside a café in Tangier, watching some handsome young Arab go by and sighing: 'Just think of the firm dusky limbs quivering beneath that fella's djellaba.'[69] Privately, meanwhile, Alec indelicately let slip that the real obstacle was Barbara's hymen, which he claimed was 'built like a concrete portcullis'.[70]

* * *

By the autumn term of 1921 Evelyn was well and truly tired of Lancing, yet typically he used his low spirits creatively, filling the school magazine with what he later described as 'preposterous manifestos of disillusionment'[71] and founding the Corpse Club 'for people who are bored stiff'.[72] Members were required to wear black silk tassels in their buttonholes, wrote to each other on mourning notepaper and whenever a new one was elected, Evelyn as self-appointed 'Undertaker' would announce that 'The Undertaker finds a mournful pleasure in announcing the interment of the late Mr . . .'[73]

The one bright spot was the prospect of going to Oxford, so besides his various official jobs Evelyn was busy cramming 'like hell' for a history scholarship. He took the precaution of writing to Arthur to tell him how 'very repugnant' he found the idea of staying on another term at Lancing and that in case he failed to get a scholarship he was prepared to go up to Oxford 'on a minimum wage'. Mindful of the trouble his son might cause if he stood in his way, Arthur promptly consented to his leaving that term and either going straight to Oxford or to France.[74] Evelyn was greatly relieved. 'I should have only stagnated and fallen in love with some underschool if I had stayed on,'[75] he wrote in his diary. A week later, however, he was still fretting that he was 'open to fall in love with someone', that 'people like Onslow and Kimmerling interest me too much' and that 'I shall have to take care if I want to leave with credit and self-respect'.[76]

In early December Evelyn travelled to Oxford to sit the scholarship exams, accompanied by his friend Preters Molson, who sought to galvanise himself with a dash of strychnine but to no avail. The other candidates struck Evelyn as 'absolute oiks but monstrously intellectual',[77] nonetheless it proved to be 'a week of pure euphoria', staying in a hotel for the first time on his own and being well looked after by Lancing old boys who had gone up to Oxford before them. The general paper, in particular, he 'simply loved', writing at length about the Pre-Raphaelites and Arthur Symons's *Life of Beardsley*, and afterwards he felt confident that he had done well. The next week two letters arrived at Lancing, one to say that he had won the £100 Hertford College open history scholarship, another from his prospective tutor C. R. M. F. Cruttwell congratulating him on his 'extremely promising' work, saying he had been especially impressed by his general paper, his question on the Reformation in English history, and above all by his English prose style which was 'about the best of any of the candidates in the group'.[78]

The next day, after saying his goodbyes and arranging for his successors to take on the school magazine, debating society and library, Evelyn caught the late train to Ditchling, leaving Lancing for good. 'I am sure I have left at the right time,' he wrote in his diary, 'as early as possible and with success.'[79]

6

....

All That One Dreams

Arthur was delighted with his son's achievement and brazenly basked in the glory that he felt reflected on himself. 'Thank you, my dear Boy,' he wrote as Evelyn made his way back to Underhill, 'for the honour & happiness you have brought to your home. May the future be worthy of this beginning.' With possibly unintended condescension, he added that next to New College (his old college), whose scholarships Evelyn had thought unduly competitive, he too would have chosen Hertford. 'It is a small but thoroughly good college, and the emoluments are the best on the list.'[1] The £100-a-year emoluments provided by Evelyn's scholarship were especially welcome for Arthur who, like most British publishers, was far worse off than he had been ten years previously and had been worrying even more than usual since the expiry of the Dickens copyright in 1920, which left a large hole in Chapman & Hall's income.[2]

Evelyn's headmaster, meanwhile, was relieved no longer to have to deal with the boy's restlessness at school. 'He had begun to grate at his surroundings,' wrote Bowlby in his final report, 'and the friction was bad for him & threw out sparks which made little fires in some of the characters about him, partly no doubt kindling, but partly destructive! For all his brilliance he is curiously young and out of touch with reality. But he is looking for it and if he will search diligently & humbly & be content with <u>some</u> beaten tracks, instead of wanting to make a new road every time, he will find it – and himself.' If Evelyn found that patronising, Roxburgh's report was more straightforwardly favourable: 'His work has great merit and is sometimes really brilliant. I think he has quite unusual ability and a real gift for writing. We shall hear of him again.'[3]

Privately, Roxburgh rebuked him for having spread the 'contagion of disillusionment'⁴ in his last term at school, however Evelyn assured Dudley Carew that he was now 'pretty full of beans'⁵ at the prospect of going to Oxford so soon. Whereas at Lancing he had felt apprehensive and resentful to be starting in the middle of the academic year, this time he was excited to be going to university as 'a lone explorer'.⁶

When he arrived in January 1922, Hertford's best rooms had all been taken by the Michaelmas freshers, so for his first two terms he made do with a poky set over the JCR buttery from where the smell of anchovy toast wafted up each afternoon.⁷ Here he lived not unlike Paul Pennyfeather or Charles Ryder before he met Sebastian Flyte, in a typical freshman's tangle of emotions. 'I am very shy and a little lonely still but gradually settling down,' he wrote to Carew a few weeks into his first term. 'I wish I could find some congenial friends.'⁸

To begin with he saw a lot of his old Lancing cronies: Max Mallowan, Rupert Fremlin, James Hill and Preters Molson – who was not yet up but being coached for another attempt at a New College scholarship, which he eventually achieved at the third go. It was with the pleasure-seeking Preters (and Hill) that Evelyn got drunk for the first time, polishing off three-quarters of a bottle of Madeira, a glass of port and two tumblers of cider and then loudly reciting Newbolt in the quad – all 'very pleasant', he told Tom Driberg afterwards. 'I don't feel the least ill after it.'⁹

For Evelyn, the effect of drink mattered far more than the taste of it. Besides being another way of going against the grain at a time when the political mood in Britain seemed to favour introducing Prohibition, getting drunk offered the perfect means of conquering his shyness and broadening his social range. According to a friend at Hertford, 'he drank to get into a world that was not his world'.¹⁰ By Evelyn's own account most of his Oxford friendships were forged while drunk and he was fervent in preaching the benefits of intoxication.¹¹ 'Do let me seriously advise you to take to drink,' he urged Driberg. 'There is nothing like the aesthetic pleasure of being drunk and if you do it in the right way you can avoid being ill the next day. That is the greatest thing Oxford has to teach.'¹²

Driberg was still at Lancing and, despite Evelyn's avowed euphoria at having left, at lonelier moments during his first Oxford term his thoughts still drifted back to his old school. To Dudley Carew, who also remained there, he affected disdain at the idea of keeping up with the past yet admitted that he was 'vain enough' to want to know what was said of him now that he had left: 'I imagine I am pretty well disliked now as good God I deserved to be. [But] I am changing pretty hard and I think for the better . . .'[13] He also could not resist writing the odd piece for the school magazine, including a robust reply (under the pseudonym Lavernia Scargill) to a conceited critic of the Corpse Club.

At Oxford, for the time being at least, he remained relatively unobtrusive. He learned to smoke a pipe and to ride a bicycle and went for long walks around the surrounding villages, bounding along with his stubby oak walking stick. He bought a cigarette box engraved with the Hertford College arms and a printed panorama of Oxford, and even played the odd game of hockey, relishing its 'pleasant old world violence'. More ominously, he had begun to spend money with reckless abandon and later explained to his cousin Claud Cockburn that he 'kept the creditors quiet in the traditional Oxonian manner of the day by simply ordering more and more goods'.[14] He never went to chapel, did not frequent the lecture room and read almost no history despite his tutor's exasperated demands: 'Damn you, you're a scholar!'[15]

Evelyn found ample time for other books, however, among which he particularly admired Lewis Carroll's *Alice's Adventures in Wonderland*, which he famously alludes to in *Brideshead* when Charles Ryder sets off for lunch with Sebastian for the first time: 'I was in search of love in those days, and I went full of curiosity and the faint, unrecognized apprehension that here, at last, I should find that low door in the wall which opened on an enclosed and enchanted garden, which was somewhere, not overlooked by any window, in the heart of that grey city.'

Equivalent glimpses of Wonderland had beckoned for Evelyn when, as a timid fresher feeling cut off from the best of what Oxford had to offer, he began to make friends with a wild, dishevelled 'second-year man' at Hertford called Terence Greenidge. In the prevailing Oxford parlance, Greenidge was 'a zany'[16] or, as Harold Acton described him, 'a dear, charming loony'.[17] His foibles included a mania for picking litter off Oxford pavements and stuffing it in his pockets, and a habit of pinching small items belonging to others – hairbrushes, nail scissors, keys and so forth – and hiding them behind books in the library.

Yet it was in Greenidge's rooms that Evelyn met the president of the Union and the editor of *The Isis*, introductions which in turn quickly led to his speaking at the Union and contributing to the magazine. Given the zeal with which he had taken to drinking, it was apt that Evelyn's maiden Union speech in early February 1922[18] should oppose a motion calling for Prohibition, although with characteristic contrariness within a few months he spoke in favour of it, saying he was a Conservative and that Prohibition ought to be a Conservative principle.* *Oxford Magazine* recorded the 'good impression' he made in his first debate,[19] however Evelyn readily conceded that he had no talent for oratory and was quite unable to assume the appropriately grave tone for the debates, besides which he was far too ignorant of the politics and current affairs that were routinely discussed.†

Perhaps more influentially, Greenidge launched Evelyn's Oxford social life and accelerated his descent into drunkenness by introducing him to the Hypocrites' Club (motto: 'water is best'), the much-mythologised dive on St Aldate's which was then in the process of being taken over by a band of hedonistic Old Etonians. Evelyn found the riotous and self-consciously childish atmosphere there immediately congenial and later described the Hypocrites' as 'the stamping ground of half my Oxford life and the source of friendships still warm today'.[20]

Many of these friendships had a pronounced homosexual flavour, not that there was anything especially unusual about that at that time. As John Betjeman later remembered, 'Everyone was queer at Oxford in those days!'[21] According to Terence Greenidge, himself an active homosexual, 'the attraction of man for man' was apparent well beyond the Aesthete set that Evelyn befriended at the Hypocrites'. Greenidge claimed to have witnessed 'many a hearty "blind", even in Athletic Magdalen, where the behaviour of the most unlikely people showed evidence of tender feeling'. The cox 'of a very sporting college' also told him stories about the private lives 'of the crews whom he used to steer so well, and they were remarkable stories'.[22]

If Evelyn had been sexually repressed at Lancing, here at Oxford he at last felt able to shed his inhibitions, emboldened as much by the overtly camp and licentious atmosphere as he was by the drink. When Anthony

---

* Douglas Woodruff, later editor of *The Tablet*, had recruited Evelyn to the debating chamber as one of the Conservatives, at that time outnumbered by the Liberal contingent. 'I proclaimed myself a Tory but could not have defined Tory policy on any current topic.' (*A Little Learning*, p. 183.) He belonged to the Oxford Carlton Club and the smaller Chatham.
† Evelyn did however enter himself for the Union elections in June 1923, coming last with twenty-five votes. His friend Christopher Hollis was elected president with 309.

Powell first saw him at the Hypocrites' he was sitting on Christopher Hollis's knee, and when Tom Driberg came for his scholarship exam he and Evelyn enjoyed 'some lively and drunken revels ("orgies" were they?), mainly homosexual in character: I remember dancing with John F, while Evelyn and another rolled on the sofa with (as one of them said later) their "tongues licking each other's tonsils"'.[23] (Perhaps not surprisingly, Driberg was unsuccessful in that scholarship attempt.) His friend and biographer Christopher Sykes averred that Evelyn frankly admitted to having passed through 'an extreme homosexual phase' while at Oxford, which 'for the short time it lasted, was unrestrained, emotionally and physically'.[24]

* * *

Towards the end of his first term, Evelyn wrote to tell Carew that Oxford was 'all that one dreams'.[25] In the summer term it got even better. 'Life here is very beautiful,' he wrote to Driberg in May. 'Mayonnaise and punts and cider cup all day long. One loses all ambition to be an intellectual.'[26]

A week before the holidays began, Evelyn again wrote to Driberg asking him to be kind to the brother 'of a friend of mine here called Pares' who was due to start at Lancing the next term. 'As far as I can gather he is a fragile & sensitive flower. If he is anything like his brother, he is also abnormally clever.'[27]

The friend was Richard Pares, widely admired among Oxford undergraduates for his bright blue eyes, flax-gold hair and, as A. L. Rowse wistfully remembered, 'red kissable lips'. Rowse admitted to having fallen victim himself to Pares's 'charm and desperation',[28] while Evelyn's later rival for Pares's affections, Cyril Connolly, beheld 'the look of a Rossetti angel with a touch of Mick Jagger'.[29]

According to Christopher Hollis, who remained a lifelong friend, Evelyn's homosexuality at Oxford represented a passing phase at a time when girls were in short supply and strictly chaperoned. Yet while the phase lasted there were at least two intense relationships, and the first of these was with Pares, 'my first homosexual love', as Evelyn later described him to Nancy Mitford.[30] A year older than Evelyn, Pares had come up to Oxford from Winchester the term before him, in the autumn of 1921. A history scholar at Balliol and a future Fellow of All Souls, he was certainly abnormally clever, however he was also strangely submissive. Years later

Hollis recalled that Pares had 'become a complete prostitute more from obligingness than anything else';[31] or as Harold Acton observed, 'My de-ar, he lends his body.'[32] His timid acquiescence was possibly a legacy of his troubled relationship with his father, the celebrated but emotionally wintery Russian expert, Sir Bernard Pares, who was 'responsible for much family unhappiness' according to Rowse. In any event, Richard was a nervous, delicate child.

Much of the attention he attracted at Winchester had been unwelcome – he 'hated being pursued by buggers', as Rowse robustly recorded[33] – however there was apparently at least one love interest before Evelyn. 'I have been inwardly faithful to one boy for more than two years,' he told Evelyn, 'and he is only dispossest this morning and by you, so I think I shall be constant to you for three years and then turn Papist. How much I shall have to confess depends on you.'[34]

Having begun sometime during Evelyn's first year – possibly during his first term – their affair seems to have peaked around Christmas 1922.* In a letter to Evelyn written during that vacation from his home in Surbiton, Pares declared himself 'tired of pretending not to be in love with you, which I have done intermittently since the fourth week of last term'. It was 'impossible not to be level-headed after receiving a letter from you, for the bare receipt of it plunges me precipitously into sentimentality which increases in geometrical progression the first five times I read the letter through . . . Thoughts of me in bed? O Come.'[35]

In the same letter, Pares wrote that his 'only fear of writing love-letters to you is that they might come to be read out in court like those of Mrs Thompson, and the counsel for the defence would say it was one of the greatest love-affairs of history – which it is – and the Judge would say it was a guilty passion – which also it is'. Edith Thompson was a young Essex housewife who was then awaiting execution for conspiring with her young lover to murder her husband. The allusion adds to the impression that Evelyn and Pares's love affair was more momentous than is often suggested.

Rowse, a notoriously inaccurate gossip, later described it as 'a very intense adolescent affair' and hazarded that Evelyn would have been the more active, masculine partner, Pares more passive and feminine. Pares

---

* '. . . my few romances have always culminated in Christmas week, Luned [Jacobs], Richard [Pares], Alastair [Graham]' (Christmas Day 1924; *EWD*, p. 194).

himself confided to Rowse that he had never before experienced anything like it. It was, wrote Rowse, 'Pares's great love affair' and 'they were inseparable in Evelyn's first year'.[36] Pares was passionate about *Alice's Adventures in Wonderland*, which may help to explain why it became such a favourite narrative template for Evelyn in his future fiction.

Theirs was an attraction of opposites. Besides his intellect – far more academic than Evelyn's – Pares was renowned for his puritanical self-discipline, yet according to another great friend, Isaiah Berlin, who regarded Pares as 'the best and most admirable man I have ever known', he 'needed, and was sustained by, the greater vitality of others, and rewarded it with grateful and lasting affection'.[37] But if he was attracted by Evelyn's fizzing energy, Pares was equally repelled by his heavy drinking. 'I loved him dearly,' wrote Evelyn, 'but an excess of wine nauseated him and this made an insurmountable barrier between us. When I felt most intimate, he felt queasy.'[38]

Evelyn demanded complete dedication from those to whom he gave affection – as with his lopsided friendship with his Lancing disciple Dudley Carew – and for a time he expected Pares to accompany him on his regular benders at the Hypocrites' and elsewhere. To begin with Pares meekly complied, even going so far as to speak at the Union in favour of drunkenness, but it soon became evident that he had neither the inclination nor the constitution for it. Moreover, despite his 'gift for absurdity and frivolity', as an article in *The Isis* recorded,[39] Pares was always far more studious than Evelyn. Eventually, as Evelyn recalled, he was 'rescued from bohemia and preserved for a life of scholarship'. He subsequently took a First, became a don and wrote a series of books on the eighteenth-century West Indian sugar trade as impenetrable as they were magisterial.

His saviour from Evelyn was the Dean of Balliol, F. F. 'Sligger' Urquhart, who lured him into his more sober salon, thereby earning Evelyn's lasting contempt. Towards the end of the spring term of 1923, another member of Sligger's circle, Cyril Connolly, admitted to being 'rather gone' on Pares. Despite Pares's promise to Evelyn that he would be 'yours for three years or ad nauseam'[40] he and Connolly were soon to be seen walking around the colleges together arm in arm. Evelyn felt sufficiently betrayed to complain later of having been 'cuckolded by Connolly'.[41]

The nature of Evelyn's love affair with Pares is difficult to define at this distance, although Evelyn's Hertford friend Tony Bushell was adamant that Evelyn's fastidiousness would have precluded a physical affair. 'The idea is preposterous,' Bushell scoffed in a television interview. 'Absolutely not possible, and I know.'[42] Christopher Hollis remembered Evelyn telling him that his affections at that time were 'much more romantic than carnal'.[43] Harold Acton also tended to the view that the relationship was 'idyllically platonic',[44] although he may have preferred to think that given his own unrequited crush on Evelyn.

If there really was no physical element, it might seem odd that Evelyn himself should have referred to the affair as homosexual to Nancy Mitford – unless he was trying to impress her with what an intrepid young libertine he had been. In letters to Carew at the time Evelyn admitted that he had been 'incredibly depraved morally' and also that 'my diary for the period is destroyed'.[45] This seems to be the only evidence that he kept a diary during his time at Oxford, however in his future life Evelyn habitually destroyed his diary covering times of greatest emotional upheaval. All the indications are that Pares's abandonment of him was more wounding than Evelyn was prepared to let on, and the painful end of the affair can be said to have given rise to the theme of faithlessness that would recur throughout his young life and again and again in his fiction.

* * *

In his third term at Oxford, Evelyn had moved to larger rooms on the ground floor of Hertford's front quad. In *Brideshead*, Charles Ryder's priggish cousin Jasper warns him: 'I've seen many a man ruined through having ground-floor rooms in the front quad. People start dropping in . . . you start giving them sherry. Before you know where you are, you've opened a free bar for all the undesirables of the college.'[46]

This certainly reflected Evelyn's own experience, just as Charles's first encounter with Sebastian recalled an evening when members of the Bullingdon came roaring out of Terence Greenidge's rooms and rushed across the quad to get back to Christ Church before the Great Bell stopped ringing. 'But there was a straggler,' remembered Bushell, 'and about the middle of the quad he turned away from the rest of them and staggered over towards Evelyn's room where he was sick through the window.'[47]

His new rooms soon became the epicentre of the self-elected 'Hertford underworld', whose chief protagonists were Evelyn, Greenidge, Tony

Bushell, the budding actor who had come second to Evelyn in Hertford's history scholarship exam, and Evelyn's Lancing friend Philip Machin. Most days at lunchtime they gathered in Evelyn's rooms for bread and cheese and plenty of beer. When his old Lancing friend Preters Molson was invited he sniffed, 'I usually prefer to have a hot lunch,' thereby lumbering himself with a new nickname.

'Hot Lunch' Molson later remembered being shocked at Evelyn's wild and irresponsible behaviour at these lunches. Tony Bushell recalled that at Evelyn 'always drank a good deal' at these events, 'a good deal'. Starting with a glass or two of Sandeman's Brown Bang, a heavy, glutinous sherry, he would then go on to beer and in the afternoon, while Bushell and the other athletes went off to play games, he 'just went on drinking'. By five o'clock, when the games players had returned and were eating their anchovy toast in the JCR, Evelyn would often be completely sozzled, 'purple in the face with blotches on the backs of his hands'. Not infrequently he would then carry on drinking throughout the evening.

Bushell recalled him as 'a wonderful drunk ... a marvellous drunk. Wonderful company, witty, funny, wildly funny'.[48] Others, though, had less wonderful experiences. Tamara Abelson, the daughter of an émigré former official in the Tsar's treasury and one of very few girls at the university in those days, made friends with Evelyn during long walks across the meadows with her Alsatian dog, Ghost. One day Evelyn turned up 'unpleasantly drunk,' Tamara recalled, 'rude and violent', and she threatened to cut him off for ever if he went to see her like that again. He never did, although with others his roistering continued unabated and he often became objectionable.

Even at the Hypocrites', never noted for its sobriety, Evelyn's behaviour occasionally went too far. On Anthony Powell's first visit there in the autumn of 1923, towards the end of Evelyn's second year, he learned that Evelyn had been banned 'for having smashed up a good deal of the Club's furniture with the heavy stick he always carried'.[49]

By this time, Evelyn had introduced another new friend to the Hypocrites', Harold Acton, whom he had met at the Newman Society, listening to a talk by G. K. Chesterton (evidence, incidentally, that Evelyn remained intellectually interested in religion even if he no longer went to chapel). By some distance the most significant influence on Evelyn's social and artistic development at Oxford – as he later acknowledged by dedicating

Decline and Fall 'in homage and affection' to him – Acton was considered by far the most striking and promising student of their era,* although his renown has not lasted anything like as well as that of Evelyn and several other protégés.

The son of an Italianized English father and an immensely rich American mother (Acton himself left $500 million when he died in 1994), Acton had grown up at a magnificent Florentine villa before being packed off to prep school in Berkshire, where he founded a precocious magazine on art and fashion and regarded standing on chairs and reciting poetry as a perfectly normal way of making new friends.[50]

At Eton he fell in with another unashamedly camp and rich half-American, Brian Howard, with whom he collaborated to produce the *Eton Candle* magazine with shocking pink wrappers, yellow endpapers and contributions from Max Beerbohm, Aldous Huxley (then a young beak at the school) and the Sitwells. Their Eton Society of Arts numbered several of Evelyn's future Oxford cronies, among them Hugh Lygon, who Anthony Powell assumed owed his membership to an unrequited 'tendresse' felt for him by either Brian Howard or Robert Byron rather than to his intellect, which was far from remarkable.[51]

When Acton arrived at Christ Church in the Michaelmas term of 1922, he painted his gloomy Gothic rooms bright yellow and festooned them with artificial flowers and wax fruit. Tall, plumpish, with a domed forehead, long black side-whiskers and oriental-looking eyes, he was an easily recognisable figure 'shouldering and mincing his way' about Oxford. Familiar accoutrements included grey bowler hat, black stock, pleated mauve trousers as wide as a skirt (the so-called Oxford bags which he popularised)† and tightly rolled umbrella.[52] Their near-contemporary John Rothenstein, later director of the Tate Gallery, recalled a near-collision with Evelyn and Acton on an Oxford street corner, 'two figures with scarves flying in the wind, one fair, shortish, with fanatical eyes set wide apart [Evelyn]; the other tall, dark, with an expression of pride oddly blended with courtliness'.[53]

---

* A. L. Rowse wrote: 'Never can there have been *such* undergraduate reclame, such publicity, such a peculiar ascendancy as that exerted by Harold Acton in his day at Oxford.' (*A Cornishman at Oxford*, p. 23.)

† Lord Boothby claimed to have started this fashion some years earlier. (*My Oxford*, ed. by Ann Thwaite, p. 32.)

Like Anthony Blanche in *Brideshead*, whose creation ('part Gallic, part Yankee, part, perhaps, Jew; wholly exotic') owed an equal amount to Brian Howard, Acton declaimed Eliot's *The Waste Land* through a megaphone from his balcony to puzzled passers-by; and when confronted by a gang of hearty rugger players, he exclaimed to a fellow aesthete: 'Oh my de-ah, we are so dec-a-dent and they are so in-no-cent.' After coming down with a cold, he wailed: 'Oh, my de-ah, I've been so mis-er-able a-all the day.'[54]

Acton's affectations – he later described his recreations in *Who's Who* as 'hunting – Philistines' – attracted occasional hostility, most notably when, in the summer of 1923, a band of 'big ruff animal louts', as he described them, smashed his window with a poker. 'I, tucked up in bed and contemplating the reflection of Luna on my walls, was immersed under showers of myriad particles of split glass, my head powdered glass-dust and my possessions vitrified.'[55] But by the time he left Oxford, when he was recognised as the pre-eminent figure in the artistic life of the university, he had won over even the athletes.

He and Evelyn were unlikely soulmates, however Evelyn was fascinated by Acton's exotic background and enthusiasms and relished their shared 'zest for the variety and absurdity of life opening to us; a veneration for (not the same) artists, a scorn for the bogus'. It was Acton who steered him away from the fusty Francis Crease, 'that nice old maid' as Acton called him,[56] whom Evelyn had continued to see during the holidays, and towards such prophets of modernism as T. S. Eliot and Gertrude Stein. In June 1923 he took him to the bizarre, under-rehearsed yet to Evelyn captivating first public showing of Edith Sitwell's *Façade* at the Aeolian Hall in London, where one uncomprehending critic complained of the poet reciting 'drivel through a megaphone'. Later that evening, at an after-party at Osbert Sitwell's house in Carlyle Square, Evelyn met Lytton Strachey and Clive Bell; however it was the Sitwells whom he really aspired to know, seeing them as torchbearers of the avant-garde and an inspiration to all those wishing to blaze a new artistic trail. They 'radiated an aura of high spirits, elegance, impudence, unpredictability, above all sheer enjoyment,' he later wrote. 'They declared war on dullness.'[57]

For his part, Acton was drawn to what he called Evelyn's 'friskiness'. More awkwardly, he also appears to have found him physically attractive – he described him achingly in his memoir as 'a prancing faun, thinly disguised by conventional apparel. His wide-apart eyes, always ready to be startled under raised eyebrows, the curved sensual lips, the hya-cinthe locks of hair . . . So demure and yet so wild!'[58] In the same book, Acton painted himself as a young Casanova, proudly recalling numerous 'bygone loves' at Oxford and of having 'kindled flames in Elgin marble breasts' and enjoyed 'ecstacies on the Thames and at Thame . . . I have not forgotten a single kiss . . .'[59] Yet if he ever did make overtures to Evelyn the signs are that he was rejected, one letter from that time hinting at jealousy of Evelyn's more passionate friendships: 'Please forgive me if I said that about "R. I. P." [Richard Pares] last night,' wrote Acton. 'Truth will out, I suppose, in spite of the fact that I had tried hard not to hurt your feelings or to "sneer" . . . You are, as I have said before, a faun, but I had never credited you with the fantastic whimsies of a faun, nor with the enigmas of one; now I do. Besides it is rather elegant to have an unhappy love affair . . .'[60]

According to Evelyn, Acton harboured similarly unrequited feelings for the 'strikingly handsome hearty'[61] – presumably Tony Bushell – who unwittingly drew him almost daily to Evelyn's offal lunches in his rooms at Hertford. While everyone else drank beer, Acton 'would sip water and gaze ardently at the inaccessible young athlete'.[62]* In return Acton gave many lunch parties of his own in his rooms at Christ Church where Evelyn made several long-lasting friendships.

Among these were three who had been at prep school with Acton as well as Eton – Mark Ogilvie-Grant, the 'reckless roof-climber' Billy Clonmore, who as an undergraduate held a supper party on the roof of an Oxford church and later became a priest, and the 'secretly studious' David Talbot Rice who, almost uniquely among their peer group at Oxford, went out with a student of the opposite sex, Evelyn's friend Tamara Abelson, whom he later married.

With the new Michaelmas intake of 1923, Evelyn's circle expanded to include several more of what was an exceptionally talented generation of Etonians – Anthony Powell, Oliver Messel, Henry Yorke (the novelist Henry Green), Robert Byron, who belied his future calling by yelling 'Down with abroad!' whenever travel was mentioned, and Brian Howard,

---

* Evelyn and Tony Bushell were not the only ones who spurned his advances. James Lees-Milne later recorded how during the Second World War he half-heartedly agreed to go to bed with Acton, who was then in uniform, but 'next morning he rebuked me for icy-cold unresponsiveness'. (James Lees-Milne, *Diaries 1984–1997*, ed. by Michael Bloch, p. 373.)

who even his close school friend and collaborator Harold Acton admitted was 'completely amoral'.[63] Later immortalised as Ambrose Silk in *Put Out More Flags* as well as Anthony Blanche in *Brideshead*, Howard was one of those whom Evelyn 'did not greatly like' but 'in my innocence, I was proud to know'.

He felt much the same way about two other Oxford contemporaries, both at Balliol, the raffish yet tediously didactic Peter Rodd, who later married Nancy Mitford, and Nancy's more wayward cousin 'Baz' Murray, whom Evelyn deemed 'a satanic young man'.[64] Evelyn later fused several of their least appealing traits in the character of Basil Seal, his Balliol-educated anti-hero in *Black Mischief* and *Put Out More Flags*. Murray was renowned at Oxford for his intellectual brilliance (he was the son of a well-known Classics don and himself a scholar), but equally for his casual approach to sex, money and personal hygiene. Like Basil Seal he later covered the Spanish Civil War as a journalist (Evelyn added 'gun-runner')[65] on the Republican side and died there in the kind of bizarre circumstances that might easily have featured in an early Waugh novel – having caught a deadly virus from a female ape he had bought in Valencia docks and reportedly cavorted with in his hotel room in a state of drunken disillusionment after a series of failed love affairs.[66]

Fifteen years previously, at Oxford, it was Murray who had helped F. A. Philbrick (later a chemistry beak at Rugby) to rough up Evelyn in retaliation for a campaign of teasing after Philbrick admitted to having rather enjoyed beating smaller boys at school – the persecution culminated when a film was shown with a scene of a man being flogged and the whole cinema erupted in a loud chant of Philbrick's name. Evelyn later took his revenge by attaching Philbrick's name to a series of disreputable characters in his early fiction.

Yet none of these enmities came close to that which Evelyn felt towards his Hertford history tutor, C. R. M. F. Cruttwell, for whom he developed a dislike that was, as his brother Alec recalled, 'mutual, instinctive and irrational as love'.[67] Seen by his fellow dons as a rather sad and lonely bachelor, Cruttwell disguised his painful shyness behind a gruff and uncompromising manner.[68] Even Evelyn later conceded that he was probably a 'wreck of the war', yet he could not resist mocking his 'petulant baby' face, his pipe 'usually attached to his blubber-lips by a thread of slime'. 'As he removed the stem,' Evelyn went on, 'waving it to emphasise his indistinct speech, this glittering connection extended until finally it broke leaving a dribble on his chin. When he spoke to me I found myself so distracted by the speculation of how far this line could be attenuated that I was often inattentive to his words.'

At Oxford Evelyn mercilessly caricatured 'Crutters' in student magazines and told anyone who would listen about the perversions he supposedly got up to with his dog. 'Now he's raping the poor brute,' he whispered to his cousin Claud Cockburn as they listened to the strange sounds coming from the rooms above Evelyn's, 'and at this hour in the morning!'[69]

Evelyn's initial gripe with Cruttwell was the don's frenzied insistence that Evelyn fulfil his obligations as Hertford's first history scholar, a demand which Evelyn early made clear his intention to ignore, seeing his scholarship as a 'reward for work done, not as the earnest of work to come',[70] and maintaining later that while he knew all about his Oxford friends' political and religious opinions, love affairs, finances, etcetera, he would have 'thought it indelicate to inquire what school they were reading'.[71] However he also affected to take against Cruttwell's undisguised misogyny (he called female dons 'drabs' or, if they were emotional, 'breastheavers') and his propensity to bully those weaker than himself.

Evelyn famously attached Cruttwell's name to an unsavoury character in each of his first five novels and seems to have resolved to pursue the feud indefinitely after Cruttwell's 'gratuitously derogatory' letters to Evelyn's first mother-in-law, Lady Burghclere, shortly before his marriage in 1930.

Long after both Cruttwell and Evelyn were dead, Evelyn's son Auberon cheerfully seized any opportunity to revive the vendetta. When the *Oxford Dictionary of National Biography* published an entry on Cruttwell which recorded, besides his various achievements as a historian, his 'passion for flowers and for country life', Auberon rebuked the publishers for omitting to mention 'the peculiarity for which he was much more widely suspected'. (Their solution was simply to remove the reference to flowers from subsequent editions.) In 2003, at an Evelyn Waugh centenary dinner at Hertford, Auberon's son Alexander surprised the assembled scholars by calling on them to raise their glasses to Cruttwell, 'that he may forever be remembered as a dog sodomist and a total shit'.[72]

7

His Poor Dead Heart

After living so uproariously during term time, Evelyn inevitably found the holidays at Underhill rather dull by comparison. In the spring of 1922 he told Driberg that north London suburbia was 'quite indescribably dreary'.[1] His relations with his father, whose stagy readings in the book-room he found increasingly excruciating as he grew older, were further strained by disagreements over his refusal to do any work and his persistent overspending. To supplement Evelyn's scholarship, Arthur had allowed him a further £220 annually, which with birthday presents and various other demands to meet unpaid debts took up more than a quarter of his earnings, then around £1,000.[2] Yet despite this generosity, friends Evelyn took home were often horrified by the way he spoke to his father. One of them shuddered to recall Arthur asking Evelyn how he could be so charming to his friends and yet so unkind to his father. 'Because I can choose my friends,' said Evelyn, 'but I cannot choose my father.'[3]

Evelyn could be equally cruel to Alec, as when he suggested that their cousin, Claud Cockburn, who was in need of £200 to pay some debts, ask him for a loan. By his own account Alec was by then making around £800 a year from his writing[4] yet nevertheless politely refused the request. Incensed that Alec should spurn his 'more deserving and artistic' cousin in this way, Evelyn muttered sternly: 'That bald-headed lecher needs a lesson in how a gentleman should comport himself' – Evelyn had conceived the theory that excessive sexual activity since the end of his marriage had caused his brother's hair to fall out. He then led several sorties from Oxford to London, during which he and his friends would burst out from hiding places and surprise Alec and his latest girlfriend, yelling 'Boo to

Alec the bald-headed lecher!'. He assured Cockburn that Alec's women were 'apt to be rendered frigid by anything unconventional'.[5]

Alec seems to have been remarkably good-natured about all this – at least he later recalled only the good times they had during this period, introducing Evelyn to his Bohemian friends in London, taking him to parties and generally feeling proud of his 'witty, lively, hopeful' younger brother.[6] For his part, in later years Evelyn paid tribute to his brother's generosity – 'a host who introduced me to the best restaurants of London, on whom I sponged, bringing my friends to his flat and when short of money, sleeping on his floor, until the tubes opened when I would at dawn sway home to Hampstead, in crumpled evening dress among the navvies setting out for their day's work'.[7]

* * *

Arthur Waugh may have worried that his younger son was frittering away his time and money at Oxford, yet amid all the drinking binges he was in fact remarkably busy across a range of activities, albeit none that bore the slightest relevance to his history degree. At that time, Evelyn still had more confidence in his talents in illustration and design than he did in his Union debating skills or indeed his writing. He later admitted that drawing made him more 'entirely happy' than he ever felt when reading or writing and, ever ambitious to get better, he took lessons during the holidays in wood-engraving and during term time went with Peter Quennell to draw the 'remarkably unalluring' nude models who sat for life classes at the Ruskin School of Art.

Throughout his time at Oxford he designed bookplates for friends and dust-jackets for Chapman & Hall, contributed woodcuts to the *London Mercury* and *Golden Hind*, and was much in demand to design head-pieces and covers for various university magazines and programmes. His distinctive and frequently macabre woodcuts were particularly admired by the university art critics.[8] At a time when his reserves of filial piety were running particularly low, one of these depicted 'That grim act par-ricide', in which a deranged young man with a pistol advances towards an older man looking not unlike Arthur Waugh, somewhat alarmed and vulnerable in an armchair. The cartoon was part of a ghoulish series por-traying Evelyn's own version of 'The Seven Deadly Sins' and appeared in

Cherwell, the most subversive of the Oxford magazines of that time and the mouthpiece for the aesthetes and intellectuals, who tended to disparage the more athletically orientated *Isis*.

The Isis paid its contributors, however, so the perpetually improvident Evelyn was more than happy to work for that magazine too, supplying numerous cartoons and other illustrations as well as light verse, short stories, film reviews and Union reports, all written under the nom de plume 'Scaramel'. On the first page of the magazine there appeared 'Isis Idol', generally a profile of a sporting hero or leading light of the Union, although Evelyn neatly turned the slot on its head by contributing a paean to Harold Acton, the mincing non-athlete *par excellence*, as well as a rather less fulsome portrait of his 'badger-like' history tutor.

References to Cruttwell were also discernible in two short stories that Evelyn published in *Cherwell* in 1923, 'Edward of Unique Achievement' in which an undergraduate develops such 'an absorbing and immeasurable hatred' for his tutor that he decides to murder him; and 'Conspiracy to Murder', in which a young man is driven mad by the 'ill-dressed and rather dirty' don who lives in the room opposite and 'snarls like a beast' whenever they pass on the stairs.

Of more biographical interest, however, were two other stories that appeared in different Oxford magazines the same year. In the first of these, the intriguing yet often overlooked 'Portrait of Young Man With Career', published in *The Isis* in May 1923, a pushy student named Jeremy visits 'Evelyn' in his rooms and asks for an introduction to Richard Pares, explaining 'I feel he is a man to know.' Evelyn calls Pares 'an amiable rogue' and protests that he hardly knows him. If this was an ambiguous dig at the lover who had recently forsaken him, the story made far more unsettling reading for his friend Hugh Molson, who immediately recognised himself in the character of Jeremy, whose deep appreciation of the sound of his own voice and tiresome ambition extend to an intention to become president of the Union, a goal Molson achieved two years later.

In the story, Jeremy fails to take Evelyn's hint about hardly knowing Pares and continues:

'Nonsense, I'm always seeing you about together. I am not doing anything 'fore lunch on Tuesday. How about then? Or Friday I could manage, but I should prefer Tuesday.'

So it was arranged.

There was a pause; I looked at my watch; Jeremy took no notice; I looked again.

'What is the time,' he said, 'Twenty-three to. Oh, good! – hours yet.'

'Before a fool's opinion of himself the gods are silent – aye and envious too,' I thought.

'I'm speaking "on the paper" on Thursday.'

'Good.'

'About the Near East. Macedonia. Oil, you know.'

'Ah.'

'I think it ought to be rather a good speech.'

'Yes.'

'Evelyn, you aren't listening; now seriously, what do you really think is wrong with my speaking. What I feel about the Union is . . .'

A blind fury, a mist of fire. We struggled together on the carpet. He was surprisingly weak for his size. The first blow with the poker he dodged and took on his shoulder; the second and third caved his forehead in . . .

The latter scene is a wish-fulfilling daydream that Evelyn has lapsed into while his visitor drones on. When Jeremy does eventually get up to leave, he parts with a final annoying request: 'Oh and Evelyn, if you know the man who reports the Union for the *Isis*, you might ask him to give me a decent notice this time.'

In so ruthlessly skewering Molson as a self-important bore, 'Portrait of Young Man With Career' effectively ended their friendship. When Molson was later asked why he and Evelyn had fallen out, he recalled that they had been on 'one of our usual long walks and I suppose I am inclined to be long-winded. I got to talking about oil and when *Isis* came out next week there was a repetition of much of what I had said . . . After that I never felt like going out for a long walk with him and telling him what was going on in my mind.'[9] Molson professed to dislike what he called Evelyn's 'intellectual cruelty', as well he might, yet in truth the friendship became unviable after he discovered what Evelyn really thought of him.

Doubtless having Molson's youthful excesses as much in mind as his overweening ambition, Evelyn could never take him anything like as seriously as he appeared to take himself. When Molson ultimately became a life peer as a Unionist politician (he is remembered now chiefly for the soundbite 'I will look at any additional evidence to confirm the opinion to which I have already come'), Evelyn could only ever bring himself to refer to him with the 'Lord' between quotation marks.

*　*　*

Evelyn's other noteworthy short story from 1923 was 'Antony, Who Sought Things That Were Lost', which appeared in Harold Acton's short-lived arts journal *The Oxford Broom*, for which Evelyn had already designed covers and produced two 'Cubist' cartoons. A macabre tale of two imprisoned lovers, Count Antony and Lady Elizabeth, who ruthlessly betrays her husband with their pockmarked turnkey, it was influenced by James Branch Cabell's mannered fantasy novel *Jurgen* (1919), as Evelyn later wincingly admitted, 'that preposterously spurious artefact which quite captivated me at the age of nineteen'. Even Acton later conceded that the story had 'seemed rather better than it was in fact' as he had been under Evelyn's 'elvish fascination' at the time. Yet however flawed it might have been in stylistic terms, with hindsight it can now be seen to contain the seeds of Evelyn's later masterpiece *A Handful of Dust* (1934), with Antony the forerunner of Tony Last, the chivalrous husband whose bored wife (Lady Elizabeth / Brenda Last) betrays him with a worthless bounder (the turnkey / John Beaver).[10] Just as *A Handful of Dust* reflected Evelyn's bitter sense of betrayal over the ending of his first marriage, 'Antony' was written while he was suffering 'the pangs of neglected love' for Richard Pares, as Terence Greenidge later maintained.[11] Both works also drew on Evelyn's nostalgia for a romantic past and his cynical belief that romantic expectations will never be fulfilled.

*　*　*

If Richard Pares's desertion destroyed nineteen-year-old Evelyn's hopes in the spring of 1923, he wasted little time before taking up with the next 'friend of my heart', as he described him, a handsome eighteen-year-old* at Brasenose called Alastair Graham, who was later disguised in *A Little*

---

* Alastair Hugh Graham was born on 27 June 1904 (see *Burke's Peerage*, Graham, Bt, of Netherby), and so would have turned nineteen in the summer of 1923.

Learning as 'Hamish Lennox'.[12] Eight months younger than Evelyn, well-born, rich and dreamy, Graham became one of the great loves of Evelyn's early life. As a muse, he made the most obvious contribution to the composite character of Sebastian Flyte in *Brideshead*, which in manuscript twice has 'Alastair' in place of 'Sebastian'.

Like Pares, Graham was seen by Evelyn's contemporaries as a catch. Anthony Powell remembered him as 'frightfully good-looking, with rather Dresden china shepherdess sort of looks ... a lot of people were undoubtedly in love with him'.[13] Among the queue of admirers was Harold Acton, who in the midst of Graham's affair with Evelyn gushed in a letter jointly addressed to the two of them: 'I had erections to think of you two angels in an atmosphere salinated with choir boys and sacerdotal sensuality!'[14] He later described Graham as a Pre-Raphaelite beauty but 'a cock-teaser',[15] and told Duncan Fallowell that he had 'the same sort of features as Evelyn liked in girls – the pixie look'. He was not a hearty, Acton added, 'but he dressed like a hearty, in the country style, plus-fours and *tweeds*'.[16]

Evelyn was fond of tweed breeches too, yet there were other more significant similarities. Unlike Pares, Graham had 'no repugnance of the bottle', as Evelyn put it, or as Harold Acton preferred, he 'drank like a fish'. Intellectually and artistically curious, he read widely throughout his life yet he was by nature also profoundly lazy. Having refused to go back to Wellington at the age of fifteen, at Oxford he was even more neglectful of his history studies than Evelyn. 'I could not have fallen under an influence better designed to encourage my natural frivolity, dilettantism and dissipation,' Evelyn later wrote, 'or to expose as vulgar and futile any promptings I may have felt to worldly ambition.'[17]

The gap in Evelyn's diaries makes it hard to say how or when their friendship began – as Graham ruefully told the diaries' eventual editor, 'a lot of his happier experiences are not recorded'[18] – however it must have been before the end of the summer term 1923, when Alastair failed his Mods and on the advice of the principal of Brasenose was removed from the university by his mother.

Mrs Graham's decision threw Evelyn into 'a momentary restlessness', as he later downplayed it, and at the beginning of the Michaelmas term he asked his father if he too might be taken away from Oxford and sent to Paris to live as a bohemian artist. Not surprisingly, Arthur did not like this idea.[19] 'I want to go down for good but I cannot explain and my parents are obdurate,' Evelyn wrote to Carew.[20] What was it that he could not explain to his parents? His love for Alastair perhaps?

Alastair meanwhile was 'settling down and writing,' his mother told the Brasenose bursar, 'so far hard'. She said he would soon be 'taking up Architecture at London University', an endeavour that was to prove even less enduring than his Oxford career.[21] But though Alastair had left the university, he and Evelyn remained 'inseparable', so Evelyn later recalled, 'or, if separated, in almost daily communication'.[22] Alastair 'continued to haunt Oxford', driving down regularly from his home in Warwickshire in his two-seater motor car, whereupon he and Evelyn would zoom off into the Oxfordshire countryside, sometimes with a third passenger squeezed in the dicky, more often just the two of them. 'We hardly saw anything of Evelyn at that time,' Acton lamented. 'He [Graham] and Evelyn were always together. An infatuation. Oh definitely an infatuation.'

In advance of one such visit, Alastair wrote a letter enclosing a photograph of himself naked, posing like some alluring wood nymph beneath an overhanging rock face, his backside pointing seductively towards the camera:*

> My dear Evelyn,
>
> I'm sending this down by David [Plunket Greene] or the Bastard John [Greenidge, elder brother of Terence], whom I'm seeing this evening. I am sad that you wouldn't come up for this party. I am afraid it will be bloody. One can always drink but it is rather a cheap path to heaven. I've found the ideal way to drink Burgundy. You must take a peach and peal [sic] it, and put it in a finger bowl, and pour Burgundy over it. The flavour is exquisite. And the peach seems to exaggerate that delightful happy Seraglio contentedness that old wine evokes. An old French lady taught it to me, who has a wonderful cellar at Lavalles. I've been in bed with pains in my ears for the last two days. May I go and call on your parents one day, or would they hate it? I do not know whether I ought to come to Oxford next week or not next week. It depends on money and other little complications. If I come, will you come and drink with me somewhere

---

* Auberon Waugh told Duncan Fallowell that whether Graham enclosed the photograph or whether Evelyn put it in the envelope later was uncertain.

on Saturday? If it is a nice day we might carry some bottles into a wood or some bucolic place, and drink like Horace. I'm afraid this is a poor wandering letter. But I cannot write letters. It was only meant to express my sorrow at your absence from this party. I wish you felt merrier, and were not so serious.

With love from Alastair, and his poor dead heart.

It seems safe to assume that Evelyn had this letter somewhere in mind when he wrote the passage in *Brideshead* in which Sebastian beckons Charles: 'You're to come away at once, out of danger. I've got a motor-car and a basket of strawberries and a bottle of Château Peyraguey* – which isn't a wine you've ever tasted, so don't pretend. It's heaven with strawberries.'[23]

Though undated, Alastair's letter was most likely written in 1924, as he would presumably not have suggested calling on Evelyn's parents before he had met them, which according to Kate Waugh's diary happened in December 1923, when Evelyn took him for supper at Underhill.[24] Evelyn later indicated that the affair had 'culminated' that Christmas.†

Evelyn went far more often to Alastair's home, Barford House, near Stratford-upon-Avon, which was by then presided over by Alastair's widowed mother Jessie, Alastair's father having died the year before he went to Oxford. 'Mrs G', as both Alastair and Evelyn called her (or alternatively 'the Queen Mother'), had been as mad about hunting as her husband – the excellent surrounding country had been the reason they had bought the house in the first place – but she no longer kept horses. Instead she 'gardened with all the fury of the chase', Evelyn recalled, although her vigour failed to rub off on her languid son, who was forever being exhorted to 'get out of the house and do something!'.

Barford is nothing like the size of Brideshead or its television alter ego, Castle Howard, which Evelyn visited only once in 1937, yet was far more akin to the stately pile he described in the novel. Nonetheless beneath Barford's handsome, peeling, white-stucco façade can be glimpsed the

---

* Peyraguey is a sweet Sauternes and remained one of Evelyn's favourite wines. He always preferred it unchilled and referred to it as 'White Claret'. (See Alec Waugh, *A Year to Remember*, p. 107.)

† '... my few romances have always culminated in Christmas week, Luned, Richard, Alastair [Graham] (Christmas Day 1924; *EWD*, p. 194). Given that Graham was abroad over Christmas 1924, it seems Evelyn was referring to the previous year.

same gold-coloured ashlar that Charles Ryder sees on his first visit to Brideshead; its front is embellished with a similar, albeit far less grand, row of Ionic half-columns; and there is even a dome and lantern on the roof, though again on a considerably more modest scale than in the book. When Charles Ryder remembers, 'I had been there [to Brideshead] before, first with Sebastian more than twenty years ago on a cloudless day in June . . .' it is perfectly conceivable that Evelyn is recalling his own first visit to Barford. He is explicit (in Chapter Four) that the June day Charles remembers is in 1923, the same summer that Evelyn's own love affair with Alastair Graham had begun. The first mention in Kate Waugh's diary of Evelyn visiting Barford is admittedly not until 3 January 1924, however all the other evidence points to her son having been there the previous summer – without perhaps telling his mother.

If Evelyn had sampled country-house life with the Molsons at Goring Hall, at Barford he gained a far fuller appreciation. Alastair Graham was far closer to a 'true aristocrat' than Hugh Molson. His mother was a Southern belle – her American family's cotton fortune being the main source of Alastair's substantial private income – his father a bona fide scion of the British landed aristocracy. The younger son of a baronet and grandson of the 12th Duke of Somerset, Hugh Graham had grown up at Netherby Hall in Cumberland and devoted his life to hunting, shooting and fishing. His sisters, Alastair's aunts, were the Duchess of Montrose, the Marchioness of Crewe, the Countess of Verulam and Lady Wittenham. Alastair was the last person to name-drop his grand relations so Evelyn may not have picked up on all this, yet while staying at Barford (which he was to do on countless occasions, occasionally for several weeks at a stretch) he gained his first meaningful entrée into the upper class world that he eventually came to inhabit.

For Alastair, who had not inherited his father's passion for field sports, Barford was a place of refuge. A natural recluse ('rather quiet', said Acton; 'buttoned-up', according to Powell), he craved undisturbed solitude, and in a later letter to Evelyn wrote: 'All the beautiful things that I have seen, heard or thought of, grow like bright flowers and musky flowers in a garden where I can enjoy their presence, and where I can sit in perfect peace and banish the unpleasant things in life. A kind of fortified retreat that no one can enter except myself.'[25]

As Evelyn fell in with Alastair's wish to shut himself off from the outside world, during his final year his Oxford friends saw less and less of him, as did the History School. A late burst of cramming in the summer of 1924 proved insufficient and he was uncomfortably aware as he left the exam room that the questions had been 'rather inconvenient'. His chances would hardly have been improved by his behaviour at a dinner party held by Cruttwell for the history candidates, 'at which I arrived tipsy and further alienated their sympathies by attempting, later, to sing a Negro spiritual'.[26] At the end of July he returned to Oxford for his viva, dressed in dark coat, scholar's gown and white tie and fortified by a whisky from his favourite wine merchant. He sensed that it was 'purely formal', however, and telegraphed his parents to warn them of 'my certain third', confirmation of which duly came the next day.

8

....

Pure as Driven Slush

Evelyn confided to his recently resumed diary that he was 'much dis-
pirited' by his Third, although on the day he got his results he deferred
the gloom with a lengthy drinking spree, eventually winding up at the
Abingdon Arms in Beckley, a village just north of Oxford where he and
Alastair had rented a leaky caravan ('sans horse', as Evelyn described it)[1]
to escape from Mrs Graham.[2]

The next week he and Alastair set off for Dublin, 'a most unattractive
place,' thought Evelyn, 'full of barbed wire and ruins and soldiers and un-
employed' – and pubs that closed at 9 p.m. Their two-week Irish jaunt was
further blighted by dingy hotels, 'ghastly' fizzy beer and towns that all
reminded him of Shoreham. It was in Ireland that Cruttwell's valedictory
letter caught up with him: 'I cannot say that your 3rd does you anything
but discredit; especially as it was not even a good one; and it is always at
least foolish to allow oneself to be given an inappropriate intellectual label
... I hope that you will soon settle in some sphere where you will give
your intellect a better chance than in the History School.'[3]

Back at Barford things scarcely improved during a week in the company of an 'extremely quarrelsome' Mrs G, and when Evelyn eventually
got back to Underhill he was irked by the presence of 'a horrible wireless
apparatus' which Arthur had recently acquired; 'contrary to modern domestic conventions,' Evelyn later wrote, 'it was he who always wished to
hear it, I to turn it off.'[4]

The onset of autumn deepened his despondency about the future, exacerbated by the prospect of Alastair's imminent departure for Africa to
spend the winter with his sister in Kenya.[5] No less depressing was the
thought that he would then have been beginning his last term at Oxford

– the ninth he needed to complete his degree having come up in a by-term – had not the certainty of his Third and Cruttwell's subsequent withdrawal of his scholarship persuaded Arthur that this would be a complete waste of money.

Prior to that Evelyn had been keenly anticipating a term of 'pure pleasure', for which he had reserved digs on Merton Street to share with his old Hypocrite friend Hugh Lygon, whom he recalled in his autobiography as 'always just missing the happiness he sought, without ambition, unhappy in love, a man of great sweetness'. Dubbed 'lascivious Mr Lygon' by Evelyn, Hughie was one of the more promiscuously homosexual Hypocrites and it has often been suggested that he and Evelyn were lovers. The timing of this supposed liaison has never been convincingly established, however, and in any case the evidence that they ever went to bed together – while perfectly possible – is far flimsier than one might imagine, comprising a mixture of hearsay and reading between the lines. Selina Hastings evidently had reservations about her three informants and accordingly played down the possibility of an affair. More recently Paula Byrne has been more emphatic about the matter, writing that Tamara Talbot Rice 'reported that John Fothergill let Evelyn have rooms at the Spread Eagle at Thame at a special mid-week rate so that he and Hugh could meet in private'.[6] That appears to clinch it, but did Tamara Talbot Rice really say that? No date or source is given for the assertion, however it appears to come from the brief note of Selina Hastings's interview with her in 1991, which is in Alexander Waugh's archive. According to the note, Mrs Talbot Rice said in that conversation that 'everyone knew' they had an affair and she also mentioned Evelyn getting a good rate at the pub. But she said nothing about them using it as a trysting place.[7]

Whatever the nature of Evelyn and Hugh Lygon's relationship, it has long been recognised that Hugh's father, the 7th Earl Beauchamp, was the main inspiration for Lord Marchmain, just as Hugh's elder brother Viscount Elmley (president of the Hypocrites' when Evelyn joined) provided the model for Bridey (the characteristics he supplied included Bridey's distaste for fox-hunting), and Hugh himself shared many of the characteristics of Sebastian – his restlessness, his self-destructive drinking, his ever-present teddy bear[8] and his ethereal beauty, described by Anthony Powell as that of 'a Giotto angel living in a narcissistic dream'.[9] Yet nowhere in the various mentions of Hugh in Evelyn's surviving diaries and letters – which contain several references to Hugh's love affairs with others – is there a hint of sexual intimacy between them.

* * *

With his Oxford plans thwarted and his finances so precarious that he had stooped to writing begging letters to friends, Evelyn now faced the bleak prospect of having to remain at Underhill indefinitely, longer at any rate than he had lived there since he first went to Lancing. By way of distraction, he spent long afternoons at the cinema and otherwise strove to make headway with a novel called *The Temple at Thatch* (about a young man dabbling in black magic at his ancestral folly) which he had started in June but already sensed would never be finished. Lacking conviction that he could make it as a writer and in search of a more definite purpose, he enrolled at Heatherley Art School, whose term began fortuitously on the same day as Alastair's embarkation, 18 September.

Then located on Newman Street, just behind Tottenham Court Road, Heatherley boasted an array of illustrious alumni – among them Burne Jones, Rossetti, Millais, Henry Moore, E. H. Shepard and Walter Sickert – however when Evelyn went there most of the students appeared to be 'respectable girls who, like myself, were believed at home to be "artistic"', while the few men seemed 'bent upon making commercial careers'.[10]

On his first day, when he was set to draw 'a thin man with no clothes but a bag about his genitalia', he recognised no kindred spirits, and from then on lunched either by himself or with his old Oxford friend Tony Bushell, who was training to be an actor at the nearby Royal Academy of Dramatic Art. Most days they made do with a pub on Tottenham Court Road where they could get a large ham roll and a half a pint of beer for sixpence,[11] but occasionally they treated themselves at Previtali's restaurant, where they celebrated Evelyn's twenty-first birthday on 28 October. Arthur took the opportunity of his son's coming of age to remit the money he had lent him during his Irish trip and gave him a further £5 besides, 'most like a gentleman', thought Evelyn.[12]

Throughout this time, in order to escape the tedium of Underhill, Evelyn relied greatly on his brother Alec, who was by then enjoying his post-divorce freedom as a bohemian bachelor about town. He had rented an elegant first-floor flat on Earl's Terrace in Kensington, with a bedroom that served as an extra sitting room for parties, separated by a curtain in stylish emulation of the Algonquin Hotel in New York. He painted the high ceilings primrose-yellow and the walls pale blue and the whole place was 'pleasantly suffused with the smell of a luxurious Russian Leather soap he used', a friend remembered.[13]

Besides the cocktail parties and suppers he held there, Alec took his brother along to soirées staged by notable 1920s hostesses such as the 'inexhaustibly hospitable'[14] Gwen Otter and the avant-garde writer Mary Butts, who had earlier studied magic with Aleister Crowley and would soon become an opium-smoking intimate of Jean Cocteau. Mary Butts held a memorable 'super-party' for Alec at her large house in Belsize Park promising 'unlimited drink, dancing, female attractions, secluded corners',[15] although it only really got going after Evelyn began lacing the claret-cup with brandy.

Among those caught up in the resulting maelstrom was the young writer Rebecca West, who later became a staunch fan and supporter of Evelyn's work and remained so until the 1950s, when they fell out irreparably over a libel suit. At similar gatherings Evelyn met luminaries such as Tallulah Bankhead and her then girlfriend Gwen Farrar: 'My family warned me about men,' the former quipped, 'but they never mentioned women!' On another occasion she boasted, 'I am as pure as driven slush.'[16] No less licentious was her lisping secretary, Sir Francis Laking (brother of Evelyn's friend Joan), whom Evelyn witnessed pouncing on Alec – much to his brother's gratification, he could not help noticing.[17] Another evening, casting himself in the role of spectator as so often, Evelyn watched as Alec 'turned up late and a little drunk and after his fashion, fixed upon the ugliest woman in the room, bore her off and lechered with her'.[18]

It was a constant source of vexation for Evelyn that his lecherous brother was always so much more successful with women than he was, especially as Alec seemed to boast no obvious physical advantages, being as one contemporary recalled 'very unattractive, tiny and stout'. His appeal seemed to lie mainly in the fact that he was so persistently keen. He was also more obviously charming and approachable than Evelyn, and according to one contemporary, perhaps crucially, he seemed to be 'very very interested in bores – the more boring the person, the more fascinated Alec became. So he was every hostess's dream guest.'[19]

It was Alec who in early 1924 first introduced Evelyn to Elsa Lanchester, one of Mary Butts's numerous lodgers. At the age of just twenty-two she had recently established a popular cabaret club, the Cave of Harmony, which soon became Evelyn's favourite nightspot. By the summer he had developed a crush on her and persuaded her to take a part in a silent film he had written with Terence Greenidge called *The Scarlet Woman*,* much of which they shot in the garden at Underhill; he later referred to it as 'the Elsa film', and when she subsequently went on to become a well-known actress and the wife of Charles Laughton, Evelyn liked to claim that it was he who had 'invented' her.

In Alastair's absence, meanwhile, Evelyn continued to visit Barford, although whenever he went into Leamington with Mrs Graham he felt 'a little sad to pass all the public houses where Alastair and I have drunk'.[20] In early November he was lured back to Oxford by John Sutro's invitation to a luncheon at which his attendance was kept a secret from the other guests – Harold Acton, Mark Ogilvie-Grant, Hugh Lygon, Robert Byron, Arden Hilliard and Richard Pares (recently elected a Fellow of All Souls) – who 'feted me spontaneously in a way to rekindle all my love of Oxford'.[21] An epic lunch of 'hot lobster, partridges and plum pudding, sherry, mulled claret and a strange rum-like liqueur' was followed by beer at the New Reform Club, dinner at Merton, more beer in the rooms of 'a charming hunting man called Reynolds', a further session at the Nag's Head pub, then on to the old Hypocrites' to drink whisky and watch *The Scarlet Woman*.

'After about this stage of the evening my recollections become somewhat blurred,' Evelyn's diary continues. 'I got a sword from somewhere and got into Balliol somehow and was let out of a window at some time having mocked Arden and Tony Powell and talked very seriously to Peter Quennell . . .'[22] He returned to Oxford every weekend for the rest of that term, each one consistently more debauched than the last, and adopted the latest Oxford fashion of wearing polo-neck jumpers, 'most convenient for lechery,' according to Evelyn, 'because it dispenses with all unromantic gadgets like studs and ties'.[23]

With his tendency to overdo it whenever he happened to venture out,

---

* They had started filming it at Oxford, including a sequence by the Littlemore Asylum. 'Evelyn had a thing about loonies at the time,' recalled Tony Bushell. 'There were poor loonies looking through the gate and all that.' The negative of that particular sequence was subsequently lost by Terence Greenidge.

Evelyn soon realised that 'it is not possible to lead a gay life and to draw well'.[24] Though he was 'by no means the worst in the class' at Heatherley, the whole business of art school had begun to pall. In December he briefly considered going to live in Sussex as pupil to the printer and bookplate designer James Guthrie, however on a two-day recce he found that, much though he liked his whole family, he was less impressed by their printing press and still less by the discomforts of their 'ugly little house' near Bognor.[25] As a last resort, he turned to the 'one profession open to a man of my qualifications' and took a job as a prep school master in north Wales.

As Evelyn prepared to take up this post in late January 1925, he reflected that he felt more desolate than he had done since Alastair's embarkation for Africa in September – only now the main cause of his unhappiness was a girl.

*   *   *

His latest infatuation was with eighteen-year-old Olivia Plunket Greene, whose brother (Richard) Evelyn had befriended in his last year at Oxford. Evelyn first met Olivia in early December and was quickly smitten. If not a classic beauty, she was curiously attractive with bobbed hair, 'minute pursed lips and great goo-goo eyes'.[26] Evelyn saw her again two weeks later and again two days after that, when they ended up in his bedroom at Underhill – albeit chaperoned by Alec and Terence Greenidge – before she eventually left at three.

The next day (Christmas Eve) Evelyn sent her a book that Alec had acquired from Oscar Wilde's son called *Irais* – an obscure 'lesbian novel' describing an intense sexual relationship between two girls at a Catholic boarding school.[27] 'I wonder whether I am falling in love with this woman,' Evelyn wrote in his diary that evening,[28] beguiled by the intensity of her enthusiasms, her forthright opinions, her ability to be outrageous without compromising her 'essential delicacy'.[29] That she seemed to enjoy getting drunk as much as he did was an added bonus.

Not everyone was charmed by Olivia – her aunt Dorothea Ponsonby thought her 'a rude, egotistical frivolous vain painted child'[30] – however to certain men she was irresistible, not least due to her reputed 'fastidious but intense appreciation of sexual pleasure',[31] as one forlorn suitor put it.

As various boyfriends discovered to their cost, she was also a notorious tease.

*   *   *

Doubtless hopeful that the sexy book might spark something between them, Evelyn spent the week after Christmas impatient for a letter from her. At last, on 30 December, she rang up and they went for a pub lunch followed by a magic show. On New Year's Eve she came for lunch at Underhill and afterwards sat by the fire and talked until tea, at which point she abandoned her previous plans and went with Evelyn to the cinema.

On New Year's Day Evelyn went for the first time to her house on Hanover Terrace (now Lansdowne Walk) in Holland Park and took an instant liking to her liberal and indulgent mother Gwen, by then separated from Olivia's father, the singer Harry Plunket Greene. He later wrote of having fallen in love with the entire family and 'focused the sentiment upon the only appropriate member'. He first told Olivia he was in love with her on 4 January in a nightclub, then wrote the next day to assure her that he had meant everything he said. For the avoidance of doubt, he said it all over again the day after that when they ended a long night out at the flat of Audrey Lucas, the daughter of Arthur Waugh's friend E. V. Lucas, who complicated the situation somewhat by telling Evelyn that she was in love with him.

Olivia evidently relished the attention yet she repeatedly resisted his advances. The Plunket Greenes' lodger Harman Grisewood later remembered her telling him that she 'couldn't possibly sleep with anybody so hideous',[32] however he was hardly an impartial witness given that he also loved Olivia 'to the painful point of being entirely consumed by it,' he admitted. 'Destroyed some might say.'[33]

On 11 January Evelyn described a 'desolate tea' with Olivia at Hanover Terrace 'in front of a gas fire quarrelling in a half-hearted sort of way. Most of the time she insisted monotonously "I don't think you love me any more" and then became aloof when I attempted to prove that I did.'[34] A week later Evelyn saw Olivia kissing his friend Tony Bushell at the theatre and reacted by being 'very rude' to her, but she was 'too drunk to mind'. The next day he turned up drunk at her house after midnight with the same Tony Bushell, broke a gramophone record and refused to go until Olivia knelt down and apologised to him, which she refused to do, 'quite rightly', he later conceded. They made up the next day, just before he forlornly departed for Wales, when she told him he was 'a great artist and must not be a schoolmaster'.[35]

*   *   *

Unlike its lavishly embellished portrayal as the towered and turreted Llanabba Castle in *Decline and Fall*, Arnold House was a bland Victorian property perched above the village of Llanddulas on what Evelyn called the 'highly geological'[36] Denbighshire coast, between Rhyl and Colwyn Bay. He completed the last leg of the 250-mile journey from London by taxi, buried beneath a pile of bags belonging to the thirty boys he had reluctantly chaperoned on the train from Euston, who had then walked up from the station. The headmaster's wife, Mrs Banks,* greeted him sternly. 'The boys know they must carry their own bags. You should not have let them do that to you, Mr Waugh.' She then handed him a message she had taken down on the telephone. 'I hope you can understand it. I certainly cannot.' Sent by Hugh Lygon and John Sutro, it read 'On Evelyn, on.'

The dislike was mutual from then on, alleviated only briefly when Alastair and Mrs Graham came to visit Evelyn a month later and impressed Mrs Banks with their evident social superiority. 'Some *very* nice friends of yours have called for you, Mr Waugh,' she said. 'I am sure Mr Banks will excuse you from all duties while they are in the neighbourhood.'[37]

Evelyn's duties were in any case fairly vague at first. 'It is the most curiously run school that ever I heard of,' he wrote to his mother soon after arriving. 'No time tables nor syllabuses nor nothing. Banks just wanders into the common room & says "There are some boys in that class room. I think they are the first, or perhaps the fourth. Will someone go & teach them Maths or Latin or something."'[38]

Evelyn rated himself 'an obvious dud' as a schoolmaster, as inept at exercising authority as he was at carving the joint in the school dining room. But although he also admitted to finding 'a certain perverse pleasure in making all I teach as dreary to the boys as it is to myself',[39] he

---

* In *A Little Learning* (p. 222) Evelyn called the Bankses Mr and Mrs Vanhomrigh – 'pronounced by some who sought her goodwill "Vanummery"'.

seems to have been quite popular. Derek Verschoyle – later literary editor of *The Spectator*, where he recruited Evelyn as a columnist – remembered being favourably struck by his tweed coat, voluminous plus-fours and high-necked jumper, and by his agreeably laissez-faire attitude in the classroom: 'It could not be said that he made any great formal effort to teach [however] if any child showed curiosity on any specific point he would attempt to satisfy it.'[40] When it was his turn to take prep, Evelyn left his charges to their own devices instead of doing the rounds, while he used the time to write. (If anyone was impertinent enough to ask he would say that he was writing a history of the Eskimos.) Verschoyle also recalled that when Evelyn was in charge of 'communal walks', the boys vied to walk near him as they found his stories so entertaining.

At games, on the other hand, Evelyn was 'so undistinguished a per-former that after a few humorous episodes it was thought better that he should not exercise with the senior boys'. Instead he was 'issued with a whistle and allowed to amble harmlessly around the football field with the ten-year olds'.[41] Even more humiliating was Evelyn's first riding lesson at a local livery yard when, having not ridden since childhood, he was put on a leading rein, only to be met 'in this contemptible situation' by the whole school returning from football.[42] Perhaps to bolster whatever was left of his dignity, he began to smoke a pipe and grow a moustache.

Midway through the term, Evelyn told Harold Acton that, while not a bad school, 'it is a sorry waste of time & energy'. Any time and energy left to him tended to be spent pining for Olivia, engraving a bookplate for her and writing letters 'full of sorrow and devotion'[43] which she either ignored or replied to with such lack of emotion as to make him even more miserable. 'All the term I have been allowing her to become a focus for all the decencies of life,' he wrote in his diary, 'which is foolish of me and not very fair to her.'[44] Drinking, as ever, provided a diversion and he enjoyed leading his common-room colleagues ('a rum lot united like defeated soldiers in the recognition of our base fate')[45] astray in the local pubs. But he could hardly wait for the Easter holidays, not least since he had been invited to stay with all the Plunket Greenes for two weeks in a rented lighthouse on the island of Lundy, off the north coast of Devon.

Back in London Evelyn quickly reverted to his bad old ways, and on the second evening he so shocked his besotted friend Audrey Lucas with his drunken behaviour that she wrote begging him never to get drunk

again. Her letter went unanswered, however, having arrived on the morning of his next spectacular misadventure, an episode later recycled as the
late-night carouse involving Charles, Sebastian and 'Boy' Mulcaster in
Brideshead. Evelyn and Olivia had organised a party to celebrate Richard
Plunket Greene and Elizabeth Russell's engagement, but the drink they
ordered failed to turn up. Evelyn accordingly went off to fetch it, persuading Olivia's cousin Matthew Ponsonby to drive him. Having retrieved
it, Evelyn announced he needed to go home to change and suggested a
pub crawl to Underhill, a further seven miles away to the north, to which
Ponsonby again meekly agreed. After two more glasses of beer there they
eventually headed back to the party, with Evelyn insisting on stopping at
yet more pubs on the way.[46]

As their erratic expedition neared its completion they were pulled over
by the police in the Strand after the inebriated Ponsonby drove the wrong
side of a traffic island. Later that night his father Arthur, a member of
Ramsay MacDonald's first Labour government, had to be woken by his
daughter Elizabeth to go and bail his son out of Bow Street police station.
He refused to do anything for Evelyn ('rather ill-naturedly, I thought'),
who was eventually released after four hours in a cell and made it to the
party just as it was breaking up. The next morning he was fined 15/6 for
being 'drunk and incapable', and reportedly 'made a bad impression as
he appeared in court in pink trousers & a green high-necked jumper and
cheeked the police'. When one officer said, 'Come along, my boy,' Evelyn
shot back, 'Don't call me "my boy", my man.'[47] Ponsonby, meanwhile, was
lucky to get away with a fine of 22 guineas – of which Evelyn offered to pay
half – and the loss of his licence for a year. *The Daily Telegraph*'s report
did not name Evelyn, but his friends and family knew perfectly who the
'incapably drunk' passenger was. 'A quantity of liquor found in the car
was afterwards claimed by this man,' the report added.[48]

Evelyn's behaviour shocked even some of his own age group. 'I am all
for a carouse now and again,' Elizabeth Russell's sister Georgiana* primly
confided, 'but I think there is something disgusting about Evelyn.'[49]
Arthur Ponsonby naturally blamed the 'disreputable' Evelyn for leading
his 'good-natured and weak' son astray, telling his wife Dolly (sister of

---

* Later Georgiana Blakiston. Known as 'Giana', later that year she was conspicuously drunk
herself at her sister's wedding. (See 22 December 1925; *EWD*, p. 238.)

Gwen Plunket Greene) that Evelyn had been 'distinctly drunk and therefore drew suspicion on M who was not sober'.[50]

Later in the year, if Evelyn's diary is to be believed, the Ponsonbys' hapless son would be involved in another far more serious motor accident while drunk, 'killing or at any rate seriously injuring a small boy'.[51] However, that Easter, as far as their family was concerned, Evelyn was very much the guilty party, and hence Matthew and Olivia's grandmother, Lady Parry, was 'disgusted' to hear that he was going to stay the next day with the Plunket Greenes 'just as if we didn't care when we are all so upset'. Frantic telephone calls passed between the cousins. Evelyn himself received what he called a 'piteous' letter from Lady Parry and no answer from Dolly Ponsonby after he wrote to her trying to mend fences.[52]

The Lundy house party included Elizabeth Russell, Julia Strachey and Terence Greenidge, who annoyed Evelyn with his 'new and disagreeable mannerism' of licking the backs of his hands, and later claimed apropos Olivia that 'she had fallen a bit for me!'.[53] Another girl there, Anne Talbot, confessed to Evelyn that she did not know what a phallic symbol was but then appeared to be the most enthusiastic participant in an 'amazing orgy' Evelyn walked in on one evening a few days later,[54] seeing her 'almost naked being slapped on the buttocks and enjoying herself ecstatically. Every two minutes she ran to the lavatory and as soon as she was out of the room everyone said, "My dear, the things we are finding out about Anne." It was all rather cruel.'[55]

On the whole it was an enjoyable two weeks for Evelyn, albeit marred by 'the insistent sorrow of unrequited love', of which he felt unable to cure himself even though he realised it was almost as trying for Olivia as it was for him. He was also troubled by the news that his own admirer, Audrey Lucas, was soon to marry Elsa Lanchester's partner at the Cave of Harmony, Harold Scott. 'It seems to be a most improper arrangement,' Evelyn mused, 'and one for which I am largely responsible.'[56] Having failed to respond to Audrey's desperate letter about his drinking, Evelyn feared she was 'marrying this vulgar man out of mockery'.[57] It proved to be an unhappy union.

From Lundy Evelyn went stay at Barford for a few days' heavy drinking with Alastair, who had arrived back from Africa just after New Year. But by that time Evelyn only had eyes for Olivia, and he continued to pursue her fruitlessly for a few days back in London before returning 'in immeasurable gloom' to Arnold House for the summer term. Within a week he was debating the 'paradoxes of suicide and achievement' and bought a revolver from the newly arrived second master, Dick Young, with the idea of killing himself.[58] Young was 'a dapper man of sunny disposition who spoke in the idiom of the army', but as Evelyn soon discovered, he was also 'monotonously pederastic and talks only of the beauty of sleeping boys';[59] as Evelyn later admitted, he provided 'certain features' for the character of Captain Grimes, his most memorable creation in *Decline and Fall*: 'When you've been in the soup as often as I have,' Grimes tells Paul Pennyfeather, 'it gives you a sort of feeling that everything's for the best, really . . . The last chap who put me on my feet said I was "singularly in harmony with the primitive promptings of humanity".'[60] In *A Little Learning* Evelyn recalled how, a few weeks into the term, Young surprised his colleagues by saying how much he had enjoyed a school trip to Snowdon in honour of the headmaster's birthday, a singularly tiresome expedition for the other masters. '*Enjoyed* yourself?,' they asked incredulously. 'What did you find to enjoy?' 'Knox minor,' he said with radiant simplicity. 'I felt the games a little too boisterous, so I took Knox minor away behind some rocks. I removed his boot and stocking, opened my trousers, put his dear little foot there and experienced a most satisfying emission.'[61]

Evelyn was fascinated by Young's cheerful recollections of past ignominies: 'expelled from Wellington, sent down from Oxford, and forced to resign his commission in the Army. He had left four schools precipitately, three in the middle of the term through his being taken in sodomy and one through his being drunk six nights in succession. And yet he goes on getting better and better jobs without difficulty.'[62] He admired his 'shining candour' and his unfailing ability to bounce back, and the development of his comic outlook as a novelist undoubtedly owed something to their fellowship. He spent many evenings with him in the pubs at Llanddulas and kept in touch after they ceased to be colleagues.

If Young helped keep Evelyn's spirits up during his second term at Arnold House, so too did his excitement about a new book, which would be published the following year as a short story, 'The Balance'. 'I am making the first chapter a cinema film and have been writing furiously ever since,' he told his diary. 'I honestly think that it is going to be rather good.'[63] He had also heard from Alec that C. K. Scott Moncrieff, the famous translator of Proust, might want him as a secretary. Happily imagining a year in Italy sipping Chianti under olive trees, Evelyn promptly gave his notice to Mr Banks. 'I never give notice,' said Young, when he heard. 'It's always the other way about with me. In fact, this looks like being the first end of term I've seen, old boy, for three schools.'[64]

Evelyn's life briefly seemed full of promise, but then came a letter from Harold Acton with his crushing assessment of *The Temple at Thatch*: 'Too English for my exotic taste. Too much nid-nodding over port. It should be printed in a few elegant copies for the friends who love you such as myself.'[65] Evelyn promptly consigned the manuscript to the school furnace. Next came the news that Scott Moncrieff did not need him after all. 'It looks rather like being the end of the tether,' Evelyn told his diary.[66]

At the end of *A Little Learning*, he described how all this drove him to leave his clothes and an appropriate quotation from Euripides on the beach one night and swim out to sea with thoughts of drowning, only to be turned back by jellyfish. 'As earnest of my attempt, I had brought no towel. With some difficulty I dressed and tore into small pieces my pretentious classical tag . . . Then I climbed the sharp hill that led to all the years ahead.'[67]

9

Becoming a Man of Letters

There is no corroboration for the drowning attempt in Evelyn's diary or letters and it may very well have been an imaginative flourish to lend a dramatic and slightly farcical finale to his account of his early years. Yet this was undoubtedly a low point. Sent on his way from Arnold House with a few 'valedictory discourtesies' from the headmaster, back in London he became acutely aware of the gulf between his own situation and that of his close friends: Harold Acton was at the height of his Oxford popularity and esteem; Tony Bushell, when Evelyn visited him in his dressing room at the Adelphi Theatre, seemed 'superbly important nowadays with Cabinet ministers waiting on him with their cars and amorous Jewesses offering him their beds';[1] Robert Byron was about to set off on the adventure to Greece that would lead to his first book; Peter Quennell was already a published poet, the most 'poetical' since Swinburne according to Evelyn's bête noire Edmund Gosse;[2] even Evelyn's school sidekick Dudley Carew had published a novel and was assistant editor on a weekly newspaper. Only Alastair Graham remained as determinedly idle and dissolute as ever.

Evelyn and Alastair were together a lot that August and a resumption of romance is hinted at in Evelyn's recollection of their having 'dined in high-necked jumpers' at Barford and done 'much that could not have been done if Mrs Graham had been here'.[3] After that visit Alastair wrote to him: 'I feel very lonely now. But you have made me so happy. Please come back again soon. Write to me a lot, because I am all by myself, and I want to know what you are doing ... My love to you, Evelyn; I want you back again so much.'[4] There is a sense here of Alastair beginning to lose his hold over Evelyn, and more palpably so in his next letter. 'Thank you for your letter,' he wrote a few days later. 'Evelyn, it was very serious for a poor careless, happy person like me. Of course I want you to treat me as your nature wishes to. I don't understand how one could treat anyone otherwise without being insincere.'⁵ Evelyn's pulling away doubtless had to do with his crush on Olivia, with whom he had gone to stay on the Norfolk coast for a week in September 1925, taking with him a kitten as a present. But in any case he appears to have been turning his attention more towards girls in general, and had confided to certain friends that he wanted to find a wife.⁶ The same month he recorded going to 'a party given by one of the homosexual painters I had met at Mary Butts. He wanted to dance with me and Bobbie [Cecil A. Roberts] but it seemed too repulsive and I am afraid we were rude.'⁷

In a bid to find more congenial work, meanwhile, he had applied to all the London art galleries and art magazines, but to no avail.⁸ So in late September he reluctantly began a new teaching job at Aston Clinton in Buckinghamshire, an Italianate pile formerly owned by the Rothschilds where backward public schoolboys were crammed for university entrance. With only thirty 'mad boys' (or 'lunatics'), as Evelyn called them, in the whole school, he had more free time here, besides which the proximity to the fleshpots of London and Oxford, as well as his entertaining Cockburn cousins just four miles away at Tring, made life far more agreeable than at Arnold House. So too did the presence in the common room of his great friend Richard Plunket Greene, to whom Evelyn acted as best man when he married Liza Russell that December, another event marred for him by his jealously over Olivia.

When some of Richard and Elizabeth's wedding party eventually ended up at the Berkeley, Evelyn looked on as Olivia did 'that disgusting dance of hers'⁹ – her version of the Charleston, which was so much the rage then among the Bright Young People.¹⁰ Much of his heartache about her stemmed from the fact that she made such a show of being sexually available to everyone. Everyone, that is, except Evelyn, who was barely allowed to touch her. A month earlier, at Matthew Ponsonby's party, Evelyn observed that 'Olivia as usual behaved like a whore and was embraced on a bed by various people'.¹¹ Harman Grisewood later insisted that she 'would never have accepted these physical caresses from anyone to whom she was herself attracted'.

She was not greatly attracted to Grisewood either, however during his four years as the Greenes' lodger, he sometimes put her to bed when she was too drunk to undress. On such occasions, he recalled, 'I was allowed – encouraged indeed – to make love to her a little . . . a macabre and an agonising experience for a man who was consumed by love for her and enthralled by her.' When it stopped, 'well before the natural outcome of such pleasures', she would say to him, 'If you live in the furnace, sometimes you are allowed a glass of water.'[12]

More regular boyfriends experienced similar frustrations. Some years later, after having become a Catholic and taken a vow of chastity, Olivia wrote to Augustus John's highly sexed son Henry, himself a recent fugitive from the Jesuits: 'If I let you hold me in your arms, it is for a variety of reasons . . . Your embraces are lessons, but most enjoyable, like a lesson in eating ice-cream or treacle.' In the summer of 1935 they had been due to go to Cornwall together when he received a six-page letter outlining various reasons why she could not have sex with him. He drove on down to Cornwall as planned but she did not follow. He was last seen on a desolate stretch of cliffs, 'walking along,' Michael Holroyd writes, 'swinging a towel, his aunt's Irish terrier at his heels'. His body was washed up on a beach two weeks later, dressed only in a pair of shorts.[13]

* * *

For Evelyn, meanwhile, any distraction from Olivia was welcome, and after a 'dreary' Christmas with the whole Waugh family crammed into Alec's flat for two nights, he agreed to go to Paris – his first time abroad – with a heavy-drinking actor-manager called Bill Silk, an ardent admirer of Tony Bushell's, who promptly took him to a male brothel.* There Evelyn was kissed by a nineteen-year-old youth whom he found 'attractive but [I] had better uses for the 300 francs which the patron – a most agreeable young man in evening dress – demanded for his enjoyment'. While Bill haggled in bad French over the price, Evelyn then arranged 'a tableau by which my boy should be enjoyed by a large negro who was there but at the last minute, after we had ascended to a squalid divan at the top of the house and he was lying waiting for the negro's advances, the price proved

---

* Unlike in Britain, where they would remain illegal until the 1960s, homosexual acts had been legal in France since the Revolution.

prohibitive and, losing patience with Bill's protracted argument with the patron, I took a taxi home and to bed in chastity. I think I do not regret it.'[14] For the rest of the trip, leaving his companion to his nightlife, Evelyn concentrated on sightseeing.

Back in London, another diversion was provided by Elizabeth Ponsonby, Matthew's fashionable elder sister, one of the first girls to have her hair shingled. Later the model for Agatha Runcible in *Vile Bodies*, Elizabeth was the fabled leader of the Bright Young People and gave the impression at least that she would sleep with anyone who wanted to sleep with her.[15] Evelyn had met her the previous autumn without being especially bowled over – 'two years ago, or less even, I suppose I should have been rather thrilled by her,' he wrote in his diary.[16] But in January 1926, at one of Alec's dinner parties, she 'made vigorous love' to Evelyn which flattered him, and on reflection he was sorry not to have accepted. 'She has furry arms,' he noticed. When he met her again the next evening, however, she seemed 'entirely to have overcome her attraction to me'.[17] She was still on his mind a month later when, on a brief dash to London, he sent 'Liz' a card asking her to come for cocktails at the Ritz 'but she did not'.[18] When Alec invited her to a cocktail party in March, she again failed to show up.[19]

The prospect of the Lent term meanwhile was made bleaker by Richard Plunket Greene's departure for a new job at Lancing. As a parting gift for his best man he had bought him a Douglas motor-bicycle, whose inaugural run 'shook off 12/6 worth of its lamp,' Evelyn recorded, 'broke its front brake and stand and number-plate' but otherwise went 'creditably'.[20] Heading back to Aston Clinton in the rain a few days later for the start of term, it went less well 'and finally outside Tring made me wheel it a long way and buy it a new tyre'.[21] Undaunted, shortly after that Evelyn set off for Oxford, more than thirty miles away, returning after dinner 'beastly wet and windy and no light on my bicycle', once falling over and 'all the time sliding all over the road'.[22] The next day he made for Barford, a 'dolorous' sixty-mile journey, again in the dark and rain, during which his bike required a lengthy repair en route when a nut came off the clutch. Three miles short of his destination he again came to a halt with the engine 'refusing to grapple with the wheel'; later he learned it had '"sheared off a key", whatever that may be'.[23]

Evelyn was soon persuaded to swap his Douglas for a smaller but more reliable Francis-Barnett, on which he proceeded to undertake even more hair-raising journeys, often in the dark, his lights usually not working, the roads wet or icy, and with plenty of alcoholic refreshments taken en route. When Dick Young, 'the lecher from Denbighshire', came to visit him in March Evelyn could not help but cast an envious glance at his 'marvellous' Sunbeam, perhaps mindful of the effect his more substantial Douglas had had on his credibility with the boys, making him, unlikely as it sounds, 'the idol of the school'.[24] The Francis-Barnett was not entirely unimpressive, however, as can be seen from the famous motorcycling photograph of Evelyn which, as Duncan McLaren has now established, shows him outside Aston Clinton astride his new machine in February 1926.

With no Richard Greene to drink with, Evelyn tolerated the odd glass with an officious cavalry officer on the staff with the suitably Wavian name of Captain Hyde-Upward, whose one redeeming feature so far as Evelyn was concerned was his habit of thoughtfully polishing and cleaning out his pipe while standing naked at his bedroom window.[25] But generally he preferred the company of the boys, especially his two favourites, Edmund and Charles, who kept house for him in the sitting room the headmaster had allowed him over the stables, while he repaid them with tea and strawberries, went for walks with them, sat with them on the golf course and read aloud from *The Wind in the Willows*. He did not entirely shirk his disciplinary responsibilities and in March recorded that 'the children have begun to be a little naughty so I have started being strict with them, which is a bore'.[26] In the summer term he 'found Edmund out of bounds and beat him with mixed feelings and an ash plant. He was very sweet and brave about it all. I have given him a Sulka tie as recompense.'[27]

Evelyn's friendship with Edmund and Charles would doubtless raise eyebrows today, especially since he seemed to think nothing of inviting Dick Young to visit him at the school, taking him to 'see the children at football', whereupon he promptly 'fell in love with Richard Hollins'. After a subsequent visit, Evelyn recorded: 'Young of Denbighshire came down and was rather a bore – drunk all the time. He seduced a garage boy in the hedge.'[28] In his autobiography Evelyn maintained that he envied Young 'his unclouded happiness but not his exploits',[29] and there is nothing in his diaries to contradict this. His own romantic sights remained firmly fixed on Olivia, and with her proving so elusive there was always still

Alastair, with whom he had been reading T. S. Eliot's poems in January, 'marvellously good but very hard to understand',[30] and went to a dance – 'only it is called a "ball" because it is in the country' – after which Alastair drove the car up the bank on the way home.

A natural drifter, Alastair was prone to disappear without warning, as when he vanished for ten days in April before being discovered drunk in the Lotti Hotel in Paris.[31] In his absence on another longer trip to Constantinople, Evelyn reflected, 'I have missed him more than I would have thought.'[32] But in all probability by this stage they were just friends, so for instance when returning in July from a jaunt to London at dawn Evelyn recorded that 'Tony [Bushell] slept in my room in the stables, Alastair in his car'.[33]

Yet they were still close enough for Evelyn to invite himself to accompany Alastair and his mother to Scotland for three weeks in the summer. Mrs G had been less warmly disposed towards Evelyn since discovering that her son was guaranteeing his overdraft and, as Alastair recalled, his 'deplorable manners' during the course of the trip 'did nothing to clear the atmosphere'.[34] The two of them then went on to France, where Evelyn reflected, 'I think I have seen too much of Alastair lately.'[35]

Alastair would in any case soon be off to take up a diplomatic post in Athens; however before leaving he wanted Evelyn to write a pamphlet for the printing press he had brought home from Turkey. Evelyn had made some notes on the Pre-Raphaelite Brotherhood the previous November at Underhill after spraining his ankle climbing out of a window, and he rattled off *PRB: An Essay on the Pre-Raphaelite Brotherhood 1847–54* in four and a half days. If it now seems rather whimsical and patronising in tone, it was a bold effort given that the Pre-Raphaelites were so out of fashion at the time. Six decades later the young Evelyn Waugh would be hailed as having been 'a lone voice crying in the modernist wilderness' and 'one of the most distinguished pioneers of the Victorian revival'.[36]

The original publication of *PRB* came a month after that of Evelyn's short story 'The Balance', which he had written the previous summer. At thirty-eight pages, Evelyn had hoped it might make a short book, however the manuscript he sent to Chatto & Windus was politely returned, as was the copy Evelyn sent to Leonard Woolf – whose rejection letter chanced to arrive the day after Evelyn recorded in his diary that he had been lent 'a novel [*Mrs Dalloway*] by Virginia Woolf which I refuse to believe is good'.[37] After yet another refusal, Alec eventually came to its rescue and included it in the volume he edited in Chapman & Hall's series of *Georgian Stories*, published in October 1926, along with contributions from Aldous Huxley, Somerset Maugham, Liam O'Flaherty and others.

As Alec said, Evelyn's was 'an *avant-garde* piece',[38] an experimental collage with abrupt shifts in form and tone, and characters and situations closely drawn from his life. Subtitled 'A Yarn of the Good Old Days of Broad Trousers and High Necked Jumpers', it features an art student recently down from Oxford called Adam Doure who tries to poison himself when the fashionable Imogen Quest blithely ends their affair, blaming her mother. If the experimental narrative techniques did not quite come off in this instance, it was nonetheless an extraordinary piece of writing for a twenty-one-year-old, and the use of cinematic descriptions to achieve greater objectivity, the one-sided telephone conversations and skilfully handled passages of sustained, unattributed dialogue all prefigured devices used to great effect in his later fiction. The *Manchester Guardian* pronounced it 'brilliant',[39] albeit 'for all the most futile reasons'[40] in Evelyn's view. The American writer Conrad Aiken came closer to the mark, acclaiming it as an 'astonishingly rich portrait of a mind' and predicting that the author might 'do something very remarkable [providing] he is not too clever'.[41]

Despite the encouraging reviews, Evelyn still lagged behind some of his contemporaries, most obviously Henry Yorke, who had begun his first novel *Blindness* while still at Eton and published it, under the pseudonym Henry Green, just before leaving Oxford that autumn. Evelyn felt 'impelled' to write and tell him 'how very much I like it. It is extraordinary to me that anyone of our generation could have written so fine a book.'[42] Two years younger than Evelyn, Yorke was now about to embark on a stint on the factory floor of the family engineering works in Birmingham, an experience that would lead to his second novel, *Living* (1929), whereas Evelyn remained glumly stranded at Aston Clinton, attempting a life of 'sobriety, chastity, and obedience' after his mother had paid off his debts yet again.[43] As he passed his twenty-third birthday, for which Arthur gave him 'some very expensive underclothes, and a pound to buy some dinner with', he was growing increasingly frustrated with schoolmastering, irritated by the boys' 'prattle'[44] yet at the same time ashamed of how rude he could be to them. At the end of term, the headmaster grudgingly gave him a £10 pay rise. 'I think next term will be my last,' Evelyn wrote in his diary.[45]

A trip that Christmas holidays to Athens, where Alastair had been posted as honorary attaché to the British Minister, Sir Percy Loraine, did little to cheer him. Alastair had been fascinated by ancient Greece since childhood, brought up on tales of his great-grandfather, the 14th Duke of Somerset, who had travelled throughout the Levant in the 1840s 'with a shotgun under one arm and a copy of Homer under the other'.[46] An additional draw was that the Mediterranean was then seen as 'the place for Anglo-Saxon gay men to escape to', as Duncan Fallowell puts it, a place where 'misfits of all kinds' could 'breathe more easily and be themselves'.[47] Alastair was a cousin of Lady Loraine, which doubtless eased his appointment; however there were whispers about Sir Percy which, if true, would also have made Alastair an appealing recruit. An ostensibly strait-laced Northumbrian landowner and able diplomat with what his friend Harold Nicolson called 'a weakness for the processional', Sir Percy was also rumoured to have a 'liking for young men and low life' and to have had an affair with the young Francis Bacon, his distant kinsman by marriage, thus helping to extend the painter's 'experience and observation'.[48]*

Whether Loraine helped extend Alastair's horizons in the same way is a matter for conjecture, but in any event Alastair seemed to be seizing every opportunity to explore his sexuality away from the restrictive laws of England; as Evelyn recorded, the modern flat he shared with another diplomat was 'usually full of dreadful Dago youths called by heroic names such as Miltiades and Agamemnon with blue chins and greasy clothes who sleep with the English colony for 25 drachmas a night'.[49]

Unimpressed by Alastair's new friends and by Athenian cafés, which he said reminded him of potting sheds, Evelyn eventually struck out alone for Olympia, where he saw the Hermes of Praxiteles that had been found by archaeologists only fifty years previously, 'quite marvellous and well worth all the trouble I have taken to see it'.[50] Yet despite his conscientious and adventurous sightseeing, he was nagged by a feeling of having

---

* Roger Mortimer recalled that in retirement Sir Percy Loraine lived in the flat below his parents at 76 Sloane Street and that he used to go abroad for the winter, during which time his butler used the flat as a brothel. 'My mother could not understand the weird noises that could be heard from 2 p.m. onwards. I think my father rather enjoyed them.' (*Dear Lumpy*, p. 126.)

inherited his father's 'homely sentiments': 'The truth is that I do not really like being abroad much. I want to see as much as I can this holiday and from February shut myself up for the rest of my life in the British Isles.'[51]

Home was eventually regained in late January 1927 via Corfu, Brindisi, Rome and Paris, after almost a month away, and he was soon back at Aston Clinton, busily corrupting a new master called Attwell, who seemed to have led 'the dullest life imaginable' at Oxford and been a virtual teetotaller before being cajoled into drunken binges by Evelyn. Returning from one of their sprees they came across another new member of staff, a matron who had recently given Evelyn a ham and struck him as an 'admirable' sort. What happened next is not clear, although Evelyn later told friends that as a joke he had said some suggestive things to her in French as she came out of the bathroom in her dressing-gown.[52] The following day, while Evelyn and Attwell were sitting by the fire laughing about the night before, the headmaster came in and sacked them both. From then on, Evelyn recorded, it became 'rather a harrassing day'. The next morning Evelyn 'slipped away feeling rather like a housemaid who has been caught stealing gloves'.[53] He warned his parents in advance by telephone that he would be coming, explaining tactfully that he had been dismissed for drunkenness, and when he got there 'dined in a very sorrowful household'.[54] The next day, feeling 'tired and discouraged' after 'trying to do something about getting a job', he wrote his diary: 'It seems to me the time has arrived to set about being a man of letters.'[55]

The same day he wrote to say goodbye to Edmund and Charles, his letter crossing with one from Edmund enclosing two photographs of himself:

Dear Evelyn,

I cannot tell you how sorry I am that you have left and that I never came to say good bye but I was too shy as you had your friend, Cecil Roberts, with you. I am writing this in bed instead of going to call you, I shall miss doing that awfully. Every one is very upset at your leaving. Watkinson asked me especially to remember him to you when I wrote. I do not know what Pig [Charles] & I will do now without your room to go up & tidy or wash up (in cold water). I went up there yesterday to see what you had done with all your things & it looked so bare without your books & candle sticks & the Ikon (I cannot spell it).[56]

* * *

Back in London following his dismissal, Evelyn had a discouraging interview with a Father Underhill to explore the idea of his becoming a clergyman before accepting a temporary job at a dismal school in Notting Hill, where 'all the masters drop their aitches and spit in the fire and scratch their genitals' and the boys 'pick their noses and scream at each other in a cockney accent'.[57]

Prior to taking up that post he 'spent two days writing a story about a Duke'[58] for the well-regarded *New Decameron* short story series. 'A House of Gentlefolks' reintroduces Ernest Vaughan, Adam Doure's dissolute friend (and Evelyn's alter ego) in 'The Balance', who has now been sent down from Oxford and befriends the Duke of Vanburgh's supposedly backward grandson and heir after being asked to take him around Europe. More straightforwardly readable if less ambitious than 'The Balance', it appeared later that year alongside stories by Michael Sadleir, G. B. Stern, L. A. G. Strong and others.

As he usually did when in London, he saw a lot of the Plunket Greenes, and after lunching with them one day he complained to his diary that 'Olivia could talk of nothing except black men'.[59] Since the opening of the Blackbirds revue the previous autumn it had become chic for Bright Young People to entertain black people at their parties, to the extent that when issuing an invitation promising no such adornment Evelyn took to saying, 'It's not a party, there won't be a black man.'[60] Evelyn had in fact seen the Blackbirds shortly after it opened and he went again several times with Olivia after leaving Aston Clinton, recording on one occasion that they 'called on Florence Mills and other niggers and negresses in their dressing-rooms. Then to a night club called Victor's to see another nigger – [the American cabaret star] Leslie Hutchinson.'[61]* It is a commonplace to accuse Evelyn of being racist in such diary entries, just as it is to describe various other pronouncements as anti-Semitic or snobbish.

---

* Known as 'Hutch', Hutchinson's romantic entanglements were a source of particular fascination to Evelyn. Despite being married with a baby, Hutch was at the time openly living with a girl called Zena Naylor (the illegitimate daughter of the art critic Langton Douglas), who soon complained of his sleeping with Olivia's sister-in-law, Babe Plunket Greene. To complicate matters further, Zena soon became the girlfriend of Alec Waugh, who had to plead with Evelyn to change a brothel sign that read 'Chez Zena' in one of his illustrations for *Decline and Fall*.

But his apparent prejudices almost invariably contained elements of self-parody or mischievous provocation, or stemmed from a compulsion to say the unsayable. Regarding his descriptions of the Blackbirds, it is worth bearing in mind that language and attitudes were very different then, and in any case the hostesses who courted and patronised black artists, treating them as fashionable and amusing accessories rather as Mrs Beste-Chetwynde does with 'Chokey' in *Decline and Fall*, were if anything more amusing to him than the black performers themselves.

In Evelyn's case there may also have been jealousy over Olivia's outspoken fascination with black men and her rumoured affair with Paul Robeson. By now Evelyn knew all too well the depressive, self-obsessed flipside of Olivia's character after witnessing such scenes as her 'packing bottles in a bedroom littered with stockings and newspaper. Fatter and larger generally, unable to talk of much except herself and that in an impersonal and incoherent way.'[62] Yet according to Harman Grisewood he remained desperately in love with her and one day, when the message finally got through that she would never sleep with him, he took hold of her hand and very deliberately burnt the back of her wrist with his cigarette. Olivia found this sadistic act strangely moving, and when she showed the scar to Grisewood she confided that she felt very sorry for Evelyn, 'sorry', as Grisewood later recalled, 'that she could feel no physical attraction for him and sorry that this knowledge should have so frightful an effect, driving him to a sort of frenzy'.[63]

For Evelyn, meanwhile, the only way of getting over his obsession with Olivia was for him to find someone else, and on 7 April 1927 he recorded in his diary: 'I have met such a nice girl called Evelyn Gardner.'

10

....

Shevelyn

There has been a certain amount of debate about when or where the two Evelyns met, Dudley Carew recalling that it was he who introduced them at his flat (and that was why Evelyn was so horrid to him in later years)* and others suggesting that it happened at the lodgings that Evelyn Gardner shared with her best friend Pansy Pakenham on Ebury Street in Belgravia. Evelyn certainly went to the girls' Ebury Street party, describing it in his diary as 'a pleasing little one',[1] however that took place in late May 1927, more than six weeks after the Evelyns' first meeting. According to Evelyn Gardner, whose written account of their relationship has not been seen by any previous biographer,† they had first met at an earlier party given by Sylvia Brooke, Ranee of Sarawak, self-styled 'Queen of the Headhunters', at her large house on Portland Place, introduced by their mutual friend Bobbie Roberts.

Recalling this first meeting, 'Shevelyn', as Evelyn's friends soon took to calling her, wrote: 'I saw a young man, short, sturdy, good-looking, given to little gestures, the shrugging of a hand which held a drink, the tossing of a head as he made some witty, somewhat malicious remark. He was easy to talk to and amusing.'[2] Besides thinking her 'a lovely girl', Evelyn never recorded his initial impressions of Shevelyn, however she later presumed 'he was interested in me because I was gay, boyish looking with an Eton crop and very slim'. A possible additional draw, she hazarded, was 'that I

---

* This is impossible as by his own account Carew did not meet Evelyn Gardner until they were fellow passengers on the Rajah of Sarawak's hired bus to the Epsom Derby, won by Call Boy, in June 1927. (See *Fragment of Friendship*, pp. 77–8.)

† Written in 1975 and running to nineteen pages, this was described by Shevelyn as 'a full account which the children can dispose of as they like after I am dead'. (Evelyn Gardner to Michael Davie, 8 December 1975, AWA.)

belonged – so he thought – to the society to which he not only wished to belong but of which he wished to become an undoubted member'.

Her father, Lord Burghclere, illegitimate eldest son of the 3rd Lord Gardner and the actress Julia Fortescue, had been a Liberal MP and President of the Board of Agriculture under Gladstone then Rosebery. Her mother, Lady Winifred, eldest daughter of the 4th Earl of Carnarvon, and a distant kinswoman of Gwen Plunket Greene, was the scholarly biographer of James, 1st Duke of Ormonde and George Villiers, 2nd Duke of Buckingham. Winifred's brother sponsored Howard Carter's Egyptian archaeological expeditions and participated in the discovery of Tutankhamen's tomb in 1922. But Shevelyn longed to escape her illustrious background. Born in 1903 (a month before Evelyn Waugh), the youngest by seven years of four daughters, she never went to school and was brought up by a nanny and governesses, her sister Mary, the next youngest, having been married off when Shevelyn was eleven, after which, as she recalled, 'the servants became my greatest friends'. She remembered the sensation of being 'as it were in a cage with no knowledge of the world or the real behaviour of others. One was enclosed and the bursting out when freedom came was not good.'

Of her parents Shevelyn far preferred her father, 'whose sunny disposition and ever-kindly wit,' according to *The Times*, 'together with his fame as an amateur actor are perhaps better remembered than his services to Liberalism'.[3] However he was fifty-seven by the time Shevelyn was born and she saw very little of him as a child, although she fondly recalled his winking at her across the table during boring lunch parties. He died in 1921, when she was barely eighteen. Her mother, on the other hand, was 'formidable' and 'absolutely terrifying' as far as Shevelyn was concerned – notwithstanding her dainty figure, tiny waist and mice-like feet.

Lady Burghclere's starchiness may have stemmed from having had to sacrifice her own adolescence. Her mother died when she was eleven, leaving it to her to entertain her father's guests at Highclere Castle (the 'real' Downton Abbey) as if she were a grown-up. Her father eventually remarried and when he began crawling around playing bears with his baby son on the drawing room floor, she was horrified that he could be so undignified. When she came to have Shevelyn, her daughter remembered no affection at all. 'One could never explain one's presumed misdemeanours,' wrote Shevelyn, 'because words froze in one's mouth or didn't even get as far as freezing. Neither my sister Mary nor I remember her ever coming into the nursery or schoolroom. There were no goodnights, loving or otherwise, or prayers being heard at bedtime.'

On the face of it the three elder Gardner daughters had all married well,* however none of the marriages was especially happy and by the time Shevelyn was grown-up two of them had already failed and there were whispers of 'bad blood' in the family, which Shevelyn presumed referred to her actress grandmother, some of whose warmth and demonstrativeness she herself exhibited in her role as the archetypal Modern Girl, calling friends 'angel-face' and 'sweetie-pie', and referring to Proust, whom she once declared herself 'buried in', as 'dear old Prousty-wousty'.[4]

Shevelyn's longing to 'burst out' was allied to a natural flirtatiousness, a slim figure, pert little nose and, like her distant cousin Olivia Plunket Greene, round 'goo-goo' eyes that men found highly attractive. By the time she was twenty-three she had been engaged nine times, often simultaneously, her assorted fiancés including a ship's purser whom she had met on a trip to Australia, where her mother had sent her to break up another unsuitable entanglement. When she met Evelyn Waugh at Sylvia Brooke's party she had recently accepted a proposal from the Ranee's handsome ADC and former boyfriend Barry Gifford, whom shellshock had transformed from dashing First World War hero to hopeless soak and 'frightful bounder' in several people's estimation. Shevelyn knew he was an alcoholic, but 'in my immature way I imagined I could cure him'; however they had to hold fire for the time being because he was still technically married.

* * *

Aside from finding Evelyn Waugh attractive and fun, the fact that he was a writer was also very appealing, given that she had recently quit her job as a *vendeuse* at the Maison Arthur fashion store on Dover Street in order to write a play, and was keen for an entrée into the literary world. When they met he had just begun a trial stint on the *Daily Express*, and

---

* In 1914 Mary married Geoffrey Hope-Morley (Morley's underwear); they divorced in 1928. In 1915 Alathea married Geoffrey Fry (Fry's chocolate); the marriage lasted but was very strained. In 1916 Juliet married Alexander Cumming-Russell of Clochan; they separated within twenty-four hours and divorced in 1922.

after their first lunch à deux at the Green Park Hotel in late May he went straight off to cover a fire in Soho, where 'an Italian girl was supposed to have been brave but had actually done nothing at all'.[5] He was sacked shortly afterwards, perhaps not surprisingly if the advice he subsequently offered budding journalists was any reflection of the attitude he displayed at work. When assigned a story, 'the correct procedure is to jump to your feet, seize your hat and umbrella and dart out of the office with every appearance of haste to the nearest cinema'.[6] There the probationer was advised to sit and smoke a pipe and imagine what any relevant witnesses might say. It was perhaps Evelyn's good fortune that in his seven weeks on the paper, not one of the pieces he filed was published.

Shortly before being let go by the *Express*, after toying with the idea of writing a book about the Mormons, he had in any case been commissioned by Duckworth's, where his friend Anthony Powell worked, to write a biography of Rossetti in time for the centenary of the painter's birth the next year. Arthur Waugh gloomily predicted that the book would never be finished and that he would have to make good the publisher's advance of £20 which Evelyn, who invariably lurched towards largesse when in funds, had spent in a week. However, after two weeks with his parents and Alec in the South of France (during which Evelyn and Alec visited the Marseilles red-light district, which may have occasioned Evelyn's first sexual encounter with a woman), he knuckled down, and after three weeks he had completed 12,000 words. A month later he was up to 40,000, helped by a stint at the Abingdon Arms in Beckley (where he and Alastair had rented their horseless caravan three years earlier), from where he went most days to Oxford to write in the Union library, which Rossetti and other Pre-Raphaelites had decorated with murals in the 1850s. Next he decided to patch up his quarrel with Mrs Graham and move on to Barford, where he could work undisturbed in a room under the roof called the cock-loft, formerly a lady's maid's 'cutting-out room', furnished with only a table and, as Alastair recalled, 'one of those headless, armless, legless dummies representing the ideal Victorian lady's figure'.[7]

Despite doing all the research as he went along – including interviewing Rossetti's former secretary Hall Caine in bed and looking 'like a Carthusian abbott', and visiting Kelmscott Manor, where Rossetti had shared a lease with William Morris, whose daughter Evelyn found to be 'a detestable woman' – he managed to complete *Rossetti: His Life and Works* within seven months. By today's standards the eventual 227 pages includes a lot of long direct quotations – comprising as much as a third of the text in some chapters – however considering that he was barely twenty-four, and that the book is studded with strikingly trenchant and at the time unfashionable opinions, it was a distinctly impressive achievement.

Did the thought of enhancing his eligibility in the eyes of Evelyn Gardner give an extra spur to his writing? Almost certainly it did. After their lunch date in May there had been a long weekend over Whitsun when they both stayed in Wiltshire with Shevelyn's sister Mary Hope-Morley, who was by then estranged from her first husband and entertaining his replacement, Alan Hillgarth, 'very sure of himself', noted Evelyn in his diary, 'writes shockers, ex-sailor'. There was then a long interval while Evelyn got on with Rossetti before he again began to pursue her in earnest in mid-September. In late November – by which time he had taken a leaf out of the Pre-Raphaelites' book and was learning to be a cabinet-maker at the Academy of Carpentry – he told his diary that he was seeing Shevelyn 'a lot', and she had recently been to dinner at Underhill to meet his parents, after which she told a friend: 'Old Mr Waugh is a complete Pinkle-Wonk. He wears a blue velvet coat at dinner, just like Papa did, and talks about actresses who were the toasts of his young days. I like that kind of thing.'[8]

A little wiser perhaps after his forlorn pursuit of Olivia, Evelyn seems to have blundered only once with Shevelyn when, 'a little too tight' one evening, as she told a friend, he was furious when she wouldn't let him take her home. 'When I got back about 1.30 the telephone rang, & a small precise voice said, "Is that Miss Gardner?" "Yes." "What I want to say is, Hell to you!" Clang went the receiver. I did laugh so much. Evelyn apologised profusely the next day, he is so sweet.'[9] 'Sweet' is a word that crops up a lot in her descriptions of him at this time.

Evelyn had been vaguely on the lookout for a wife for the past two years, and it had evidently already crossed his mind that Evelyn Gardner might be the one. When one day she let slip out of the blue that she was thinking of going to Canada, he realised he could afford to dither no longer. Three days later, on 12 December, Evelyn took her out to dinner at the Ritz Grill and proposed. 'Let's get married and see how it goes,'[10] is how he phrased it, according to Shevelyn, who recalled there being no mention of love. She asked for time to think about it but the next day rang up to accept.

She later admitted that, much though she 'liked Evelyn and admired him sincerely', she 'should have considered it far longer than I did. But I was anxious to get married and settle down.' Her sense of urgency had been heightened by two recent developments. Her closest sister Mary, whom she idolised to an extent unfathomable to her friends, had announced that she was going to marry the cocksure shocker writer Alan Hillgarth (to whom Hevelyn had taken a virulent dislike, as had her flat-mate Pansy Pakenham) and follow him to South America. And Pansy had also just got engaged to the painter Henry Lamb. 'Suddenly there was the danger of my having to return home,' recalled Shevelyn. 'I did not think that my mother would allow me to live alone [and was afraid she] might cut off my allowance.'

To give her her due, besides the sheer convenience of marriage at this time she also felt that Evelyn would be far more stimulating company than the 'solid 100% he-men' with whom she had previously consorted, whose appeal, she told a friend, lay 'in their directness and sex-appeal' yet whose charms tended to wear off to the point when they became 'hum-drum'.[11] Her acceptance of him was encouraged by Pansy, who told a friend at the time that 'after all these toughs & cavemen that make up her usual clientele, E. Waugh seems like claret after whisky [and] seems to be kind and bracing at the same time'.[12] Pansy had been equally instrumental in persuading Evelyn to take the plunge when he did. 'I was <u>greatly</u> in favour of this,' she wrote to a friend just after the engagement, 'as I thought E. Gardner had lost her nerve about marriage & that if she didn't do it at once she would let it peter out out of sheer funk.'[13]

Evelyn's proposal does not sound all that romantic, it is true, and is often adduced as proof that he was not especially in love with her. Equally plausible, however, is that he was nervous and unsure of her response and anxious to protect himself against her possible rejection, which would have been perfectly understandable with Barry Gifford still lurking about, and given all the knocks his confidence had suffered at the hands of Olivia. In any case, Shevelyn later implied that his breezy suggestion was far less threatening and more appealing to her than a passionate declaration of love, telling Michael Davie that she interpreted it as meaning that absolute faithfulness was not required by her. 'I had been brought up to believe everything that people said. I believed him. I was a ninny.'[14]*

Whatever the depth of his feelings for her, Evelyn was also keen to get away from home. 'How I detest this house [Underhill],' he had reflected earlier that autumn, 'and how ill I feel in it. The whole place volleys and thunders with traffic. I can't sleep or work . . . The telephone bell is continually ringing, my father scampering up and down stairs, Gaspard [the dog] barking, the gardener rolling the gravel under the window and all the time the traffic. Another week of this will drive me mad.'[15]

It was nonetheless there that Evelyn asked his fiancée to spend five days over Christmas, after which Shevelyn wrote to Kate thanking her 'for the happiest Christmas I have ever had. I loved being at Hampstead & wish I were with you still. I have never thanked you properly for the letter you wrote me, when I got engaged to Evelyn. It was so much the nicest letter I have ever had. Somehow, I thought that you wouldn't be pleased, because Evelyn is such an exceptional person, and I know how fond you are of him. I hope I shall be able to make him happy. I think when one loves someone, as much as I love Evelyn, one is terrified of disappointing them.'[16]

Shevelyn was to go to Underhill many times after that, giving her ample opportunity to observe the Waugh household. When talking to her, Alec Waugh referred to Underhill as 'the little house', hinting that she might find it rather humble compared to what she was used to, however it struck her as far more of a home than the various places in which she had grown up. She was occasionally taken aback by the tensions between the two brothers and also by Evelyn's ill-concealed aversion to his father's sentimentality. But overall she found the Waugh parents far easier to get along with than her own mother, of whom she had recently observed that 'unless you agree with her every word she is furious. The great thing is to say "quite" to every remark she makes.'[17]

Lady Burghclere – known unaffectionately as 'the Baroness' by her daughter's friends – had already made it plain that she was not remotely in favour of her daughter marrying an 'impoverished, suburban trainee carpenter', as Evelyn's grandson later put it.[18] How much snobbery there

---

* In his obituary of Evelyn Gardner in the *Independent*, Davie wrote that the casual nature of the proposal 'gave Evelyn Gardner the impression, she explained later, that Waugh was not wholly committed to the marriage'. However the notes of his interview with her say nothing about Waugh's implied lack of commitment, but rather: 'Implication seemed to be that absolute loyalty not required of her, she thought.' (Michael Davie interview with Evelyn Gardner, 24 February 1973; AWA.)

was on her part and how much subsequent embroidery by Evelyn is anyone's guess, however years later he told Nancy Mitford that 'it never occurred to me to think I wasn't a gentleman until Lady Burghclere pointed it out'.[19] One thing was made perfectly clear from the start: she was never going to give her consent to their marriage while Evelyn was without a job. However when he subsequently sought one at the BBC, she used her connections (her one remaining son-in-law Geoffrey Fry wrote to Evelyn's interviewer, Lance Sieveking, who happened to be a friend of his*) to make sure he did not get it.[20]

Lady Burghclere meanwhile began gathering all the evidence she could of Evelyn's unsuitability, even visiting Cruttwell at Oxford to grill him about Evelyn's career there. As Shevelyn reported, the embittered don was 'palpitating with perverse vices' and assured Lady Burghclere that Evelyn drank copious amounts of vodka and absinthe, went about with disreputable people, lived off his parents, ill-treated his father, had no moral backbone or character, would soon cease to love Shevelyn and would drag her 'down into the abysmal depths of Sodom and Gomorrah'.[21]

After listening to this lurid list Lady Burghclere made a last desperate attempt to reclaim her daughter, asking her to stay for a fortnight in early May with the inducement of publicly announcing the engagement. It had been eighteen months since Shevelyn last spent the night under her mother's roof, however she was worried about money and anxious not to lose her mother's support, so accepted. On arrival she was confronted with Cruttwell's charge sheet and an ultimatum that the marriage could not possibly take place for two years. Evelyn was then summoned and, according to Pansy's account, 'behaved with admirable firmness, threatening to get married in a week', whereupon Lady Burghclere tearfully collapsed and agreed to consent to a wedding providing Evelyn found a job first.[22] 'Victory to the Evelyns!' declared Shevelyn.[23]

* * *

Lady Burghclere's demand that Evelyn get a job was not surprising, although hindsight renders it slightly absurd, and Pansy and her fiancé

---

* Lance Sieveking had met Evelyn a few times at parties and liked him and he later recalled going 'conscientiously through the motions for half an hour, discussing and assessing his abilities and ending up with a voice test. I was really sorry to turn him down.'

Henry Lamb, who had recently painted Evelyn's portrait (since lost) with pipe in one hand, pen in the other, hovering over the manuscript of *Decline and Fall*, were among those who felt that way at the time, accusing her of 'gross materialism' and predicting that Evelyn was 'obviously going to be a successful author in a few years' time', that the couple could scrape along till then, and that in the meantime 'a job' would only waste his energies.[24] As a writer herself, Lady Burghclere cannot have been blind to his potential, having received an advance copy of *Rossetti* (inscribed 'with kind regards' as opposed to 'with love') in April, and then presumably seen the favourable reviews, most prominently in *The Observer*, where J. C. Squire paid tribute to Evelyn's 'terse elegance and unobtrusive wit', and the *Nation & Athenaeum*, which called it 'both lively and reliable'. Almost equal admiration was elicited a month later by Evelyn's sublime rebuke to *The Times Literary Supplement* for referring to him throughout its far less enthusiastic notice as 'Miss Waugh'. 'My Christian name, I know is occasionally regarded by people of limited social experience as belonging exclusively to one or other sex,' Evelyn wrote; 'but it is unnecessary to go further into my book than the paragraph charitably placed inside the wrapper for the guidance of unleisured critics, to find my name with its correct prefix of "Mr". Surely some such investigation might in merest courtesy have been taken before your reviewer tumbled into print with phrases such as "a Miss of the sixties".'[25] Rebecca West considered this 'a model of how one might behave to that swollen-headed parish magazine' and expressed the hope that 'you will go on being so much more intelligent and amusing than most people in such a useful form'.[26] What Lady Burghclere made of all this is not recorded.

Unbeknown to her, meanwhile, throughout the spring of 1928, Evelyn had also been working hard on *Decline and Fall*, the novel that would make his name. He had first mentioned it to Duckworth's the previous September, and read the first 10,000 words – which were scarcely altered later – to Anthony Powell towards the end of that year. Powell recalled thinking it 'extremely funny', although when he subsequently asked about the novel's progress Evelyn replied disconcertingly, 'I've burnt it.'[27]

Dudley Carew then remembered being regaled with 'the first fifty pages or so' in January 1928 at Underhill, with Evelyn sitting in the chair from which Arthur used to declaim after dinner. 'A happiness, a hilarity sustained him that night, and I was back giving him my unstinted admiration as I did at Lancing. It was marvellously funny and he knew that it was. As was his habit in those old, innocent days, he roared with laughter at his own comic invention and both of us at times were in hysterics.'[28]

Buoyed by the prospect of marriage and the growing realisation that he was finally creating something that would do justice to his extraordinary talent as a writer, Evelyn was probably as happy that spring as he had ever been, and his exuberance comes through clearly in the book. A stint writing at The Bell at Aston Clinton was followed by several weeks in March and April in Dorset at the Barley Mow pub in Colehill, two miles from where Shevelyn and Pansy were lodging in a boarding house at Wimborne, also writing novels – Pansy's would be published a month after *Decline and Fall* as *The Old Expedient*. Henry Lamb had rented a house at Poole, seven miles away on the coast, in which to paint while he waited for his divorce from his first wife to come through.

Shevelyn was struggling with her own novel – which concerned 'the thoughts of a man and a girl during twelve hours [going] back through their lives, looking at the same situations from different points of view'[29] – but was proudly delighted with Evelyn's. 'It is really screamingly funny and I think there is a good chance of its being a success, if not a bestseller,' she told a friend, 'but I don't think our mothers will approve of it, certainly mine won't!'[30] During their stay in Dorset Pansy thought Shevelyn seemed 'really much better than I have seen her in a long time'. 'I don't think she is wildly in love with E. W.,' she continued, 'but I doubt if she is capable of sustained passion. However she is very fond of him & looks up to his brains & respects his strength of character. At any rate she will not be able to despise him when the first raptures are past which would have inevitably happened with Barry & his like. She has to work hard for him which is the best thing for her.'[31]

In mid-May they all moved back to London, Evelyn initially to Underhill and the girls to new lodgings at 7 Upper Montagu Street, kept by a charming if rather slatternly Irishwoman. 'I suppose this will be the last abode that Evelyn and I will share together,' wrote Pansy:

It has been a strange little partnership and I am afraid I have been no help to her in her struggles. Perhaps she never does struggle, only drifts with the tide & that is why she gets into such difficulties. Her marriage still seems remote & it is hard to imagine how much she cares for the other Evelyn.

Not enough to follow him barefoot through the world, certainly, but on the other hand she is happier with him & since their engagement than she has been for a long time. The absence of Mary & the necessity to share & intrigue with her is also a great relief ... Now the only issue is whether they are to raise a little money & elope or wait until the maternal sanction wafts them to St Margaret's Westminster. Evelyn Waugh is for the former course, EG for the latter. That's why I don't consider her passion for him can be illimitable, or has she prematurely exhausted her capacity for passion? I wonder if the emotions can be worn out from too much use? I don't see why not.[32]

Two weeks later Evelyn recorded in his diary: 'Evelyn and I were married at St. Paul's [sic]* Portman Square, at 12 o'clock. A woman was typewriting on the altar. Harold best man. Robert Byron gave away the bride, Alec and Pansy the witnesses. Evelyn wore a new black and yellow jumper suit with scarf. Went to the 500 Club and drank champagne cocktails under the suspicious eyes of Winifred Mackintosh and Prince George of Russia. From there to luncheon at Boulestin. Very good luncheon. Then to Paddington and by train to Oxford and taxi to Beckley.'[33]

. * More correctly St Paul (no 's) Portman Square, built in 1779 as a proprietary chapel for the Portman Estate.

A Common Experience, I'm Told

Like so much in Evelyn's diaries, his account of the wedding service was a mix of fact and fantasy. According to Shevelyn, no one was typing on the altar, although she did remember the sound of a typewriter coming from the vestry as they went in and being a little disconcerted by the mustachioed clergyman who married them, with his Cockney accent and heavy black boots.[1] Harold Acton recalled her being so overcome by the whole occasion that she could barely bring herself to say the words 'I do'.[2] Her jitters beforehand had been sufficiently advertised for Robert Byron to complain to his mother of having 'to *fetch* Evelyn Gardner to the church and I know she won't come'.[3] However after honeymooning at Beckley, of all places, where Evelyn and Alastair had shared their caravan, she declared herself happy with married life. The Waugh parents were holidaying in France at the time of the wedding but were telegraphed on the day and took the news in their stride. 'Arthur well again, Evelyns married,' Kate noted nonchalantly in her diary.[4] Lady Burghclere, though, was furious, 'quite inexpressibly pained', she told Evelyn after Geoffrey Fry[5] eventually broke it to her in mid-July, although years later Nancy Mitford could clearly recall her saying how pleased she was that her daughter should marry into 'such a good literary family'.[6] In any event, she immediately announced it in *The Times* 'to avoid scandal and misconstruction', as she charmingly told Shevelyn.[7]

Inconveniently for Evelyn's writing career, meanwhile, Lady Burghclere's sister was married to Sir George Duckworth, the brother of Evelyn's publisher Gerald Duckworth,* who had thus known all about Lady

---

* The Duckworth brothers were also, incidentally, the elder half-brothers of Virginia Woolf, who later accused them of having molested her during her childhood and adolescence.

Burghclere's disapproval of her prospective son-in-law. When Evelyn had submitted the manuscript of *Decline and Fall* in May, 'Uncle Gerald'[8] (as Evelyn dubbed him) personally intervened to demand the omission of many of the more indelicate scenes, whereupon Evelyn promptly took it down the street to Chapman & Hall, figuring that with his father abroad it would be easier for them to accept it, which they did, albeit ultimately with alterations only slightly less extensive than those that had been insisted on by Duckworth's. Soon after his return from honeymoon Evelyn set about designing the wrapper and going through the proofs and noted testily in his diary that 'Chapman's <u>not</u> an easy firm to deal with'.[9] At that point he and his new wife were briefly occupying dingy rooms at 25 Robert Adam Street, just off Baker Street, which Evelyn had taken shortly before their wedding to enable them to marry at the nearby church of St Paul. For the rest of the summer they lived at Underhill, before renting a flat in September on a handsome if then slightly dilapidated Georgian square in Islington.

The move to 17a Canonbury Square, their first proper marital home, coincided with the publication of *Decline and Fall*, an event that very quickly and profoundly changed Evelyn's life. The first review to appear, in *The Observer*, pronounced it 'richly and roaringly funny' and praised the author's 'exquisite ingenuousness of manner combined with a searching ingenuity of method; he is a critic of life, whose weapon is the joke disguised as a simple statement; he is an important addition to the ranks of those dear and necessary creatures – the writers who can make us laugh'.[10] The verdict that really mattered, however, came two weeks later, when England's grandest and highest-paid literary journalist Arnold Bennett, whose weekly column in the *Evening Standard* was splashed along the sides of London omnibuses, hailed the arrival of 'a genuinely new humorist' and 'an uncompromisingly and brilliant malicious satire, which in my opinion comes near to being quite first-rate'.[11]

Besides the universal acclaim in the press, Evelyn was congratulated equally effusively by his new friend Rebecca West, for whom it was 'one of the few funny books that have really made me laugh', and perhaps more surprisingly by the left-leaning Naomi Mitchison, who wrote to tell him she thought it 'perfectly plumb'. 'The really odd thing about it is the unity; you've kept it up all the time, so that at the end one is laughing in the same tone (and with the same violence) as at the beginning. And it's so ridiculously intelligent. I adore funny books, but when one looks for them one never finds anything but P. G. Wodehouse, and after all one is a high-brow.'[12] John Betjeman, whom Evelyn had befriended while both were schoolmasters, later recalled that to many of Evelyn's friends *Decline and Fall* seemed 'so rockingly funny, there could never be anything quite so funny again'.[13]

Gratifying as all this was, Evelyn was embarrassed a month later when J. B. Priestley and Cyril Connolly both drew attention to the enormous gulf in quality between his brilliant novel and Harold Acton's aptly named *Humdrum*, which had come out shortly after. Evelyn had dedicated *Decline and Fall* to Acton 'in homage and affection', however Priestley was adamant that 'Mr Waugh owes no homage to Mr Acton as a novelist, for the latter's story is a poor thing, showing us nothing but a vast social superiority to everybody and everything. I have always heard that Mr Acton is one of our brightest young wits, but "Humdrum" seems to me to be really tedious. Perhaps his title was too much for him.'[14] Connolly was scarcely less damning, observing that whereas *Humdrum* 'falls rather flat', *Decline and Fall* 'seems to possess every virtue which it lacks'.[15]*

The friendship between Evelyn and Acton thus entered a decidedly awkward phase, with Evelyn's star now clearly in the ascendant and Acton's reputation equally obviously in decline, a state of affairs to which the former mentor evidently found it hard to adjust. 'I don't know what to say to Harold,' Evelyn confided to a mutual Oxford friend around that time. 'If I tell him that I am going to lunch at the Ritz, he says "Of course you're a famous author but you can't expect a nonentity like me to join you there." If I suggest that we should go to a pub, he says, "My dear, what affectation – a popular novelist going to a pub."'[16]

Others were upset by *Decline and Fall* for different reasons. Eddie Gathorne-Hardy and Paddy Brodie (the latter a notably wild and drunken man about town who once mistook the bar at the Ritz for a *pissoir*)[17] had flown into 'a furious rage',[18] so Acton told Evelyn, after their names were borrowed for the extravagantly camp character Martin Gaythorn-Brodie – it was changed to the Hon. Miles Malpractice in the second edition in November for fear of libel. Similarly, Robert Byron wrote to say how '<u>very</u>

---

* While praising *Decline and Fall* in a letter to Arthur Waugh, Charles Scott Moncrieff also referred to *Humdrum*: 'It seems that only a very rich young man can afford to write as badly as this.' (25 October 1928; AWA.)

cross'[19] he was about the character of Kevin Saunderson (subsequently renamed Lord Parakeet), who arrives late and drunk to Mrs Beste-Chetwynde's weekend party and walks around 'birdlike and gay, pointing his thin white nose and making rude little jokes at everyone in turn in a shrill, emasculate voice'.[20] This was too obviously Gavin Henderson, an equally mincing friend of Byron and Brian Howard's, whom Evelyn confided to his diary he found 'most trying'.[21] Though briefly married, Henderson was, as one contemporary put it, 'a roaring pansy', and after succeeding his grandfather as the 2nd Lord Faringdon famously began a speech in the Upper House, 'My dears . . .'[22] Just as recognisable was Cecil Beaton, whom Evelyn had bullied so mercilessly as a schoolboy in Hampstead and who now found himself caricatured as the photographer David Lennox who accompanies Gaythorn-Brodie/Malpractice to King's Thursday: 'They emerged with little shrieks from an Edwardian brougham and made straight for the nearest looking-glass.'[23]

Evelyn shrugged off the offence his book caused. 'I am threatened with four civil actions and a horse whipping,' he wrote cheerfully to his publisher.[24] In any case the shedding of uncongenial acquaintances was offset by the new friendships he was beginning to make through his marriage and the more strategic contacts he had begun to cultivate following his establishment as the newest of London's literary lions, entertaining Arnold Bennett to dinner one night at Canonbury Square, and the next day having Cyril Connolly to lunch, an occasion that left Connolly with a lasting memory of the two Evelyns as 'this fantastic thing of the happily married young couple whom success had just touched with its wand'.[25]

Connolly was equally struck by their 'very small spick and span bandbox of a house', filled with odd bits and pieces lent by friends or bought from local junk shops and altered by Evelyn or made by a local carpenter. Portraits of each of them by Henry Lamb hung in the tiny dining room. When Harold Acton visited he found Evelyn crouched on the floor, sticking postage stamps onto a coal scuttle then applying a coat of varnish, 'endowing it with a patina of Sir Joshua Reynolds'. 'The atmosphere was that of a sparkling nursery,' recalled Acton. 'One hoped to see cradles full of little Evelyns in the near future, baby fauns blowing through reeds, falling off rocking-horses, pulling each other's pointed ears and piddling on the rug.'[26] But that was not to be.

Throughout that autumn and winter, Shevelyn was plagued by

ill-health. According to her written account of their marriage, she suffered severe period pains for which she underwent an operation – without which, her surgeon then discovered, she would never have been able to have children, although she recalled that she and Evelyn had no immediate plans in that regard, having 'decided to wait until we were better off'.[27] Sometime after that, in early October, Evelyn came home one day to find her feverish – 'a touch of influenza', he noted nonchalantly in his diary;[28] however the next day she became delirious as her temperature soared to 104. A few days later her mottled face led their doctor ('a cross between a butcher and vet in appearance', Evelyn recorded)[29] to diagnose German measles. Her sister Alathea and brother-in-law Geoffrey Fry suggested she go and convalesce at their house at Oare in Wiltshire; however it was two weeks before she was strong enough to travel down there.

They stayed at Oare for the best part of a fortnight while she recuperated and Evelyn got on with the various newspaper assignments organised by A.D. Peters, the then up-and-coming literary agent Alec had introduced him to in order to capitalise on the success of *Decline and Fall*. 'Please fix up anything that will earn me anything,' Evelyn wrote to Peters after he was taken on, 'even cricket criticism or mothers' welfare notes.'[30] Several were written from the standpoint of the nation's youth but providing he was well paid, he was happy to write about anything, so when the *Evening Standard* misunderstood his proposal to write about 'The Manners of the Younger Generation' and asked for a piece on 'The Mothers of the Younger Generation', he promptly dashed off 1,000 words on mothers instead. In June the next year he was similarly unhesitant when asked for a piece by *The Birth Control Review* of New York.

A handsome country house spectacularly situated beneath the Downs, Oare is nonetheless described by Pevsner as 'townish' and Evelyn found there 'an epicene preciosity or nicety about everything that goes better with cigarettes and London clothes than my tweeds and pipe'.[31] Originally Georgian and more or less square, the house had recently been enlarged and modernised by Clough Williams-Ellis, whose scheme had been written up in *Country Life* in March 1928 while Evelyn was still working on *Decline and Fall*. As Duncan McLaren suggests, the featured revamp may conceivably have prompted Margot Beste-Chetwynde's request to her architect Professor Silenus to replace her Tudor country house King's Thursday with 'something clean and square'. Equally, Alathea Fry, who struck Evelyn as 'extraordinarily ingenuous with a fluttery eagerness', may have contributed something to the creation of Margot herself, who arrives at the Llanabba sports 'like the first breath of spring in the Champs Élysées'. Like Margot and Paul Pennyfeather, Alathea was ten years older than Evelyn, and she had been photographed by Curtis Moffat in mannered poses not entirely dissimilar to the photographs taken by David Lennox of the back of Margot's head and the reflection of her hands in a bowl of ink.[32]

Alathea was arguably the most beautiful of all the Gardner sisters, however her looks were apparently wasted on her husband Geoffrey, who was far more interested in the various young men he had to stay at Oare, one of whom Evelyn described on the first weekend of their stay: 'Young Mr. Wayman [an accountant] appeared first in riding clothes and rode, then in white flannels and played tennis, then in tweeds and went out shooting – "having a smack at the longtails" as someone described it to Geoffrey – then in evening clothes and talked about architecture.'[33] Oblivious of Geoffrey's previous deviousness over the BBC job, Evelyn seemed equally unaware that he and Shevelyn were still under the scrutiny of this outwardly graceful and witty yet essentially rather cruel and calculating man. At the end of November, when Shevelyn was well enough, the Evelyns threw a house-warming cocktail party at Canonbury Square, cramming their flat full of guests cheerfully celebrating what most assumed to be the start of a long and happy marriage. However Mary Pakenham later recalled that as she left with Geoffrey, who gave her a lift home, he remarked: 'And when they buried her the little town had never seen a merrier funeral'[34] – presumably an intimation of his forebodings about Shevelyn's health and/or their marriage, neither of which was set to prosper over the course of the next year.

After spending Christmas in Wiltshire with Henry and Pansy Lamb, whose wedding they had gone to shortly after their own, in February 1929 the Evelyns set off for a cruise around the Mediterranean, a trip conceived as a kind of belated honeymoon and an opportunity for Shevelyn to recuperate properly while Evelyn earnt some money by writing articles and a book. *The Daily Express* marvelled that *Decline and Fall* had been so successful that the young author was able to afford this luxurious expedition out of his royalties,[35] whereas in fact Evelyn's enterprising new agent had managed to obtain free passages in return for favourable publicity.

Evelyn's eventual travel book, published in 1930 as *Labels*, accordingly devoted several pages to extolling the *Stella Polaris*'s 'quite remarkable' comfort, 'almost glacial cleanliness' and 'Jeeves-like standard of courtesy and efficiency'.[36]

But what had looked set to be a delightful adventure quickly became a nightmare for Shevelyn, who began to feel feverish as soon as they reached Paris. A dose of crème de menthe (unhelpfully suggested by a friend of Evelyn's) did no good at all and by the time they were in the train heading south she was 'beginning to feel very ill indeed', she later recalled.[37] In *Labels*, Evelyn disguised himself and his wife as 'Geoffrey and Juliet', the author's intermittent travelling companions, 'a rather sweet-looking young English couple – presumably, from the endearments of their conversation, and marked solicitude for each other's comfort, on their honeymoon, or at any rate recently married. The young man was small and pleasantly dressed and wore a slight, curly moustache [Evelyn had recently grown one in line with his original idea to call his travel book 'Quest of a Moustache'];[38] he was reading a particularly good detective story with apparent intelligence. His wife was huddled in a fur coat in the corner, clearly far from well . . . Every quarter of an hour or so they said to each other, "Are you quite sure you're alright darling?" And replied, "Perfectly, really I am. Are *you* my precious?" But Juliet was far from being all right.'[39]

As Shevelyn's condition worsened they eventually moved to a more comfortable carriage – though Evelyn fretted about the expense – and on arrival at Monte Carlo she 'trudged miserably beside Evelyn through falling snow from hotel to hotel until we found one that would take us in'. Two days later, an English doctor consented to her going aboard the *Stella Polaris* providing she remained in her bunk, however as soon as the ship slipped out of port she began to cough up blood. By now suffering from double pneumonia and pleurisy (as it was later diagnosed) and unable to sleep because of her cough, it was 'a horrible voyage', she recalled, 'imprisoned in that little cabin with its closed port-hole and dark walls at which I looked for so long'. At Haifa they hired a nurse, 'a pallid, skinny Israeli who cannot have had much training for all she did was to insist on scraping my tongue with a spoon'. When they reached Port Said she was taken ashore by stretcher 'looking distressingly like a corpse',[40] and rushed to the British Hospital.

At first it was feared that she might not survive and Evelyn sent a post-card to Pansy Lamb saying that by the time she got it, Shevelyn would probably be dead.[41] She did eventually pull through, however, and after ten days she was 'sitting up in bed knitting and reading and falling deeply in love with her doctor', Evelyn reported.[42]

Evelyn visited the hospital every day to read aloud from P. G. Wode-house but otherwise wrote articles to help defray their escalating expenses, pondered a new novel and disconsolately loitered about the 'intolerably dull'[43] Port Said: 'This is not the town I should have chosen for a month's visit,' he wrote to Henry Yorke. 'There is one expensive hotel with a jazz band and bugs, innumerable bars where the P & O stewards may be seen getting mildly drunk on Guinness at 2/6 bottle, two brothels, one Euro-pean one Arab . . . and this [Union] club where the shipping office clerks attempt to create an Ethel M. Dell garrison life.'[44] Occasionally he was entertained by the consul and his 'harlot' wife, who led the women guests away after dinner saying, 'Goodbye darling men. Keep your naughtiest stories for us.' On another evening at a dance, Evelyn reported, 'she opened her mouth and invited me to throw sugar into it'.[45]

Alastair Graham briefly visited from Athens and took Evelyn to Cairo for some 'varied and vigorous nightlife'; he also gave them £50 so they could 'struggle along for another week or two'.[46] Of the Cairo trip Shevelyn recalled that she 'didn't grudge Evelyn the invitation or its acceptance' but also remarked: 'I don't think he would have done that if he'd really loved me, would he?'[47]*

At the end of March they travelled south to the Pyramids and a two-week stay at the Mena House Hotel, 'very enormous & hideously expensive but sunny & I think a good place for Evelyn's recuperation', Evelyn told Harold Acton. It was a chance too to see the Tutankhamen discoveries, 'real works of art – of exquisite grace,' Evelyn reported, 'just as fine as anything which has survived of Athenian Art'.[48]

From there they headed to Malta to rejoin the *Stella Polaris*, Shevelyn by now well enough to organise the ship's fancy-dress ball, while Evelyn, unlikely as it sounds, joined the onboard Sports Committee, 'which is

---

* The demonic voices who accuse Pinfold of being 'queer' in *The Ordeal of Gilbert Pinfold* (1957) later demand: 'I want the truth, Pinfold. *What were you doing* in Egypt in 1929?' If this hints at an illicit dalliance with his former lover, the voices' naming of the Mena House Hotel where Evelyn stayed with his wife seems to suggest otherwise.

very serious indeed'.[49] At Athens they saw Alastair Graham and Mark Ogilvie-Grant, and at Constantinople they joined the Sitwells for 'a brief & rather uneasy luncheon party at the Embassy'.[50]

Approaching Venice in early May, Evelyn told Harold Acton that it was at last turning into a delightful voyage. 'Evelyn is growing stronger every day. There is plenty of sun and a calm sea and a very good background of ludicrous fellow travellers to amuse us in between ports. In the Bosporus a Greek tried to seduce first Evelyn & then me & then the bar-steward. Evelyn & I were flattered & delighted but the bar steward furious & the Greek had to leave the ship.'[51] As they headed for home (via Barcelona – where Evelyn was dazzled by the buildings of Gaudí – and Lisbon), he reported that they were thinking of 'taking a minute house & settling somewhere in the country for the summer', partly on account of being so 'hideously' broke but also so that he could get on with writing his new novel, *Vile Bodies*.[52]

Although she sequestered herself in the country in later life, Shevelyn cared little for rural seclusion at that time and so was perhaps never especially keen on that idea. The voyage had evidently also gone on too long as far as she was concerned, and towards the end she told a friend that 'we are getting a little fed-up and shall be glad to get home'.[53] In *Labels*, written after the devastating events of the coming summer, Evelyn described being woken several times in the night by the ship's foghorn as they neared Harwich, 'a very dismal sound, premonitory, perhaps, of coming trouble, for Fortune is the least capricious of deities, and arranges things on the just and rigid system that no one shall be happy for very long'.[54]

When they reached London at the end of May Evelyn's publisher at Duckworth's, Tom Balston, confided to Anthony Powell that he thought the Waughs' marriage seemed strained, although Shevelyn declared herself 'frightfully well – really much better than before I caught that beastly pneumonia'.[55] Having already missed so many parties in the three months they were away, she was loath to go and sequester herself in the country just as the most vibrant London season since the war was reaching its peak.

Thus, as Evelyn soon reported to Henry Yorke, they came to a fateful arrangement whereby she went to live at Canonbury Square, accompanied by her old friend Nancy Mitford, while he went off to write his book in a pub.[56] In the meantime they stayed a few days at Underhill and on

5 June Kate Waugh noted innocently in her diary: 'Evelyns lunched with J Heygate.'

John Heygate had been a friend of both Evelyns since the previous autumn, introduced coincidentally by the same Bobbie Roberts who had brought the Evelyns together at the Ranee's party. For a time they made 'such a happy trio', Heygate later recalled. The slightly louche son of an uncompromisingly conventional Eton housemaster, and heir via his equally strait-laced uncle to an Irish baronetcy and some 5,000 acres in County Londonderry, Heygate also descended through his mother from the diarist John Evelyn, and had very nearly been named Evelyn himself after his distinguished ancestor, which, as his friend Anthony Powell drily remarked would have added an extra layer of confusion to future events.[57]

Tall, reasonably good-looking, with 'an easy rather lounging carriage', as Powell described it, he was reputed to be 'agreeably successful with women', albeit 'well short of being anything like a professional woman-izer'.[58] He used to say that his chief misfortune was that stupid people thought him intelligent and intelligent people thought him stupid. After Oxford he had gone to Heidelberg to learn German and formed a lasting romantic attachment to that country, but after failing to get into the Diplomatic Service he had suffered a breakdown, possibly exacerbated by his heavy drinking, and began hallucinating that everyone around him in a London club was talking German. By the time he met the Evelyns his troubles were reasonably well hidden – although they would re-emerge later – and he was working as an assistant news editor at the BBC. Evelyn would later describe Heygate as 'radically contemptible', however according to Powell he 'was very much taken' with him when he first got to know him.[59] Shevelyn maintained that she had initially thought Heygate 'a nice young man but nothing more'.[60]

While Evelyn took himself off to the Abingdon Arms to write, Heygate was among those entrusted with chaperoning Shevelyn and Nancy Mitford, who recalled a succession of costume balls so endless that 'we hardly ever saw the light of day, except at dawn'.[61] The summer of 1929 was a particularly hectic one for the well-connected partygoers known as the Bright Young People who were about to be definitively satirised in Evelyn's new novel:

The Waughs in 1890. From left: Elsie, Connie, Dr Alexander Waugh ('the Brute'), Alick, Annie (Mrs Waugh), Arthur and Trissie.

The Brute: Annie was terrified lest Arthur's birth interfere with his first day of partridge-shooting.

Their house at Midsomer Norton: Evelyn relished its dark hidden corners and assorted interesting smells.

The Raban family
circa 1892, with
Arthur and Kate
top left.

Kate and Arthur
about to explore
the lanes of
Buckinghamshire,
and (below)
posing after their
engagement; as
Evelyn later saw
it, his father was
'acting all the
time'.

(Left to right) Alec, Arthur and Evelyn, circa 1906.

Evelyn on the steps of 11 Hillfield Road with his nanny, Lucy Hodges.

Kate, Arthur, Evelyn, Alec (with cricket bat) and their poodle on holiday at Midsomer Norton, 1904.

Alec, Kate and Arthur in the garden of the newly built Underhill, 1909.

Evelyn (second from right) with the Pistol Troop, circa 1910.

Evelyn, aged eight.

Above: Evelyn (second top row, third from left) at Heath Mount, with his bête noire Cecil Beaton (same row, third from right).

Right: Alec, Evelyn, Kate and their poodle in 1912.

Head's House during Evelyn's desolate first year at Lancing, 1917. Evelyn is sitting second from the left on the ground, next to the other 'new man', Roger Fulford, far left. The Rev. Bowlby is behind the cup in a dog collar

From top to bottom: Evelyn at Lancing in 1921, at Oxford in 1923 and teaching at Aston Clinton in 1926.

Evelyn's first love at Oxford, Richard Pares, seen here in the Alps with Cyril Connolly (wearing beret); Evelyn complained of having been 'cuckolded by Connolly'.

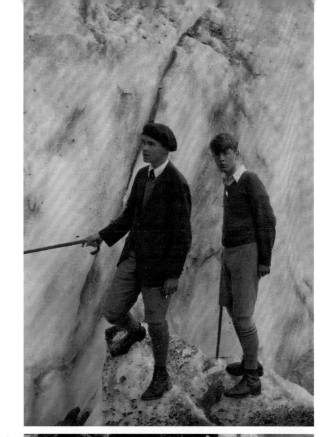

Evelyn's next 'friend of my heart' was Alastair Graham (below), pictured here shortly before they met at Oxford, and (right) the photo he sent beckoning Evelyn to 'come and drink with me somewhere'.

Lundy Island, Easter 1925: (left to right) Richard, Olivia, Gwen and David Plunket Greene, Terence Greenidge and Elizabeth Russell. Evelyn is seated in foreground.

On the same Lundy holiday: Olivia Plunket Greene, Patrick Balfour, David Plunket Greene and Matthew Ponsonby.

Evelyn on his Francis-Barnett motor-bicycle at Aston Clinton in February 1926.

'Oh Nina, *what a lot of parties*' (... Masked parties, Savage parties, Victorian parties, Greek parties, Wild West parties, Russian parties, Circus parties, parties where one had to dress as somebody else, almost naked parties in St John's Wood, parties in flats and studios and houses and ships and hotels and night clubs, in windmills and swimming-baths, tea parties at school where one ate muffins and meringues and tinned crab, parties at Oxford where one drank brown sherry and smoked Turkish cigarettes, dull dances in London and comic dances in Scotland and disgusting dances in Paris – all that succession and repetition of massed humanity... Those vile bodies...)

For a time Evelyn's writing regime worked well, and on 12 June 'Dragoman' (his friend Tom Driberg) reported in the *Daily Express* that he had telegrammed his wife: 'Novel started splendidly. All characters horribly seasick.'[62] By 20 June Evelyn reckoned he had written 25,000 words in ten days. 'It is rather like P. G. Wodehouse all about bright young people,' he told Henry Yorke. With Evelyn 'chained hand and foot' to his novel, Shevelyn and Heygate came to Beckley to see him and they all went for lunch at the Trout Inn just north of Oxford with Heygate's girlfriend Eleanor Watts, a twenty-year-old undergraduate at the university. Shortly afterwards Heygate proposed to Eleanor but she was unsure, and when they subsequently went to a party in London – she later recalled that it had been held by Bobbie Roberts, a curiously catalytic figure in the whole Shevelyn story – Heygate got so drunk that Eleanor left without him. Shevelyn was also there and ended up going home with Heygate; they were found together at his basement flat in Cornwall Gardens the next morning by a manservant.[63] Shevelyn later recalled that the realisation that she was 'very seriously in love' with Heygate came as an 'emotional thunderbolt'.[64]

Oblivious of all this and happy with the progress of his novel, Evelyn told Henry Yorke that he was toying with the idea of coming up to London for Bryan and Diana Guinness's 1860s party on 25 June 'if I thought there would be anyone who wouldn't be too much like the characters in my new book'.[65] He did not go in the end, but afterwards the indubitably safe Harold Acton thoughtfully reassured him that he had 'danced blissfully' with Shevelyn. Later that evening, however, Heygate had taken Shevelyn and Nancy Mitford on to another party aboard the schooner

Friendship, moored off Charing Cross pier, where *The Tatler* inadvertently photographed them lounging on deck in 'a very amiable position', as Heygate later described it.[66] There was another couple in the foreground yet Heygate was clearly recognisable and Shevelyn, with her back to the camera, could also be identified from the costume in which she had been photographed by *Sketch* at the Guinnesses' party.[67]

The next evening, Thursday, 26 June, Shevelyn and Heygate were both among the guests at a small dinner party held by Tom Balston when Heygate, having been up till dawn the previous night, fell asleep between courses. The day after that they went to Anthony Powell and Constant Lambert's cocktail party at Tavistock Square. On that occasion Evelyn did travel up from Beckley, however Powell remembered that he and his wife arrived separately, neither of them seemed to enjoy themselves and they left early, together, after what appeared to be a brief altercation between Shevelyn and Heygate. 'This was the first public occasion when there was a sense of something being wrong between the Waughs,' wrote Powell. 'Quite how wrong I did not even then take in.'

The next day the two Evelyns went to stay at Heygate's parents' house on the Solent. Powell was again a witness and remembered 'no special tensions throughout the visit',[68] although when they went to tea at Beaulieu Elizabeth Montagu observed that 'Waugh seemed bored and monosyllabic, whilst his wife and Heygate tried rather too hard to compensate.'[69]

Shortly after this, on 13 July, Powell and Heygate set off on a motoring trip to Germany and according to Powell spoke little about 'the embroilment in which Heygate now undoubtedly found himself'. (Nor, incidentally, did they talk much about the rise of Hitler, even though Heygate later admitted that on a previous trip to Bavaria he had carried with him a letter that began: 'Dear Hitler, this is to introduce John Heygate, a young Englishman interested in your movement.')[70] After two weeks they reached Munich, where various urgent cables awaited them: 'Instruct Heygate return immediately Waugh.'[71]

The events leading up to this stern missive had begun with the appearance of the incriminating photograph in the 3 July issue of *The Tatler*, which threw Shevelyn into a desperate quandary, knowing that many of their friends would have seen it. Her sister Mary begged her to say nothing, however her flatmate Nancy Mitford advised her to tell Evelyn that she loved him and to say that her attitude in the photograph was not what it appeared. 'But I *don't* love him,' said Shevelyn, explaining that she had never loved her husband and that she had only married him to escape the tyranny of her mother.[72]

By now anxious to come clean, she wrote a letter to Evelyn (which he received on about 9 July and promptly destroyed) saying she was in love with Heygate, and when Evelyn returned to London three days later she confessed that she had already slept with him. Evelyn's subsequent divorce petition stated: 'My wife and I had a long talk upon the subject, and I agreed to forgive her if she would give up Heygate. This she promised to do.'[73]

There followed a miserable fortnight during which Shevelyn told Alec Waugh that Evelyn was drinking far too much and making himself ill, and then accusing her of trying to poison him. When Alec remarked that they had always seemed so happy together she replied: 'Yes I suppose I was,' then after a pause, 'but never as happy as I've been with my sisters,' which struck Alec as a peculiar thing for a wife to say about a husband.[74]

They were photographed looking distinctly gloomy at Vyvyan Holland's 'Tropical' party on the *Friendship* – one caption commenting that the author of *Decline and Fall* appeared 'somewhat scared even though there were no fierce Zulus on board'[75] – and at Henry Yorke's wedding on 25 July the groom's aunt, who had presumably got wind of Shevelyn's predicament, wryly noted her 'outward mood of butter not melting in her mouth'.[76]

The next day Evelyn and Eleanor Watts took the train to Crewe to stay for a few days at Haslington Hall, her family home in Cheshire. Shevelyn was supposed to have gone too but, as Heygate later recalled, 'she changed her mind and returned to me'.[77] This is probably the point at which Evelyn realised once and for all that the reconciliation was not going to work so sent the famous cable summoning Heygate from Germany.

At Haslington, Evelyn and Eleanor sat around miserably drinking Black Velvets, Eleanor by now regretting having turned Heygate down and Evelyn so distraught that he suggested a suicide pact in the rhododendrons. Eleanor later told Selina Hastings that she suspected Evelyn was not so much madly in love with Shevelyn as flattered that such an attractive woman had been prepared to marry him.* She urged him to put her out of his mind, to which he replied, 'I can't, I can't.'[78]

Shevelyn's desertion could hardly have come at a worse time as far as Evelyn's work was concerned, with *Vile Bodies* barely half written and *Labels* not even started although he had promised to deliver it to Duckworth's by the end of July. 'The last few weeks have been a nightmare of very terrible suffering,' Evelyn wrote to his publisher, 'which, if I could explain, you would understand. You shall have the book, unless I go off my head, as soon as I can begin to rearrange my thoughts. At present I can do <u>nothing</u> of any kind.'[79] A few days later he asked Balston to omit the dedication to his wife in all subsequent editions of *Rossetti*.

Evelyn returned home to an empty flat on 1 August and the next day received a letter from Shevelyn saying that she was living with Heygate, at which point he decided to file for a divorce and asked Alec to tell their parents. 'It's going to be a great blow to them,' said Alec, to which Evelyn retorted, 'What about me?'[80] Arthur reacted as predicted. 'Your poor, poor mother,' he said when Alec broke the news, 'your poor, poor mother.' Only Kate seemed to think about her wretched son.[81]

A few days later Evelyn wrote to his parents: 'I asked Alec to tell you the sad & to me radically shocking news that Evelyn has gone to live with a man called Heygate. I am accordingly filing a petition for divorce. I am afraid that this will be a blow to you but I assure you not nearly as severe a blow as it is to me . . . My plans are vague about the flat etc. May I come & live with you sometimes?'[82] He added that 'Evelyn's defection was preceded by no kind of quarrel or estrangement. So far as I knew we were both serenely happy. It must be some hereditary tic. Poor Baroness.'[83]

Clearly the marriage had not been as happy for Shevelyn as Evelyn thought. At the time she was heard to complain that her husband was 'bad in bed',[84] and she later told Michael Davie that she suspected Evelyn of being homosexual. It is true that Evelyn had had very limited sexual experience with women, and the opportunities to make up for this during their marriage were doubtless limited by Shevelyn's various illnesses. Nonetheless it seems just as likely that their incompatibility was due

---

* Mary Pakenham's view was that Evelyn had been 'tremendously gratified when this aristocratic, chic, honeypot consented to be his wife, and naturally when she threw him over it was shattering' (see Note by Lady Mary Clive on Evelyn Gardner [1987], copy in AWA).

to a straightforward lack of chemistry as any deficiencies in his sexual technique or orientation. He would have several passionate affairs with women in years to come and went on to have seven (six surviving) children from his second marriage. While he was always frank about his earlier homosexual experiences and did not go out of his way to deny being to some extent bisexual, the weight of evidence points to his having been predominantly heterosexual by the time he married.*

For his own part, Evelyn told Harold Acton that his reason for seeking a divorce was 'simply that I cannot live with anyone who is avowedly in love with someone else . . . I did not know it was possible to be so miserable & live but I am told that this is a common experience.'[85] Acton was glad Evelyn was 'making a gesture of it for Heygate is too contemptible, and he ought to be made to realize how monstrously he has behaved'. However he was so tactless about the possible reasons for Shevelyn's betrayal ('Are you so very male in your sense of possession?'[86]) that Evelyn complained to Henry Yorke that 'homosexual people however kind & intelligent simply don't understand at all what one feels in this kind of case'.[87]

On 6 August, two days after being told of Evelyn's troubles, Arthur and Kate went to meet Lady Burghclere and Geoffrey Fry to see if anything could be done to save the marriage. They all decided that if Evelyn could be persuaded to hold fire with the divorce proceedings, it might be a good idea for Shevelyn to go to Venice with her sister Alathea, 'in order to think it over once more,' as Shevelyn recalled, 'and perhaps on my return it might be possible for Evelyn to take me back'.

While she was away Heygate went to stay at the Watts's beach house at Selsey where, evidently anxious to keep his options open, he again asked Eleanor to marry him in case Shevelyn did change her mind and went back to her husband. Eleanor 'would not hear of it', she later recalled.[88] Heygate then cabled Shevelyn to let her know that he was waiting for her and she promptly returned to London to be with him. Evelyn's divorce petition was duly served on 9 September.

---

* Anthony Powell recalled having been on a train once with Evelyn later in life when a very good-looking young man entered their compartment pushing a tea trolley. After he had gone, Powell asked Evelyn if he preferred men or women, to which Evelyn replied: 'I suppose I must say I prefer women – but when I see a boy like that I get an awful pang!' Selina Hastings to author, February 2016.

12

....

Perversion to Rome

In the months following the break-up several of Shevelyn's closest friends switched their allegiance to the man she had thrown over. Pansy Lamb, whose husband Henry told Evelyn how profoundly he admired his 'magnificently patient & generous'[1] response to the 'catastrophe', was herself not vastly impressed by her former flatmate's justification that 'Waugh was too difficult to live up to & that he secretly hated her when he was ill!' or the fact that 'she really seems to enjoy the publicity her conduct entails'.[2] Shevelyn had been staying at the Lambs' Dorset cottage in mid-August when the first lawyer's letter arrived announcing that Evelyn was suing for divorce, prompting her to exclaim, 'Well, you can't call life dull!'[3]

Nancy Mitford had given Shevelyn a dinner party to celebrate their engagement the previous year and she regarded her as her best friend,[4] yet as soon as she became aware of the affair she moved out of the flat at Canonbury Square. Shevelyn later maintained that Nancy left 'not because of her admiration for Evelyn but because Lord or Lady Redesdale insisted',[5] but in any event the two friends never saw each other again and instead Nancy set about developing a lifelong friendship with Evelyn, someone whom she and her sisters did not yet know well but nevertheless idolised as the author of their favourite book, *Decline and Fall*.[6]

Nancy's twelve-year-old sister Jessica later recalled her excitement when 'Evelyn Waugh, a writer feller and one of the main Swinbrook sewers'[7] promised to immortalise her pet sheep Miranda by substituting the word 'sheepish' for 'divine' in his forthcoming *Vile Bodies*, and duly did so with his description of Edward Throbbing's 'perfectly sheepish house in Hertford St'.

Nancy, meanwhile, began meeting Evelyn regularly for lunch at the Ritz, where he teased her for being 'a dangerous red' and advised her on her doomed love affair with the homosexual Hamish Erskine, explaining to her about 'sexual shyness in men',[8] of which he may have had some experience, but also suggesting she 'dress better & catch a better man'. 'Evelyn is always so full of sound common sense', Nancy wrote to Mark Ogilvie-Grant.[9]

For a time, Nancy's nineteen-year-old sister Diana was even more instrumental in mending Evelyn's broken heart. The most beautiful of the Mitfords, a ravishing blue-eyed blonde described by James Lees-Milne as 'the nearest thing to Botticelli's Venus that I have ever seen',[10] Diana had at her disposal several luxurious houses where Evelyn could lick his wounds and catch up with his writing.

As with Nancy, Evelyn had got to know the Guinnesses through Shevelyn, and in July he had written the introduction to their catalogue of works by 'Bruno Hat', the imaginary German artist whom Bryan claimed to have discovered in a shop in Sussex and whose spoof exhibition was held at their house on 23 July, towards the end of the Evelyns' failed reconciliation fortnight. After his return from Cheshire to find Shevelyn had gone for good, Evelyn miserably took refuge at the Guinnesses' house on the Sussex coast. On separate occasions that month and the next he also stayed with them in Ireland at Knockmaroon, just west of Dublin's Phoenix Park, after which he buried himself away at a pub in north Devon in a painful attempt to finish *Vile Bodies*. 'It has been infinitely difficult,' he wrote to Henry Yorke in September, 'and is certainly the last time I shall try to make a book about sophisticated people. It all seems to shrivel up & rot internally and I am relying on a sort of cumulative futility for any effect it may have. As soon as I have enough pages covered to call it a book I shall join Bryan & Diana in Paris.'[11]

In early October, after scrawling 'The End Thank God' across the last page, he duly made his way to the large Guinness flat in the 7th arrondissement. Each morning, with Diana by then pregnant with her first child and resting in bed, Evelyn made a start on his Mediterranean travelogue *Labels* while Nancy worked on her first novel, *Highland Fling* – which she subsequently had to alter 'quite a lot as it is so like Evelyn's [*Vile Bodies*] in little ways,' she told Mark Ogilvie-Grant, '*such* a bore'[12] – and Bryan was busy with *Singing Out of Tune*, a portrait of a failed marriage and also, like *Vile Bodies*, an indictment of a way of life. (It is often said that his idea came from the Waughs' marriage, although by the time the book came out in 1933 Bryan and Diana had themselves separated following her affair with Oswald Mosley, and Bryan begged his wife to tell everyone that it was *not* their story.)

Back in London, Evelyn took to arriving at the Guinnesses' house at 10 Buckingham Street (now Buckingham Place) in the morning and staying all day. Diana was fascinated by dazzlingly clever men and equally capable of fascinating them. Having recently struck up a close rapport with Lytton Strachey, she now found herself similarly taken with Evelyn. They would 'laugh all day long', she remembered. 'You couldn't help loving him. He was so funny and so unlike anyone else.'[13]

During her confinement, with Bryan out most days reading for the Bar, Diana became increasingly dependent on Evelyn for her entertainment and in due course he began to fall in love with her. A decade later, in his unfinished novel *Work Suspended*, Evelyn described the novelist-narrator John Plant's growing infatuation with the pregnant heiress Lucy Simmonds, which he later admitted to Diana was 'to some extent a portrait of me in love with you'.[14]

On his usual morning call, John is greeted by Lucy 'lying in bed in a chaos of newspapers, letters and manicure tools':

> Couched as she was, amid quilted bed-jacket and tumbled sheets – one arm bare to the elbow where the wide sleeve fell back and showed the tender places of wrist and forearm, the other lost in the warm depths of the bed, with her pale skin taking colour against the dead white linen, and her smile of confident, morning welcome; as I had greeted her countless times and always with a keener joy . . . her beauty rang through the room like a peal of bells . . . So another stage was reached in my falling in love with Lucy, while each week she grew heavier and slower and less apt for love, so that I accepted the joy of her companionship without reasoning.

The similarities between fact and fiction extended to the narrator's sense of losing her after the birth of her child, however for the time being Evelyn had Diana all to himself, sitting on her bed during the morning while she dealt with her correspondence, then accompanying her on various excursions in the afternoon – 'carriage exercise' in her chauffeur-driven

Daimler to the zoo and occasional visits to Underhill for tea – before re-turning for dinner in the evening.

Seeing Evelyn almost every day as she did at this time, and with him doubtless striving to be as cheerful and amusing as he could, Diana became convinced that the break-up of his marriage had not hurt him as severely as many of his old friends supposed and that there was even 'a good deal of relief' stemming from his recognition that he had made a mistake in marrying Shevelyn in the first place. 'But his pride was hurt, naturally, & the very fact that everyone felt so loudly sorry for him was salt in the wound, even if the wound was superficial.' In any case, she added, 'one couldn't have had him constantly in the house if he'd been saddled with the other Evelyn, who though very pretty wasn't much else'.[15]

When *Vile Bodies* was published in January 1930 Evelyn dedicated it to the Guinnesses, whose numerous kind gestures had also included giving him a birthday lunch at the Ritz and sending him a Christmas stock-ing 'full of lovely things including a gold watch!!' as Kate was thrilled to record.[16] He in turn sent them the leather-bound manuscript of his book as a belated Christmas present with apologies that it 'will never be of the smallest value'. In 1984 it was sold at Christie's for £55,000, enough in those days to buy a small house in west London.[17]

His divorce also came through that month, and in a preface to a later edition Evelyn admitted that the 'sharp disturbance in my private life' had upset the latter part, where the tone shifts dramatically at the begin-ning of Chapter Seven, the point at which he resumed writing after being abandoned by his wife.

His nominal hero Adam Fenwick-Symes becomes the hard-pressed gossip columnist 'Mr Chatterbox', who resorts to 'snaps and snippets about cocktail parties given in basement flats by spotty announcers at the BBC' – a caustic reference to Heygate, whom Evelyn derided as 'the Basement Boy', presumably because he lived in a basement flat.* When, in the next chapter, Adam takes Nina, whom he hopes to marry, and Ginger Littlejohn, the rival who steals her, to a party on an airship moored in a 'degraded suburb', it is hard not to think of the incriminating photograph of Shevelyn and Heygate taken aboard the *Friendship*: 'There were two

---

* Anthony Powell thought the tag resulted from Evelyn's having met Heygate at Powell's basement flat, however it is a little hard to imagine Evelyn coining it due to Heygate's occa-sional presence in *someone else*'s basement.

people making love to each other near him . . . reclining on cushions.' The scene also includes clear allusions to Shevelyn's casual attitude to their marriage:

'Nina,' said Adam, 'let's get married soon, don't you think?'

'Yes, it's a bore not being married.'

'I don't know if this sounds absurd,' said Adam, 'but I do feel that a marriage ought to *go on* – for quite a long time, I mean. D'you feel that too at all?'

Critics once again praised the book's great wit and originality, however the reviews this time were not quite so universally glowing, with Arnold Bennett regretting 'the lack of a well-laid plot' which 'resulted in a large number of pages which demand a certain obstinate and sustained effort for their perusal'.[18] Interviewed by the *Paris Review* more than thirty years later, Evelyn himself called it 'a bad book, I think, not so carefully constructed as the first'.[19]

However, as he also recalled, he had 'popularised a fashionable language like the Beatnik writers today, and the book caught on'.[20] With *Vile Bodies* selling 2,000 copies a week, expressions such as 'shy-making' and 'too too sick-making' soon spread far beyond the Guinnesses' circle of friends where Evelyn had first heard them. Within a month of publication, the *Daily Mirror* reported that black suede shoes (among the various spoof fashions propagated by Adam during his stint as Mr Chatterbox) were being 'much worn up at Oxford just now'.[21]

Evelyn's own stock also rose dramatically. 'My dear Waugh,' his old mentor J. F. Roxburgh wrote to him, 'You are now so eminent that I dare not use your Christian name as I once did!'[22] Sought out by literary lion-hunters such as Sibyl Colefax and Emerald Cunard, he soon became a fixture in fashionable society, his diary routinely recording lunch with Noël Coward ('a simple, friendly nature. No brains.'), tea with the Labour Prime Minister Ramsay MacDonald ('a nasty and inadequate man'), and dinner with the Duke of Marlborough ('such a mundane mind,' whispered the duchess, 'will go to any party for which he is sent a printed invitation'). Not in the least bit shy about capitalising on his fame, he wrote after one evening: 'After dinner I went to the Savoy Theatre and said "I am Evelyn Waugh. Please give me a seat." So they did.'[23]

The huge success of *Vile Bodies* earned Evelyn considerable sums in royalties and simultaneously completely revived the fortunes of Chapman & Hall, whose business had been precarious ever since the lapse of Dickens's copyrights in 1920. It also enabled Evelyn to demand increasingly exorbitant rates for his journalism. 'I will only do <u>feature</u> articles,' he told his agent, '– not side columns like Heygate – with photograph of me and general air of importance.' To editors he was equally forthright. 'I should quite like to broadcast but what will you pay?' he wrote to the BBC. 'It isn't any good my taking up your time with a voice test if at the end, you find my avarice insupportable. Broadcasting is clearly more exacting work than journalism. I get £20 a thousand words' writing. I suggest £25 a thousand for speaking. If that's too much don't answer.'[24] The response on this occasion was 'Too expensive, have a cocktail?',[25] however enough newspapers did meet his demands and in May he was elated to record that his regular annual income had temporarily rocketed to £2,500 a year.

That spring, 1930, he finished writing *Labels* while staying at the Guinnesses' seaside house in Sussex. The book was published in late September and again dedicated to Bryan and Diana, 'without whose encouragement and hospitality this book would not have been finished'. Diana's baby was born at the beginning of March, a boy who was soon christened Jonathan partly due to the fact that Evelyn, who stood godfather, was at the time contemplating a biography of Jonathan Swift.

After recovering from giving birth, with her old nanny engaged to look after the baby, Diana was keen to make up for lost party-going time and although Evelyn continued to see her regularly for a while, with so many other people now vying for her attention he resented the loss of their previous intimacy and in due course started to behave as objectionably as only he knew how. In July he went to stay with them at Pool Place in Sussex: 'Diana and I quarrelled at luncheon,' he recorded in his diary. 'We bathed. Diana and I quarrelled at dinner and after dinner. Next day I decided to leave. Quarrelled with Diana again and left.'[26] At various parties over the next few weeks he went out of his way to avoid her. Eventually he wrote her a note: 'When I got back last night I wrote you two long letters and tore them up. All I tried to say was that I must have seemed unfriendly lately and I am sorry. Please believe it is only because I am puzzled and ill at ease with myself. Much later everything will be all right. Don't bother to answer. E.'[27]

A few weeks later Bryan wrote innocently to say how glad Diana was to receive his letter: 'We had both been very upset by your coldness. If it was due to anything she had done or said perhaps the cause can be explained away. But I daresay it was something too elusive to put into words. Anyway you must remember that we are missing you a great deal; and if you should be able to change your mind and come over for a few days nothing would make us more happy.'[28] But Evelyn kept refusing their invitations, so Diana reluctantly concluded that he no longer wished to be her friend. It was one of the deepest friendships in each of their lives, yet it lasted barely a year. During Diana's pregnancy, Evelyn's visits to her served as a bubble within which he could forget about the trauma of his marriage, and it seems that as soon as Diana began to see other people he felt his humiliation all over again.

It was not until a few weeks before he died that Evelyn attempted to explain: 'You ask why our friendship petered out. The explanation is very discreditable to me. Pure jealousy. You (and Bryan) were immensely kind to me at a time when I greatly needed kindness, after my desertion by my first wife. I was infatuated with you. Not of course that I aspired to your bed but I wanted you to myself as especial confidant and comrade. After Jonathan's birth you began to enlarge your circle. I felt lower in your affections than Harold Acton and Robert Byron and I couldn't compete or take a humbler place. That is the sad and sordid truth.'[29] It was one of the last letters he wrote.

Diana had consoled herself by telling Nancy that his behaviour had latterly become 'so horrid when he did come that one didn't miss him at all'.[30] Yet she remained fiercely loyal to his memory and quick to refute whatever misconceptions she perceived about him. She maintained, for instance, that to call him a snob was nonsense – which is perhaps debatable, although it is certainly true that he was never drawn to grandeur for its own sake and did not choose his friends on account of their rank or worldly position. Neither did he go out of his way to court popularity among aristocrats; indeed his behaviour towards them was often so far from sycophantic as to be downright rude – which is perhaps why so many of them ended up with a grudge of some sort or another against him and a (snobbish) tendency on their own part to accuse him of social climbing. 'He liked people,' wrote Diana, 'as I do, because they amused him, or he was fond of them, or he found them stimulating; sometimes he sought their company because of some oddity which delighted the novelist in him. He disliked those who bored or irritated him, and needless to say they, too, were all sorts of men and women ... there was never any question of him trying to get to know grandees. The boot was on the other foot.'[31]

It is probably true that Evelyn, for his part, did not 'aspire to Diana's bed', although that is not the same thing as saying that he did not find her attractive, which he almost certainly did. As with a lot of men, the more unobtainable the girl, the more attractive she became.

The reverse had been the case with Audrey Lucas, the only daughter of a domineering father whose more submissive demeanour Evelyn evidently found less alluring. But she had remained keen on him, and he began to see a lot of her after his divorce, by which time her marriage to Harold Scott was also going badly (they later divorced and she married the actor Douglas Clarke-Smith). Even if Evelyn knew that he was unlikely to fall in love with Audrey, he may have figured that with his sexual confidence shattered by his wife's desertion, an affair might help to rebuild it. Alec Waugh, whose travel book *Hot Countries* sold 80,000 copies that year, first got wind of their liaison when Evelyn visited him for five days in the South of France at Easter and told him that he was on his way to a romantic rendezvous in Monte Carlo.[32] Arthur Waugh innocently observed that Evelyn returned from that holiday to Underhill 'very tired but well'.[33] A month later Audrey announced she was pregnant. 'I don't much care either way really,' Evelyn noted nonchalantly in his diary, 'so long as it is a boy.'[34] He remained as non-committal as ever and two weeks later he went to bed with another married woman, Dorothy Varda, a noted beauty and renowned man-eater who was by then separated from her husband, the porcelain collector Gerald Reitlinger: 'Went back and slept with Varda,' Evelyn recorded, 'but both of us too drunk to enjoy ourselves.'[35] A week after that Audrey told him she was not pregnant after all, 'so all that is bogus', wrote Evelyn. Audrey was at least shrewd enough not to let him have his way with her whenever he chose, and after a party later that evening Evelyn recorded that he had 'waited for hours to sleep with Audrey but she was too tired'.[36] Their on-off affair continued until the end of the summer.

The fling with Audrey was presumably good for morale, however with the failure of his marriage still very much on his mind Evelyn was inclined to play down the importance of sex within marriage in his journalism. In an article that summer entitled 'Tell the Truth About Marriage', he wrote that to say that you cannot lead a happy life unless your sex life is happy was 'just about as sensible as saying, "You cannot lead a happy life unless your golf life is happy"'. The modern attitude, he added, was that 'the moment a couple's physical interest in each other starts to slacken, it is their duty to look for other mates'. He advocated teaching children that sex 'is not infinitely important or infinitely satisfying'. 'Teach them fully about birth control and encourage them to find out for themselves exactly how much sex is likely to mean in their own lives: they will not then marry out of curiosity or inexperience. Arrange a system of legal marriage, registered, like any other legal contract, by mutual consent. Then leave it to the Church to show the sacramental importance of marriage to her own members.'[37]

The last sentence reflected momentous recent developments in his own spiritual outlook. The previous year, after informing Alec that Shevelyn had left him, he said: 'The trouble about the world today is that there's not enough religion in it. There's nothing to stop young people doing whatever they feel like doing at the moment.'[38] Evelyn later admitted that at the time of writing *Vile Bodies* he himself was 'as near to an atheist as one could be',[39] however Alec was in no doubt that the break-up of his marriage and the ensuing feeling of emptiness hastened his conversion to Roman Catholicism.

Since his divorce Evelyn had seen a lot of Gwen and Olivia Plunket Greene, both recent Catholic converts, and he later told a friend that during their various discussions Olivia 'bullied me into the Church'.[40] However according to Father Martin D'Arcy, the Jesuit priest to whom Olivia recommended Evelyn go for instruction at Farm Street in July 1930, 'no one could have made up that mind of his for him'.[41] Evelyn later explained that the first ten years of his adult life as an atheist had proved to him that life was 'unintelligible and unendurable without God',[42] that he had come to the conclusion that Western civilisation owed its entire existence to Christianity, and that Christianity in turn seemed to exist in its 'most complete and vital form' in the Roman Catholic Church. He realised that 'Catholicism was Christianity, that all other forms of Christianity were only good in so far as they chipped little bits off the main block'; hence it was 'a conversion to

Christianity rather than a conversion to Catholicism as such'.[43]

In Father Martin D'Arcy he could scarcely have found anyone more in tune with his growing revulsion with the 'barbaric' modern world and his hazily conceived romantic nostalgia for the old English Catholic past. Evelyn candidly admitted that he didn't 'feel Christian in the absolute sense',[44] however D'Arcy was so impressed by his unsentimental conviction as to the truth of the Catholic doctrine that he was prepared, as Evelyn later put it, 'just to get the seed in anyhow & hope some of it would come up'. D'Arcy, who remembered it as 'a special pleasure to make contact with so able a brain',[45] received him into the Roman Catholic Church at Farm Street on 29 September. The only witness he asked along was Tom Driberg, who interpreted it as part of his remit to inform his *Express* readers about Evelyn's conversion the next day. His only godparent was a charwoman who happened to be working there that day.

Evelyn had told his parents two days before, whereupon Arthur recorded that Kate was 'very, very sad over news of Evelyn's secession to Rome' (although she was typically reticent about her feelings in her own diary). To Arthur, whose family had for so long been steeped in Anglicanism, it felt like a betrayal and he later referred to Evelyn's 'perversion to Rome'.[46] For both parents, perhaps the saddest aspect of their son's 'going over' was that it seemed to extinguish any hope of his marrying again and giving them grandchildren owing to the fact that the Catholic Church did not recognise divorce. Father D'Arcy was later adamant that at the time Evelyn took his decision, the possibility of having his first marriage annulled had not yet been foreseen, and that by becoming a Catholic he was effectively committing himself to remaining a bachelor for the rest of his life.

Terence Greenidge also remembered Evelyn telling him at the time that he was now 'tied to Evelyn G for life unless [Greenidge] bumped her off(!)' but that Catholicism would at least prevent his 'making a fool of himself again over marriage'.[47] Yet his sacrifice was particularly poignant given that he had spent so much of his adult life yearning to be married and had recently begun to fall for one of the great loves of his life.

13

....

The Dutch Girl

Known then as 'Baby' – a name she never liked and eventually managed to discard – Teresa Jungman was the younger daughter of the prominent London hostess and talent-spotter Mrs Richard Guinness, who was herself generally referred to as 'Gloomy Beatrix' or 'Gloomy Guinness' or just plain 'Gloomy', not so much for her curious habit of closing the curtains during lunch parties as for her very deep voice and doom-laden conversation – she was once overheard demanding of a startled milliner's assistant: 'I want a hat for a middle-aged woman whose husband hates her.'[1]

Baby and her elder sister Zita were from Gloomy's first marriage to Nico Jungman, an impoverished Dutch-born artist 'greatly beloved', according to his obituary, 'for his artless charm of manner and almost childlike simplicity of character'.[2] The obit tactfully left unspecified the 'successive misfortunes, often cruelly undeserved' that befell this naive and generous-hearted man, however they included being abandoned by Baby's mother while he was interned in Germany for four years during the First World War (Baby was barely ten when they divorced in 1918) and she fell in love with the far wealthier Dick Guinness, scion of the banking branch of that family and himself chairman of the Mercantile & General Insurance Company.

The new Mrs Guinness soon became a dedicated salonnière and by the late 1920s their house at 19 Great Cumberland Place was a hub of fashionable London society, where clever young politicians like Bob Boothby mixed with writers and artists such as the Sitwells, Noël Coward, David Cecil, Oliver Messel and Cecil Beaton. Loelia Ponsonby (a close friend of the Jungman sisters whose subsequent marriage to Bendor Westminster, the 2nd Duke – of whom more later – was memorably described by James Lees-Milne as 'a definition of unadulterated hell') met Evelyn at one of the many gatherings there and thought he looked like a furious cherub, watching with his 'glaring eye', missing nothing and giving the impression with his pungent remarks that he was 'an unhappy man who found in the world much to amuse but little to admire'.[3]

Mrs Guinness's guests tended to find her similarly alarming, however her daughters remained remarkably unfazed by her relentless teasing and their striking beauty and spirited attitude to life soon rendered them among the most dazzling of the Bright Young People. With their equally high-spirited friends Eleanor Smith (Lord Birkenhead's daughter) and Enid Raphael (who once quipped, 'I don't know why they call them private parts – mine aren't private') they initiated the nocturnal treasure hunts and masquerades that came to define high society in the late 1920s. Both sisters were much photographed by Cecil Beaton, who admired Baby's 'Devonshire cream pallor and limpid mauve eyes' and 'her hair, spun of the flimsiest canary-bird silkiness' which fell 'lankly over her eyes' or was 'thrown back with a beguiling shrug of the head'.[4]

Beside her pale beauty, Baby was renowned for her pranks, one of which was to borrow her mother's Rolls-Royce and mink coat and go about pretending to be a widowed Russian émigré who had been forced to sell her jewels to educate her 'poor leedle boy'. In the same guise she attended a garden party with two borzois and approached an old general gushing about how she would never forget the night they had spent together in Paris during the war. The general, who was with his wife, coldly replied that he had only spent one night in Paris during the war. 'Zat was zee night,' said Baby, before melting away into the crowd.[5]

Notwithstanding her mischievousness, Baby also did regular charitable work and was a very strict Catholic, her faith inherited from her mother, whose family had moved to Birmingham as followers of Cardinal Newman. Thus she blended the beauty and zest of Evelyn Gardner with the intelligence and underlying seriousness and unavailability of Olivia Plunket Greene. For Evelyn it was an irresistible combination, as it was for several other disappointed suitors, including Pansy Pakenham's brother Frank (much later Lord Longford), who had 'a tremendous walkout' with Baby after meeting her at the Birkenheads' in 1928,[6] although, as he admitted, 'no one ever got anywhere with her sexually'.[7]

Exactly how or when Evelyn first came across her is unclear, although when he died his prayer book was found to contain a pressed orchid and fern next to which he had written '19 January 1930' – thought by some to be the date in question.[8] After a gap of eighteen months from the time when he and Shevelyn were setting up home together in Islington in November 1928, Evelyn's surviving diary does not resume until the beginning of May 1930. The first mention of Baby Jungman is on the 26th of that month, when they both dined at the Savoy with Frank Pakenham. It was evidently not their first meeting and Evelyn may already have let on that he liked her, given his observation that Baby seemed 'anxious to be friendly and very sweet'. Six days later, however, at lunch with Desmond Parsons (Robert Byron's great unrequited love), Baby arrived very late, left early and 'sat at the other end of the table so I couldn't speak to her'.[9] The following week she accepted an invitation to a lunch party Evelyn was giving at the Ritz but chucked at the last minute, telling him via a friend that she wouldn't be able to come after all as she was going to the country, which provoked a rant by Evelyn in the *Daily Mail* the next week – headlined 'Such Bad Manners!' – against 'incompetent young women who just do not know how to organize their affairs'.[10]

Baby's mother later told Evelyn that Baby was in tears after their resulting 'tiff', and when he went to lunch at their house in July Evelyn 'sat at a side table with Baby who was sweet'. Subsequent encounters were rarely more encouraging than this but they seemed to do nothing to diminish Evelyn's ardour. A consummate if perhaps unintentional heartbreaker, for the next few years Baby Jungman neither surrendered to his advances nor discouraged him from continuing to press his suit, telling him on various occasions that she enjoyed his being in love with her 'too much not to encourage it as much as I can in a subconscious way' and that 'If you weren't married you see it would be different because I might or I might not want to marry you . . .'[11]

* * *

Foreign travel was one way that Evelyn could relieve the torment of unrequited love, and in the six years after the break-up of his first marriage he travelled a great deal. The first of these trips, to Abyssinia, resulted from a conversation he had while staying with the Longfords at Pakenham Hall (now Tullynally) in Ireland in the early autumn of 1930.

It was his second visit there that year, both times at the invitation of Frank Pakenham (a younger brother of the then earl, Edward Longford), whom he had met through Pansy in 1928 and latterly got to know at Gloomy Guinness's parties in Great Cumberland Place, a few doors along from the Longfords' townhouse where Frank was born. They became closer after Evelyn's marriage ended and, as Frank modestly recalled, 'climbed the slopes of London society together'.[12] It was during this period that Evelyn, keen to spend as much time as possible away from Underhill, 'discovered the delights of the large country house', as Alexander Waugh puts it. That summer, besides the Longfords and Guinnesses, he also went to stay at Sezincote with the Dugdales and at Renishaw with the Sitwells, the latter in Cyril Connolly's assessment 'exactly the sort of aristocrats he longed to be himself'.[13] But to give Evelyn his due, he did not pretend to be anything other than an outsider, affecting an attitude to the upper classes that was more sardonic than sycophantic. 'No-one has a keener appreciation than myself of the high spiritual and moral qualities of the very rich,' he wrote in the *Daily Mail*. 'I delight in their company whenever I get the chance.'[14]

John Betjeman, sometimes bracketed with Evelyn as a fellow social climber from the middle classes, had been at the same house party at Sezincote and when Evelyn went to Pakenham for ten days in September, he was there too. Not nearly as well known as Evelyn by that time, Betjeman nonetheless seemed far more at ease with himself to the extent that, in Evelyn's eyes at least, he became 'a bore rather',[15] endlessly belting out revivalist hymns and joking about eccentric Irish peers. Evelyn by contrast appeared nervous and self-conscious and said very little at mealtimes, although their hostess did remember him coming down to breakfast and demanding 'Who's got any funny letters this morning?'[16]

Evelyn was presumably aware that Frank Pakenham had been as besotted as he was with Baby Jungman, which may explain why, after dinner on the last evening, he took it upon himself to whisper to the beautiful girl Frank had invited to stay on this occasion: 'Go after Frank. Go up with him. Follow him. Go on.' The girl was Elizabeth Harman, whom Frank had briefly fallen for at Oxford but then forgotten about for two years while he courted Baby. There may have been an element of self-interest in Evelyn's advice but Elizabeth was not to know that and she obediently followed Frank up into his bedroom, where, as she recalled, 'we conducted an ardent but chaste and anxious conversation about ourselves far into the night'.[17] Evelyn himself recorded in his diary: 'Frank and Harman slept together on Frank's last evening but did not fuck.'[18] They were married the next year.

Evelyn, meanwhile, was assumed by the other guests at Pakenham to have resumed his love affair with Alastair Graham, whom he had brought along with him from Renishaw, where Alastair had irritated Georgia Sitwell by 'boasting' that his mother was the model for Lady Circumference in *Decline and Fall*.[19] The suspicion that they were once again lovers was scarcely allayed by Evelyn's tendency to camp it up and put on a high-pitched voice whenever they were together, which was most of the time.[20]

Alastair was at the time on leave from Cairo, where he and Mark Ogilvie-Grant had followed Sir Percy Loraine when he moved there from Athens in 1929. Loraine's biographer records Cairo society being rather taken aback by 'the sparkling intelligence and decidedly informal air of these young aesthetes'. Known as 'the Embassy girls', they were famous for their laziness and incompetence and it was a mystery to those unaware of the rumours about Sir Percy that such a stickler was prepared to put up with them for so long.

In any event the posting provided Alastair with a fund of good stories, and the richly embellished one he told one evening in the library at Pakenham about the visit of two Abyssinian princes, who declined to take off their bowler hats and silk capes during a stuffy High Commission lunch party, promptly persuaded Evelyn to attend the coronation of the Emperor Haile Selassie in Addis Ababa that November instead of going to China and Japan as he had originally intended.

Soon after returning from Ireland, Evelyn went on his own to stay at Barford as a guest of Mrs Graham. In the ballroom – which she had built onto the house in 1925 in order to throw a party for Alastair's twenty-first, which in the event never took place – there was a large *Times Atlas of the World* from which, in a curiously rash act of vandalism, Evelyn tore a page for use on his forthcoming Abyssinian trip. Mrs Graham was so horrified when she discovered this that she banished him from her house. He returned there a year later, however, when he was trying to start *Black Mischief* but found it impossible to work with Alastair. 'We just sit about sipping sloe gin all day,' he complained. 'I am reading all the case histories in Havelock Ellis and frigging too much.'[21] The last appearance of Evelyn's name in the Barford visitors' book was in 1932, by which time he had stayed there on more than twenty occasions, sometimes for several weeks at a stretch.[22] After that they disappeared from each other's lives. Years later, when Alastair's niece asked him why their friendship had ended, he replied vaguely, 'Oh, you know, Evelyn became such a bore, such a snob.'[23]

By the time he said this, while Evelyn had carried on, as Alastair perhaps saw it, moving in ever grander circles to the point at which he eventually married into the aristocracy and installed himself in a Palladian country house with his coat of arms over the portico, Alastair had completely withdrawn from high society to live in a remote fishing village on the west coast of Wales.

Soon after leaving the diplomatic service in 1933, when Sir Percy Loraine was transferred to Ankara, Alastair had been warned by the police to leave London 'or go to prison'[24] following the discovery of his illicit (the laws of the land being what they then were) affair with the Welsh poet Evan Morgan, soon to be Viscount Tredegar.[25]*

In 1936 he bought a rambling white house just outside New Quay called Wern Newydd, where he lived as a virtual recluse. His mother had died two years previously and he took with him a few old retainers from Barford and had a rumoured £10,000 a year. Occasionally he threw parties for his neighbours, who at various times included Augustus John and Dylan Thomas. The latter described Alastair as 'the thin-vowelled laird',[26] and in *Under Milk Wood* used him as the model for Lord Cut-Glass, who 'lives in a house and a life at siege', and has 'a fish-slimy kitchen', presumably a reference to the pickled herring Alastair served at his parties and the pamphlet he wrote entitled *20 Different Ways To Cook New Quay Mackerel*, a testament to his fondness for sea-fishing as well as cooking.

However, neither Thomas nor anyone else in New Quay seemed to know that Alastair had also been the model for Sebastian Flyte in *Brideshead*. He remained more or less incognito in this respect until the late 1970s, when he was encountered in the Dolau Inn by the writer and critic

---

* Their trysting place was the Cavendish Hotel, whose proprietress Rosa Lewis had begun her career as a kitchen maid for Alastair's uncle, Willie Low, a crony of the future King Edward VII. Rosa was thus generally very well disposed towards Alastair and his friends, however she was so offended by Evelyn's portrayal of her as Lottie Crump in *Vile Bodies* that she banned him from the premises.

Duncan Fallowell. Not knowing who he was, Fallowell chanced to fall into conversation with him about Evelyn Waugh, about how 'well-endowed' he was as a writer and so forth, at which point the well-spoken stranger at the bar suddenly interjected: 'He wasn't well-endowed in the other sense, I'm afraid.'[27]

Fallowell never established whether he was referring to Evelyn's private parts or to the fact that he never had any money and Alastair was always having to bail him out. When the Granada television series of *Brideshead Revisited* went on air in 1981, Fallowell returned to New Quay, knocked on Alastair Graham's door and asked him out to dinner. Alastair replied that he had had a stroke and was 'not fit to be seen!'. He could not remember anything, he said, it was all so long ago, then remarked, somewhat cryptically, 'he was older than me you know'.[28] Alastair Graham died the next year, in 1982, 'taking his secrets with him'.

* * *

The Abyssinian trip that Alastair had inadvertently sparked, and on which Evelyn embarked a month after leaving Pakenham in 1930 armed with press accreditations to the *Graphic*, *Times* and *Express*, lasted five months in all and also took in Zanzibar, Kenya and Cape Town, providing him with material for the travelogue *Remote People* as well as what he promised his parents on leaving Addis would be 'a first rate novel'[29] – *Black Mischief*.

Near the end of his journey, he wrote to Baby: 'I am just going to a lake called Tanganyika where everyone dies of sleeping sickness. I have also caught typhus in a prison, malaria in a place called Hawash, and leprosy in a Catholic church, so I am fairly sure not to come back.'[30] A few weeks after arriving home in the spring of 1931 he fell ill with a temperature of 101 and ulcers on his throat. But rather than having contracted any of the exotic diseases enumerated to Baby, he was found to have been poisoned by some watercress eaten at a hotel by the Thames.

That summer all four Waughs went on holiday to Villefranche in the South of France, only the second time that Evelyn's parents had ventured to 'the palms, the sunlight and the South',[31] as Alec put it, and by Alec's account it was a great success, even though Arthur insisted on wearing the same tweed suit that he wore in England together with scarf, vest and long-legged underpants, maintaining 'I like to feel the wool against my skin.'[32]

Arthur had brought with him the proofs of his soon-to-be published autobiography *One Man's Road*, a sentimental tome which bizarrely contained no reference whatsoever to his younger son's writing career, despite the fact that *Vile Bodies* had already established Evelyn as one of the country's most celebrated young novelists and his books had done much to rescue the fortunes of Arthur's troubled publishing house. Instead Arthur made plain his distaste for what he saw as the kind of vulgar self-publicising that Evelyn had been so conspicuously guilty of each week recently in the press, pointedly bemoaning the fact that 'nobody seems content to do his work nowadays without blowing a horn to call attention to his proficiency'.[33] Arthur's determination to deny his son any further publicity may also have stemmed from recent friction between them after they found themselves living under the same roof again after Evelyn's divorce – although Evelyn kept away whenever he could, borrowing flats from friends or going to stay in the country. Unbeknown to Evelyn, relations had been further strained when Arthur's curiosity got the better of him one day and he began reading the bound volumes of Evelyn's diaries, which he kept on a shelf in the former nursery that Arthur was now using as a study. The diaries contained numerous unflattering references to Arthur which left him 'immensely humiliated and distressed' according to Alec, who recalled: 'My mother told me that he never really got over it, that he kept harking back to it.'[34]

Equally, Arthur may not have appreciated his portrayal in *Vile Bodies* as the dotty Colonel Blount who allows his house, Doubting Hall, to be used as a film location providing he can appear as an extra – just as Arthur had done with Evelyn and Terence Greenidge's student film, *The Scarlet Woman*, in 1924. Nor could he have failed to recognise himself in another of the book's characters, Adam's publisher Mr Rampole, who is based, like Arthur, in Henrietta Street and is described as a 'benign old gentleman' who is nonetheless notoriously stingy in his dealings with young authors. When Arthur looked back on 1931 he wrote in his diary, 'Much kindness at home and abroad. Particularly from K [Kate] and Alec.'[35] There was no mention of Evelyn.

* * *

Besides entertaining their parents, the Waugh brothers saw various others in the South of France, among them Cyril Connolly, Aldous Huxley and Somerset Maugham, the last of whom they visited twice at his villa on nearby Cap Ferrat and Evelyn offended by addressing him as 'Dr' Maugham and feigning ignorance of his literary reputation. Evelyn's rudeness was partly a symptom of his growing restlessness with the family holiday and he soon went himself off to an uncomfortable monastery in the hills in a bid to try and finish *Remote People*, which he took back with him to his publishers in June 1931; it was eventually published that autumn to reviews which mostly reflected the haste in which it had been written. 'I think you have the most important of the young English writers in Evelyn Waugh,' his new American publisher, John Farrar, was informed by a respected littérateur, 'but my God, will you stop him writing travel books!'[36]

When Evelyn returned to the Riviera in mid-July he was accompanied by a very pretty thirty-three-year-old divorcee called Pixie Marix, to whom he had been introduced by his friend Patrick Balfour, and whom he quickly whisked off to a hotel well away from his brother. 'Evelyn has gone wenching down the coast,'[37] Alec told Balfour. Evelyn's paramour was more respectable than Alec made her sound, however she was reputed to enjoy what she called 'brinking', leading men on but stopping short of what Alec delicately termed 'a bestowal of ultimate favours'.[38] Evelyn evidently grew frustrated with this and complained to Balfour: 'That girl has made a fool of me & taken all my money . . . It is all very distressing & humiliating. Apart from anything else she is so boring and so American at heart. I could drown her with pleasure.'[39] Eventually, Pixie realised that unless she gave him what he wanted she would have to make her own way home, so she changed tack and decided to let him have 'so much of it that he would wish he had not brought the matter up'.[40] At night she kept him at it until two or three in the morning and at dawn she would 'bound into his room, eager and voracious'.[41] A week later, Evelyn wrote to Balfour again: 'I said some hard things about Mrs. Marix. Well subsequent events have not justified my first estimate of her character . . . [she] is a nice girl really.'[42]

* * *

It was in France that summer that Evelyn first read in a newspaper about a divorce suit involving an aristocratic Liberal politician whose predicament would later give him the idea for *Brideshead Revisited*. The petition had been filed by Countess Beauchamp, the mother of his Oxford friends Hugh Lygon and William Elmley. Although the newspapers did not say so at the time, her grounds had to do with Earl Beauchamp's homosexuality, evidence of which had been rigorously compiled by the Countess's jealous and vindictive brother, Bendor Westminster, and at the Duke's insistence was set out in unsparingly explicit detail in the petition: 'THAT throughout their married life at 13 Belgrave Square, Madresfield Court, and Walmer Castle, aforesaid, the Respondent habitually committed acts of gross indecency with certain of his male servants, masturbating them with his mouth and hands and compelling them to masturbate him and lying upon them and masturbating between their legs . . .'[43]

Lord Beauchamp's fondness for his footmen, whose faces were routinely powdered, was an open secret, and when Evelyn read about the divorce his first reaction was 'So the story has broken.'[44] But while he had known the sons at Oxford, he had never been to their vast moated manor house in Worcestershire or met their sisters, even though they were great friends of Baby Jungman and the Mitfords. He went to Madresfield Court, the house that would cast such a famously powerful spell over him, for the first time that autumn after obeying Baby's suggestion that he attend Captain Hance's famous riding academy in nearby Malvern and subsequently being invited by Mary Lygon (whom he chanced to meet lunching with Mrs Guinness) to stay with them while he was doing so.

With Lady Beauchamp having recently decamped to a house on the Westminster estate in Cheshire with their youngest brother Richard, and Lord Beauchamp, known as 'Boom' in the family for his resonant voice, driven into exile on the Continent by the threat of criminal prosecution, the three unmarried Lygon girls now had the run of the fully staffed Madresfield and regularly filled it with their friends. The eldest, twenty-four-year-old Lady Sibell, later admitted to finding Evelyn 'rather tiresome and terribly rude',[45] however her two younger sisters, Lady Mary and Lady Dorothy, then aged twenty-one and nineteen, took to him at once, relishing his endlessly entertaining banter and apparent unwillingness to take anything seriously, least of all himself. He was equally entranced by them and quickly adopted them as yet another of his surrogate families. 'I miss you both very much at school and in play time,' he wrote to them after one of his early visits.

Mary had been known since childhood as Maimie and Dorothy as Coote, and to these Evelyn soon added Blondy and Poll respectively, while giving himself the mock-Masonic sobriquet of Boaz (which he later bestowed on the Azanian Minister of the Interior in *Black Mischief*). Certain traits of their friends were incorporated in a secret code, thus 'Dutch' came to denote anyone or anything problematic or uncooperative, a reference to Evelyn's enduring and much-discussed difficulties in wooing Baby Jungman, whom he generally referred to as 'the Dutch girl'; 'Highclere', the Hampshire seat of the Earls of Carnarvon, was used for anything imposing and luxurious; and to laycock (or lacock) meant to chuck a social engagement, coined after a genial but evidently forgetful young cavalry officer called Robert Laycock (later Evelyn's wartime commanding officer in the commandos) whom Evelyn routinely referred to as 'Chucker': 'Very very sorry for lacocking tea,' Evelyn wrote to Maimie.

Evelyn's irreverent mischievousness was such that it was 'like having Puck as a member of the household', Coote recalled.[46] The sundial in the garden at Madresfield was inscribed: 'That day is wasted on which one has not laughed.' Standing by this one day, Maimie said to Evelyn: 'Well, you and I have never wasted a day, have we?'[47]

The laughter helped alleviate the Lygon girls' sadness over the loss of their father, to whom they were devoted despite his extreme love of formality – always referring to his children by their courtesy titles and insisting that liveried footmen stand behind each chair in the dining room – not to mention his notoriety as a prowler, which meant they had to warn any handsome male guests they had staying at Madresfield to lock their doors at night. They were never reconciled meanwhile to what they saw as the treachery of their mother, a pious and unworldly woman who famously declared after failing to grasp the essentials of what her husband was accused of: 'Bendor tells me that Beauchamp is a bugler.' Bendor, meanwhile, charmingly wrote to Beauchamp after his downfall: 'Dear Bugger-in-law, you got what you deserved.'

Soon looked upon by the sisters as an extra brother, Evelyn found the family's plight deeply affecting and told Baby that the Arts and Crafts chapel that Lady Beauchamp had given her husband on their marriage (the only part of Madresfield that Evelyn eventually borrowed for his creation of Brideshead Castle) was 'the saddest thing that ever I saw'.[48] He shared the sisters' concern about their brother Hugh, whose alcoholism and general profligacy led to his going bankrupt in the spring of 1932, which in turn prompted a breakdown and a brief spell in an asylum. And he was at one with their growing antipathy towards their stiff elder brother William, Lord Elmley, the only one of the siblings remaining at Madresfield not to have taken their father's side.

However much he loved being at Madresfield, Evelyn knew that he had to tear himself away from time to time in order to get on with the various articles he had promised as well as the novel that eventually became *Black Mischief*. Towards the end of October he wrote to Patrick Balfour: 'I am having a healthy time riding all day and romping with the bright young Lygons in the evenings but not doing any work or making money – in fact spending pots so must get away quick.'[49] He proposed joining Balfour for a stint at the Eastern Court Hotel near Chagford in Devon, a low-ceilinged, old thatched farmhouse which was to become his favourite writing refuge for years to come. 'I pretend to my London chums that I am going to hunt stags,' he told the Lygons, 'but to you who are intimates and confidantes I don't mind saying that I shall sit in my bedroom writing books, articles, short stories, reviews, plays. Cinema scenarios, etc. etc. until I have got a lot more money.'[50] Within a few days of getting there, he admitted that he had been 'fox catching on Thursday with a pack called South Devon. We galloped like mad for five hours over Dartmoor. My horse fell down once but it wasn't my fault & I made a "plucky remount". I pretend I am a farmer & don't pay any money.'[51]

Having previously groaned to Baby Jungman that he was 'lonely and depressed here & the book [*Black Mischief*] is going badly',[52] he felt better after his day's hunting: 'Sweet Tess,' he wrote afterwards, 'I have done only 2 pages of the novel but they are masterly. I don't see how narrative could be finer, of its kind.'[53] His feelings for her remained as unreciprocated as ever, however, which tended to produce quarrels whenever they met. 'If you look on me simply as a pair of trousers for your mother's parties,' he wrote after one painful scene, 'you can't mind if I ask to be released from an engagement to watch your dogs go to the lavatory. If you regard me as a friend of your own you mustn't be disagreeable in quite that way. Isn't that reasonable!'[54]

On this occasion he could at least look forward to seeing her again over

Christmas at Madresfield. But on that occasion Baby proved no more receptive to his endearments than usual and in the new year the same old pangs returned: 'I hope you have every kind of success and amusement and marry a rich marquess,' he wrote in January, 'or a brilliant young novelist or something equally exciting.'[55]

Another regular guest at Madresfield was Stanley Baldwin's younger son Windham, known by Evelyn as 'Frisky' and more widely as 'Bloggs'. In common with Evelyn, the ginger-haired and bespectacled Baldwin had had the occasional dalliance with Pixie Marix while also being hopelessly smitten with Baby Jungman, on the basis of which he and Evelyn had formed a mutually commiserative alliance, bolstered by the fact that neither saw the other as much of a threat in the looks department: 'Mrs Reginald Marix is back in London,' Evelyn informed Frisky in mid-January 1932, 'Theresa is hunting in Leicestershire. Make the best you can from these Words to the Wise.'[56] Their shared lack of success as suitors cemented what proved to be a lasting friendship and in later life Baldwin recalled that Evelyn was 'always wonderfully unrude to me and my wife; I can't think why; and I've always been grateful'.[57]

*　*　*

In February, staying the Spread Eagle at Thame where he was working on two short stories (possibly 'Bella Fleace Gave a Party' and 'Cruise'), Evelyn again wrote to Baby, telling her that he had 'thought of you this morning and yesterday and in fact every day since I left London' and that he was 'sorry that I am so consistently tiresome with you'. He would shortly be going abroad, he added, in a bid 'to leave loneliness by being alone for a bit as I used to be able to do'.[58] He was away for barely two weeks, much of the time spent travelling to and from Spain, where he went to look at Gothic cathedrals and from where he inevitably again wrote to Baby, imploring her to 'think of me now and then between telephone calls'.[59] When he returned and she went off to stay with some friends in Ireland, another letter followed her. 'How you must be missing me,' he wrote optimisti-cally, 'but cheer up. These separations are the very manure of love.'[60] He went on to tell her about the recent first night at the Vaudeville Theatre of the stage version of *Vile Bodies*, at which 'everyone laughed very loud and the criticisms this morning seem pretty genial'. Yet as he lamented to

Frisky Baldwin: 'Did little Miss Jungman send me a line of good wishes from Ireland? Not on your life.'[61]

He spent Easter at Stonyhurst, the Catholic boys' public school where his old Oxford friend Christopher Hollis was teaching and where he went several times in the early years of his Catholicism. On this occasion he spent much of his time there working on his novel, the delivery of which John Farrar in New York was now beginning to hassle his agent about: 'You can tell these troublesome yanks that the novel will be called BLACK MISCHIEF and will be ready for them in about 3 weeks,' Evelyn wrote Peters in early May. 'It is extremely good.'[62]

Begun in September 1931 and mostly written during his various stays at Madresfield and Chagford, *Black Mischief* had taken him eight months to complete, far longer than his first two novels, partly a measure of how distracting he found life at Madresfield, where he groaned every time he shut himself away in the old nursery to write. 'Oh how I should love to live in your Liberty Hall,' he wrote to Coote in the spring of 1932, 'but the trouble about poor Bo is that he's a lazy bugger and if he was in a house with you lovely girls he would just sit about and chatter and get d.d. [disgustingly drunk] and ride a horse and have a heavenly time but would he write his book? No, and must he? By God he must.'[63] He found it impossible to stay away for long, however, and in May he was back there again – when the girls and their guests posed as models for the drawings he did for *Black Mischief* – as he would be in June, August, October and several times in November and December.

* * *

On 21 May 1932, after putting the final touches to *Black Mischief*, Evelyn caught the early aeroplane to Paris, from where he was to take a train to Rome to be privately confirmed by Cardinal Lépicier.[64] His unlikely travelling companion for this pilgrimage was a singularly undevout Catholic friend called Raymond de Trafford, 'a fine desperado', as Evelyn described him, from a Lancashire landowning family whom he had met the previous year in Kenya. Having supplied several of the characteristics of Basil Seal in *Black Mischief*, de Trafford would later feature in James Fox's *White Mischief* as the wildest of the notorious Happy Valley set. He was particularly renowned for having been shot by his lover Alice de

Janzé at the Gare du Nord in Paris in 1927 (an attempted murder-cum-suicide) and then marrying her five years later, in February 1932, before leaving her again three months after that, his final gesture being to hurl a cocktail in her face at a Parisian café and then burst out laughing.[65] It was very shortly after this that he met up with Evelyn on his way to Italy.

To Evelyn's great relief, Hugh Lygon was due to join them later in Rome. 'My word I am glad Hugh is coming to Italy,' he wrote to Coote, 'because between you and me and the w.c. Raymond de T. is something of a handful. v. nice but so BAD and he fights & fucks and gambles and gets D.D. all the time. But Hugh & I will be quiet & chaste and economical & sober.'[66] For the time being Evelyn was held up in Paris by Raymond's wayward behaviour: 'He arrived at the Ritz in evening dress having not been to bed,' Evelyn reported to Baby. 'He slept all yesterday until ten – I left him tight at four this morning just off for gambling at Le Cercle Haussman. If I don't manage to move him tomorrow I shall go alone.'[67]

When they did eventually reach Rome, they were joined not only by Hugh Lygon but also by his sisters Coote and Maimie. They had all come along in order to see their father, who was renting Lord Berners's opulent apartment overlooking the Forum for the summer. It was there that they all stayed, despite the fact that there was only one bedroom, which was generally occupied by Lord Beauchamp and his handsome young valet Robert Byron, whom he had recruited while wintering in Australia. 'Wasn't it extraordinary that we were all there in one room?' Evelyn wrote years later to Maimie.[68]

This was the first time that Evelyn had met Lord Beauchamp, whom he had heard so much about. They went sightseeing together and by all accounts got on very well, admiring each other's intelligence and interest in art and church architecture. On a trip to join Maimie Lygon in Venice later that summer in August, Evelyn inadvertently gathered more material for future use in *Brideshead*: 'On some days life kept pace with the gondola, as we nosed through the side-canals and the boatman uttered his plaintive musical bird-cry of warning; on other days, with the speed-boat bouncing over the lagoon in a stream of sun-lit foam . . .'[69]

In both Rome and Venice that summer Evelyn also hit it off with Lady Diana Cooper, the actress and renowned beauty at whose fortieth birthday party on one of Venice's islands he had witnessed the famous brawl begun by Richard Sykes and Randolph Churchill which inspired a new word in his private vocabulary – to 'sykes', meaning to hit or smash up. Evelyn had first met Lady Diana that spring in London through Hazel Lavery, with whom he had been having a casual on–off affair. He soon became as infatuated with her as he had been with Diana Guinness, yet despite their often ferocious quarrels their friendship proved considerably longer-lasting. Beside the fact that she was bright, beautiful and very grand, Evelyn admired Diana's cleverness, her unusual wit, her sense of adventure and her extraordinary self-confidence – like all his great women friends, she never allowed herself to be bullied. Diana meanwhile was 'enraptured by [Evelyn's] wit, his sensibility, his gusto, his affection for her', yet equally dismayed by his black rages and random cruelty. She was one of the few women who could call him to order. That autumn, when Evelyn joined her in Birmingham while she was touring the provinces in a revival of *The Miracle*, a red-faced man approached them and breathlessly asked if he was going the right way to the railway station. Evelyn replied that indeed he was, knowing full well that the station was in the opposite direction. When it dawned on Diana what he had done she refused to speak to him again until he ran after the man, corrected the mistake and helped him with his heavy suitcase.[70]

It was a measure of how greatly Diana delighted in Evelyn's company that she was prepared to forgive such indefensible badness and welcomed his frequent visits over the next few months as she moved about the theatres of Manchester, Glasgow and Edinburgh. He would sit loyally with her in her dressing room and later take her out to dinner; by day they toured the great houses of the district – Chatsworth, Hardwick, Belton, and her two old family homes, Haddon and Belvoir.

Mindful perhaps of her husband's well-known infidelities, Evelyn was at first not entirely averse to the idea of an affair, however that was the last thing Diana wanted. When she later learned how Evelyn had snorted at the notion of her as a *'grande amoureuse'*, she retorted: 'How the hell can he tell if I am or not? Just because I never responded to his dribbling, dwarfish little amorous *singeries*, he need not be so sure!'[71] If that sounded cruelly dismissive, she could be equally eloquent on the subject of her devotion to him, later recalling that during this time she had 'wanted to bind Evelyn to my heart with hoops of steel'.[72] In a possible reference to Baby Jungman, she wrote to him: 'You know perfectly well that you have no Baby as loyal as this Baby and if you believe anything else you are very foolish.'[73]

Black Mischief was published at the beginning of October, dedicated 'With love to Mary and Dorothy Lygon'. An exuberantly tasteless black comedy about the absurd attempts of Oxford-educated Emperor Seth to modernise the fictional African island of Azania, it met with mixed reviews. The most glowing came from L. A. G. Strong in *The Spectator*, who pronounced it 'a brilliant book', 'exceedingly funny', 'amazingly well-written'. 'No one but Mr Waugh could have written a single page of it.'[74] Eric Linklater in *The Listener* was similarly effusive: 'The manner in which Mr Waugh controls his widely varied matter is admirable. His narrative is swift and picturesque, and his cutting – if one may borrow a Hollywood term – is masterly. "Black Mischief", indeed, shows an all-round growth of strength.'[75] Others, though, were less convinced, among them James Agate in the *Express*, who found the satire 'heavy-handed', while Geoffrey West in *Bookman* complained that 'Mr Waugh still seems to suffer from his early illusion that the vapid fatuities of Ronald Firbank are funny.'[76] None of this greatly bothered Evelyn, not least since it was the Book Society's choice as Book of the Month, the first impression of 15,000 copies sold out before publication, and by early October a third was already in the press.

In matters of the heart, however, Evelyn's situation remained as bleak as ever. The marriage later that month of his brother Alec to an Australian heiress called Joan Chirnside served only to underline his own lack of progress with Baby Jungman, as did the fact that he was unlikely to be able to marry anyone at all now that he was a Catholic divorcee. At the wedding itself Evelyn was seen to behave 'like a malignant demon with a red hot poker' and loudly announced to anyone within earshot that he had now set his sights on the attractive Surrealist painter Eileen Agar, ignoring the fact that she was there with her six-foot-tall Hungarian boyfriend (later husband) Joseph Bard. Evelyn subsequently renewed his acquaintance with Eileen while staying the weekend with Alec and Joan, where Eileen recalled how he tried to 'lure, charm and finally push me into the bushes on our walks through the woods' and later that night boldly called for her outside her bedroom door, which she rewarded only with a chaste kiss on the brow, 'cool as a coconut, but with perhaps a hint of indulgence', as she recorded. She was perfectly happy with her 'calm and steady' existing lover and 'had no desire to rush into a passionate and agitated affair which would leave me no chance to pursue my all-consuming interest – painting'.[77]

Evelyn was evidently neither Baby Jungman nor Eileen Agar's type, however he was then still impishly good looking, as well as affectionate, charming, clever and extremely funny, and there were undoubtedly women who did find him attractive. A year or two later, he had an affair with a married actress in her early twenties called Clare Mackenzie (stage name Clare Brocklebank), whom he took to stay at Chagford and then evidently abandoned: 'That was the unkindest cut of all,' she wrote to him afterwards. 'Was it absolutely necessary to leave me when I needed you so desperately badly? . . . I can't believe you would willingly kick me so hard once I was down. One kind word last night would, I believe, have saved me cracking so badly . . . My hand is so shaky this morning I can hardly hold the pencil steady, but the doctor's given me some soothing medicine which may help. And God do I need it after your note this morning. I shan't stay here long now; what's the use, I should only be miserable without you . . . I still can hardly believe you've really done this . . . Please ignore a telegram in very bad taste if it reaches you I hope it doesn't. I'm afraid I felt so ill I lost all sense of proportion & broke the rules.'[78]

He cast an even more powerful spell on Joyce Gill, two years his senior, whom as Joyce Fagan he had first met via Alec while he was at Oxford, and smuggled into an all-male party with her posing as Terence Greenidge. She was the only guest to dinner at Underhill on his 21st birthday and it was her flat in Canonbury Square that Evelyn rented after his marriage to Shevelyn in 1928. At some point after the marriage ended, Evelyn and Joyce began an affair. To outward appearances she remained devoted to her American husband, Donald Gill, yet throughout her marriage Joyce had wrestled with a side of her nature that was bohemian, flirtatious, impulsive and adventurous, and she later admitted having agonised over a suggestion of Evelyn's that she abandon her family and accompany him on one of his expeditions in the 1930s. In 1938, after Evelyn had remarried and was about to become a father, Joyce wrote him a letter that said much about the intensity of their relationship:

> It is too difficult not to write to you now, Evelyn, because things have not been going well, because it's nearly March 13th which was the day you

jokingly suggested that we might meet each year until I am 70. And so I suppose that day will be for me a kind of lovely agony for ever and ever . . . I have arranged my life now, as I think best, to give the least trouble to you or to Don. When you were married I found that to drive the children back to their Prep-School I had to pass very near to you. So, to be out of temptation, I arranged to have them living at home. It is better so, anyway . . . And in compensation, I do what you suggested & what in my foolishness I thought almost a crime. I think of you all the time when I am making love, until the word and Evelyn are almost synonymous! And in the darkness each night & in the greyness of each morning when I wake I remember your face & your voice and your body and everything about you so earnestly and intensely that you become almost tangibly beside me. And after that I can forget you for the day (except when I am alone). It is a kind of exercise which, together with being tied hand & foot by the family, keeps me from behaving like the pitiable sort of fool I was 2 years ago. At least I hope it will keep me from it. It is only for the next few years. After I am 40 I won't want to see you. Then it will just be dismal aged despair! Then even the impossible possibility of having your child will be gone. And I suppose that is at the root of this – this – I can't call it infatuation because I know that that is an unworthy word for it; because I know, darling, that love is a juster description. And every night I tell myself that your wife now has your child in her body and I think of it and of you always, so that when I do hear or read about it I shall not be unprepared. I tried to do the same thing about your marriage, but darling, it was the dearest kindest thing of you to write about it, and it is because you are like that – because you are Evelyn, that I shall try most terribly hard to conform to the normal convention of 'decency' (Christ! what a phrase) and not bombard you with love letters. And if I do ever write darling, it is not a 'begging letter' only because I remember that once you said 'write to me if it helps'. I know that was before you were married again – so I shall not write every day . . . Almost I could be contented if every night I could write & say 'Evelyn I love you' & every morning I could say Evelyn God bless you! But what nonsense! Of course I could not be content. I have only to remember your eyes – your mouth and my heart aches as if it were a stone cut by a diamond . . . Goodnight & good morning and good day for always, dearest.[79]

*   *   *

In the autumn of 1932 travel again seemed to offer Evelyn the best means of distraction from his lovesickness, and after pondering a variety of far-flung destinations – Moscow, Borneo, Peking – he finally settled on the Amazon jungle. When he sent Baby a copy of *Black Mischief* in late September 'simply to show you that I was still thinking of you', he breezily added that he was 'Off to British Guiana quite soon'.[80] However the prospect of leaving appeared only to intensify his feelings for her. In October he told her from Chagford that it seemed 'all make-believe being genial and friendly with you just as much as it was before when I was disagreeable because when the natural relationship is love everything else is a fraud'.[81]

Sometime later, on a final visit to Diana in Glasgow before setting off to South America, he wrote again to Baby: 'I miss you but I won't go on about that.'[82] Two days before he left she joined him for lunch at the Ritz with a Guiana-hand called Lieutenant-Colonel Ivan Davson: 'She sat quiet while he and I spread a map on the table and talked of Guiana,' Evelyn recorded.

On his last evening, 1 December, they dined together at Quaglino's (caviar aux blinis, cold partridge, marrow on toast) and the next morning attended Mass at Spanish Place followed by breakfast over which she presented him with a medal of St Christopher, the patron saint of travelers, to wear round his neck – 'gold, Cartier, very expensive,' he told Diana, 'saved out of her pocket money. Deeply moved.'[83] They motored down to the docks at Tilbury in her mother's car. 'Deadly lonely, cold, and slightly sick at parting,' Evelyn wrote in his diary. 'Teresa drove off to lunch with Lady Astor in London. We sailed at about half-past two. Down the river in heavy rain and twilight. Heart of lead.'

14

....

Off to the Forest

Shortly before leaving for Georgetown Evelyn told Diana Cooper that he had spent 'a very pious few days going to church with that Dutch girl'.[1] They had even discussed the possibility of their both 'taking up the religious life', as he recalled in a letter to Baby en route, albeit adding that on reflection it now seemed very presumptuous to have been talking about it 'as though it were joining a club'. 'Here am I going off to the forest to see if it would suit me to be a missionary,' he wrote. 'It is just like the people who used to be continually coming to my father and saying they would like to be novelists because it was congenial indoor work with no fixed hours and long holidays.'[2]

As he implied, he was not perhaps obvious missionary material, yet however seriously he ever viewed that aim, the mordant account he subsequently wrote in *Ninety-Two Days* (the title itself brought to mind a prison sentence) suggests that he did look upon the journey as a form of penance – even if the artist in him also hoped that this distant and barbarous place might yield 'experiences vivid enough to demand translation into literary form'.

His choice of British Guiana (now the independent republic of Guyana) came from the fact that it had always seemed to him on a map to be 'absurdly remote'.[3] However he may have been additionally prompted by Peter Fleming's recent reports in *The Times* describing a harebrained expedition to try and find the explorer Colonel Fawcett, who had vanished seven years earlier in the Brazilian jungle while searching for the lost city of El Dorado. Two days before leaving Evelyn had had tea with Fleming 'to talk of equipment for forests'.[4] The next day he had packed a suitcase and grip: 'A few tropical suits, camera, books, a pair of field boots and settler shirt and shorts.'[5]

Evelyn's previous travels, including the trip to Abyssinia, had never taken him far from the company of other Europeans or for that matter a hotel, however his expedition to British Guiana was to be of an altogether different order, 'sterner stuff', as Eric Newby later classed it, involving travel 'much more in the manner of a Victorian explorer: with guides who were at best unpredictable, through country in which there was a considerable degree of danger'.[6]

The discomforts began as soon as he boarded the SS *Ingoma* at Tilbury. This sluggish cargo vessel was 'not at all like Highclere',[7] he told Maimie Lygon, but instead resembled 'an Irish packet-boat with the second-class decks removed to leave a clear deck for the accommodation of two prize bulls, a race horse, a couple of fox hounds and some hens'.[8] The heating system did not work – a particularly unfortunate defect in midwinter – and it creaked noisily 'like a pair of new boots'.

For the first week until they were well past the Azores the sea was very rough, however while most of the other thirty passengers were 'being sick or else very sullen & quiet', Evelyn, who was a good sailor, resiliently strode about the boat with a big cigar feeling like 'no end of a swell', as he told Maimie Lygon.[9] Otherwise he lay in the three-berth cabin he had managed to secure for himself, smoking, studying maps of the jungle and reading – histories of Guiana, D'Arcy's *Nature of Belief* and two books of Thomist philosophy.

He thought a lot about Baby and wrote to tell her that he 'could have cried at any moment' as they parted. 'I wanted very much to kiss you goodbye but didn't have the heart to [risk] another escape.'[10] The next day he wrote again: 'Your St Christopher comforts me and gives me a feeling of not being quite alone. Think of me sometimes.'[11] A few days later he told her that she was 'very often in my thoughts – closer and dearer than ever before', and in another letter: 'Don't go falling in love with anyone while I'm away. I thought it would be a good thing but now I know I couldn't bear it ... I'd sooner have your love with all the unhappiness it would probably cause both of us, than anything I can think of at the moment.'[12]

After two weeks at sea they finally reached Antigua and two days after that Barbados. On Trinidad Evelyn was shown around by a man who disconcertingly disclosed that he was Baby Jungman's first cousin, and more awkwardly he was invited to stay by the manager of a hotel that Alec had insulted at length in *The Coloured Countries*. Plied with multiple rum swizzles and lent silk pyjamas and a dressing-gown 'gayer than I should have dared choose for myself', he pronounced all this an 'exemplary manner in which to accept criticism'.[13] Privately, however, he recorded that except for the new bed, 'the hotel had all the defects Alec complained of'.[14] 'General impression of Trinidad,' he concluded, 'that I don't want to see it again.'[15]

His first glimpse of Guiana, on 22 December, was no more uplifting: 'misty palm-fringe through pouring rain and a few factory chimneys . . . dreary wind-swept wharfs; some corrugated iron roofs of warehouses'. On the bright side there was a cable from Baby and an interview with a local paper which produced the headline: 'Handsome and Well-Formed Novelist'.[16] Nonetheless he recorded: 'General impression of Georgetown that I don't mind how soon I leave it.'[17]

Obliged to stay there for ten days while he planned his venture into the interior, he was looked after over Christmas by the Governor, Sir Edward Denham, and his wife, lunching with them on Christmas Eve at Government House, dining there again on Christmas Day – 'Rather a pathetic evening of the Denhams' charming attempts to be homely among childless officials . . . I sat between a black attorney general and a white archdeacon'[18] – and the day after Boxing Day embarking on a three-day trip up the great Essequibo River on their comfortable steam yacht.

At last all was ready for his own expedition and on New Year's Eve he wrote to Baby: 'Unless anything odd happens you won't hear from me for some time as I am just starting on a journey up country and there are no post offices there. I don't quite know where I am going yet.'[19]

His guide was an emaciated eccentric called Mr Haynes (Mr Bain in *Ninety-Two Days*), commissioner for the Rupununi district. 'Half black and more than half crazy',[20] as Evelyn described him to Diana Cooper, Haynes was soon regaling Evelyn with accounts of his horse, which supposedly swam underwater, and how he found his way through the bush with the help of parrots which flew on ahead on reconnaissance.

On 3 January 1933 they caught a slow train down the coast to New Amsterdam and the next day a paddle steamer up the Berbice River with 'monotonous vegetable walls on either bank' to Takama. They continued from there by horse south to Kurukupari ('I had no idea where Kurupukari was, but it sounded as good as anywhere else'),[21] covering the ninety miles in six days, with Mr Haynes constantly discoursing on subjects such as his own extraordinary honesty, courage, efficiency, generosity, horsemanship, physical prowess and sex appeal. He had a fair amount to say too about the local fauna and in *Ninety-Two Days* Evelyn later recorded a few of the choicest examples of his guide's 'experienced ear':

'Listen,' said Mr Bain one day, 'that is most interesting. It is what we call "the six o'clock beetle", because he always makes that noise at exactly six o'clock.'

'But it is now quarter past four.'

'Yes, that is what is so interesting.'[22]

'Throughout the week's ride,' Evelyn wrote in his diary, 'Haynes did not once stop talking, except at night when he kept me awake with asthma and retching.'[23] By the time they reached Kurukupari – a single wooden house in a clearing on a slight hill – he had had quite enough of his companion and left him behind as he pressed on towards the ranch of a man named Christie, a further five days' ride away.

When he eventually arrived there on the afternoon of 20 January after an 'intolerably hot ride' through bush and savannah, a few hours ahead of his two bearers and cook, Evelyn found Mr Christie 'reclining in hammock and sipping cold water from the spout of a white enamelled teapot'. Christie had 'a long white moustache and white woolly head; his face was of the same sun-baked, fever-blanched colour as were most faces in the colony but of unmistakeable Negro structure'. When Evelyn greeted him and asked where he could water his horse, Christie smiled at him dreamily and told him that he had been expecting him:

'I always know the character of any visitors by the visions I have of them. Sometimes I see a pig or a jackal; often a ravening tiger.'

I could not resist asking, 'And how did you see me?'

'As a sweetly-toned harmonium,' said Mr Christie politely.[24]

That night they drank a lot of rum and talked about Christie's preaching and his translation of the scriptures into Macushi. Christie recalled seeing in another vision 'the Love of God' and, as Evelyn recalled, 'pronounced it to be spherical in shape and slightly larger than a football'.[25] Evelyn later wondered if he had dreamt the whole encounter until he read in a mission magazine about a previous visitor to Mr Christie's ranch, a priest who had offered his host one of the medals of Our Lady which he carried for distribution among converts. Christie studied it for a moment before giving it back: 'Why should I require an image of someone I see so frequently?' he said. 'Besides, it is an exceedingly poor likeness.'[26]

The next morning Evelyn was off again at 6.45 a.m. and by eleven he had reached the next ranch on the border with Brazil, where he wolfed down 'a dish of fried eggs, minced tasso fried with herbs, bananas and delicious Brazilian coffee'.[27] At the next ranch, a few more hours on, he gratefully accepted a lift in a motor van to Bon Success, which did the journey in a third of the time it would have taken by horse, albeit rather less comfortably. From Bon Success he then drove on up beside the Takutu River to the Jesuit mission at St Ignatius, 'as lonely an outpost of religion as you could find anywhere'.[28] There he spent a very affecting ten days as a guest of Father Mather, 'the kindest and most generous of all the hosts of the colony', whose skill at carpentry reinforced Evelyn's view of the priest as craftsman, 'a man with a job which he alone was qualified to do'.

Evelyn eventually moved on on 1 February and three days later reached Boa Vista, a town whose name ('lovely view' in Portuguese) combined with Haynes's misleading description had led him to imagine rather more than the ramshackle huddle of squalid buildings that greeted him. Gone in an instant was the mirage he had conjured of 'shady boulevards; kiosks for flowers and cigars and illustrated papers; the hotel terrace and the cafés; the baroque church built by seventeenth-century missionaries . . .'[29] More alarmingly, no one seemed to know anything about the fast motor launches that supposedly plied constantly between there and Manaós and by which Evelyn hoped to be able to return to civilisation via the Amazon River. At the Benedictine mission where Father Mather had arranged for him to stay, the monk told him that it was quite impossible to predict when another boat would leave.[30] During his days of waiting he found little to occupy himself other than to wander desultorily about the town and every so often call in at the wireless office to see if there was any news of the boat. 'Goodness the boredom of Boa Vista,' he wrote to Diana Cooper after he had been stuck there a week, 'I am already nearly crazy. No one here speaks a word of English. The Benedictine priest (Swiss) knows a few sentences of French but for the last four days he has been

down with fever. There are no books except an ant-eaten edition of Bous-
set's sermons and some back numbers of a German pious periodical for
children. One cannot get drunk as the only liquor in the village is some
very mild, very warm beer, which I can drink at a table in the store in a
cloud of flies stared at by Brazilians in pyjama suits and boaters. There
are of course no cars or boats for hire and nowhere to go in them if there
were. No roads outside the village at all – bush on one side, pampas on the
other, vast shallow river full of sand banks on other sides. No hotel or café
or life of any kind. Everyone asleep most of the day . . . I shan't ever again
undertake a journey of this kind alone. I am getting homesick and shall
return direct as soon as I get to Manaós.'[31]

As so often with Evelyn, boredom eventually gave way to a burst of
creativity, and five days later he sent his agent what he described as 'a
grade A short story', almost certainly 'The Man Who Liked Dickens', the
superbly chilling tale which later served as the penultimate chapter of *A
Handful of Dust*, the novel now seen as his greatest masterpiece. According to Evelyn's diary the story was written in just two days between 12 and
14 February, although evidently it had been brewing in his imagination
ever since he left Mr Christie, who is the clear original in the short story
of Mr McMaster (Mr Todd in *A Handful of Dust*), the sinister settler who
takes the hapless Paul Henty (Tony Last) captive on his isolated ranch and
makes him read Dickens to him day after day for the rest of his life.

'The Man Who Liked Dickens' draws on Evelyn's feelings of being
stranded in Boa Vista combined with the remembered sensation of en-
trapment he had felt while his father sat in the book-room at Underhill
reading aloud from Dickens – a memory doubtless revived by the stash of
Dickens novels Father Mather kept at St Ignatius. McMaster, incidentally,
was the name of one of Arthur Waugh's closest friends.

Henty has stumbled on McMaster's ranch while on an expedition
aimed at winning back his unfaithful wife. When a rescue party of three
Englishmen does finally arrive, Henty misses them because he has been
drugged by McMaster, who calmly tells him when he wakes:

'I thought you would not mind – as you could not greet them yourself I gave
them a little souvenir, your watch. They wanted something to take home
to your wife who is offering a great reward for news of you. They were very
pleased with it. And they took some photographs of the little cross I put up

to commemorate your coming. They were very pleased with that too. They were very easily pleased. But I do not suppose they will visit us again, our life here is so retired . . . no pleasures except reading . . . I do not suppose we shall ever have visitors again . . . well, well, I will get you some medicine to make you feel better. Your head aches, does it not . . . We will not have any Dickens today . . . but tomorrow, and the day after that, and the day after that. Let us read *Little Dorrit* again. There are passages in that book I can never hear without the temptation to weep.'

Unlike Henty, after two weeks in Boa Vista Evelyn did eventually manage to escape, albeit by horse as the promised trade boats had failed to show up, and back towards Georgetown having given up on the idea of Manaós. On the second day, after going on ahead of his guide, he contrived to get lost and was extremely fortunate to stumble upon a hut belonging to an English-speaking Indian just when he and his horse could go no further, a stroke of luck the odds of which Evelyn estimated at 54 million to one. The Indian also happened to be heading to Bon Success, so within a couple of days Evelyn was safely back with Father Mather at St Ignatius, from where he wrote to Baby on Ash Wednesday telling her that he had been 'saved by the miraculous intervention of St Christopher' and bade her look forward to his return 'on account of my bearing and beauty and wit and nobility of character'.[32]

He did not reach Georgetown for a further six weeks, however, having rashly chosen a 'very unpansy'[33] route over the Pakaraima Mountains to the upper waters of the Potaro and so down to the Essequibo. 'One has to walk all the time as there is no trail for lamas,' he wrote to Baby, 'and one has a party of Indians in front with choppers clearing the path so it is very slow going.'[34] It was an even grimmer journey than he had envisaged, beset by heavy rain, kaboura flies and jiggers that regularly had to be dug out of the soles of his feet. When he eventually made it back he was relieved to find two 'delightful' letters from Baby and he replied that he had got 'a small dead alligator for Wincey [her dog]'.[35] He reached London a month later and promptly took himself off to a hotel in Bath 'to be in good architecture for a little after all those huts and forests', he explained to Baby,[36] and to attend to his backlog of mail.

Evelyn was mildly annoyed to see that an article he had written describing the Rupununi cattle trail had been rechristened by the *Daily Mail*

'My Escape from Mayfair' ('It will be about two years before I dare look anyone in the face again,' he told Baby). Rather more vexing, though, was the discovery that while he was away he had been accused of blasphemy and obscenity in a review of *Black Mischief* by Ernest Oldmeadow, the moralistic editor of Britain's oldest Catholic journal. '*The Tablet* says I am no Catholic,' Evelyn wrote to Baby, 'and yet I carried a torch for two miles in front of the B [Blessed] Sacrament in Trinidad [at Easter on his way home] and I was the only white man.'[37] Gratifyingly, twelve prominent Catholics had sprung to Evelyn's defence and in his absence written to *The Tablet* expressing their 'regard for Mr Waugh' and protesting at the journal's 'bad faith'. Evelyn himself now wrote a scathing 4,000-word 'open letter' to the journal's proprietor, Cardinal Bourne, the Catholic Primate of Great Britain, which Baby sensibly persuaded him not to publish ('Did I tell you I took your advice and rather deferred to your wishes, about the Cardinal's pamphlet?')[38] but which he nonetheless distributed among friends.

From Bath Evelyn went to Madresfield, where he got it into his head one 'bad night' that Baby was about to announce her engagement to Sir Michael Duff, a handsome, bisexual landowner from north Wales, and wrote to her withholding his congratulations 'until I am convinced that he is the solution for our particular problem'.[39] He realised the next morning this was not the case but sent her the letter anyway hoping it would amuse her. The four months away seemed only to have intensified his devotion and he was not shy of saying so. 'I think of you all the time,' he wrote in July. 'I believe you are the first woman I have ever been in love with . . . I love you so much.'[40] When he borrowed the Coopers' house by the sea at Bognor to make a start on *Ninety-Two Days* (dashed off at an astonishing rate within a month), he told Diana: 'Trouble is I think of the dutch girl all day – not sweet voluptuous dreams, no sir, just fretful and it sykeses the work.'[41] The same day he told Baby that he had wasted three sheets of notepaper from not knowing how to begin a letter to her – 'I wrote Sweet Tess and that looked silly and Dear Heart which was sillier still, and Lovely Teresa, which was better . . .'

Two days later, while staying with the Montagus at Breccles Hall in Norfolk, he wrote again: 'I don't think of much except you – your beauty, so fragile and intangible, a thing of fresh water and early morning and the silence of dawn and mist just alloyed with gold and deep, saturated restful greens, like sunrise on that river I travelled down last winter – and your intricate character, all mystery and frustration, a labyrinth with something infinitely secret and infinitely precious at its centre ... I couldn't understand anyone less and want anyone more ... Darling Tess your beauty is all around me like a veil so that every moment apart from you seems obscure and half real.'[42]

However fond Baby was of Evelyn, her inability fully to reciprocate his feelings continued to cause friction. 'It is hard to believe that you can't see me without wanting to have an affair with me,' she wrote to him, 'but if that is so I do implore you not to feel bitter about it and not to behave as if we didn't perfectly understand each other and weren't very fond of each other indeed quite apart from anything else. Please do try and understand what I mean and not be so unkind – You may have so many friends that you can afford to quarrel with me but there can't be many who are as fond of you as I am. So do please, Evelyn, be generous enough not to feel bitterly about me – If only you would be less obstinate about having evil intentions we could perfectly well go on seeing each other like we used to.'[43]

'I am afraid it must be my fault that you are cross with me,' she went on, 'perhaps you feel I made too much use of you during those weeks when I was sad – Forgive me if I did – it was only because I felt you were sympathetic and trusted you completely – not only because you were a Catholic because after all there are a good many others who might have been able to produce priests and advice for me!'[44]

In this instance Baby's unhappiness seems to have stemmed from some kind of religious crisis and Evelyn told her how he had recently been asked by Lady Juliet Duff if it was true that she was going into a convent: 'No, I said, nothing is less likely except her marriage to someone she doesn't love.'[45] He had by then moved on to stay at Madresfield, where he hoped 'to do the work that got upset when I fell in love'.[46] The only other people were Maimie, Coote and Hughie, the latter 'deep in disgrace', so Evelyn told Baby, 'having been tipsy all the weekend and sykesed up the servants and attempted to murder C. Brocklehurst [a Sussex landowner and another of Baby's admirers – years later he left her money in his will]'. Evelyn was sleeping in 'oriental squalor' in Lady Sibell's old room, 'full of bad taste objects', and as usual had nursery as his study. 'My love to you all the time, everywhere,' he wrote to Baby.[47]

With Baby herself about to leave for a holiday in Italy with her mother and sister Zita, Evelyn had allowed her to persuade him to go on what he imagined would be a 'nightmare' Hellenic cruise with a group of fellow Catholics organised by Father Martin D'Arcy. 'You will think me insane when I tell you,' he wrote to Nancy Mitford, 'and you will be jolly well right.'[48] But Baby's imminent departure prompted yet another lovelorn outburst, possibly exacerbated by her confusing ambivalence:

Darling Evelyn,

Don't be cross with me and keep ringing off all the time – you <u>know</u> how fond I am of you and that you were the first person I wanted to see when I was miserable – so please don't ever doubt that, will you? But what do you expect me to do when you say that you might fall in love with me and that your intentions are evil! You see I enjoy that situation too much not to encourage it as much as I can in a subconscious way – and as I mean to try as hard as I possibly can not to behave badly, it wouldn't be very consistent of me to go on seeing you all the time, would it! And quite apart from that I have got such a <u>revulsion</u> suddenly from the ungenerousness of encouraging people as much as I can and then being prim in taxis – I know you will understand this although I explain it very badly – For once in my life I am <u>not</u> just being tiresome and enjoying creating a situation – at least I don't think I am! I am <u>really</u> very fond of you and should like to go on being your friend for the rest of our lives – and I should like to do some enormous thing for you so that you would know that I really mean all this – And if you are ever miserable and want anybody to be sympathetic I only hope that I shall be able to be as sweet to you as you have been to me – Thank you a <u>million</u> times for it, darling Evelyn – you have been an angel – and please do forgive me and not laugh at me for being priggish but I know you will understand me because you always do – If you weren't married you see it would be different because I might or I might not want to marry you but I wouldn't be sure – As things are, I <u>can't</u> be so unfair as to go on when I am quite determined about what I mean to do – Bless you – I might be Helen of Troy from the conceited things I find myself saying![49]

In the weeks leading up to his trip, while staying at Bognor, Evelyn had taken up skipping so as 'to make me prettier for the papist cruisers', he told Baby.⁵⁰ The cruisers were to have included 'old Hazel' [Lavery], but she missed the boat, which was a relief to Evelyn, who had been doing his best to avoid her since getting back from Guiana.

In the meantime, Evelyn spared Baby few of his yearnings: 'I love you and that's all there is to it and I know you a little and so realize that you find it hard to do both the hard and the good things that come easily to less remarkable people. You have almost every lovely quality – tolerance, temperance, patience, family affection, discretion, reticence, purity – all unattainable to me. But you're also lazy, cold and undecided. I knew all that long before I fell really in love with you.'⁵¹

Besides wanting to occupy himself while Baby was in Italy, another of Evelyn's motives for going on the cruise was to try and coax his old friend Alfred Duggan away from the bottle and back towards his lapsed Catholic faith, a mission which Evelyn was to pursue doggedly for many years to come and with eventual success, although on that particular trip Alfred was conspicuously drunk for much of the time and, as Evelyn told Diana, 'broke up badly during last days of voyage on account of switching from beer to Jugo-Slavian brandy'.⁵²

Evelyn's more immediate achievement aboard SS *Kraljica Marija* was to make friends with two families of great importance to him in the future, the Asquiths and the Herberts. Of the latter, he made a sufficiently favourable impression on twenty-one-year-old Gabriel Herbert, a first cousin of his first wife, to be invited to go and stay at her family's house at Portofino after the cruise, and in the intervening week he persuaded Katharine Asquith and her son to join him for a few days sightseeing in Ravenna and Bologna.

Katharine, then aged forty-eight, was the widow of H. H. Asquith's brilliant son Raymond, who had been killed on the Somme in 1916. The next year her brother Edward had also been killed in action and she inherited what was left of her family's Mells estate in Somerset and its beautiful sixteenth-century manor house, built for one of her Horner ancestors after the dissolution of Glastonbury Abbey.

A convert to Catholicism during widowhood and in some respects rather pious and high-minded, she nevertheless found Evelyn 'exceedingly amusing and a great collector of the ship's gossip',⁵³ as did her seventeen-year-old son Julian, 'Trim', who had succeeded his grandfather as the 2nd Earl of Oxford and Asquith in 1928 and whom Evelyn found 'studious, holy and respectful';[54] and her 'very doe-like and sweet' twenty-five-year-old daughter, Lady Helen, a teacher.[55]

The cruise was far more enjoyable than Evelyn had feared and he admitted to Baby he was 'glad you sent me'. Besides his various old and new friends, the ship was 'full of people of high rank,' he told the Lygon sisters, 'including two princesses of ROYAL BLOOD'. That there was 'not much rogering' appeared not to bother him unduly, nor that the food was 'appalling'. In fact the only obvious impediment to his enjoyment was the news that Baby had cut short her Italian trip to return to London. 'If I had realised you would be back so soon I wouldn't now be in the sea of Marmora,' he wrote to her on 1 September. 'If you had been a more enterprising girl you should have joined this cruise at Athens.'[56]

The ship eventually returned to Venice on 12 September, and after the few days sightseeing with the Asquiths, Evelyn made his way to Portofino, and to 'Altachiara', which the Herberts had named in translation of Highclere, although, like Guy Crouchback's 'Castello Crauccibac' in *Sword of Honour*, the locals always referred to it as the Villa Carnarvon. The house party there was presided over by Gabriel's mother Mary Herbert, a 'very decent hostess', according to Evelyn, and included Mary's Catholic friend Hilaire Belloc, various young friends of her children and the four Herbert siblings. The second-youngest of these, Laura, then aged seventeen, would eventually become Evelyn's second wife, although there is no evidence of the merest frisson on this first encounter; indeed he seems barely to have noticed her at all, beyond describing her in a letter to the Asquiths as 'a white mouse'.

* * *

Evelyn was of course still fixated by Baby Jungman, and in any case as a divorcee there seemed no prospect of his marrying anyone at all within the rules of the Catholic Church. Another of his friends on the recent cruise, Christopher Hollis, had noticed how Evelyn had gone to great trouble each day to obtain an English newspaper even though he had never seemed much interested in current affairs. 'Oh,' replied Evelyn when Hollis asked him why he did this, 'just to see if there is any good news – such as, for instance, the death of Mrs Heygate.'[57] For a time after his conversion, Evelyn had indeed taken it for granted that Shevelyn would have to die before the

Church would allow him to remarry, however by this time he had begun exploring with Catholic friends the possibility of applying to the Church to have his marriage annulled. It was presumably to talk about this that Evelyn had lunched with Shevelyn in July – an event referred to in passing in one of his letters to Baby. ('I wrote to my wife and she said lunch with me next week. I have grown my hair long and it has twelve white ones she said.'[58]) By this time Shevelyn's marriage to John Heygate was becoming unstuck and she was keen to do what she could to make amends so far as Evelyn was concerned. 'I felt that the whole thing was my fault,' she wrote later, 'and to pretend innocence was a lie . . . I was naturally anxious that he should get his annulment.'[59]

In October, Evelyn wrote to Coote Lygon: 'I shall be in London on Wed to take my poor wife to be wracked by the Inquisition.'[60] Beforehand the two Evelyns had lunch together again, during which Evelyn was 'pleasant,' Shevelyn recalled, 'and told me exactly what to say, which priest to be aware of and who was on his side. He was anxious to marry again and was afraid the girl would not wait.'[61]

The hearing itself took place in a large, gloomy room adjoining Westminster Cathedral, with 'a bevy of priests at a seemingly never ending table' as Shevelyn recalled, and four additional witnesses: Alec Waugh, Pansy Lamb, Shevelyn's sister Alathea and her husband Geoffrey Fry. Evelyn requested an annulment on the grounds of 'the lack of real consent', contending that, first, he and his wife had entered the marriage on the understanding that it could be dissolved at the wish of either party and, second, that children had been excluded for an indefinite period.

The second argument was eventually rejected over its failure to meet the required standard of proof, but the first argument prevailed after both Evelyns described themselves as nominal Anglicans (at best) at the time of their marriage, and testified that their church wedding had been a 'conventional formality' and that the words of the ceremony had meant nothing.[62] In support of Evelyn's case, Pansy Lamb went so far as to recall that 'They came to an agreement in my presence that, if the marriage was not happy, they would not be bound by it, and Miss Evelyn said to me that she had no intention of remaining married if the marriage did not turn out well. The arrangement was not a written contract but a mutual agreement, each accepting divorce as a definitive solution to possible misfortune.'[63] Even though the Westminster judges expressed doubts at the

The Evelyns photographed by Alastair Graham in the garden at Barford, shortly after their engagement in May 1928.

Their 'spick and span bandbox of a house' at 17a Canonbury Square, and (below right) the portrait painted by Henry Lamb for Bryan Guinness – hence the glass of stout – earlier the same year, 1928, shortly after Evelyn had finished *Decline and Fall*.

AS A CHILD IN THE YEAR 1860: THE HON. MRS. EVELYN WAUGH.

Shevelyn photographed by *Sketch* at the Guinnesses' 1860 party in the same costume as she was seen by *The Tatler* at a later party, lounging on deck in 'a very amiable position' with John Heygate.

The Evelyns at a 'Tropical' fancy-dress party during their failed reconciliation-fortnight.

After the collapse of his marriage, Evelyn sought refuge with Bryan and Diana Guinness, seen here on honeymoon in 1929.

Right: House party at Pakenham Hall, 1930: Alastair Graham, Evelyn, Elizabeth Harman (later Longford), and, just out of shot with a tennis racket, John Betjeman.

Below: Evelyn in observation mode at Pool Place, with Rupert Mitford (Nancy's uncle), Nancy Mitford and Pansy Lamb, 1930.

Below right: Evelyn in Kenya in 1931.

Alec and Evelyn at Villefranche, South of France, 1931.

Teresa 'Baby' Jungman, whom Evelyn fell deeply in love with in 1930, and (left) below, posing with her sister Zita as the Gemini sign of the zodiac.

Another who eluded his advances was Eileen Agar (above) but more receptive girlfriends included (clockwise from above right) Joyce Fagan, Audrey Lucas, Hazel Lavery and Pixie Marix.

AUDREY SCOTT

Evelyn (above) with Sybil Colefax,
Phyllis de Janzé and Oliver Messel in
1931.

Alec Waugh and Joan Chirnside after
their engagement in 1932.

Left: Evelyn, Hamish St Clair Erskine, Coote Lygon and Hubert Duggan at Madresfield, early 1930s.

Below: Evelyn between Maimie and Coote (in specs) Lygon.

Left: Evelyn at Captain Hance's riding academy, labelled by himself.

Madresfield as it looks today.

Evelyn is congratulated by his father after winning the Hawthornden Prize in 1936.

Evelyn with Penelope Betjeman and her horse in the drawing-room at Faringdon House.

time about this evidence on the basis that it seemed to say 'more than the parties said themselves', the Rota eventually dismissed their reservations and granted a declaration of nullity: 'It is established beyond doubt on the evidence that the parties excluded the indissolubility of the bond of marriage by a specific act of will.'[64]

Almost three years were to pass before this judgment was delivered, however, due to what the Rota called 'reprehensible delays' in Cardinal Bourne's office at Westminster, where the papers concerning Evelyn's case lay forgotten until he eventually asked about them again in 1935. But at the time Evelyn was confident that his marriage would soon be annulled and so he felt free at last to propose to Baby Jungman. 'Just heard yesterday that my divorce comes on today,' he wrote to Maimie Lygon, 'so was elated and popped question to Dutch girl and got raspberry. So that is that, eh. Stiff upper lip and dropped cock. Now I must go. How sad, how sad.'[65]

15

....

I Can't Advise You in My Favour

After such a long and anxious build-up it was something of a relief for Evelyn finally to have got his proposal off his chest – even though the response was not the one he had wanted. Shortly afterwards the archbishop's office told him that while they were confident he would get his annulment, it was unlikely to come through for at least eighteen months. 'It is funny how things turn out,' he wrote to Baby when he heard this. 'Imagine my impatience and despair if I had been honourable and decided to wait till I was free before popping the question. Now having popped it and got my answer it is all more or less O.K.'[1]

Whether or not he was putting a brave face on it, in other respects Baby's rejection marked the low point of a difficult and desolate autumn, much of which he had spent by the sea at Diana Cooper's house in Sussex working on *Ninety-Two Days*, which he finished in the second week of November. 'It is a very sad life I lead,' he wrote to Coote Lygon, 'very lonely, very uncomfortable, in a filthy cottage in the ugliest place in England with only mice for company like a prisoner in the tower. Still I write my boring book, hand over fist and that is something.'[2]

Though he was buoyed by writing as fast as ever, rattling off up to 4,000 words a day, his birthday had been a forlorn and introspective affair. 'I was thirty on Saturday & feel sixty,' he wrote to Maimie Lygon. 'I celebrated the day by walking into Bognor and going to the Cinema in the best 1/6 seats. I saw a love film about two people who were in love; they were very loving and made me cry.'[3] Reaching the milestone had hit him hard, 'not the time wasted but the 45 years or so to come', he told Baby. 'You are between 20 and 30 and can always die young and that is all right, high promise unfulfilled, and so on. No one ever dies between 30 and 75.'[4]

However calmly he affected to take Baby's refusal to marry him, it was not long before Evelyn began beseeching her again. 'Of course what I asked for last night was out of all reason,' he acknowledged in early December. 'It is just that there are periods when one has to hope for a miracle because there seems no possibility of things going right by natural causes.'[5] Baby told him that she could no longer accept kisses or presents from him and sent back the chain he had bought her as a Christmas present, but as so often the messages soon became mixed again and when Evelyn went to Madresfield for Christmas, she sent him a sponge, which seemed to set him off again: 'I have clung to the last sponge you gave me through many changes of bathroom; I threw its shreds away today and will stick to the new one for months to come.'[6]

* * *

At such times the easiest way for Evelyn to cope was to go abroad and on 29 December he wrote to Baby from the SS *Raisai I Huid* bound for Morocco. 'You will say it was sly to go away without saying anything . . . But please believe it isn't only selfish – running away from pain (though it has been more painful than you know, all the last months, realizing every day that I was becoming less attractive and less important to you) – but also I can't be any good to you without your love and it's the worst possible thing for you to have to cope with the situation that had come about between us.'[7]

After disembarking at Tangier he took the overnight train to Fez, 'a city of astonishing beauty,' he wrote to Katharine Asquith, 'with running streams & fountains everywhere and enormous covered gateways in very narrow streets – no wheeled traffic, miles of bazaar, elaborate medieval fortifications, hills all round dotted with forts, olive trees, sand cliffs & spring grass, waterfalls. Dense crowds of moors and a few French soldiers – mostly Senegalese or Foreign Legion – practically no touting for tourists.'[8]

The more worldly Diana Cooper (who had seen him off) and the Lygon girls were treated to his tales from the red-light district: 'It was very gay and there were little Arab girls of fifteen & sixteen for ten francs each & a cup of mint tea. So I bought one but I didn't enjoy her very much because she had skin like sandpaper and a huge stomach which didn't show until she took off her clothes & then it was too late.'[9] More to his liking was a girl called Fatima whom he got to know on subsequent visits and briefly thought about installing in his own lodgings. 'She is not at all Dutch in her ways,' he told Maimie. 'She is brown in colour and her face is tattooed all over with blue patterns v. pretty but does not play the piano beautifully, she has a gold tooth she is very proud of but as we can't talk each other's language there is not much to do in between rogering.'[10]

Evelyn's other priority in Morocco was to write the novel he had been thinking about during the previous year and made a tentative start on in December at Chagford. Explaining the genesis of what eventually became *A Handful of Dust*, he later recalled that after writing 'The Man Who Liked Dickens' in British Guiana, 'the idea keeps working in my mind. I wanted to discover how the prisoner got there, and eventually the thing grew into a study of other sorts of savages at home and the civilised man's helpless plight among them.'[11]

The civilised man in his new book was Tony Last, innocent squire of Hetton Abbey, the savages his unfaithful wife Brenda and her young lover John Beaver. Like all Evelyn's previous novels, it was firmly rooted in his own experience, drawing on the bitterness he still felt over Shevelyn's betrayal coupled with his more recent rejection by Baby Jungman; however he was now attempting something much more serious than his previous black comedies. 'I peg away at the novel which seems to me faultless of its kind,' he wrote to Katharine Asquith. 'Very difficult to write because for the first time I am trying to deal with normal people instead of eccentrics. Comic English character parts too easy when one gets to be thirty.'[12] In early February 1934 he told her: 'The novel drags on at 10,000 words a week. I have just killed a little boy at a lawn meet & made his mother commit adultery & his father get drunk so perhaps you won't like it after all.'[13] Every so often he sent instalments back to his agent in London to be typed up. Though still undecided how it would end, he told Peters that the dénouement might possibly be the same as that of 'The Man Who Liked Dickens'.

Eventually it was, and when the book was published later in the year Henry Yorke was among those who found the ending 'so fantastic that it throws the rest out of proportion. Aren't you mixing two things together? The first part of the book is convincing, a real picture of people one has met and may at any moment meet again. Then comes the perfectly feasible, very moving, & beautifully written death of that horrible little boy after which the family breaks up. Then the father goes abroad with that very well drawn horror Messinger. That too is splendid & I've no complaints. But then to let Tony be detained by some madman introduces an entirely fresh note & we are in phantasy with a ph at once. I was terrified towards the end by thinking you would let him die of fever which to my mind would have been false but what you did do to him was far far worse. It seemed manufactured & not real.'[14]

Evelyn was unperturbed by his friend's assessment: 'Very many thanks for your letter of criticism,' he replied. 'You must remember that to me the savages come into the category of "people one has met and may at any moment meet again". I think they appear fake to you largely because you don't really believe they exist ... I think I agree that the Todd episode is fantastic. It is a "conceit" in the Webster manner – wishing to bring Tony to a sad end I made it an elaborate & improbable one. I think too the sentimental episode with Therese in the ship is probably a mistake. But the Amazon stuff had to be there. The scheme was a Gothic man in the hands of savages – first Mrs Beaver etc. then the real ones finally the silver foxes at Hetton. All that quest for a city seems to me justifiable symbolism.'[15]

In his introduction to a 2003 edition of the novel, William Boyd suggested Evelyn was being disingenuous here, contending that what really happened was that he 'needed an ending and realized he had already written something that would do', and that 'rather than any huffing and puffing about Websterian conceits' the author's primary objective had been to bring Tony to a sad end in line with his belief in the cruel and frequently unfair workings of Fate. It is true that Tony's hellish destiny was in keeping with Evelyn's pessimistic world view and that he frequently reused what he had already written before – his letters abound with passages shamelessly lifted word for word from those to other correspondents. However the Websterian conceit had not been dreamt up on the spur of the moment in response to Yorke but had been in Evelyn's mind as early as February, when the book was still only half finished and he told Diana Cooper that it was 'rather like Webster in modern idiom'.[16]

* * *

187

Evelyn returned from Morocco in late February 1934, 'sweetened by solitude', he told Diana, and took himself straight off to Chagford to finish his novel, after which he planned to go and live in Oxford to write a life of Pope Gregory the Great. In the meantime, the American magazine *Harper's Bazaar* asked for an alternative ending to *A Handful of Dust* before they would agree to serialise it, given that 'The Man Who Liked Dickens' had appeared the previous year in *Cosmopolitan*. 'I'll get the happy ending done by Saturday,' he told Peters testily in early April, intending to rattle off 5,000 words describing Tony and Brenda's reconciliation. Evidently he procrastinated and several weeks later, when *Harper's* began to pester him about delivery, he exploded: 'God how I hate Americans ... They can't have the end tomorrow because it's not written but I'll do it this week <u>if necessary</u>.'[17]

By early July he was back in London and dropped in at the Lygons' townhouse off Belgrave Square where he found Hughie drinking gin in the library. Hughie announced that he was going to the Arctic island of Spitsbergen in two days' time with a young explorer named Alexander ('Sandy') Glen (later Sir Alexander Glen, chairman of the British Tourist Authority), whom Hugh had met recently though his sister Sibell. On the spur of the moment Evelyn decided to go with them.

After giving Glen £25 for his fare and buying some kit – skis, ice axes, balaclava helmets, windproof clothes, sleeping bag and mackintosh cover – he spent the evening before he left with Winnie, his favourite girl from Mrs Meyrick's 43 Club, who 'put up a good show of being sorry for my departure',[18] he recorded. The next morning he went to Farm Street Church 'to confess Winnie' and bought a birthday cake for Baby Jungman.

Having studiously refrained from contacting Baby for the past six months, now he was off on his travels again he felt emboldened to send 'My Darling Tess' his love for her birthday: 'You are nearly always in my thoughts wherever I am,' he wrote. 'Have a happy year and if ever you aren't happy and you think I could help you are to ask for me.'[19] By the time her birthday arrived they had reached Bergen and Evelyn noted in his diary that Baby 'ought now to be receiving a series of parcels from me with no name attached. It is more fun for her that way.'[20] A few days later, after threading their way northwards towards Tromsø, he wrote to Diana: 'I don't like Norwegians at all. The sun never sets, the bar never opens, and the whole country smells of kippers.'[21]

In the early evening of 17 July they finally caught sight of the south cape of Spitsbergen: 'Black mountains with glaciers flowing down to the sea between them – occasionally a magnificent burst of light on a narrow silver strip between iron grey sky and iron grey sea, the glaciers brilliantly white, the clouds cutting off the peaks of the mountains.'[22] From Advent Bay they took a whaling boat up the west coast to some remote mining huts, where Glen committed the cardinal sin of giving the whaler crew their bottle of rum as he said goodbye, causing 'very little pleasure to them and great concern to Hughie and me', according to Evelyn.

They spent the next two days on this desolate shore lashing the sledge, waxing their skis and repacking their provisions before rowing their small boat across the bay to another derelict hut: 'Seals bobbed in the water around us,' wrote Evelyn; 'there were innumerable small icebergs, some white and fluffy, others deep green and blue like weathered copper, some opaque, some clear as glass, in preposterous shapes, with fragile, haphazard wings and feathers of ice, pierced by holes. The whole bay was filled by their music, sometimes a shrill cricket-cry, sometimes a sharp, almost regular ticking, sometimes the low hum of a hive of bees, sometimes a sharp splintering, sometimes a resonant boom . . .'[23]

The plan was to climb a glacier and sledge across inland ice to some unexplored territory in the north-east of the island, but first they had to lug all their gear for three miles up a muddy mosquito-infested valley, requiring two trips a day with loads of up to 40lbs, 'beastly work' by Evelyn's account. They had hoped the worst would be over by the time they reached the ice, however an exceptional thaw had rendered the ice rough and hummocky and the snow so soggy that they could only manage five miles a day in ten hours of extreme labour. The glacier itself then proved too badly crevassed to negotiate, so they turned west towards the shore, where Glen promised they would find a trappers' cabin and a boat left by his last expedition.

Glen's invincible and to Evelyn's mind foolhardy optimism had long since begun to grate, besides which Evelyn did not especially relish taking orders from a twenty-two-year-old undergraduate. In his diary he referred to Glen sarcastically as 'the leader' and sprinkled the only account he published of their expedition (subtitled 'Fiasco in the Arctic') with a series of digs: 'G tried to swim, but quickly scrambled out, blue and shuddering, saying that it had warmed him . . . G had said that on the coast we could "live on the country". He and Hugh went out with their guns but came back empty-handed . . . G assured us that we should have a craving for fat as soon as we were on the ice. We did not find it so.'[24] Evelyn also chided him for being too eager to shoot seals just in case they might need to eat them, lecturing him on the sanctity of life for animals as well as humans.

It came as no great surprise to Evelyn that when they eventually reached the cabin the boat was not there. After sleeping for six or seven hours, Glen and Hugh set off to retrieve their sledge which exhaustion had obliged them to abandon en route, leaving Evelyn to sort out the cabin. When he had done that he lay down on the furs covering the bunk and sank into a deep sleep – from which he was urgently roused by Glen. One of the small streams that they had all crossed with ease a few hours earlier had since become a raging torrent and while Hugh, who was tall and strong, had managed to cross it and go on to fetch the sledge, Glen could not and thought Hugh would be extremely hard pushed to get back across without help. As Evelyn and Glen hurried back there, they heard the roar of the water half an hour before they reached it. 'When finally we stood on the bank the sound was so great that we could barely make ourselves heard, shouting in each other's ears,' Evelyn recalled. 'The flow was terrific, of no great depth as yet, and still divided by shingle banks into four or five streams, running at a dizzy speed, full of boulders and blocks of ice, whirling down in it.'[25]

Glen and Evelyn roped themselves together at the waist and began wading across water so cold that 'we did not feel the ice-blocks that pounded against us' and flowing so fast that it was impossible to stand without the support of the cord. When they eventually got to within reach of Hugh on the far bank they threw him the rope on a ski stick and began dragging him back across. But just as Glen reached shore the cord broke and Hugh and Evelyn were swept away and dashed against numerous rocks and ice blocks. It seemed an age before they eventually scrambled to safety and Evelyn had long since assumed they would not make it. To regain base camp avoiding the river they now had to make a three-day trek up into the mountains without map, tent, ice axes or rope. 'If I hadn't joined the Church of Rome,' Evelyn told Glen in the midst of this, as they sheltered from a storm beneath a rock, 'I could never have survived your appalling incompetence.'[26] When eventually they returned to England in late August he was scathing about the whole venture, describing it to Tom Driberg as 'hell – a fiasco very narrowly retrieved from disaster'.[27]

* * *

Ninety-Two Days was published in the spring to far better reviews than Evelyn had expected – *The New York Times Book Review* hailing it as a departure from 'the distortion of truth and the tawdry self-exploitation of the travel books of the recent degenerate era'[28] – yet when *A Handful of Dust* appeared on his return from the Arctic few critics considered it anything approaching the masterpiece it is now held to be, although Peter Quennell in the *New Statesman* thought it 'certainly the most mature and the best written novel Mr Waugh has yet produced'.[29] As far as Evelyn was concerned it was a success, however, not least since it was the Book Society's Book of the Month and was into its fifth impression by the end of the fourth week. 'Wherever I go,' he wrote to Maimie Lygon, 'the people shout Long Live Bo & throw garlands of flowers in my path.'

He was by then back staying with his parents, who had recently sold Underhill and moved to a flat on Hampstead Lane in Highgate. 'At present it is all dignity & peace,' he reported, 'but I expect we shall soon have a quarrel & black each other's eyes & tear our hair & flog each other with hunting crops like the lovely Lygon sisters. I am going to spend a very studious autumn writing the life of a dead beast. I think I shall stay here so that I shall not be tempted to the demon at the Savile and to go out with whores & make myself ill as I do if I am away from good parents.'[30]

The 'dead beast' was Edmund Campion, the sixteenth-century Jesuit priest and martyr, and the resulting biography not only raised Evelyn's stock in Catholic circles but also gave him a far deeper understanding of his adopted faith and 'a conception of the value of total surrender', as Christopher Hollis put it. When he had had enough of living under his parents' roof he went down to Chagford, where he interspersed his writing with days hunting and visits to friends such as the Asquiths at Mells. He also wrote two short stories, 'Mr Loveday's Little Outing'* and

---

* Originally entitled 'Mr Cruttwell's Little Outing', which would not have been wholly inappropriate as Cruttwell was to end his life insane.

'On Guard' – described to Coote Lygon as 'a funny short story about a looney bin and a very dull one about a dog who bit a lady's nose'.[31]

After Christmas Evelyn was asked by Gabriel Herbert to go and stay at Pixton Park in Somerset. It was his third visit to the cheerful and chaotic Herbert family home whose Irish shabbiness – 'pyramids of books on every table – dogs' dinners on sofa etc'[32] – would later inspire his portrait of Boot Magna Hall in *Scoop*, some of which was written there. Set in rolling parkland on the edge of Exmoor and originally surrounded by an estate of some 5,000 acres, this handsome stuccoed house had been built by the 2nd Earl of Carnarvon in 1803–5 and given to Gabriel's father, Aubrey, younger son of the 4th Earl (and half-brother of Shevelyn's mother), on his marriage to Mary Vesey in 1910. When Evelyn arrived he found a large party of boisterous young people and 'God they did make me feel old and ill', he told Maimie. But amid all the exhausting bouts of hockey and hunting and charades he soon found himself falling in love with the youngest of the Herbert sisters, Laura, the silent 'white mouse' whom he had barely noticed before but now confided to Maimie that he had taken 'a <u>great</u> fancy' to.

'What is she like? Well fair, very pretty, plays peggotty beautifully . . . She has rather a long thin nose and skin as thin as bromo as she is very thin and might be dying of consumption to look at her and she has her hair in a little bun at the back of her neck but it is not very tidy and she is only 18 years old, virgin, Catholic, quiet and astute. So it is difficult. I have not made much progress yet except to pinch her twice in a charade and lean against her thigh in pretending to help her at peggotty.'[33]

Ostensibly shy, reserved and rather frail, Laura was very different to her more garrulous, hunting-mad elder sisters, as she was to all the girls with whom Evelyn had previously fallen in love. Yet as he perhaps sensed, behind the quiet, unassuming façade lay a resolutely independent character with an original, ironic sense of humour and a surprisingly violent temper, which she occasionally suppressed by taking herself off to bed until she had cooled down.

Her self-reliance may have stemmed from her distant relationship with her domineering mother – like her sister-in-law Winifred Burgh-clere, Mary Herbert was more obviously devoted to her husband than to her children – and the loss of her remarkable father when she was only seven after he contracted blood poisoning while having some teeth extracted as a supposed cure for his failing eyesight. Following the death of Aubrey Herbert – later immortalised in his granddaughter Margaret FitzHerbert's fine biography *The Man Who Was Greenmantle* – Laura's mother had promptly converted to Catholicism, however Laura stoutly resisted following her lead until she was well into her teens and thus old enough to know her own mind.

By the time she caught Evelyn's eye she was training to be an actress at RADA, having earlier attended a small boarding school in Wimbledon followed by a year at a Catholic finishing school just outside Paris (the Convent of the Holy Child at Neuilly, where 'Kick' Kennedy was finished a few years later). Besides the age gap and the fact that there was no immediate guarantee of his marriage being annulled, the most obvious impediment to Evelyn's courtship was the resistance of Laura's mother, who was far from thrilled about the reappearance of this slightly un-gentlemanly – as she reportedly saw him – character who had caused so much trouble for her sister-in-law several years earlier. 'I thought we'd heard the last of that young man,' remarked Lady Victoria Herbert, maiden aunt of both Laura and Shevelyn.

Mary Herbert was likened by James Lees-Milne to 'a magnificent, im-perious stag by Landseer, perhaps an eagle . . . masterful and very clever . . . full of opinions and Catholic prejudices'.[34] Her first meaningful encounter with Evelyn at Portofino in 1933 had not been especially auspicious and early on during his stay she had pelted him with hard Italian buns and driven him from the house after he was rude about Ireland, where she had grown up at Abbeyleix as the only child of Viscount and Viscountess de Vesci. In general, though, he had been on his best behaviour, polite almost to the point of smarminess and as a recent convert keen to in-gratiate himself with her famous Catholic guest Hilaire Belloc, whom Evelyn had met briefly on several previous occasions, most recently with Diana Cooper at Bognor. When Evelyn had gone and Mary Herbert asked Belloc what he made of him, he replied rather disconcertingly: 'He has the devil in him.'[35]*

Following the stay at Pixton just after Christmas, Evelyn's courtship of

---

* Many years later, Diana Cooper wrote to her son that while Graham Greene was 'a good man possessed of a devil' Evelyn 'contrary to this is a bad man for whom an angel is strug-gling'. John Julius Norwich (ed.), *Darling Monster: The Letters of Lady Diana Cooper to her son John Julius Norwich, 1939–1952*, p. 436.

Laura ran far from smoothly. In early February 1935, having invited her to London, he greeted her with a hangover and 'could only eat 3 oysters and some soda water,' he told Maimie Lygon, 'and I was sick a good deal on the table so perhaps that romance is shattered'.[36] In early May, while pegging away at the Campion biography at a succession of country houses, he wrote to tell Laura that he had begun to despair of ever seeing her again.[37] The next month he told Katharine Asquith that 'estranged is the word re M Herbert. High estimate of her charm and character undiminished but not able to see her without embarrassment.'[38]

In late July he had a final go: 'Darling Laura,' he wrote to her from St James's Club in Piccadilly, 'I am sad and bored and need your company. If you have a spare evening between now and when you leave London, please come out with me. Any time will suit me as I have no engagements that I cannot gladly break. Ask your mother first and tell her I wanted you to ask. That is, supposing you want to come. Perhaps you don't. I don't know where I shall be in the autumn so it may be a long time before we meet. Please come. I will behave respectfully, I promise.'[39]

His uncertainty as to his whereabouts in the autumn referred to his imminent departure for Abyssinia to report on the looming invasion by Mussolini, and it seems to have been the prospect of this, combined with Laura's mother's rigid opposition to him and Laura's equally determined independence from her, that eventually persuaded Laura to see him again. Soon after receiving the letter she asked him to Pixton for the weekend and it was on that occasion that she fell in love with him. 'I'm writing to you rather before I meant to,' she wrote boldly after he had left, 'but I feel like it – You can't know how happy I was & how much I loved having you here this weekend – I don't think I've ever loved anything so much . . . all my love to you darling I do love you so very much more than I can say – I do hope Abyssinia's fun & not dangerous.'[40]

'Darling darling Laura,' wrote a greatly relieved Evelyn from the Adelphi Hotel in Liverpool, as he prepared to embark for Africa, 'please don't find that you are just as happy without me. I am not nearly as happy without you. Bless you my darling love child.'[41]

A consummate opportunist when it came to his journalism, Evelyn had asked his agent to capitalise on his previous experience of Abyssinia when news broke of Mussolini's coming invasion. However in the end it was a word in Lord Rothermere's ear from his friend Diana Cooper – just

about the award, Henry Yorke wrote
on it if it were not for the fact that y(
generation & that recognition of this
time. It may sound ungracious to pu
I do feel hotly that there is not one
not very far beyond the books they l
It takes time for outstanding work t(
was presumably this prize that persu
Who that Evelyn might at last merit
appear for the first time in its 1937 e(
'travelling'), a scarcely believable seve
first entry in the hallowed annual refe

Evelyn replied to Henry that it w
prize should go 'to a specifically Catl
this could do no harm to his reputai
damaged his marriage prospects tha
Mrs Herbert, Maurice Bowra, again
recently published collection of short
'Mr. Waugh, like Mr. Maugham, su(
attempts,' wrote Bowra. 'He manages
touch of an accomplished master . . .
abandon biography to lesser men and
stories like these?'⁵

But Evelyn relied heavily on his nor
vent, and with his expenses sure to ris(
the reluctant conclusion that he nee(
up his half-written book with a con(
conquest had turned out. After going
he travelled out to Africa via Rome
told Katharine Asquith. 'I am sick of
It was fun being pro-Italian when it
losing cause. I have little sympathy wi
arrived to find the fledgling colony in
appears to be Wops in jam,' he wrote
he came to finishing his book he was
as having brought about the 'spread o(
medicine, in a disgraceful place'; it wi

as in *Scoop* Mrs Stitch mentions the young novelist John Boot to Lord Copper – that led to his highly lucrative employment as a correspondent by the *Daily Mail*, which had lost its star reporter (Sir Percival Phillips, who like Evelyn had reported on the coronation of Haile Selassie in 1930) to *The Daily Telegraph* just as the crisis loomed.

Besides his knowledge of the country – an extremely rare commodity on Fleet Street at that time – Evelyn could be counted on as an unflinching advocate of Rothermere's pro-Italian stance, viewing Mussolini as the most effective barrier against Hitler and Abyssinia as a barbarous country at the mercy of a capricious and violent government unable to cope with its lawless elements. 'It is entertaining to find a country where the noblemen feast on raw beef,' Evelyn had written in the *Evening Standard* earlier that year, 'but less amusing when they enslave and castrate the villagers of neighbouring countries.' The Abyssinian empire, he argued, had been taken bloodily and was held 'so far as it is held at all' by force of arms. 'In the matter of abstract justice, the Italians have just as much right to govern; in the matter of practical politics, it is certain that their government would be for the benefit of the Ethiopian Empire and for the rest of Africa.'⁴²

As with previous trips, besides the *Daily Mail* contract, Evelyn looked to get two books out of his adventures: a non-fiction volume about the war, *Waugh in Abyssinia*, for which he was paid what was then the huge advance of £950 by Longman's, where his friend Tom Burns commissioned it; and a novel, which eventually became *Scoop*, inspired by the scorn he felt for the rest of the press corps, among whom he found the conscientious Stuart Emeny of the *News Chronicle* particularly ridiculous: 'All events for him had only one significance and standard of measurement – whether or no they constituted a "story". He did not make friends; he "established contacts". Even his private opinions were those of his paper . . .'⁴³

But while Evelyn was inclined to disparage the whole business of journalism and his own aptitude for it, he actually possessed many of the qualities of an excellent newspaper reporter. One of his fellow correspondents in Abyssinia, W. F. 'Bill' Deedes, recalled: 'His ear was well attuned to the idiocies of this world. He was curious, thorough in any inquiry he made, very quick on the uptake, persistent and observant, and never nervous of embarrassing anyone.'⁴⁴ Deedes, whose quarter-ton of luggage famously found its way into Evelyn's portrait of William Boot in

Scoop, also admired Evelyn's br[...]
foe and to bluff his way out of a t[...]
to be endowed with many of the [...]
to possess'.[45] And he noticed tha[...]
adept at conversing with people [...]
fling them with his brand of wit. [...]
to him, which is why dialogue in [...]

Deedes may have recognised [...]
cover himself in glory as far as th[...]
biggest gripe was that he mana[...]
by *The Daily Telegraph* on the m[...]
concerning a master of foxhoun[...]
who, on behalf of the brazenly n[...]
ment Corporation, managed to c[...]
other natural resources over half [...]
America, to which countries the [...]
cial interest in the maintenance [...]

Evelyn had chanced to travel [...]
at the time thought there was sor[...]
explanation that he was on a mi[...]
yssinian Orthodox Church and [...]
he received en route, which he [...]
'From my huntsman. He says the [...]
instead of tailing Rickett to find [...]
the eccentrically roundabout rou[...]
to Penelope Betjeman (several we[...]
whether her Berkshire neighbou[...]

When *The Daily Telegraph* br[...]
Evelyn was four days away from [...]
Italy was most likely to invade) [...]
file follow-up pieces until the st[...]
irreparably damaged his relation [...]
up with their bad-tempered teleg[...]

---

* Auberon Waugh later attested to his [...]
came to play Christmas carols each year [...]
was certainly not something he cultivate[...]
it, he had it.' Auberon Waugh, *Will This [...]*

of the American peoples, the dispossession of the Indian tribes and the establishment in a barren land of new pastures and cities'.[8]

Leaving Laura this time had proved far more affecting than he expected. 'How I wish you were here,' he wrote to her from Assisi. 'Sweet poppet it seems such a waste to see lovely things & not be with you. It is like being one-eyed & goggling out of focus. I miss you & need you all the time. Most of all when I'm happy.'[9] The next day he wrote again:

> I need you all the time – when I'm vexed and uncertain & tired – but more than ever on a night like this when everything is unearthly & lovely. You see, darling child, so often when people fall in love & want to be married, it is because they foresee a particular kind of life to which the other is necessary. But I don't feel that. Sometimes I think it would be lovely to lead the sort of life with you that I have led alone for the last ten years – no possessions, no home, sometimes extravagant & luxurious, sometimes lying low & working hard. At other times I picture a settled life with a large household, rather acrimonious & rather frugal, and sometimes a minute house, and few friends, and little work & leisure & love. But what I do know is that I can't picture any sort of life without you. I have left half of myself behind in England and I am only dragging about a bit of myself now. And I don't at all regret the haphazard, unhappy life I've led up till now because I don't think that without it I could love you so much. Goodnight my blessed child. I love you more than I can find words to tell you.[10]

He told Mary Lygon: 'I cry a great deal on account of not seeing LAURA. But Lady Horner says absence is like the wind – it extinguishes a little flame & fans a big one with greater heat.'[11] However with Laura's mother insisting on their delaying the announcement of their engagement, Evelyn evidently did not feel bound by absolute fidelity just yet, and on his way back through Rome he recorded that he had 'intended to bathe, change, fuck, and eat a luxurious dinner. Instead spent the evening driving to pay my debt to the English College [presumably to do with his annulment] in smuggled lire.'[12] If there had been any lingering uncertainty in Laura's mind, Evelyn's absence in Abyssinia seems to have removed it. 'I have definitely made up my mind that I want to marry you more than anything I want in the world,' she wrote to him while he was away. 'I hope you're still wanting to marry me. I think I love you more every day.'[13]

the *Mail*,' he wrote to Diana Cooper. 'It was no good they sent me offensive cables twice a day & I took umbrage & they wanted me to stay in Addis and I took despair.'[48] But with book contracts still to fulfil he could not afford to leave Abyssinia just yet, and when his replacement was held up in Djibouti, he stayed on working for them until they finally terminated his contract at the end of November. He was away for more than four months in all, during which time he sent frequent letters to the girl whose love he had been assured of on leaving. 'I wonder how you are,' he wrote to Laura shortly after his arrival in Addis. 'In fact I wonder about you most of the day . . . The thing I think about most is your eyelashes making a noise like a bat on the pillow. How compromising that sounds – you know what I mean, but the Ethiopians won't who read all my correspondence & telegrams . . . Darling child I feel very far away from you.'[49] In October he hoped to be home by Christmas: 'I am lonely and bored and have all the material for a jolly good novel about journalists which I want to do before it gets stale to me.'[50]

In the event he spent Christmas in Bethlehem, followed by an overnight jaunt by charabanc across the desert to Baghdad for a weekend, then visits to Damascus and finally Rome, where he was 'crossed examined by beasts [priests] re my wife', he wrote to Maimie Lygon, and came away impressed after an interview with Il Duce. He returned to London at the beginning of February 1936, arriving 'in a lion-skin,' so his father recorded, 'which much excited Tuppence [their dog]'.[51] Laura was even more eager to see him providing her mother would let her. 'Please ring me up as soon as you reach London,' she had written. 'I've kept all this week free on the chance of your getting back & of my being allowed to see you. Darling Evelyn I can't tell you how happy it makes me thinking that you are coming back so soon – Even if I can't see you, it makes the whole difference knowing that you are near & out of any danger . . . I am so longing to see you or even to hear your voice.'[52]

Evelyn was soon hard at work on his non-fiction book, *Waugh in Abyssinia*, much of which he wrote as a guest of Perry Brownlow, a distant cousin of Diana Cooper via her natural father Harry Cust and a great friend and lord-in-waiting of King Edward VIII, as he had just become, who like Evelyn spent a fair amount of time at Belton House, Lord Brownlow's stately home in Lincolnshire. In the spring of 1936, while writing his Abyssinia book, Evelyn stayed at another Brownlow property in

Shropshire, where he inhabited a flat above the estate office. 'So now I live here looking after the great Ellesmere estates,' he wrote to Maimie Lygon, 'god it is a responsibility I have afforested & deforested & distrained & debentured & still it won't come right.'[53]

Two weeks later from there he wrote Laura what amounted to an exceptionally straightforward and realistic letter of proposal:

Tell you what you might do while you are alone at Pixton. You might think about me a bit & whether, if those wop priests ever come to a decent decision, you could bear the idea of marrying me. Of course you haven't got to decide, but think about it. I can't advise you in my favour because I think it would be beastly for you, but think how nice it would be for me. I am restless & moody & misanthropic & lazy & have no money except what I earn and if I got ill you would starve. In fact it's a lousy proposition. On the other hand I think I could do a Grant [Eddie Grant, married to Laura's sister Bridget] and reform & become quite strict about not getting drunk and I am pretty sure I shall be faithful. Also there is always a fair chance that there will be another bigger economic crash in which case if you had married a nobleman with a great house you might find yourself starving, while I am very clever and could probably earn a living of some sort somewhere. Also though you would be taking on an elderly buffoon, I am one without fixed habits. You wouldn't find yourself confined to any particular place or group. Also I have practically no living relatives except one brother whom I scarcely know. You would not find yourself involved in a large family & all their rows & you would not be patronized & interfered with by older sisters in law & aunts as often happens. All these are very small advantages compared with the awfulness of my character. I have always tried to be nice to you and you may have got it into your head that I am nice really, but that is all rot. It is only to you & for you. I am jealous & impatient – but there is no point in going into a whole list of my vices. You are a critical girl and I've no doubt that you know them all and a great many I don't know myself. But the point I wanted to make is that if you marry most people, you are marrying a great number of objects & other people as well, well if you marry me there is nothing else involved, and that is an advantage as well as a disadvantage. My only tie of any kind is my work. That means that for several months each year we shall have to separate or you would have to share some very lonely places with me. But apart from that we could do what we liked & go where we liked – and if you married a soldier or stockbroker or member of parliament or master of hounds you would be more tied. When I tell my friends that I am in love with a girl of 19 they look shocked and say 'wretched child' but I don't look on you as very young even in your beauty and I don't think there is any sense in the line that you cannot possibly commit yourself to a decision that affects your whole life for years yet. But anyway there is no point in your deciding or even answering. I may never get free of your cousin Evelyn. Above all things, darling, don't fret at all. But just turn the matter over in your dear head.[54]

16

....

Goodness She is a Decent Girl

Evelyn was never going to be the world's easiest husband, however no one could accuse him of not having been entirely upfront about how difficult he was likely to be. In any case Laura's reply to his proposal must have been reasonably favourable as he told Diana Cooper in June 1936 that he had been periodically leaving his desk in Ellesmere for trips to see her and 'loving her a lot and she being exquisitely unDutch. Goodness she is a decent girl.'[1]

Yet however keen they were on each other, they could still not get married before the Pope had annulled Evelyn's first marriage and, while Laura remained a minor, her mother had given her consent. The first obstacle was removed on 7 July, when Evelyn returned to his club at dawn after a pilgrimage to Lough Derg in Ireland to find a telegram from Cardinal Godfrey in Rome: 'Decision Favourable.' That morning he found Laura and her mother at Farm Street Church, knelt behind them and after the service told Laura the news in the porch. For the next week he saw her every day, doing crosswords together, attending Mass, going to the cinema, dining twice at the Café Royal and once in Nancy Mitford's bedroom. On 16 July he was interviewed by Laura's mother at her townhouse on Bruton Street, where she told him that he and Laura must wait until October to be engaged and Christmas before being married.

Mary Herbert's resistance had possibly been softened by the announcement in late April that Evelyn had won the Hawthornden Prize, at that time Britain's most prestigious literary award, for *Edmund Campion*, which had been published the previous autumn while he was in Abyssinia and which his fellow Catholic convert Graham Greene hailed in *The Spectator* as 'a model of what a short biography should be'.[2] After hearing about the award, Henry Yorke wrote to Evelyn: 'I would congratulate you on it if it were not for the fact that you are the outstanding writer of our generation & that recognition of this kind has been due to you for a long time. It may sound ungracious to put it in the way I have just done but I do feel hotly that there is not one book you have published which is not very far beyond the books they have given the prize for up till now. It takes time for outstanding work to get through their thick skulls.'[3] It was presumably this prize that persuaded the dozy publishers of *Who's Who* that Evelyn might at last merit a mention in its pages – he was to appear for the first time in its 1937 edition (listing his sole recreation as 'travelling'), a scarcely believable seventeen years after his brother Alec's first entry in the hallowed annual reference work.

Evelyn replied to Henry that it was particularly gratifying that the prize should go 'to a specifically Catholic book' – knowing full well that this could do no harm to his reputation at Pixton.[4] Neither can it have damaged his marriage prospects that a week before his interview with Mrs Herbert, Maurice Bowra, again in *The Spectator*, had praised his recently published collection of short stories *Mr Loveday's Little Outing*. 'Mr. Waugh, like Mr. Maugham, succeeds at every kind of writing he attempts,' wrote Bowra. 'He manages the short story with the confident touch of an accomplished master . . . Is it too much to ask that he will abandon biography to lesser men and give us more novels and more short stories like these?'[5]

But Evelyn relied heavily on his non-fiction and journalism to stay solvent, and with his expenses sure to rise after his marriage he now reached the reluctant conclusion that he needed to return to Abyssinia to beef up his half-written book with a concluding account of how the Italian conquest had turned out. After going to Pixton to say goodbye to Laura, he travelled out to Africa via Rome 'full of gloomiest forebodings', he told Katharine Asquith. 'I am sick of Abyssinia & of my book about it. It was fun being pro-Italian when it was an unpopular and (I thought) losing cause. I have little sympathy with these exultant fascists now.'[6] He arrived to find the fledgling colony in an ostensible state of chaos. 'Truth appears to be Wops in jam,' he wrote in his diary.[7] However by the time he came to finishing his book he was inclined to see the Italian invasion as having brought about the 'spread of order and decency, education and medicine, in a disgraceful place'; it was akin to 'the great western drive of the American peoples, the dispossession of the Indian tribes and the establishment in a barren land of new pastures and cities'.[8]

Leaving Laura this time had proved far more affecting than he expected. 'How I wish you were here,' he wrote to her from Assisi. 'Sweet poppet it seems such a waste to see lovely things & not be with you. It is like being one-eyed & goggling out of focus. I miss you & need you all the time. Most of all when I'm happy.'[9] The next day he wrote again:

> I need you all the time – when I'm vexed and uncertain & tired – but more than ever on a night like this when everything is unearthly & lovely. You see, darling child, so often when people fall in love & want to be married, it is because they foresee a particular kind of life to which the other is necessary. But I don't feel that. Sometimes I think it would be lovely to lead the sort of life with you that I have led alone for the last ten years – no possessions, no home, sometimes extravagant & luxurious, sometimes lying low & working hard. At other times I picture a settled life with a large household, rather acrimonious & rather frugal, and sometimes a minute house, and few friends, and little work & leisure & love. But what I do know is that I can't picture any sort of life without you. I have left half of myself behind in England and I am only dragging about a bit of myself now. And I don't at all regret the haphazard, unhappy life I've led up till now because I don't think that without it I could love you so much. Goodnight my blessed child. I love you more than I can find words to tell you.[10]

He told Mary Lygon: 'I cry a great deal on account of not seeing LAURA. But Lady Horner says absence is like the wind – it extinguishes a little flame & fans a big one with greater heat.'[11] However with Laura's mother insisting on their delaying the announcement of their engagement, Evelyn evidently did not feel bound by absolute fidelity just yet, and on his way back through Rome he recorded that he had 'intended to bathe, change, fuck, and eat a luxurious dinner. Instead spent the evening driving to pay my debt to the English College [presumably to do with his annulment] in smuggled lire.'[12] If there had been any lingering uncertainty in Laura's mind, Evelyn's absence in Abyssinia seems to have removed it. 'I have definitely made up my mind that I want to marry you more than anything I want in the world,' she wrote to him while he was away. 'I hope you're still wanting to marry me. I think I love you more every day.'[13]

Evelyn arrived back in London on 12 September to the shattering news that Hugh Lygon had died while on a motoring tour of Bavaria, having mysteriously fallen over and hit his head on the curbside, conceivably after drinking or suffering from sunstroke after driving in an open car. 'It is the saddest news I ever heard,' Evelyn wrote to Mary Lygon. 'I shall miss him bitterly.' During what *The Times* euphemistically described as Hugh's 'varied and adventurous career',[14] an unhappy stint in the City had been followed by an abortive attempt at training racehorses and a brush with the bankruptcy courts, but while he never overcame his alcoholism he had at last seemed to be making a success of his most recent venture of running one of the farms at Madresfield. 'It is so particularly tragic that he should have died just when he was setting up house and seemed happier than he had been for many years,' wrote Evelyn.[15]

Hughie's death had come only a few weeks after that of his mother, and while Lord Beauchamp, who was still living in exile in Venice, had been prevented from attending his wife's funeral after being warned as he prepared to disembark at Dover that he would be arrested if he set foot ashore, he determined to go to Hughie's funeral at Madresfield on 24 August come what may. On this occasion, to the fury of the Duke of Westminster, the Home Secretary suspended the warrant for his arrest. The next year, after his warrant was finally withdrawn, Boom returned to spend the last year of his life at Madresfield, in much the same way as Lord Marchmain returns in *Brideshead Revisited*.

As the final chapter of *Brideshead* shows, all this made a deep and lasting impression on Evelyn's imagination, however for the time being he had the distraction of his forthcoming marriage to Laura, in contented contemplation of which he was even prepared to make peace with John Heygate, who had written to him shortly after he returned from Abyssinia: 'I have done you a great wrong. I am sorry. Will you forgive me?' Evelyn replied on a postcard: 'O.K. E.W.'*

He had still not told his parents, but two weeks after he got back they heard from Alec on the telephone that his annulment had been accepted

---

* Heygate had originally written to Evelyn shortly after Shevelyn ran off with him, but received no reply. In 1936 a bishop told him that before being allowed to take Communion he must try and obtain the forgiveness of the man he had sinned against, whereupon he wrote again. As Heygate later told Auberon Waugh, the bishop 'seemed rather surprised' when he showed him Evelyn's answer, 'but was satisfied'. (Sir John Heygate to Auberon Waugh, 11 November 1973; AWA.)

by the Pope and that he hoped to be married after Christmas. 'But he has not written to us!' protested Arthur in his diary.[16] Five days later Kate received a note from Evelyn announcing that he was to be married in February and the day after that he finally got round to writing to his father, obliquely apologising for his 'unfilial' delay in telling him of his engagement.[17] A week or so later he brought Laura to Highgate. 'Great preparations for Evelyn & Laura,' Arthur recorded. 'The evening was delightful. She behaved charmingly; he was at his best; and the dinner was good.'[18] The next day, Arthur and Kate 'had a pleasant talk over dinner about our happy evening with Evelyn & Laura. Was very glad to see her so happy. By last post a dear little note came to K from Laura, thanking us for being "so sweet" to her, which sent us to bed happier still.'[19]

Evelyn also wrote to Baby Jungman, telling her that he wanted her to be the first to know – though of course one or two others knew already:

> She [Laura] is very young indeed. Very thin and pale with big eyes and a long nose – more like a gazelle really than a girl; completely free of any literary, artistic or social ambition, silent as the grave, given to fainting at inopportune moments, timid, ignorant, affectionate, very gentle, doesn't sing, Narcissus complex, looks lovely on a horse but often falls off, student of acting, but doesn't take it too seriously. Catholic but doesn't take that too seriously either, owns pretty nasty dog called Lump, but he looks like dying soon. I love her very much and I think there is as good a chance of our marriage being a success as any I know.[20]

The letter to Baby was written from Mells, where he was writing the final chapter of *Waugh in Abyssinia*, which he finished on 2 October. By the middle of the month he had moved on to *Scoop*, noting in his diary that he had 'made a very good start with the first page of novel describing Diana's early morning'[21] – Diana Cooper serving as his model for Mrs Stitch, some of whose less amiable traits betrayed Evelyn's growing ambivalence towards her on account of her pointed unfriendliness towards Laura. Within two weeks he had completed the second chapter, however his speedy progress was soon halted by his perennial need to make money and in early November he went to see the editor of *Nash's Magazine*, where he 'accepted money for jam job, thirty guineas a month for less than 2,000 words on anything I like'.[22]

Work aside, much of that autumn was spent looking for somewhere for him and Laura to live. The area around Mells seemed as good a place to start as any, not only because he was there at the time but also because it was very close to his aunts' home at Midsomer Norton and a convenient stop-off between London and Laura's family home at Pixton. Both soon set their hearts on an exceptionally pretty Georgian manor house within the bailey of the ruined castle at Nunney, however the owner, a 'homicidal squireen' in Evelyn's estimation, proved impossible to pin down. A few days before Christmas, having by then extended their search north into Gloucestershire, Evelyn recorded in his diary: 'Saw two no-good houses then Piers Court, Stinchcombe. Absolutely first-rate, delighted.'[23] 'Laura and I have found a house of startling beauty between Bath and Stroud,' he told Diana Cooper, 'so that is where we shall live.'[24]

Situated just above the village on the western escarpment of the Cotswolds, some twenty-two miles north-east of Bristol, Piers Court commanded spectacular views from its garden across the Berkeley Vale (a panorama since spoilt somewhat by the M5 motorway) to the Severn estuary and Forest of Dean beyond. But behind its handsome Georgian stuccoed façade the house itself was in considerable disrepair, without water, gas or electricity, and after spending Christmas at Pixton – hunting, shooting (or in Evelyn's case beating), and enduring what he wryly recorded as the Herberts' 'family fun' – they returned there in the new year to assess what needed to be done. With a view to having a carving placed on the blank pediment over the porch, around this time Evelyn also wrote to Alec to enquire about the validity of the Waugh coat of arms. On 22 January 1937 his offer of £3,550 for Piers Court and its surrounding forty acres was accepted – a week after he had spent the evening with his parents in Highgate and told them that Laura's grandmother, Lady de Vesci, was giving them £4,000 as a wedding present with which to buy the house.

Unable to compete with this, Arthur modestly asked them to choose some silver from what he had left of his grandfather's, wrapped up in flannel under his bed, and said he would give them £25 to buy 'something definite & lasting – to remind you of me'. 'I think that's decent,' Evelyn wrote to Laura, 'considering his reduced circumstances & the fact that he forked out handsomely for my mock marriage some years back.'[25]

Evelyn's grateful and sympathetic response made a change from his often curt attitude towards his father, with whom he had tended to be by turns sullen and censorious of what he called his 'affected conversation'.[26] To strain relations further, on one of his rare recent visits to his parents he had contrived to set Arthur's library alight, inadvertently destroying, as he later admitted, 'hundreds of inscribed copies from almost every English writer of eminence' – Arthur having had by Evelyn's reckoning 'more books dedicated to him than any living man'.[27] In the past few months, however, Evelyn had shown a good deal more tolerance and affection towards him, a welcome development that Arthur attributed to Laura's influence. 'Certainly we have had much more kindness from him,' he noted in his diary on New Year's Eve.[28] Two months later, after lunch at the Savoy Grill prior to Evelyn joining the board of Chapman & Hall, Arthur recorded pathetically: 'Evelyn very gracious & attentive to me.'[29]

But beyond the initial favourable impressions of his 'charming' prospective daughter-in-law, Arthur could never really fathom Laura. He was plainly extremely well disposed towards Alec's wife Joan, not so much because she was very rich – having inherited a fortune that Alec put at £300,000[30] (i.e. more than eighty times what Evelyn paid for Piers Court) from her Australian father – but mainly because she seemed so appreciative of everything about him that Evelyn found so annoying. However Arthur never felt anything like the same affinity with Laura. A few years later he wrote to Joan: 'Certainly my two daughters-in-law write very differently, and have very different temperaments. I shall never be able to make anything of Laura. We live in other worlds and talk another language. But I miss nothing. I find everything I want in Joan, the daughter of my heart.'[31]

Whether or not Evelyn picked up on Arthur's favouritism, he was rather less misty-eyed about his sister-in-law and brazenly mercenary when it came to her offer of some linen for their wedding present after she had already promised to pay for their honeymoon. 'I think now you should write to her,' he suggested to Laura from his writing den on Dartmoor where he was polishing off a lucrative film treatment* for Alexander Korda: 'say Evelyn has told you of her kind offer etc. and make out a big

---

* Evelyn had gone to Korda's studio to be told the plot of 'a vulgar film about cabaret girls'; the working title was 'Lovelies from America'. He was paid £750 for the script but the film was never made. *EWD*, p. 413*n*.

list of what we need – two double beds, three single (at least) & towels for five guests. You might hint at table cloths, table napkins etc. Sorry to put all this on you, but I really am very busy trying to get the film done & as it is correspondence takes ½ my morning.'[32]

The result evidently failed to come up to scratch: 'Joan Waugh is mean as hell,' remarked Evelyn sometime later. 'Well I suppose I must pay for having neglected her these last 2 years.'[33] Hers was not the only offering deemed below par. 'Presents have come in, mostly of poor quality,' Evelyn recorded in his diary in early February, 'except from the Asquiths who have given us superb candelabra, sconces, and table.'[34] The Coopers' glass chandelier would have been equally appreciated were it not for the fact that when it arrived, three months after the wedding, the Waughs' new butler gloomily announced 'a box full of broken glass outside for you'. As it turned out only a few bits were broken, and as Evelyn told Diana: 'If we can get it mended [which they soon did] it will be a superb ornament, in fact the whole of our hall and staircase has been planned and painted round it.'[35]

The wedding took place at eleven o'clock on a showery Saturday morning, 17 April, at the seventeenth-century Catholic Church of the Assumption (originally the chapel to the old Portuguese Embassy) on Warwick Street in Soho, preceded by a cocktail party for all the guests the evening before at 14 Gloucester Gate on the edge of Regent's Park, where the reception was also held. Among the three officiating priests, Father D'Arcy gave the address, although Evelyn thought him 'sensationally ignorant of simplest professional duties'. Laura's brother Auberon gave her away, having spent the journey to the church begging her to change her mind.[36]* The church was full of family and friends, including, as Tom Driberg reported in the *Express*, 'many fair women: Lygons, Jungmans [Baby and Zita], Lady Diana Cooper (straight from Windsor Castle), the Hon Mrs Peter Rodd (novelist Nancy Mitford: she wore a hat made of

---

* Auberon Herbert's disapproval of Evelyn was described by Alexander Waugh as 'the aristocrat's natural dislike of the *arriviste* or, as my father preferred, the "traditional jealousy between privilege and actual achievement". Auberon was no fool. He spoke six languages fluently, had a natural and unusual wit and was adored by figures as random and far apart as Sir Isaiah Berlin and Karol, his Polish butler, but to Evelyn, who deplored his manner of speech, the habitual twisting of his wrists by his face as he spoke, and the suffocating odour of his scent that wafted oppressively about his person, Auberon was no more than a spoiled idler.' *Fathers and Sons*, p. 272.

red and dark blue ostrich feathers, held together by bits of ribbon, which wasn't nearly as gauche as it sounds)'.

Among the more notable absentees was Evelyn's best man from his first marriage, Harold Acton, who had settled in Peking in 1932 to teach at the university and translate Chinese poetry after becoming fed up with his falling literary reputation in Britain. The reception was 'all over' by a little after one and Arthur Waugh recorded with apparent satisfaction that he was 'home by 1.40 to a slice of brawn and cheese'.[37]

Evelyn, meanwhile, repaired to his club bedroom to be toasted by his best man, Henry Yorke, along with Francis Howard, Douglas Woodruff, John Sutro, Perry Brownlow, Billy Clonmore and Hubert Duggan, after which he and Laura drove to Englefield Green to say goodbye to eighty-five-year-old Lady de Vesci, who had not made it to the wedding but may well have paid for it. They then flew from Croydon to Paris, where they caught the overnight express to Rome, arriving at Portofino the next afternoon by horse-drawn cab. 'Lovely day,' wrote Evelyn in his diary that evening, 'lovely house, lovely wife, great happiness.'[38]

Three weeks later Evelyn wrote to Katharine Asquith: 'Well it is o.k. being spliced. Very decent indeed ... so far the marriage is an unqual-ified success.'[39] After ten days in Portofino he had taken Laura to Rome to be blessed by the Pope, who proved disappointingly inattentive, then Florence, then back to Portofino, where he resumed work on *Scoop*, which he admitted to his agent needed to be 'entirely rewritten' but promised would be ready in time for publication before Christmas.[40] Returning to England at the end of May, they borrowed a house in Chelsea from Laura's sister before moving finally into Piers Court in July where, as Evelyn told Diana Cooper, 'we are well and very happy indeed and the beauty of the house waxes daily'. They both became happier still when Laura discov-ered she was pregnant.

Work on the house, which they tended to refer to as Stinchcombe, or more often 'Stinkers', continued well into the next year, with Evelyn taking a keen interest in almost every detail. Besides designing his library and various other bits of joinery around the house, he filled the house with fine furniture and pictures, among them Rossetti's charcoal nude *Spirit of the Rainbow* ('My word it is ugly,' he told Diana) and Holman Hunt's painting *Oriana*, and a good collection of Victorian genre paint-ings, including works by George Smith and George Elgar Hicks.

He set about re-landscaping the garden, doing much of the physical work himself. Much is often made of Evelyn's supposed eager adoption of squirearchical ways, strolling about in his loud tweeds and chomping on a cigar. Yet he far preferred pulling brambles, planting trees and pegging out new lawns in the garden to hobnobbing with the local county set.

Several good friends lived within a fifty-mile radius – the Betjemans at Uffington in Berkshire, the Lygons at Madresfield, the Asquiths at Mells – although as neither Evelyn nor Laura had yet passed their driving tests, visiting them meant hiring a man to sit beside them in their car. Others from further afield were persuaded to come and stay, among them Pansy Lamb and Patrick Balfour, who reported to his mother: 'Lovely house: quite big, almost a "place". Evelyn v. happy & exaggeratedly domestic: they hardly see anybody. All right in the meantime, but I should think she would begin to want something more sooner or later. She is v. young & very much under Evelyn's thumb, & the question is how long she'll be content to stay under it. Wives must have *some* life of their own.'[41] But there would never be any evidence of the restlessness that he predicted.

When Diana Cooper came to stay after the birth of their first child she was assured beforehand that she would 'not notice baby or dog they are kept away'. Graham Greene, whom Evelyn had known for years but only recently befriended as a contributor of weekly book reviews to his short-lived literary magazine *Night and Day*, also came to stay with his wife Vivien: 'Yes, I normally wear a dinner jacket in the evenings,' Evelyn wrote to Mrs Greene, 'Laura a dressing gown. Do whatever is most convenient. I have asked a particular fan of Graham's & am sure he will dress for the meeting.'[42]

Local grandees held rather less appeal however. 'Count d'Oyley rang up to ask us to weekend at Berkeley,' runs a typical entry in Evelyn's diary. 'Refused, controlling temptation to explain that I do not go visiting the immediate neighbours.'[43] 'Started work again on novel,' he noted wearily on another occasion, a few months after they had moved in. 'Another lady with double-barrelled name called.'[44]

Across the fields at Stinchcombe Hill lived yet another double-barrelled name and unlikely soulmate for Evelyn, the keen yachtsman and shot Major Sir Francis Fetherston-Godley, then chairman of the British Legion and later retrospectively notorious for having consorted with the leaders of Nazi Germany on a visit there in 1935.* 'Dined with Lady Featherstone [sic] Godley,' recorded Evelyn after an evening chez the mustachioed major and his wife. 'Bad dinner, bad wine, middle-aged military men boasting about their ancestry.'[45] His opinion of the Catholic Misses Leigh at Nympsfield was initially more favourable – 'acute and decided and amusing' – although when they came with the local vicar to tea Evelyn noted: 'Sticky party'.[46]

By and large he got quite enough social life on trips to London, where he went from time to time to shop for books, artwork, architectural salvage and even basic ironmongery, as well as to discharge his new responsibilities as a director of Chapman & Hall. 'The month's figures showed a perceptible improvement,' he recorded after a board meeting that November, 'all directors accordingly highly sceptical.'[47] Their doubts were shared by Arthur, who wrote in similar vein early the next year: 'Heard that profits for 1937 exceeded 1936. Amazing but gratifying.'[48]

*　*　*

On 9 March 1938 Laura gave birth to their first child, a girl. 'The daughter large & blond,' Evelyn told his agent. 'No one has had the insolence to suggest it is like me.'[49] To Thomas Balston he wrote: 'I foresee that she will be a problem – too noisy for a nun, too plain for a wife. Well standards of beauty may change in the next 18 years.'[50] And to Baby Jungman: 'Dearest Tess, We have got a daughter – very large and ugly – and are going to christen it early next week. Would you be a godmother? Please do.'[51]

The little girl was christened Maria Teresa on 16 March at the church where Evelyn and Laura had married eleven months earlier, with Francis Howard and Katharine Asquith's son Julian (Trim) Oxford standing as the other godparents. Afterwards Evelyn wrote to Baby: 'It was sweet of you to be godmother and to come to the christening. I do hope that we shall see more of one another again one day.'[52]

Scoop was finally published in May, having taken Evelyn far longer to write than any of his previous novels. Described by Christopher Hitchens in 2000 as 'Waugh at the mid-season point of his perfect pitch; youthful

---

* A possible prototype for Colonel Hodge, owner of Much Malcock Manor, in Evelyn's short story 'An Englishman's Home' (1938).

and limber and light as a feather',[53] at the time it received favourable if not ecstatic reviews. 'Superb entertainment', said *The Tablet*;[54] 'exceedingly amusing', thought the *New Statesman*.[55] 'His job is to provide laughter,' declared *The Daily Telegraph*'s critic, 'and how well he does it.'[56] Perhaps the most perceptive review came from Evelyn's former pupil at Arnold House, Derek Verschoyle, who admitted that he found Europe 'a more effective background to his [Waugh's] characters than the other continents', but wrote that almost all his contemporaries could take lessons from him in technique. 'His books are so easy to read that it is possible to overlook how intricately they are organised. They are exactly of the length and of the form which their subject requires; there is never a word wasted or an emphasis misplaced.'[57]

It was in the afterglow of this latest success that Evelyn's parents paid their first visit to Piers Court, which Arthur pronounced himself 'delighted' with,[58] evidently relishing the luxury of having the butler unpack his suitcase and bring him his morning tea. There may have been vague feelings of bemusement and perhaps even envy that both his sons had ended up in such relatively large country houses, Alec and Joan having recently bought Edrington, a Queen Anne rectory on the Hampshire–Berkshire border which Evelyn had then sent them Sibyl Colefax to decorate. In both cases the money to buy the house had come from the wife's side of the family, however the difference was that Alec always felt that Edrington was Joan's and that his writing did not support it and had thus chosen a tiny room in the attic as his study. In Evelyn's case his pen paid for all the family's expenses and accordingly he felt no compunction about choosing the best room on the ground floor for his library, installing bookshelves in a series of handsome bays and a fine writing desk – all of which would be dismantled and transported in their entirety after his death to the University of Austin in Texas. The room was already filling up with a collection of books that Arthur admired on his visit and in years to come served as an essential place of refuge for Evelyn from the distractions and annoyances of family life. A few years later Kate Waugh asked two of his young children whether they had ever been inside it. 'Oh no,' they said, 'but we have peeped through the window.'[59]

Evelyn managed to be friendly for most of his parents' four-day visit, meeting them at Stroud station when they arrived, showing them around the garden and taking them on various expeditions to see the surrounding sights. On the final evening, though, Arthur perhaps sensed that he was once again beginning to get on his son's nerves: 'Evelyn and Laura both very tired,' he recorded in his diary. 'Too much entertaining! After dinner K & Laura played chess. Evelyn read & I kept quiet.'[60]

Scoop was more successful commercially than any of Evelyn's previous novels, yet with a family to feed he remained as receptive as ever to new opportunities for making money and very shortly after its publication accepted a lucrative commission from the oil magnate Viscount Cowdray's son Clive Pearson – 'a very rich chap,' so Evelyn described him to Peters, who 'wants me to write a book about Mexico'.[61] The Mexican President Cárdenas had recently expropriated several oilfields belonging to the Pearson family, along with those of various other foreign companies; and in return for an expenses-paid trip for himself and Laura and a cheque for £989, extracted by Peters before they set off, Evelyn agreed to write a book exposing the rank injustice of all this and countering the impression propagated by Britain's left-wing press that General Cárdenas was a progressive reformer. An additional draw for Evelyn was the opportunity to denounce the regime's persecution of the Catholic Church.

Evelyn and Laura left on 30 July and travelled out via New York and Havana, arriving in Mexico City in mid-August and putting up at the Ritz: 'Uncle Clive's beneficence followed every state and we have had the smoothest possible journey,' Evelyn wrote to his mother-in-law. 'Mexico is a puzzling place & I cannot say we feel at all at home here yet. It is like sitting in a cinema, seeing the travel film of a country one has no intention of visiting. Thousands of American tourists, a handful of disgruntled English businessmen, homicidal traffic, noise, dust – all very far from Stinkers.'[62]

The Mexican trip lasted almost three months and the resulting book, whose provocative title *Robbery Under Law* further fulfilled Evelyn's obligations towards 'rich Pearson', was not finished until April 1939, when Evelyn described it to Diana Cooper as 'like an interminable *Times* leader of 1880', a reasonable appraisal of the uncharacteristically stodgy chapters dealing with oil and the Catholic Church. But although Harold Nicolson, generally a great admirer of Evelyn's writing, called it a 'dull' book in *The Daily Telegraph*, others were surprisingly enthusiastic, not least *The Guardian*, which praised Evelyn for recounting his experiences 'with great agreeableness'.[63] In America, which unlike Britain still maintained an embassy in Mexico and where it thus bore the more diplomatic title *Mexico: An Object Lesson*, the book found even more favour with *The New York Times*: 'Soberly conceived and wittily executed in the best traditions of the familiar essay, it is one of those astringent volumes which appear every now and then as an antidote to complacency, sweetness and light. The evident sincerity of the author, the high quality of his literary talent and the calm logic with which he pursues his theme entitle him to a hearing in this country.'[64]

Although Evelyn was a hired gun, the thrust of what he had contracted to write was very much in line with his conservative political outlook, so there was an integrity to his account which reviewers responded to, besides which it may not have escaped their notice that his friend Graham Greene, whose political views were a long way to the left of Evelyn's, had reached many of the same conclusions in his own more famous travel book on Mexico, *The Lawless Roads* (inspiration for *The Power and the Glory*), which came out shortly before *Robbery Under Law*.

In any event, by the time Evelyn's book appeared in June 1939 the British public cared very little about what was going on in Mexico due to ominous developments much closer to home, Hitler having invaded Czechoslovakia in March and more recently told his military commanders to get ready for war against Poland in order to expand Germany's *Lebensraum* in the east and secure its food supplies via the Baltic port of Danzig. Evelyn himself had been mentally hunkering down since the beginning of the year: 'We are here immovable until the outbreak of war,'[65] he wrote to Baby Jungman from Piers Court on New Year's Day 1939. He saw the looming conflict as a crusade against the forces of totalitarianism in whichever form and on 22 August, shortly after his parents' second stay at Stinchcombe, he recorded: 'Russia and Germany have agreed to neutrality pact so there seems no reason why war should be delayed.'

Since finishing *Robbery Under Law* he had been working hard on a new novel (eventually published unfinished as *Work Suspended*), but had lately found himself restless and unable to concentrate and had instead been throwing his energy into the garden. On 24 August he recorded: 'Working in the afternoon in the garden, clearing the alley, I thought: what is the good of this? In a few months I shall be growing Swedes and potatoes here and on the tennis court; or perhaps I shall be away and then another two or three years of weeds will feed here until the place looks as it did when we came here two years ago.'

With Laura expecting their second child that November he was as happy and settled as he had ever been, yet at the same time he was uneasily aware that their idyll was likely to be brief. Not unnaturally, he did his best to shut the international crisis out and prided himself on being 'the only English family to eschew the radio'.[66] When Diana Cooper came to stay with her devoted friend and admirer Conrad Russell, she wrote afterwards to say how impressed she was by the 'excellencies' of his 'terribly covetable' house and how delighted she was to see him 'so happy and so serene'. Yet she failed to understand why the international crisis – 'a subject which by its nature must be constantly present in all our minds' – had to be so taboo. Evelyn had forbidden her even from getting her radio from the car to listen to a speech by the Foreign Secretary, Lord Halifax, and when at the end of dinner she attempted to bring the subject up she was met with a 'very nasty snub' from Evelyn. 'I saw both butlers blanch at your tone,' she told him. 'Why is it Bo?'[67]

On Monday, 26 August, with Germany poised to attack Poland, the local schoolmistress called to tell Evelyn that Piers Court had been designated as a billet. 'My heart sank,' he recorded. 'But it is not for children but for five adults who are coming to arrange for children's arrival and go in a week's time.' Having made arrangements, however, 'removing all valuable objects from the rooms I am giving them', they learned that there were fewer evacuees than anticipated and they would be spared after all, so instead they took a bed and some clothes to a destitute family the vicar was sheltering in his stable loft.

After breakfast on Sunday, 3 September, Evelyn gave in to temptation and listened to the Prime Minister, Neville Chamberlain, broadcast on the radio that war had begun. 'He did it very well', he told his diary. Two days later he placed an advertisement in the personal columns on the front page of *The Times*: 'MR. EVELYN WAUGH wishes to LET PIERS COURT, near DURSLEY, GLOS. FURNISHED for duration of war. Old house recently modernized: 4 reception, 10 bed, 4 bath, & co.: 4 acres or more. Low rent to civilized tenant.'[68]

17

A War to End Waugh

'How sad it all is!' wrote Evelyn's mother when she saw they were letting Piers Court. 'May the duration of the war be short & your return to your lovely home be soon.'[1] But Evelyn was pessimistic about how long it might last and although he had given the impression of ignoring its approach, privately he had been thinking about little else. The obvious thing for him to do was to apply to the Ministry of Information, where friends such as Graham Greene and Tom Burns were soon busy peddling propaganda. However as an artist and adventurer he felt drawn towards something substantially more active and exciting. 'My inclinations are all to join the army as a private,' he confided to his journal. 'Laura is better placed than most wives, and if I could let the house for the duration very well-placed financially. I have to consider thirty years of novel-writing ahead of me. Nothing would be more likely than work in a Government office to finish me as a writer; nothing more likely to stimulate me than a complete change of habit. There is a symbolic difference between fighting as a soldier and serving as a civilian, even if the civilian is more valuable.'[2]

With no takers yet for his patriotic services or his house, life at Piers Court continued much as usual for the time being, with Evelyn devoting his time to planting box hedges, building a wall and erecting a Gothic balustrade with the help of the gardener Prewitt. But at the end of September some Dominican nuns took the house for £600 a year for use as a girls' school and Evelyn and Laura decamped to Pixton, where they found a household of fifty-four, including twenty-six evacuated children. 'We ate in the hall,' Evelyn recorded that evening, 'making a fine target for the children's spittle from the top landing.'[3]

'I can't think of a worse torture,' Henry Yorke wrote to commiserate, 'than being stuck with your in-laws & the frightful children.'[4] Evelyn grabbed every opportunity to escape to London and in late October he had an interview there with Ian Fleming – then only a slight acquaintance – for a job in naval intelligence. The next day he was delighted to be accepted by the Welsh Guards, only to be told a few days later that they were full up after all. By now beginning to despair, Evelyn suspected 'there must be someone at the War Office occupied in blocking my chances',[5] which was conceivable given his words of admiration for Mussolini in *Waugh in Abyssinia* and for Franco in *Robbery Under Law*, although subsequent whispers that his interviewers had thought his suede shoes 'unsuitable'[6] suggests it was more likely pure snobbery on their part.

On his return to Pixton he recorded that 'a fresh wave of lice has effected an entry'.[7] And the next day: 'Work out of the question as the evacuated children are now admitted to the garden at the back of the house under my windows. Impetigo, thrush, and various ailments are rampant.' The only thing for it was to take himself off to his writing refuge at Chagford. 'It was sweet of you to let me go without protest,' he wrote to Laura from the Easton Court Hotel. 'It was the only sensible course. I shall be able to work here. I hope to get the novel really under way before the birth.'[8] A couple of days later he reported: 'I work all morning. Then walk. Then a little work. Then a bath, a cocktail, dinner, and the crossword and early bed & long sleep. Except for one thing [Laura not being there too] an idyllic existence – but that one thing makes the crucial difference.'[9]

Within four days he had added 4,000 words to the 15,000 he had completed before war broke out. Laura came to meet him in Exeter on his birthday and again the following weekend, but otherwise he toiled on alone with the novel, by now sufficiently absorbed to have temporarily ceased worrying about not being on active service.[10] On 16 November he moved to a boarding house near Pixton to await the birth of their baby and the next day drove over after Laura went into labour. Afterwards he told Maimie Lygon: 'Laura has had a son. Will you be its god-mother? It is to be called Auberon Alexander. It is quite big and handsome & Laura is very pleased with it.'[11] Maimie had herself recently married the Russian émigré wine merchant Prince Vsevolod Ivanovich Romanov, nephew of the last Tsar, and was thus now Princess Romanovsky Pavlovski, which Evelyn promised her Auberon would be made to say as soon as he learned to speak. Laura seems to have minded far more than Evelyn about having a boy. 'I am fretting about your anti-daughter feeling,' Evelyn had written to her beforehand. 'Daughters are a great comfort to their parents compared that is with sons.'[12]

Four days after Auberon's birth, Evelyn went up to London to see the Royal Marines, his application having been 'strongly supported'[13] by Winston Churchill at the instigation of Brendan Bracken, whom Evelyn had known vaguely since the early 1930s.* Staying at Highgate, Evelyn found his parents 'markedly unsympathetic to my project of joining the war'.[14] His interview the next day was preceded by a medical examination in a flat in St James's: 'I went first to have my eyes tested and did deplorably,' he recorded. 'When asked to read at a distance with one eye I could not distinguish lines, let alone letters. I managed to cheat a little by peering over the top. Then I went into the next room where the doctor said, "Let's see your birthday suit. Ah, middle-aged spread. Do you wear dentures?" He tapped me with a hammer in various organs. Then I was free to dress.' At the interview itself at the Admiralty, a friendly colonel told him: 'The doctors do not think much of your eyesight', but after asking him to read a large advertisement across the street he accepted him nonetheless, adding breezily: 'Anyway most of your work will be in the dark.'[15]

Evelyn's day got even better that afternoon when the editor of the American *Life* magazine commissioned two articles 'at the startling price of a thousand dollars', which went a long way towards settling his immediate debts. Cue champagne at his club, a magnum at dinner with Patrick Balfour, then three more bottles and one of rum with Kathleen Meyrick at a nightclub. 'I was sick at about five.'[16]

Required to report for duty with the Marines on 7 December, he spent the intervening week recovering from this bender at Pixton with Laura, who was now suffering from pleurisy. Travelling down to Chatham, his fellow officers struck him as 'the kind of nondescript body one might have conscripted out of the first omnibus one saw in the Strand'. But he perked up on arrival, when they were greeted with pink gins and he was given a large bedroom to himself with a fire continually blazing in it. 'The food is

---

* After their first encounter, in 1931, staying with the Brownlows at Belton, Evelyn whimsically told Maimie Lygon that 'there was a pretty auburn-haired girl called Brendan Bracken dressed up as a man' and that he could not resist sleeping with her (Christopher Sykes, *Evelyn Waugh*, pp. 113–14). However much Evelyn subsequently owed to Bracken as a fixer, he always thought him a preposterous fraud and, later feeling let down, used him as the basis for the obnoxious Rex Mottram in *Brideshead Revisited*.

absolutely excellent,' he told Laura. 'On the first evening there was a cold supper on account of a play which was being given us in our own theatre. I was led to the supper table with profuse apologies and found lobster, fresh salmon, cold birds, hams, brawn exactly like the cold table at the St. James's. Afterwards several rounds of excellent vintage port.'[17]

The next week they began a six-week intensive infantry course consisting of map-making, sanitation, small-arms, military law, endless arms drill and the dreaded PT.[18] Evelyn was the first to admit that even with his newly grown moustache, 'as smart a little moustache as Errol Flynn,' as Diana Cooper described it,[19] he did not look very impressive in his uniform: Mary Pakenham said he was the only person she knew who was made less distinguished-looking by wearing it. But he nonetheless thought himself quite good at ordinary military drill, an assessment with which his colour sergeant did not always agree: 'Lieutenant Wuff, press on that rifle butt and keep your precious eyes to the front. To the front I said! You're not 'ere to collect daisies!'[20]

On the whole, though, the life suited him very well. 'Marine barracks are like a senior common room without the bore of dons talk,' he told Helen Asquith, '– good Georgian architecture, old silver & mahogany, vintage port – all the concomitants of university murder stories with enough physical exercise to give one an appetite; no responsibilities, no intellectual exercise except in attempting to convince the Protestant chaplain of the authenticity of Our Lord's miracles.'[21]

After all this, Christmas at Pixton with its notoriously bad cooking came as a rude shock, especially since the house was now full of 'slum children' and 'silent professional spinsters, ironically called "helpers"'. With Laura still convalescing in bed, he chose to eat most of his meals on a tray in her room. Returning to Chatham just after New Year, he spent the next weekend with Tom Burns in London and was touched to be reconciled with Baby Jungman over cocktails. 'The Dutch Girl has got a new youth out of the war,' he told Laura, '(and the death of her King Charles spaniel). She dances with Canadian soldiers at night clubs three nights a week and sits up in an A.R.P. post the other four.'[22] That summer she would be swept off her feet by one of her dance partners, a walrus-mustachioed Scot called Graham Cuthbertson who was serving in a Canadian regiment. Frank Pakenham later recalled: 'He obviously had plenty of sexuality. Perhaps it needed someone like that to overcome Baby's chasteness, which possibly he did not even notice.'[23] Most of Baby's former suitors seemed to think he was a bounder, however Evelyn chivalrously told her that her marriage was 'the first good news since the Graf Spee' and that her husband 'must be a prodigy to have triumphed where so many have fallen'. 'Do let us all four meet. Laura joins with me in sending her true love. I pray you may be as happy in marriage as I have been these last three years.'[24] The marriage soon produced two children, yet despite Evelyn's prayers it was not long before the couple drifted apart.

*   *   *

In mid-January the Marines moved to a grim disused holiday camp at Kingsdown near Deal, which was so cold and uncomfortable that Evelyn sought refuge whenever he could at 'a club for old buffers' – the Deal & Walmer Union. Their affable new colonel, Godfrey Wildman-Lushington, expected them to be under canvas by April, which Evelyn did not much like the sound of. The colonel also spoke of 'extreme athletic fitness as essential for active service,' Evelyn told Laura, 'so I think you can rest easy in your mind that I shall be left behind with the luggage when the more sensational adventures are attempted'.[25] Yet despite being a conspicuous bon viveur who evidently hated PT and was growing stouter by the day due to overindulgence in the officers' mess, Evelyn managed the gruelling thirty-mile marches with all his kit remarkably well; one regular officer later noted that he had 'a very good pair of lungs on him' and was 'surprisingly fit'.[26]

The brigade commander, Albert St Clair-Morford, was a striking character and the obvious prototype for the lovably bloodthirsty Brigadier Ritchie-Hook in *Sword of Honour*: '[He] looks like something escaped from Sing-Sing,' Evelyn recorded after the brigadier's first lecture, 'and talks like a boy in the Fourth Form at school – teeth like a stoat, ears like a faun, eyes alight like a child playing pirates, "We then have to biff them, gentlemen." He scares half and fascinates half.'[27]

The next month, Evelyn visited St Clair-Morford at his home, 'a depraved villa of stockbroker's Tudor,' as Evelyn perceived it. 'I said in a jaggering way, "Did you build this house, sir?" and he said "Build it! It's 400 years old!" The Brigadier's madam is kept very much in her place and ordered about with great shouts. "Woman, go up to my cabin and get my boots." More peculiar, she is subject to booby-traps. He told us with great relish how the night before she had had to get up several times in the night to look after a daughter who was ill and how, each time she returned, he had fixed up some new horror to injure her – a string across the door, a jug of water on top of it etc. However she seemed to thrive on this treatment & was very healthy & bright with countless children.'[28]

Evelyn was as infected by the brigadier's bellicosity as he was entertained by his eccentricity and told John Betjeman, who had been turned down by the RAF on medical grounds:[29] 'Don't on your life get into a pansy mobile base defense unit. Infantry brigade is the thing ... The only way to bring this business to a happy conclusion is to kill great numbers of Germans. If we go on thinking only of defence there will be nothing worth defending. Why do you prefer defence? I can't understand it.'[30]

Evelyn had seen a lot more of Laura since Christmas, lodging with her for a time away from barracks in a local hotel and spending weekends together in London. In April, just as she had begun to feel well again for the first time since the birth of Auberon, she was somewhat less than elated to find she was pregnant yet again. 'It is sad news for you that you are having another baby and I am sad at your sorrow,' Evelyn wrote to her. 'For myself, surrounded with the spectacle of a world organized to kill, I cannot help feeling some consolation in the knowledge that new life is being given. Your suffering will be to give life, ours, if we have to suffer, to take it. A child that is a danger & distress now may be your greatest happiness in the future. If I do not live through this war, you will have your children's love & their need of you.'[31]

The consensus among the vast majority of chroniclers of Evelyn's military career is that he was 'not good with men' and was disliked by his troops because of his sarcasm and impatience and tendency to talk over their heads – he was once memorably overheard gently advising a group of nineteen-year-olds that 'Whistling and catcalls is a form of courtship that rarely leads to union.'[32] There was almost certainly some truth in reports of his unpopularity, however the evidence for it seems to consist almost entirely of the testimony of his fellow officers rather than the recollections of the troops themselves, several of whom gave evidence to the contrary. There are also several other indications that for much of the time Evelyn got along perfectly well with his men, who enjoyed his boldly nonconformist approach to soldiering even if his irritability sometimes got the better of him. He defended his men in several courts-martial and in defiance of the colonel's orders gave one young marine a night's leave so that he and his 'young lady' could compete in a dancing competition. As Evelyn told Laura, the man returned 'with a silver cup as high as himself, champion of the South of England'.[33] At the beginning of April he told Laura that he was the only temporary officer in his battalion to have been given command of a fighting company. 'But I am sad to leave my platoon whom I was greatly attached to.'[34]

The next month brought promotion to captain and a predominantly favourable report from Colonel Wildman-Lushington and Brigadier St Clair-Morford: 'A natural commander and experienced man. He works hard and gets good work out of his subordinates but must curb a tendency to lean on his 2nd in Command. Possesses any amount of moral courage and has self-confidence when on subjects he knows. A little impatient. I believe that with more military experience he will make a first class Company Commander.'[35]

In August, however, Evelyn was abruptly relieved of his command after he was overheard loudly berating his quartermaster sergeant in front of the men for the lack of drinking water on their train to Birkenhead, en route for Scapa Flow and then – after a two-week voyage – West Africa. Shortly prior to this he had gone to see Brendan Bracken about transferring to the commandos being formed by Sir Roger Keyes as director of Combined Operations, however he now worried that it would look like he was leaving under a cloud, and just as his battalion was about to see action for the first time. Rather than take up the offer of immediate transfer, he therefore accepted an appointment as battalion intelligence officer, an information-gathering role that was perhaps better suited to his particular talents than that of company commander. The action that he had been hankering for, however, proved elusive. Their part in an attempt to install General de Gaulle and the Free French in Dakar was eventually aborted due to a combination of what nowadays might be termed adverse weather conditions and the general not receiving as cordial a welcome as hoped. Afterwards Evelyn wrote to Laura that in the hours leading up to what had promised be a very hazardous operation, 'my thoughts were with you, & with you only, all the time' but that ultimately 'bloodshed has been avoided at the cost of honour'.[36]

A few days later he wrote to her: 'I realised [then] how much you have changed me, because I could no longer look at death with indifference. I wanted to live & I was pleased when we ran away.' But whenever he did see action in future Evelyn showed himself to be almost entirely impervious to danger and his subsequent enforced retreats, far from bringing any sense of relief, seemed to cause only profound feelings of shame and disillusionment.

* * *

It was on his way back in Gibraltar that Evelyn received a letter from Lieutenant-Colonel Robert Laycock to say he had a post for him in his commando, which Evelyn rather tactlessly described to his worried parents as 'a more melodramatic force than the Marines'.[37] A vague acquaintance since the early 1930s through the Lygons, Bob Laycock was the officer Evelyn would come to admire above all others he served with. Then aged thirty-three, four years younger than Evelyn, brave, charming and supremely well connected, he was the son of the raffish Nottinghamshire landowner Brigadier-General Sir Joseph 'Joe' Laycock, KCMG, DSO, who was said to have fathered two children with Edward VII's mistress Daisy Warwick before luring Bob's famously beautiful mother away from her previous husband, the Marquess of Downshire.[38] Bob Laycock was himself married to a daughter of Freda Dudley Ward, chief mistress to the Prince of Wales before Wallis Simpson. After Eton and Sandhurst he had joined the elite Royal Horse Guards in 1927 and combined a glittering cavalry career with such adventures as sailing halfway round the world before the mast in a Finnish windjammer.[39] On the outbreak of war his scientific expertise had taken him to Cairo as an anti-gas staff officer, a dull and dead-end job from which he managed to escape with the help of David Niven, the film star.

Niven was soon to marry Laycock's niece and had no hesitation in recommending his future uncle to his boss at the War Office, Dudley Clarke, who was founding the commandos to carry out offensive raiding operations behind enemy lines in occupied France, inspired by the Boer horsemen who had harried the British in his native South Africa. Laycock's sailing background meant he was ideally suited to seaborne raids and landing operations and by Niven's account, Clarke 'immediately decided that this was just the man he wanted'.[40] Laycock thus set about raising 8 Commando. An officer of great initiative, imagination and daring, within three years he would be the youngest major-general in the army.

'The business of forming a unit of volunteers, officered by my own friends, seemed, and still does seem to me, the pleasantest way of going to war,' Laycock recalled.[41] Many of his officers were recruited at the bar of his club, White's, of which Evelyn was not yet a member but soon would be. Although Laycock's officers were chosen from those who, like Evelyn, had volunteered for hazardous service, he was looking for those whom he felt he could trust. A great fan of Evelyn's novels, Laycock later remembered agreeing to Bracken's suggestion that he take Evelyn on the grounds that he was 'often even funnier in fact than in fiction' and 'could not fail to be an asset in the dreary business of war'.[42]

* * *

Before joining his new unit in Ayrshire, Evelyn spent his leave at Pixton and visited Piers Court, which he found 'over-flowing with refugees' and the garden 'rapidly relapsing into jungle'. He also went to London at height of the Blitz, staying with his parents at Highgate, where he also saw Alec who had been evacuated from Boulogne after the fall of France and was now taking the opportunity of his family's absence in Australia to pursue a love affair with a tall, bosomy, much younger woman, whom Evelyn had first met at their writing retreat in Devon and christened 'the Chagford giantess'.

In mid-November Evelyn travelled north to Largs on the Ayrshire coast where 8 Commando was stationed, with the town's Marine Hotel serving as their officers' mess. There he found various friends and acquaintances, including the former Reuters correspondent Robin Campbell, whose father had been ambassador to Paris until France fell.[43] There was also Harry Stavordale, whom he knew from Oxford, whose spectacular family home, the Jacobean Holland House in London's Holland Park, had just been destroyed in the Blitz; and Randolph Churchill, the prime minister's spoilt and rumbustious son with whom Evelyn had had a love-hate relationship since they had both been made godparents to Diana Guinness's son Jonathan. These plus a few others led by Earl Fitzwilliam's ill-fated heir Peter Milton* – 'very agreeable but a bit much for me', Evelyn told Laura – made up 8 Commando's 'smart set', a group of rich playboys whom Evelyn could not afford to join yet looked upon with indulgent amusement. 'The smart set drink a very great deal,' he told Laura, 'play cards for high figures, dine nightly in Glasgow, and telephone to their trainers endlessly.' Having reverted to the pay of a lieutenant, Evelyn was meanwhile obliged to live in 'dignified poverty'.[44]

Evelyn relished the smart set's unconventionality and thought their 'gaiety and independence' would prove an asset in action.[45] To begin with he served as liaison officer with Campbell and Stavordale. 'I have done nothing so far except take a cuckoo clock to pieces & play a lot of ludo,' he told Laura. 'All the officers have very long hair & lap dogs & cigars & they wear whatever uniform they like.'[46] A week later he reported that life in 8 Commando was growing 'more like a house party daily & I think a minor operation might be salutary to check the lotus eating . . . Today there was a grand inspection & I walked behind with the staff detecting, with my trained, Marine eye many imperfections which escaped the foot guards.'[47]

At the end of November Evelyn was to have undergone training in field-craft at Inverailort Castle in the Highlands, accompanied by Randolph Churchill, who had been expelled from the previous course by Lord Lovat for heckling one of his NCO instructors, several of whom were ghillies or stalkers on his estate at Beaufort.[48] (Another instructor was Shimi Lovat's cousin, David Stirling, later to found the SAS.) In the event Evelyn did not go because on the evening of Saturday, 30 November Mary Herbert telephoned from Pixton to say that Laura had gone into labour early with the baby she had been expecting since that spring.

Evelyn caught the sleeper the next day, arriving at Tiverton station at 10.30 on the Monday morning. 'Laura's baby was born prematurely on Sunday and lived for only twenty-four hours,' he wrote to his mother later that day. 'She was baptised, Mary, before she died & will be buried in Brushford churchyard tomorrow.' The letter then bizarrely went on: 'It was an easy birth and Laura is in excellent health . . . I have got three days' leave & return to my commando on Friday. Life is more easygoing there

---

* Heir to an estimated £45 million, including England's largest country house, Wentworth Woodhouse, Viscount Milton was later romantically linked to the widowed Marchioness of Hartington, the former 'Kick' Kennedy, sister of the future President J. F. Kennedy. In 1948 they were both killed when the plane in which they were travelling crashed in France.

than in the Marines; many old friends and acquaintances are with me, and I find the life highly enjoyable . . .'[49]

Arthur, who had always longed for a daughter, was shocked by Evelyn's apparent lack of concern at losing one of his own and additionally hurt by the fact that the news had not reached him until after the funeral. 'There seems something quite pathetic in this little star of life,' Arthur wrote to Alec's wife Joan in Australia, 'which just flickered and went out. She wasn't wanted and she did not stay. Evelyn announced her coming as "to the regret of all and the consternation of some". Well, she didn't trouble them for long, and she is spared a great deal.'[50]

Evelyn's grandson later attributed his strangely dispassionate reaction to an instinctive compulsion to 'prove his immunity to Arthur's worst fault – sentimentality', as a result of which Evelyn 'struck attitudes of immoderate detachment, exaggerated often to the point of absurdity. The more emotional Arthur became, the more Evelyn vaunted his *sangfroid*.'[51] This seems perfectly plausible, although Evelyn's account of the loss of his daughter in his diary was also curiously unemotional, apart from the sorrowful admission: 'Poor little girl, she was not wanted.'[52]*

By 7 December, Evelyn was back with the commandos in Scotland and soon off to the Isle of Arran to train for an assault on the Italian island of Pantelleria. He had been 'very sad leaving you alone', he told Laura, but doubted he would be able to make it back to Pixton for Christmas: 'You well know how glad I am to avoid that.'[53] He was glad too that Penguin had agreed to publish his unfinished novel under the title *Work Suspended*. There was, he told Laura, 'too much good material there to let it disappear',[54] and he thought it the best thing he had written as far as it went. With its first-person narrative and descriptive, nostalgic prose, *Work Suspended* is the stylistic precursor of *Brideshead Revisited* and may conceivably have become the better novel had the war not intervened.[55]

In the event, Christmas Day was spent aboard the troopship *Glenroy*, whose captain enlivened dinner by setting the tablecloth on fire and then being sick where he sat. Evelyn spent most of the day asleep. Not

---

* Although she lived for barely twenty-four hours, Mary had the distinction of being the only one of Laura's children who was breastfed, the doctor having said that that was her only hope. Perhaps because of the trauma of losing her, Laura later remembered that her daughter had lived for a week, but Evelyn's diary appears to refute that.

long afterwards the planned Pantelleria raid was cancelled, much to the exasperation of Keyes, who knew that his commandos had been brought to a peak of readiness for action and that it would become far more difficult to keep them motivated if they were continually stood down. It was against this background in late January that Evelyn's unit was suddenly told to pack their bags for North Africa as part of 'Force Z' (later renamed Layforce) under the overall command of Bob Laycock.

Keyes, whose son Geoffrey was serving with 11 Commando, saw them off himself and afterwards wrote to Churchill that they were 'the envy of all those who were left behind. I gave your love to Randolph, who is delighted to be one of the lucky ones. So many of our mutual friends have sons in that splendid party. It is the flower of my striking force.'[56]

Evelyn had been appointed acting brigade major and on the long voyage out round the Cape of Good Hope shared a small cabin with the prime minister's son and Harry Stavordale, 'both of whom have brought luggage enough for a film star's honeymoon,' he told Laura. While Churchill grew a moustache, Evelyn attempted a beard. 'At present it looks peculiarly repulsive,' he admitted to Laura, 'a mass of isolated, coarse hairs of variegated colouring, but it gives me an interest as they say, like a pet or a pot flower.'[57] Two weeks later he wrote: 'As the voyage goes on the commando gets more & more like the Russian cavalry of Tolstoy's *War & Peace*. At the last settling day for gambling poor Randolph was £800 down. Poor Pamela will have to go to work.'[58] (This proved to be the last straw in the Churchills' already unhappy marriage; they eventually divorced in 1946.) Evelyn, meanwhile, made do with 'a little poorer game with the poor', he told Laura. 'All my gaming winnings are for you. There is another pound or two coming to you at next settling day.'[59]

Before leaving, Evelyn had written to his butler Ellwood asking him to be his batman but got no reply and a nineteen-year-old archaeologist called Ralph Tanner had volunteered instead – 'very high brow,' Evelyn described him to Laura, 'a pleasant young man'. Scarcely credible though it seemed to Evelyn's would-be detractors, Tanner found his new employer equally pleasant. When, years later, an interviewer from *Punch* magazine suggested that Evelyn had been 'so unpopular that he had to be protected from other soldiers', Tanner replied: 'Absolute rubbish. He fitted in very well. He was everything you'd expect an officer to be.' 'A bit of a tyrant, you mean?' asked the doggedly sceptical interviewer. 'Not at all,' said Tanner. 'He didn't exploit you the teeniest, weeniest bit?' 'I'd say he behaved as a model employer to a servant'. 'Oh . . .'[60]

Evelyn's reputation for rudeness was 'totally alien to the Waugh I knew', Tanner added, recalling that he was ticked off only a couple of times when he served hot gravy with cold meat and when he got polish on the wrong side of his Sam Browne belt so that it came off on his uniform. In another unpublished interview, Tanner also recalled having had 'some absurd idea that if you went into the tropics, you had to have flannel spine pads, and I remember saying to him, "Do you wish me to make spine pads for you?" He looked a little bemused, but said, "No, I don't think that will be necessary." He wasn't at all sarcastic.'[61]

So considerate was Evelyn that Tanner recalled 'waiting up for him with some hot water, just to return the courtesy'. The only gossip Tanner heard about him among the troops, meanwhile, was that he was 'a bit fond of the honourables'[62] and that he had insisted on sharing a cabin with Randolph Churchill and Lord Stavordale. The implication is of course that Evelyn was a snob, which was perhaps not an entirely outrageous assessment, yet in fairness to him both of these were old friends of his and in any case he would have been hard pushed to find cabin mates among the officers of 8 Commando who did not, broadly speaking, fit the 'honourables' description.

* * *

Layforce eventually entered the Suez Canal in early March with promises that they would soon have a 'bellyful of fighting'.[63] But just as they began serious training for yet another abortive mission – an attack on the island of Rhodes – the Germans reoccupied Cyrenaica and General Wavell felt he could no longer spare the air cover and destroyer escorts that would allow them to strike in the Dodecanese or anywhere else.

Layforce was ordered to Alexandria, but while their commanding officer strove to get his men into action, his commandos were repeatedly called back from operations on which they had been sent out. One wag suggested they be renamed 'Belayforce' and some mock-Churchillian graffiti appeared on the troop deck: 'Never before in the history of human endeavour have so few been so buggered about by so many.'[64]

On 19 April they at last went into action with a night raid on the

Libyan coastal town of Bardia, which reports suggested was held by 2,000 of Rommel's *Afrika Korps*. The aim was to disrupt the enemy's lines of supply and communication and cause Rommel to 'look over his shoulder' and divert his troops away from the front line. But as they crept ashore it soon became apparent that the town was deserted apart from a solitary motorcycle patrol, which evaded their clumsy attempts to shoot it down and was thus fortunately able to relay news of the raid, with the result that a German brigade was diverted from the front line at a crucial time. In almost all other respects the operation was a shambles: one boat failed to get into the water; another ran aground and had to be destroyed; an officer was shot and killed by his own men; another man was injured by his own grenade; a party of sixty commandos returned down the wrong wadi and was left ashore and later captured. Evelyn later obligingly portrayed the raid as a success in a propaganda piece he had lucratively been contracted to write for *Life* magazine – 'it seems that you are being asked for a piece of fiction rather than an article,'[65] his agent told him – however he knew perfectly well that it had been botched. In his diary Evelyn recalled that some of the officers complained to him that their commanding officer, Lieutenant-Colonel Felix Colvin, had behaved badly. However, Evelyn thought that 'no one had behaved well enough for them to be able to afford a post-mortem' so did not pass their criticism on to Laycock. 'Perhaps if I had we might have been saved some shame in Crete,' Evelyn reflected.[66]

Crete was to be the scene of Layforce's next action, their arrival on the island coming six days after the German airborne invasion of 20 May. Before leaving Alexandria Evelyn recalled hearing that 'the Maleme aerodrome garrison was hard-pressed' but that otherwise the situation 'well in hand'.[67] This misinformation owed much to the reluctance of the Allied Commander-in-Chief on Crete, Major-General Bernard Freyberg VC, to admit to Wavell how quickly the airport had fallen and to warn him that the island could no longer be held.

In any event by the time Layforce reached Suda Bay on the island's north coast close to midnight on 26 May, the battle was already lost and they were greeted by scenes of apocalyptic chaos. The lighters which came to take them ashore were full of wounded and a bedraggled and hysterical naval officer burst through the captain's door with anguished cries of: 'My God, it's hell, we're pulling out!' The commandos all stared at him aghast and Evelyn was contemptuous of what he saw as the man's cowardice, desperate as he was to have a proper go at last at the Germans.[68] Laycock later recalled telling the wretched man to shut up.

With very limited time to land, they had to dump most of their kit before going ashore. Once on the quayside, Laycock and Evelyn, acting as his intelligence officer, then left their brigade major, Freddy Graham, to get the men into defensive positions while they went off in search of the commander of British troops on the island, Major-General E. C. Weston, whom they found asleep on the earth floor of a rustic hovel serving as his headquarters. There they were told the full extent of the retreat and that, far from raiding aerodromes and seaports as promised in Alexandria, they were to assist in the rearguard covering the withdrawal over the White Mountains to Sphakia, a small fishing harbour on the south coast. It was getting light by the time they reached 'Creforce' headquarters, where Laycock asked Freyberg whether they were to hold the defence 'to the last man and last round', to which the general replied: 'No, a rearguard. Withdraw when you are hard pressed.'[69]

Back with his commandos, Laycock drew up instructions for a timed rearguard action lasting two days and Evelyn set off with Tanner to deliver the orders to Lieutenant-Colonel Colvin, the officer he had shielded from criticism after Bardia. Driving through no man's land, Evelyn appeared oblivious to the Stukas circling overhead and later dismissed their sorties as 'like German opera – too long and too loud'.[70] When the truck could go no further, he left his companions and proceeded on foot, walking for half an hour through scrub and rock before eventually coming across a commando officer who took him to a farm building and pointed under a table. There was Colvin, as Evelyn recorded, 'sitting hunched up like a disconsolate ape'.[71] Evelyn saluted the shell-shocked colonel (who was to serve as the model for Major 'Fido' Hound in *Sword of Honour*), gave him his orders and eventually took him back to headquarters, where, by Evelyn's pitiless account, every time a plane went over the wretched man 'lay rigid with his face in the gorse for about four hours'. At sunset Colvin went back to his battalion, only to return a few hours later 'with a confused account of having been ambushed on a motor cycle,' Evelyn wrote. 'His battalion was fiercely engaged he said (this was balls), and without explaining why he was not with them he gave us the order to withdraw. It all seemed fishy . . .'[72] They nevertheless obeyed and marched all through the night, with Colvin telling them 'We must get as far as we can before light'. The moment daylight came the colonel 'popped into a drain under the road and sat there', recorded Evelyn. After an hour's sleep, Evelyn decided to assess the situation for himself and walked back across the hills through various villages they had passed in the night to within half a mile of where the enemy was being held, where he eventually found Bob Laycock. They drove back to Colonel Colvin, still in his drain; 'Bob as a politely as possible relieved him of his command'[73] – this was later repeated with some 'good round swearing'[74] after the colonel was found to have ordered his men to retreat from its position covering the redeployment of another Layforce battalion.

That night Evelyn and Laycock took the truck and fell back as far as Imbros, on the southern side of the White Mountains, from where the road descended 2,000 feet down a deep ravine to Sphakia. After resting up in a vineyard, at noon they continued on down a series of sharp hair-pins past caves full of ragged stragglers in vain search of an embarkation officer. That evening they eventually found the cave now serving as General Freyberg's headquarters, where they were given half a cupful of sherry and a spoonful of beans and told: 'You were the last to come so you will be the last to go.'[75]

Their return journey in the dark proved far more difficult and 'after an hour or two's scrambling and a bad fall for Bob' they spent the rest of the night at a little shrine on the hilltop, from where they could hear the shouts of Royal Navy sailors embarking troops on the coast below. Layforce spent the next day and a half protecting the Sphakia gorge before Evelyn and Laycock returned to the Creforce cave in the afternoon for further orders ahead of what was to be the last night of the evacuation. At around three o'clock that night, they and just over 200 members of Layforce were evacuated on the last ship to leave the island.

* * *

Over the past twenty-five years, Bob Laycock has been widely accused of lying and acting in direct contravention of orders and jumping the queue for evacuation from Crete, while Evelyn has been charged with falsifying the Layforce diary to cover up for him. These allegations were first made by Antony Beevor in his highly acclaimed and prize-winning book *Crete: The Battle and the Resistance* (1991), and with added vigour in an article he wrote for *The Spectator* – punningly entitled 'The First Casualty of Waugh' – shortly before the book's publication. His thesis has been has been almost universally adopted since. Leaving aside for a moment the direct evidence for the alleged wrongdoing – which is less compelling than one might imagine – one can see why the theory has caught on, stemming as it does from the strong sense of disillusion that permeates Evelyn's fictionalised account of the retreat from Crete in *Officers and Gentlemen*, the second novel in his *Sword of Honour* trilogy, and in particular his depiction of the discreditable flight of Ivor Claire, whose Hookforce diary is later burnt by Guy Crouchback to remove the only evidence of his questionable conduct. *Officers and Gentlemen* was published in 1955 and dedicated 'To Major General Sir Robert Laycock KCMG CB DSO. That every man in arms should wish to be.'

When Evelyn sent his mischievous friend Ann Fleming a copy, she telegraphed back: 'Presume Ivor Claire based Laycock dedication ironical Ann.' Evelyn's response was: 'Your telegram horrifies me. Of course there is no possible connexion between Bob and Claire. If you suggest such a thing anywhere it will be the end of our beautiful friendship . . . For Christ's sake lay off the idea of Bob = Claire . . . Just shut up about Laycock, Fuck You, E Waugh.'[76]

The violence of Evelyn's reaction indicated to many people that he had been rumbled, and as Beevor reasonably remarked, his subsequent diary entry hardly dispelled the suspicion: 'I replied that if she breathes a suspicion of this cruel fact it will be the end of our friendship.'[77] However since then a substantial body of contrary evidence has been excavated from scattered military archives by the Waugh scholar Professor Donat Gallagher and now several other key documents – including a previously unseen memoir by Bob Laycock – have come to light that go a long way towards refuting the accusations against Evelyn and his military mentor. So it is worth re-examining what happened after Evelyn and Laycock reached the Creforce cave on the afternoon of 31 May.

* * *

When they got there they found General Weston in charge, Freyberg having left the island by flying boat the previous evening. As Laycock recalled in his memoir, Weston seemed to be in extremely low spirits and warned them that both ammunition and food were in very short supply. Laycock reassured the general that his commandos had been trained to forage and that, having picked up countless rounds abandoned during the retreat, they also had more ammunition than they could possibly shoot off. They left the cave with orders which Evelyn later recorded in the Layforce war diary: 'Final orders from CREFORCE for evacuation (a) LAYFORCE positions not to be held to the last man and last round but only as long as was necessary to cover withdrawal of other fighting forces. (b) No withdrawal before order from H.Q. (c) LAYFORCE to embark after other fighting forces but before stragglers.'[78]

That evening Laycock was again summoned to Weston's cave and 'found him looking more utterly dejected than I can describe'. Weston was due to leave in a few hours by aeroplane and, as Laycock recalled:

> He looked at me without appearing to see me for a moment or two and then said very slowly and very quietly: 'I am now going to say something which, even in my most ghastly nightmare, I never dreamed that I could say to a British officer on the field of battle. Take down this order.' I turned to Freddy [Graham] who produced a notebook and pencil. Again in a voice so subdued that we could hardly hear him General Weston started to dictate. 'From GOC Crete to Remnants Creforce. You will provide yourself with a white flag. Tomorrow morning at first light you will seek out the Commander of the German forces and surrender to him.'
>
> When he had finished, Freddy handed the message to me. I gazed at it for some time before asking Weston whether he would consider it very insubordinate if I flatly refused to obey it.

Laycock pointed out that his commandos had plenty of fight left in them and suggested to Weston that either he could stay and organise guerrilla warfare in the hills, which some of his commandos eventually undertook on their own initiative, or he could evacuate as many of his brigade staff and men as could get down to the beach in time. After some thought Weston told Laycock that the second alternative seemed more likely to pay dividends for the future war effort. The general also took account of the fact that the Germans appeared to be 'making no attempt to give us the coup de grace', as Laycock wrote, and therefore as far as he was concerned 'the responsibility of Layforce to provide a rearguard to a force which was due to surrender in a few hours time had lapsed'.[79] By his own account, Laycock was thus authorised to delegate the responsibility for surrendering, a task which he initially assigned to Lieutenant-Colonel Colvin but which was eventually undertaken by a more senior New Zealander.

Beevor later accused Laycock of lying about his authorisation to evacuate, apparently overlooking the fact that General Weston recorded in his dispatches that he had sent for Colvin to make the surrender, thus effectively corroborating Laycock's testimony that he had been given permission to go. Freddy Graham recalled the circumstances of the crucial last meeting with Weston rather differently, however the conclusion was essentially the same – that Laycock was at liberty to evacuate his brigade headquarters along with as many of his men as he could muster. It is unclear whether Evelyn was at the same meeting, however in his private diary he later recalled that Weston 'had at first charged Bob with the task but later realised that it was foolish to sacrifice a first-class man for this and chose instead Colvin . . . Weston said that we were to cover the withdrawal and that a message would be sent us by the embarkation officer on Sphakia beach when we could retire.'[80]

In the event no message arrived and sometime after midnight Laycock grew concerned that time was running out for his commandos to make it from their various rearguard positions to the beach in time. He thus took Evelyn and Graham and hurried to Sphakia to try and find the beach officer, but the officer had already left by flying boat along with Weston and the rest of the Creforce staff at 11.50 p.m. Laycock now took matters into his own hands and sent Evelyn's batman, Tanner, as a runner with orders to his troops protecting the perimeter to withdraw.

By his own account, Evelyn meanwhile 'rescued a party of Greek boatmen whom the Australians wished to shoot as spies' and, deciding that there was nothing more they could do, he and Laycock and the rest of Layforce brigade HQ embarked in a small motor boat and boarded the destroyer *Kimberley*, which would be the last ship to leave at around three o'clock in the morning.

Evelyn later wrote in the Layforce diary: 'On finding that the entire staff of Creforce had embarked, in view of the fact that all fighting forces were now in position for embarkation and that there was no enemy contact, Col. Laycock on own authority, issued orders to Lt-Col. Young to lead troops to Sphakion by route avoiding the crowded main approach to town and to use his own personality to obtain priority laid down by Div. orders.'[81] In his *Spectator* piece Beevor wrote: 'It would be hard to compress more distortions of the truth into a single sentence.'[82] Yet everything that Evelyn recorded seems to have been perfectly correct. There was no enemy contact because the Germans chose to fight during the day and rest at night and so fighting had stopped at 8.45 p.m. Beevor contends that Evelyn's most serious fabrication was the assertion that 'all fighting forces were in position for embarkation', given that by Beevor's reckoning neither the Australian 2/7th Battalion nor the Marines, both of which had priority over Layforce, had then reached the beach. However both these units arrived at the entrance to the small beach before Laycock issued his orders to withdraw, only to find their way blocked by a combination of violent rabble and overzealous Movement Control officers. The time can be fixed because one of them recalled hearing General Weston's Sunderland take off soon after they got there.[83] Most of Layforce's troops found their way similarly blocked in the narrow sunken path to the beach. The few commandos who did manage to get away had hurried from the far western perimeter and made it onto the beach via a far less crowded side lane. The first 120 of them clambered aboard the last landing craft to leave, at 2.30 a.m.[84]

The fact that around 550-higher priority Australians and Marines failed to get away despite having reached the shore at around the same time owed far more to the complete breakdown in organisation than any supposed queue-barging by Layforce's commandos. The total taken off that night was 1,000 fewer than the planned 5,000 and numerous testimonies tell how the last landing craft were loaded with any soldiers to hand, including a great many who were not designated fighting troops. By all these accounts it seems most likely that, had the commandos not boarded when they did, their places would have been taken by lower-priority troops. Had there been better organisation many more fighting troops would have got off, including the Australians and the Marines, however that was hardly Bob Laycock or Evelyn Waugh's fault.

Freddy Graham later told Michael Davie that Evelyn had never so much as hinted that he thought Laycock should have stayed behind on Crete 'perhaps because he [Evelyn] had a personal horror of being captured!'.[85] Evelyn's strong aversion to the idea of being taken prisoner was also attested to by Laycock, who recalled Evelyn telling him that he was

'determined not to suffer the ignominy of capture' and wanted to ask a
padre whether it would be considered suicide if he drowned in an attempt
to swim back to Egypt.[86] Their evacuation removed the necessity for this
drastic action, however Evelyn was evidently not entirely happy as they
embarked on the last ship to leave the island, as Laycock recalled: 'By
the look on his face at the time I gathered that Evelyn believed this to be
a dishonourable thing to do though it made sense to me for, at least, we
lived to fight another day.'[87]

But given time for reflection, the moral rightness of their departure
became less clear to Bob Laycock too:

Was I right in using arguments which influenced Weston to countermand
his original orders? Should I, personally, have embarked that night knowing
that nearly three-quarters of my command was still ashore? Probably not.
There is much to be said in support of the principle that the Captain is the
last to leave the sinking ship. At the time, however, my motive seemed reasonable enough and I am confident that my Brigade Staff, with the possible
exception of Evelyn, heartily agreed with my contention that we would be
more use to our country by returning with the remnants of Nos. 7, 50 and
52 Commandos to rejoin Nos. 8 and 11 in Egypt than by spending the rest
of the war in a prisoner of war camp. Once the order to surrender was given
I maintained that every able-bodied man who succeeded in getting back to
Egypt had done the right thing. 'Qui s'excuse s'accuse.' I have never been
happy about leaving Young and his gallant men behind.[88]

Evelyn's violent response to Ann Fleming and the apparently incriminating reference in his diary to 'this cruel fact' was possibly his way of
acknowledging that the discreditable flight of Ivor Claire did in some way
embody his remembered sense of moral unease and uncertainty during
their evacuation from Crete. At the same time he still hero-worshipped
Bob Laycock as the commander par excellence, besides being a steadfast
friend and supporter. Evelyn was doubtless therefore genuinely appalled
that a notorious gossip such as Ann Fleming might start putting it about
that Laycock's evacuation from Crete was equivalent to that of Claire, who
had deserted his men and contrived to get himself evacuated contrary to
orders to fight until the last man and then surrender.

In *Officers and Gentlemen*, the character most like Laycock is Tommy

Blackhouse, who falls down a companionway on the way out to Crete and is thus saved him any responsibility for the ensuing debacle. Ivor Claire, meanwhile, contained elements of several members of 8 Commando's 'White's Club gang', none of whom were with them on Crete. According to Laycock, Claire's numerous apparent models included Eddie Fitz-clarence, Bones Sudeley, Peter Beatty, Randolph Churchill, Philip Dunne and Peter Milton.[89]

If Evelyn later felt ashamed over what he called 'my bunk from Crete', there was doubtless also an element of guilt about the fact that so many – including most of Layforce's commandos – had been left behind to sur-render. Others who got away felt much the same way. There was also a feeling that he had taken part in a military disgrace, and a deep sense of disillusionment at the way the Allies as a whole had capitulated so tamely when the island could and should have been held. As Beevor himself neatly summarised it: 'The loss of Crete was the most unnecessary defeat in that initial period of Allied humiliation at the hands of Hitler's Wehrmacht.'[90]

Christopher Sykes remembers Evelyn telling him shortly afterwards that he 'had never seen anything so degrading as the cowardice that in-fected the spirit of the army; said that Crete had been surrendered without need; that officers and men had been hypnotised into surrender by dive bombing'. Tanner, too, told Beevor that 'it struck me that everyone was being cowardly, no-one was moving as a military unit, everybody was out for himself'.

Antony Beevor is an outstanding and very readable military historian, however his case against Bob Laycock and Evelyn Waugh is highly de-pendent on supposition, much of which is refuted by evidence that has come to light since he wrote his book. In any event, for whatever reason, it appears from the transcript of his interview with Evelyn's batman Ralph Tanner that he had already made up his mind about the queue-jumping before he spoke to the witness who, one would think, was reasonably well placed to tell him what happened. 'There's no question that Laycock was a very brave man,' Beevor said to Tanner during the conversation, 'but there's no doubt about it, he tried to get out before they were supposed to, and tried to get as many of Layforce off as he could, but they were very much jumping the queue, in front of the Australians and the Marines.'[91]

It is perhaps telling that in her own fine biography, Selina Hastings mistook this quote as having come from Tanner and cited it in support of

Laycock and Evelyn's supposed misdeeds. The shorthand typist had begun transcribing the theory advanced by Beevor during his conversation with Tanner with a capital 'T', short for 'The' ('The controversial area is . . .') as opposed to 'Tanner' as Selina Hastings presumably thought. The slip is understandable given that Tanner said nothing in the whole interview to imply that Laycock and Waugh had acted in any way improperly or irresponsibly. In answer to the suggestion that Evelyn falsified the Layforce diary, Tanner said: 'As far as I knew, all Evelyn Waugh's comments in his diary were accurate.'[92]

Neither was there any accusation of wrongdoing from the Layforce officers who were left behind, Colonel Young saying he was 'strongly of the opinion' that Laycock going was 'justified' and 'required'. The official British 'Narrator' of the campaign, Colonel E. E. Rich, recorded that 'Layforce was ordered late in the evening to embark' and regretted the failure of them all to 'reach the boats'.[93] The Narrator's report is especially significant as it was submitted to all senior officers for their comments. The Inter-Service Committee report under Brigadier Guy Salisbury-Jones said much the same, amid some very blunt criticisms of senior officers. It is also hard to believe that Laycock would have gone on to the plum wartime jobs that he did had there been any suspicion regarding his actions on Crete hanging over him.

18

....

Head Unbloodied but Bowed

With so many of Layforce taken prisoner on Crete, the unit was soon disbanded and at his own request Evelyn rejoined the Royal Marines. His route back to England avoiding U-boats again took him via Cape Town, then across the Atlantic to Trinidad, up the American coast and across to Iceland before finally reaching Liverpool in early September 1941. He put the two-month trip to use writing *Put Out More Flags*, a riotous satire chronicling Basil Seal's non-military adventures during the Phoney War which seemed to capture the zeitgeist better than any of his books since *Vile Bodies* in 1930, albeit while suffering from similar defects of disjointedness. Although Evelyn dismissed it in a letter to his father as 'a minor work dashed off to occupy a tedious voyage', it promptly sold 18,000 copies early the next year, despite wartime paper restrictions.

Less than a month after Evelyn got back to London, his brother Alec left for Syria on a two-year posting as publicity agent to General Spears which, as Evelyn told Laura, 'is sad for my parents & for me as it means I now have them on my conscience'.[1] At the age of seventy-five and in frail health, Arthur Waugh felt particularly forlorn at the prospective departure of his favourite son, fearing that he might never see him again. In this rare instance he was relieved when Evelyn rang to invite himself to lunch on the day Alec left, recording in his diary that 'as it turned out it was a very good move, as he was amiable and cheerful and helped to stave off the anxiety of Alec's departure. He and Evelyn left us at 4 p.m. It was a ghastly wrench to say goodbye, especially as he was so kind and gentle. But his taxi vanished through the drive and we were left sorrowing.'[2]

Alec caught a sleeper to Glasgow that evening after a small leaving party in his flat, with champagne and sandwiches made by his mother. Evelyn initially declined his brother's invitation as he had just been given clearance from Brendan Bracken to do his piece about the Bardia commando raid for *Life* magazine and wanted to get it done before he rejoined the Marines. He was still struggling with it late the next evening and wrote to Laura that 'everything I try to write comes out in clichés'.[3] The finished article certainly has its *Boy's Own* moments, however a greater difficulty for Evelyn was that Peters had syndicated it to the London *Evening Standard* without telling him and a melodramatic report by Beverley Nichols subsequently appeared in the *Sunday Chronicle* describing Evelyn as a 'hard-bitten, sun-scorched Commando, with the dust of the desert in his eyes, and a rifle in his hand . . . The ex-dilettante, writing exquisite froth between cocktails, has proved one of the toughest of the lot . . . Few of us in the old days could have imagined Evelyn crawling up the escarpment at Bardia in the dead of night . . .'[4]

Nichols's portrayal was perhaps slightly tongue-in-cheek, however one can well imagine it infuriating certain other commandos who regarded themselves as rather tougher than Captain Waugh. It also earned Evelyn a stern reprimand for not having sought the approval of the Marine Office after Brendan Bracken, as Evelyn saw it, 'backed out of his responsibility' – thereby sowing the seeds for his unflattering portrayal as Rex Mottram in *Brideshead Revisited*, 'half a man posing as a whole one'.

On his last day in London before resuming military life, Evelyn saw Baby Jungman, as he still referred to her despite her marriage, now 'with a vast baby solely in her charge', he told Laura. 'She has changed a great deal with contact with rough Canadians and loss of virginity and is now frank in thought, coarse in speech & likes a stiff whisky. Very surprising.'[5] He returned to duty at Hayling Island on the Hampshire coast 'with the most profound misgiving'.[6] Unable to recapture the adventurous enthusiasm with which he joined up at Chatham, he told Laura that life at his new base was 'squalid, idle & lonely', albeit philosophically adding that it was 'suitable payment for fun with the commando & for my safe & happy return from Egypt'.[7] In November they moved north to Hawick, 'a grim, picturesque little town', as Evelyn described it, made grimmer by the intense cold and wind and rain, and the dreaded wireless playing ceaselessly in the mess. 'Weary, wet, lonely, bored,' he concluded a letter to Peters. 'There is no one here with any sense of humour,' he complained to Laura, 'but they never stop laughing.'[8] His boredom was relieved only by the books that *The Spectator* and *The Tablet* sent him to review, and in early January 1942 by a company commander's course which chanced to take place at Bonaly Tower, on the outskirts of Edinburgh, where Evelyn recognised the Cockburn coat of arms on the staircase and discovered that it had been built (by the architect William Henry Playfair in 1836) for his great-great-grandfather, Lord Cockburn.

At his suggestion, Laura joined him for part of the time ('it is absolutely glorious that you can come', he told her)[9] and they stayed at the Caledonian Hotel on Princes Street before transferring to humbler and more economic quarters, with Evelyn taking a taxi each day out to Bonaly. He thought the teaching staff 'admirable', apart from the intrusively perceptive psychoanalysts: 'I was interviewed by a neurotic creature dressed as a major, who tried to impute unhappiness and frustration to me at all stages of adolescence.'[10]

In February he returned to Hawick with his thoughts about the war growing gloomier by the day, the alliance with the Soviet Union having removed its 'heroic and chivalrous disguise', as he saw it, and rendered it instead 'a sweaty tug-of-war between teams of indistinguishable louts'. 'Do you understand now,' he wrote to Diana Cooper, alluding to his brusqueness when she came to stay at Piers Court in 1939, 'why I would have no wireless or talk of Central Europe at Stinchcombe? . . . Are there corners where old friends can still talk as though they were free? If there are, they must say in those corners that there is nothing left – not a bottle of wine nor a gallant death nor anything well made that is a pleasure to handle – and never will be again.' It was in this foul mood that on 2 April he made his first appearance on a BBC radio discussion programme, *The Brains Trust*, during which he managed roundly to offend all the other panellists by refusing to have lunch with them beforehand, making fun of them during the broadcast and finally suggesting that they all give their fees to the War Fund.

Desperate to get back to soldiering among friends, he wrote to Bob Laycock: 'I wish I were back with you. I suppose that there is no opening?' Laycock had recently returned from Egypt to command the Special Service Brigade, having earlier gone missing after the abortive raid on Rommel's headquarters in Libya, when Geoffrey Keyes was killed and posthumously awarded the VC and Evelyn's friend Robin Campbell severely wounded in his leg, which he eventually lost in a prisoner-of-war camp. 'It looks unlikely that [Laycock] has survived,' Evelyn noted at the time; 'but in White's everyone says he is too "fly" to be caught.' Sure enough, Laycock had miraculously presented himself to some British troops on Christmas Day after six weeks living off berries behind enemy lines, attributing his survival to his knowledge of the habits of foxes, in gratitude for which he never went hunting again. Though he knew perfectly well how difficult Evelyn could be, Laycock remained fond of him and in addition had been much impressed by his courage and coolness under fire on Crete. He agreed to have him back as an intelligence officer. '"The Blues" [Royal Horse Guards] have accepted me,' Evelyn wrote to Laura, 'so I can now grow my hair long and wear a watch chain across my chest, and you can have a suit made of their check tweed.'[11] After joining his new unit at Ardrossan on the Ayrshire coast, Evelyn wrote to Coote Lygon from 'a nice black market hotel where I have grape fruit and large dishes of eggs daily'. 'Chucker Laycock has proved most unchucking,' he purred, 'and I am back with him & Philip Dunne and other old chums.'[12]

Two weeks later, still feeling chipper, he wrote a much-quoted letter to Laura which showed how much he delighted in things going wrong, to say nothing of his flair for embellishment and preference for the most picturesque form of whatever story he happened to be telling:

So No.3 Cmdo were very anxious to be chums with Lord Glasgow [whose Kelburn estate lay just north of the commandos' base at Ardrossan] so they offered to blow up an old tree stump for him and he was very grateful and he said don't spoil the plantation of young trees near it because that is the apple of my eye and they said no of course not we can blow a tree down so that it falls on a sixpence and Lord Glasgow said goodness you are clever and he asked them all to luncheon for the great explosion. So Col. Durnford-Slater D.S.O. said to his subaltern, have you put enough explosive in the tree. Yes, sir, 75 lbs. Is that enough? Yes sir I worked it out by mathematics it is exactly right. Well better put a bit more. Very good sir.

And when Col. D. Slater D.S.O. had had his port he sent for the subaltern and said subaltern better put a bit more explosive in that tree. I don't want to disappoint Lord Glasgow. Very good sir.

Then they all went out to see the explosion and Col. D.S. D.S.O. said you will see that tree fall flat at just that angle where it will hurt no young trees and Lord Glasgow said goodness you are clever.

So soon they lit the fuse and waited for the explosion and presently the tree, instead of falling quietly sideways, rose 50 feet into the air taking with it ½ acre of soil and the whole of the young plantation.

And the subaltern said Sir I made a mistake, it should have been 7½ lbs not 75.

Lord Glasgow was so upset he walked in dead silence back to his castle and when they came to the turn of the drive in sight of his castle what should they find but that every piece of glass in the building was broken.

So Lord Glasgow gave a little cry & ran to hide his emotion in the lavatory and there when he pulled the plug the entire ceiling, loosed by the explosion, fell on his head.

This is quite true.[13]

Laura was at this time expecting another child and in advance of the birth Evelyn suggested: 'James if a boy; if a girl it is kinder to drown her than to bring her up like her poor sister.' If this was not meant to be taken too literally, Evelyn was genuinely concerned that Teresa had not been getting enough attention at Pixton. Staying there that Easter, he had found Bron 'sanguine and self-confident' and Teresa 'contrary to accounts, a civil, intelligent and self-possessed little girl', however also 'inarticulate and pasty faced'. He thought a 'long visit' to his mother in Highgate might 'undo some of the mischief of Pixton neglect', so after Easter they went up to London, Laura taking the children to Highgate while Evelyn treated himself to a night on the tiles with Frank Pakenham and Maimie Lygon, eventually crawling into bed at the St James's Club. Two weeks later, by which time he was back with his unit, he received a letter from his father: 'I am enjoying Teresa's visit very much. And find her a gentle affectionate & lovable little creature . . . Mother has given up her time to her entirely – having ceased to play bridge or attend at the Red Cross depot.'[14]

Laura's baby girl was born on 11 June 1942 at Pixton and christened Margaret Evelyn two weeks later. Evelyn got there shortly after the birth but was recalled before the christening to a photographic interpretation course in Derbyshire, where he soon made a point of reciprocating Bob Laycock's loyalty to him by reporting some 'insolent' remarks he had heard in a lecture about the Rommel raid, which Laycock admitted 'made my blood boil'.[15] 'I think this wicked colonel [the lecturer] will be severely beaten,' Evelyn smugly told Laura.

However in August he undid his good work somewhat by arriving at dinner with the Laycocks considerably the worse for wear after 'a hard day's drinking'. 'From that evening I began to trace a decline in my position in Bob's esteem,' he recorded. 'The next ten days I wandered aimlessly in the triangle Ritz, St James's, Claridge's, spending most of the time with Randolph or Phil [Dunne].' That autumn Evelyn's diary chronicled regular binges culminating in assorted minor disasters. After a 'beautiful day of overeating and overdrinking' at the home of Harry Stavordale at Evershot, near to the Sherborne camp where they were stationed after Ardrossan, he recorded: 'Called at 6.30 [a.m.]. Still very confused with drink and smelling of "orange gin". Drove as far as Camberley in a stupor where we had a collision which destroyed the car.'[16] 'You see,' he wrote to Laura, 'I do get into mischief when I am Whiskerless do I not.'[17] (Whiskers was Evelyn's pet-name for Laura.)

That Christmas he described a party of 'great drunkenness' at Longleat with another old friend, Daphne Weymouth, the morning after which he called on Olivia Plunket Greene, to whom he had remained characteristically steadfast as she had descended into alcoholism. She was by then living in a cottage on the Longleat estate and Evelyn 'found her with no trousers on completely drunk and Gwen blacking the grate. Then I came back to Sherborne and off we went again, to a great dinner party given by Bill Stirling & Peter Milton. Last night I suffered from the delusion that black rooks were flying round and round my bed room.'[18]

* * *

On 28 October, his thirty-ninth birthday, Evelyn had recorded: 'A good year. I have begotten a fine daughter, published a successful book, drunk 300 bottles of wine and smoked 300 or more Havana cigars. I have got back to soldiering among friends. This time last year I was on my way to Hawick to join 5 R.M. I got steadily worse as a soldier with the passage of time, but more patient and humble – as far as soldering is concerned. I have about £900 in hand and no grave debts except to the Government; health excellent except when impaired by wine; a wife I love, agreeable work in surroundings of great beauty. Well that is as much as one can hope for.'[19]

However he still yearned for more military action, the dearth of which was highlighted by Laycock's acceptance of 'sporting invitations far ahead', as Evelyn ruefully noted in his diary, not to mention the various successful raids recently carried out by other commandos, most notably by No. 4 Commando at Dieppe in August 1942, where Shimi Lovat's capture of the Varengeville battery had earned him a DSO to add to the MC he had been awarded after an earlier raid at Boulogne. Lovat was one of the most dashing commandos of them all, a fearless Highland chieftain famously described by Winston Churchill as 'the handsomest man to cut a throat', however Evelyn thought him a show-off and privately pronounced him 'a *Palais de Danse* hero'.[20] Years later in the *Sword of Honour* trilogy he mercilessly caricatured him as the former hairdresser Trimmer/McTavish.

Evelyn was at first impressed by Lovat's qualities as a soldier. After watching the film of Dieppe at the Combined Operations Club and hearing a fairly full account of the operation, he could only conclude that 'Shimi Lovat did brilliantly, the only wholly successful part of the raid'.[21] But in due course his admiration for him was overtaken by feelings of irritation: 'I have had a very great victory in a very minor battle [a dispute about maps] with Shimi,' he told Laura in October, 'and hate him instead of Wakefield.'[22] Sometime later he reported: 'Shimi has tried to make me lecture to his commando so I have countered by offering a series of lectures on imperial geography to be followed by a written examination for all ranks or, alternatively, a popular talk in praise of David Stirling. That will annoy.'[23] And the next year: 'Shimi's conceit is boundless. I thought perhaps that now he had done something he might pipe down a bit. Instead he is planning to become the Voice of the Army in the House of Lords.'[24] The dislike was evidently mutual, and years later Lovat devoted three pages of his autobiography to vilifying Evelyn as a slovenly soldier and brazen social climber, 'a greedy little man – a eunuch in appearance – who seemed desperately anxious to "get in" with the right people'.[25]

The simmering tension between the swaggering aristocrat and impertinent parvenu came to a head in the summer of 1943 after Bob Laycock departed for North Africa as part of Operation Husky – the Allied invasion of Sicily – leaving orders that Evelyn continue in his recent post as liaison officer at Combined Operations Headquarters in London before joining him when transport became available.

Though annoyed not to be included in the initial party, Evelyn was distracted for the time being by the death of his father in the early morning of the same day that Bob Laycock left. Evelyn was with Laura in London at the time and spent the next few days staying at his parents' Highgate flat going through his father's papers – 'he kept up a large correspondence with very dull people,' Evelyn noted – and having bookplates engraved so that he and Alec could keep his books together in their respective libraries. He displayed little emotion either in his diary or in his replies to letters of condolence, his main concern being for his mother, whose nerves had already been shattered by the Blitz. 'It is a disagreeable world for the old and I think he was glad to leave it,' Evelyn wrote to Tom Driberg, who had recently been elected an independent MP. 'His only regret would be leaving my mother. I am in a backwater of the war at the moment but hope for adventure soon.'[26]

Evelyn wanted very much to go to North Africa in early August and wrote to Alec suggesting that if he could get home from Syria, 'it would be a good thing as our mother is desoeuvree and lonely . . . the best thing would be for you to live with her . . . I hope you will be able to get back to see to things after I have left.'[27] However Shimi Lovat suggested that a course at the fearsome commando training depot at Achnacarry in Scotland might not go amiss after so long at a desk job. This was a distinctly unattractive proposal for Evelyn as it threatened to delay his departure to the point at which he could no longer be of any use to Laycock in Sicily. It would also have entailed his coming under the jurisdiction of the training depot's commandant Colonel Vaughan, an ex-drill-sergeant and renowned stickler with whom he had recently clashed, accusing him of making a homosexual pass after the colonel reprimanded him for acknowledging him disrespectfully with a casual wave of his riding crop.

Evelyn responded that Laycock had explicitly stated that he should remain in his post until embarkation and that he had 'good personal reasons [following his father's death] for wishing to remain in London as long as possible'.[28] Lovat wrote back that Laycock's orders had been 'automatically cancelled' (by his superior, General Charles Haydon) and that Evelyn was to report to the depot on 1 August. 'You will not proceed overseas unless passed fit by Achnacarry. I hope I have made myself clear.'[29]

Interpreting this as a deliberate act of provocation on Lovat's part motivated by personal malice – a fellow officer at Brigade HQ later described it as 'a childish and obvious bit of intimidation'[30] – Evelyn requested an interview with General Haydon to discover why an exception was being made in his case, pointing out that if doubt existed about the fitness of an officer for foreign service, the usual procedure was to refer him to the medical authorities; Evelyn had incidentally been pronounced fit by a Harley Street consultant after referring himself. But Haydon proved even less amenable and insisted that he not only do the depot course but also an intelligence course. He concluded their interview by saying that Evelyn had brought nothing but discredit to the Brigade since he joined and advised him that for the Brigade's good he should leave as soon as possible. Calculating that by the time he had done the two courses it would be too late anyway for him to go to Sicily, Evelyn complied, explaining afterwards to Bob Laycock: 'A cad [Lovat] and a lunatic [Haydon] make a formidable couple when they are hunting together.'

For his part Haydon later wrote to Laycock to explain that 'Evelyn Waugh has caused trouble and is going', adding: 'I know very well that this will disappoint and probably annoy you, because I am aware that you have a high opinion of Waugh's personal courage in the field. This is not in question . . .' Laycock certainly was annoyed and when he heard from another officer how Evelyn had been 'bullied by Lovat and Haydon', he remarked to his wife, 'How feeble of them – I am angry'.[31] His reaction appears to refute the suggestion made by both Christopher Sykes and Shimi Lovat that he had never intended for Evelyn to join him in Sicily.

Evelyn's tendency to rub certain people up the wrong way had clearly contributed to his own downfall – even Laycock had earlier warned him that he was 'so unpopular as to be unemployable'. Given that Evelyn recorded Laycock's comment without protest in his diary, he was evidently alive to his own shortcomings when it came to getting on with people whom he disliked. Less forgivable as far as some of his fellow officers were concerned was his occasional tendency to tease, or as some saw it 'bully',[32] his own men, although on the other hand several he commanded later recalled how much they liked him. But while Laycock was well aware of Evelyn's faults, the idea that he had somehow secretly connived in his sacking – even if Evelyn initially believed this to have been the case – is not only contradicted by the surviving correspondence but also seems unlikely given the past tensions between Bob Laycock and Shimi Lovat.

'My dear Shimi,' Laycock had written to him the previous year. 'When will you learn some tact? I know that it is uphill work dealing with officers who, to put it snobbishly, do not come from the same social status as those

Laura Herbert: 'I love her very much,' Evelyn told Baby Jungman, 'and I think there is as good a chance of our marriage being a success as any I know.'

Laura's family home, Pixton Park, whose Irish shabbiness inspired Evelyn's portrait of Boot Magna Hall in *Scoop*.

Evelyn and Laura leaving the church after their wedding in 1936.

Piers Court in Gloucestershire, a wedding present from Laura's grandmother.

Evelyn with the infant Teresa and (right) Laura, at Piers Court shortly before the outbreak of war.

The drawing room at Piers Court.

Evelyn in the Royal Marines, with 'as smart a little moustache as Errol Flynn', as Diana Cooper described it.

Bob Laycock: 'That every man in arms should wish to be'.

Evelyn and Randolph Churchill in Croatia, on the British Military Mission to Tito's partisans.

Left: Hollywood, 1947: Evelyn and Laura with Sir Charles Mendl and Anna May Wong.

Below The Piers Court household, 1947. Middle row, from left: Gladys Attwood (cleaning lady), Hatty, Laura, James, Evelyn, Evelyn's mother, Meg, and old Mrs Attwood. Teresa and Bron are sitting in the foreground. Directly behind Evelyn stands the butler, Ellwood. Behind Meg is their nanny, Vera, next to the cowman, Norman Attwood.

Evelyn and Laura returning to Plymouth from New York in the *Ile de France*, November 1950.

Evelyn in the library at Combe Florey.

Combe Florey, 1959. From left: Bron, Meg, Evelyn, Septimus, Teresa, James, Giovanni Manfredi, Hatty, Laura, Maria Manfredi.

Evelyn at the front of Combe Florey. The sign reads 'No Admittance on Business'.

Evelyn, Laura, James and the gardener, Walter Coggan – 'my rival Coggins' as Evelyn called him.

Evelyn and Meg on their trip to British Guiana in 1961.

Evelyn with Maime Lygon and the newly-married Meg and Giles FitzHerbert.

At Combe Florey in 1965. Back row, left to right: James, Bron (holding Alexander and Sophia), Laura, Evelyn, Teresa (with her son Justin), Margaret (with her daughter Claudia). Kneeling in front are Hatty and Septimus, with Emily FitzHerbert in the foreground.

with whom you used to deal with in peacetime . . . yet nevertheless you *must* learn to bear with them.'[33] And on another occasion, after receiving a complaint about 'one of your temperamental prima donnas in the shape of Lovat',[34] Laycock rebuked him for 'pointless bad manners when dealing with junior staff officers' and 'not giving a damn for anyone and telling all and sundry where to get off'.[35]

The account Shimi Lovat wrote in his autobiography* of Evelyn's 'sacking' from the Special Service Brigade was published well after the other main protagonists had died and went unquestioned by Evelyn's subsequent biographers, even though the author was hardly an impartial witness. The claim that Evelyn had spent his compassionate leave mostly at White's was perfectly consistent with his normal habits yet seems unlikely in this particular instance given all he had had to do sorting through his father's papers and dealing with the funeral and so forth. 'It has been marvelous to have had Evelyn in London,' his mother wrote to Alec on 3 July, four days after the funeral, 'he has seen to everything in a kindly and efficient manner . . . I don't know what I should have done without him.'[36]

Several of Lovat's other assertions are equally questionable – for instance his claim that Evelyn 'stormed in unannounced to General Haydon's office' when he plainly wrote to request an interview; and the notion that he was 'sacked on the spot for insubordination', when even by Haydon's account Evelyn was advised to resign. These may seem rather pedantic points, yet when taken together and then exaggerated by subsequent chroniclers they have further distorted the truth about Evelyn Waugh's war. Whilst more than capable of putting people's backs up and far from the ideal company commander, there were other ways in which Evelyn could be very useful to the military. He had an extremely good brain, of great value when it came to planning operations, at headquarters and in the field; he excelled at knocking the long-winded written drafts into concise and readable shape; and above all he was extraordinarily brave and cool under fire. Laycock was himself a well-read and witty man and undoubtedly found Evelyn very entertaining. However it is hard to believe that he would have wanted him on his staff had he not also been impressed by some of his qualities as a soldier.

At first Evelyn felt extremely aggrieved at his treatment and wrote a

---

* *March Past*, (Weidenfeld & Nicolson, 1978).

long letter to Laycock setting out 'the facts relevant to my leaving the Brigade so that when you have the leisure to look at them, you will know that it is not I who has let you down'.[37] He wrote an equally long letter to the head of Combined Operations, Lord Louis Mountbatten, however by the time he eventually saw him, in early August, he had grown bored of the whole saga and they met on 'terms so cordial as to be almost affectionate'.[38] At the end of that month, back with the Royal Horse Guards at Windsor, he reflected:

> I dislike the Army. I want to get to work again. I do not want any more experiences in life. I have quite enough bottled and carefully laid in the cellar, some still ripening, most ready for drinking, a little beginning to lose its body. I wrote to Frank [Pakenham] very early in the war to say that its chief use would be to cure artists of the illusion that they were men of action. It has worked its cure with me. I have succeeded, too, in dissociating myself very largely with the rest of the world. I am not impatient of its manifest follies and don't want to influence opinions or events or expose humbug or anything of that kind. I don't want to be of service to anyone or anything. I simply want to do my work as an artist.[39]

The opportunity to return to writing would come sooner than he thought, however for the time being he persisted in trying to get back into action as a soldier and began badgering Shimi Lovat's cousin Bill Stirling about a place in 2 SAS, which he had formed after the capture of his brother David in North Africa. 'I dread the prospect of organization and training and a hundred new acquaintances,' Evelyn wrote in his diary. 'But after my treatment by Haydon I must "make good" as a soldier. Nothing can upset him more than to find me promoted as a result of his intemperance.' Evelyn had stayed with Stirling at Keir, his palatial home in Perthshire, the previous year while his brother David was still missing after the Benghazi raid and they had since furthered their acquaintance at the bar of White's. For the time being Stirling put Evelyn to work drafting a cogent case to be presented to the War Office for the regiment's expansion. 'He is a great change as a master from Bob,' Evelyn wrote to Laura, '– vague, mystical, imaginative, impatient, chivalrous, moral, slow witted, unconventional, unsmart, aristocratic, – in every quality dramatically opposed to Bob and in many ways preferable.' With his posting eventually fixed, Evelyn was all set to go out with Christopher Sykes and join the rest of the SAS in North Africa in mid-November, however the Allied campaign in the southern Mediterranean went far better than expected and they were eventually deemed surplus to requirements. Instead they were sent on a parachuting course at Tatton Park in Cheshire, from where Evelyn wrote to Laura: 'Parachuting is without exception the most exhilarating thing I have ever done. All the tedium of the last months has been worthwhile for the few seconds of first leaving the aeroplane. I felt absolutely no reluctance to jump – less than in taking a cold bath.'[40] In his diary he recalled stepping from the noisy aeroplane 'into perfect silence and solitude and apparent immobility in bright sunshine above the treetops'. Years later, when the whole experience had fully ripened in his memory, he described the rapture felt by his fictional alter ego Guy Crouchback on his first parachute jump,

> . . . something as near as his earthbound soul could reach to a foretaste of paradise, *locum refrigerii, lucis et pacis*. The aeroplane seemed far distant as will, at the moment of death, the spinning earth. As though he had cast the constraining bonds of flesh and muscle and nerve, he found himself floating free; the harness that had so irked him in the narrow, dusky, resounding carriage now imperceptibly supported him. He was a free spirit in an element as fresh as on the day of its creation.[41]

But Evelyn's foretaste of paradise was as short-lived as Crouchback's and on his second jump he landed badly and cracked the fibula in his left leg, an injury that would eventually grant him the time he needed to write *Brideshead Revisited*, the climax of which had been forming in his mind ever since his efforts that October to save the soul of his dying lapsed Catholic friend Hubert Duggan.

A stepson of Lord Curzon, Duggan had been Conservative MP for Acton for more than a decade and Evelyn had known him vaguely since being at Oxford with his elder brother Alfred, although he and Hubert had only really become friends in the early 1930s at Madresfield after both had been deserted by their wives in strikingly similar circumstances and Hubert began an affair with Maimie Lygon. They had grown closer still during the war, when Hubert was the only one of Evelyn's friends he made a godparent to his daughter Margaret. By this time Hubert was living 'in sin' with Diana Cooper's long-standing friend Phyllis de Janzé, a renowned beauty and fellow divorcee ten years his senior (and the ex sister-in-law of Alice de Janzé who had shot Evelyn's friend Raymond de Trafford), but Phyllis died in April 1943 and shortly afterwards Hubert fell gravely ill with tuberculosis.

'The news of Hubert is very bad indeed,' Evelyn wrote to Laura that September. 'He is allowed to see no one ... He never sleeps and drugs put him into a delirium but not to sleep. He is in the blackest melancholy and haunted by delusions. There is nothing which can be done for him medically. Supernatural aid needed.' For three weeks Evelyn visited his stricken friend almost daily at his house on Chapel Street in Belgravia, until eventually one day Hubert began to talk about religion 'and of re-turning to the Church', as Evelyn put it, however Hubert worried that it would be a betrayal of Phyllis to profess repentance of his life with her. The next day Evelyn consulted a Catholic chaplain and was given a medal. 'Just hide it somewhere in the room,' said the priest. 'I have known most wonderful cases of Grace being brought about in that way.'

When Evelyn got to Chapel Street later that morning, Lady Curzon told him that Hubert was not expected to live through the day, so Evelyn went immediately to Farm Street to fetch Father Devas. Like Lord Marchmain's mistress Cara in *Brideshead*, Hubert's sister did not want the priest there, but Evelyn brought him in nonetheless and after he had given Hubert absolution Hubert said, 'Thank you father!' which was taken as his assent. Evelyn returned to the house that afternoon to find the sister still hostile, yet Father Devas gently explaining his intention to anoint Hubert. 'Look all I shall do is just to put oil on his forehead and say a prayer. Look the oil is in this little box. It is nothing to be frightened of.'

'And so,' Evelyn recorded, 'by knowing what he wanted and sticking to that, when I was all for arguing it out from first principles, he got what he wanted and Hubert crossed himself and later called me up and said, "When I became a Catholic it was not from fear", so he knows what happened and accepted it. So we spent the day watching for a spark of gratitude for the love of God and saw the spark.'[42]

Believing that he had been granted God's pardon, Hubert briefly rallied but died twelve days later. Evelyn attended a Requiem Mass for him at Farm Street on 3 November and in late January 1944 he asked for time off from the Army in order to write his book. The letter was addressed to the commanding officer of his regiment, the current Duchess of York's grandfather Colonel A. H. Ferguson, from whom Evelyn requested three months' leave on the basis that 'entertainment is now regarded as a legitimate contribution to the war effort'. He went on: 'It is a peculiarity of the literary profession that, once an idea becomes fully formed in the author's mind, it cannot be left unexploited without deterioration. If, in fact, the book is not written now it will never be written.'[43]

Ferguson at first refused, taking the view that his time would be better spent training the Home Guard at Windsor; however after enlisting the support of Brendan Bracken at the Ministry of Information, Evelyn eventually got his leave. Laura not unreasonably saw this as an opportunity to see more of her husband and suggested they take a cottage at Pixton, but Evelyn was always the most ruthlessly self-protective of artists and that idea was quickly scotched. 'The reason is that I long for your company at all times except one,' Evelyn explained. 'When I am working I must be alone. I shall never be able to maintain the fervent preoccupation which is absolutely necessary to composition, if you were at close quarters with me . . . I shall see if they can take me at Chagford.'[44]

Thus on the last day of January he checked into the Easton Court Hotel determined to begin writing by ten the next morning. 'I still have a cold,' he noted in his diary that evening, 'and am low in spirits but I feel full of literary power which only this evening gives place to qualms of impotence.' He remained ensconced there for the next four weeks, intensely engaged in what he already believed was going to be his most significant and self-revealing book, at once a highly romanticised representation of aspects of his own life and, as he later wrote for the dust-jacket, 'an attempt to trace the workings of the divine purpose in a pagan world, in the lives of an English Catholic family'.

19

....

A Book to Bring Tears

On 2 February 1944 Evelyn wrote to Laura from Chagford: 'So the nut started rather stiff & I had to write the first thousand words of magnum opus three times before they came right but now things are going better and I have done 2,387 words in 1½ days. It shall be 3,000 this evening & soon I hope to get 2000 a day. It is v. high quality about Col. Cutler* and how much I hate the army.'[1]

By the end of the first week he was up to 10,000 words and wrote to his agent that if left undisturbed by the military he hoped to finish the book by the middle of May. He suggested that Chapman & Hall might like to reserve some paper in order to publish it for Christmas but was concerned that their production standards might not do his great work justice. 'I should like this book to be in decent form,' he told Peters, 'because it is very good.'[2] From time to time he got bogged down rewriting. 'Every day I seem to go over what I did the day before and make it shorter. I am getting spinsterish about style.'[3] But at other times progress was far more satisfactory and on one day he sat down after dinner and rattled off 3,000 words in three hours. By the end of the fourth week he had completed 33,000 words and had reached the end of the third chapter, when Charles watches Julia drive away from Brideshead Castle and Sebastian tells him 'We'll have a heavenly time alone.'

But before he could start on the next chapter he was summoned to London to become ADC to Major-General Ivor Thomas, to whom he promptly behaved so obnoxiously that the general refused to have him.

---

* Colonel S. G. Cutler had been his commanding officer in the Royal Marines in 1942, a 'pompous booby' in Evelyn's estimation and one of his chief military bugbears alongside Tom Churchill, Shimi Lovat and Roger Wakefield.

'The primary lack of sympathy seemed to come from my being slightly drunk in his mess on the first evening,' Evelyn nonchalantly recorded. 'I told him I could not change the habits of a lifetime for a whim of his.'[4] To Laura he wrote: 'The worst I did was to pour claret in his lap.'[5] But no sooner had he escaped from one general than another one was conjured for him. Evelyn knew the next one vaguely of old, a substantially more easy-going Old Etonian called Miles Graham whom he deemed 'a slightly superior type': 'So the new general is very much less assuming than Tomas [*sic*],' he told Laura, '& fully appreciates, or appears to appreciate, the importance of a gentleman leading his own life.' Graham immediately gave him six weeks' leave but twenty-four hours later cancelled their arrangement altogether, perhaps having reflected on what he was letting himself in for.

Returning to Chagford after his ten-day break, Evelyn took a while to get back into his stride, but eleven days later he sent off another 13,000 words to be typed up, and six days after that a further 7,800. 'I am writing a very beautiful book,' he told Coote Lygon, 'to bring tears, about very rich, beautiful, high born people who live in palaces and have no troubles except what they make themselves and those are mainly the demons sex and drink which after all are easy to bear as troubles go nowadays.'[6] He was greatly relieved to be back doing what he loved best and also away from London where, as he admitted to Coote, 'it is not unfair to say I never draw a sober breath. I was beginning to lose my memory which for a man who lives entirely in the past, is to lose life itself.'[7] The hotel's other guests were mostly elderly women who did not disturb him apart from when it was sunny and they emerged 'like lizards' and annoyed him by sitting right outside his window.[8] Despite this and a few brief intrusions by trysting couples, by 29 March he had written a total of 62,000 and was up to the end of Book Two.

* * *

It was at this point that Laura came for her last brief visit to Chagford before the birth of her fifth child, Harriet, who was born in May. Neither Evelyn nor Laura ever appeared greatly to relish having children and Evelyn had greeted the news of Laura's latest pregnancy with his customary commiseration. 'I do hope that your nursery life is not proving unendurable,' he wrote to her. 'I think I have not said enough about how deeply I admire your patience & resignation in this and in the threat to your future happiness in the birth of another child. If I have seemed to make light of it, that is my rough manner; my heart is all yours & sorrowing for you.'[9] Their son Bron later recalled his mother as having scarcely featured in his early life at Pixton and being unaware that motherhood involved 'any particular emotional proximity'. His father, he remembered, 'featured not at all'.[10]

Bron had vague memories of him occasionally turning up in uniform, but most of the time Evelyn evinced a breathtaking determination to stay away. 'I shall not visit my children during Christmas leave,' he had written to Laura in December 1941, 'they should be able to retain the impression formed of me for another three months. I can't afford to waste any time on them which could be spent on my own pleasures. I have sent them some kippers as compensation.'[11] And the next year: 'I am very glad not to be with my children for Christmas. There is an hotel at Shaftesbury with a very splendid sideboard. I think we might take a week end there soon when you are fuckable.'[12]

But as much as Evelyn recoiled – or at least affected to recoil – from spending time with his children, he constantly craved the company of his wife. 'If by any chance my children should die,' he wrote to Laura at the time of her latest pregnancy, 'do come to London. I miss you every hour.'[13] Though he sometimes chided her for her careless appearance – 'Try and get your teeth white before we meet,'[14] he wrote before a brief rendezvous that spring – or bombarded her with bossy instructions about their house or children or how to liven up her correspondence, his letters to her were more often tender as well as funny, abounding in heartfelt expressions of his love for and need of her, and the various ways he missed her – 'bitterly', 'unspeakably', 'unbearably', 'unendurably' and so on. After the evacuation from Crete in June 1941 he had written to her: 'What a lot we shall have to say to each other when we meet. I feel that all our future life will be spent in telling how we have spent this year apart. In danger I have one fear, that it means further separation from you.'[15]

* * *

Just before Easter, Evelyn was again summoned to London for a proposed assignment to conduct journalists around the Second Front, which was due to open that summer. 'It is not quite as disastrous as it might be,' he reflected, 'for I have come to a suitable halting stage in the book and a week or two away from it may do no harm.'[16] But, as so often, the job never materialised and instead he passed an idle two weeks at White's catching up with old friends and drinking 'a great deal of good wine which is getting scarce daily but still procurable by those who take the trouble'.[17] He then went down to Pixton, where he completed the revision of the first two sections of *Brideshead*. Lady de Vesci's ancient stepmother Grace, Lady Wemyss, was also staying and as Evelyn recorded, 'Auberon surprised her in her bath and is thus one of very few men who can claim to have seen his great great grandmother in the raw.'[18] Returning to London he gave dinner to his old friends John Sutro and Harold Acton, the latter of whom had been working for RAF intelligence in India. Feasting on gulls' eggs, consommé, partridge, haddock on toast and nearly a bottle a head of Perrier-Jouët 28, Evelyn was riveted by what he called Harold's 'descriptions of service life as seen by a bugger . . . He combines his pleasures with keen patriotism.'[19]

With nothing yet fixed for him to do, Evelyn returned for a week to Chagford, where he 'painfully picked up the threads of a very difficult chapter of love-making on a liner'.[20] He managed to despatch the first chapter of Book Three (12,000 words) a week later yet was unsure as to the success of this section. 'I feel very much the futility of describing sexual emotions without describing the sexual act,' he recorded in his diary; 'I should like to give as much detail as I have of the meals, to the two coitions – with his [Charles's] wife and Julia. It would be no more or less obscene than to leave them to the reader's imagination, which in this case cannot be as acute as mine. There is a gap in which the reader will insert his own sexual habits instead of those of my characters.'[21]

Back in London he again enlisted the help of Bob Laycock to rescue him from the spectacularly unsuitable jobs that the War Office kept proposing (the current choice was between adjutant to a transit camp in India and assistant registrar in a hospital) and to persuade Bill Stirling to take him back at 2 SAS with as much leave as he needed to finish his book. Deeply appreciative of Stirling's help, Evelyn promptly asked him to be one of Harriet's godparents, along with Basil Bennett, owner of the

Hyde Park Hotel where he now tended to stay when in London; Mary Herbert's secretary Miss Haig, 'an inexplicable whim of Laura's' as Evelyn put it; and Laura's other choice, Gretel Coudenhove-Kalergi, an elderly Austrian countess who had been staying with her maid at Pixton when war broke out and decided to remain there for the duration, and then for a few more years after it had finished, all the time 'occupying two of the best bedrooms on the first floor', so Evelyn's son Bron later recorded with a degree of retrospective bewilderment, and 'joining a large population of retired nannies, housekeepers and maids who occupied different parts of the house, living their own lives and jealously protecting their own territory'.[22]

Harriet's fifth godparent was Nancy Mitford, to whom Evelyn looked 'not so much for spiritual instruction,' he assured her, 'as for knowledge of the world, savoir faire, joie de vivre and things of that kind'.[23] Evelyn had known Nancy since his marriage to Evelyn Gardner and later throughout his brief but deep friendship with Nancy's sister Diana Guinness, during which time Evelyn mentored Nancy in her early endeavours as a novelist. In the early 1930s they often saw each other with literary friends such as the Sitwells, Cyril Connolly, Robert Byron and John Betjeman and at house parties with the Weymouths, Pakenhams and Churchills. After Nancy married Peter Rodd, whom Evelyn disliked for his curious combination of pedantry and fecklessness, there was a distinct lull in their friendship, however by 1939 that marriage was all but over and Evelyn soon became a regular patron of Heywood Hill's bookshop in Mayfair where Nancy worked for much of the war and which he regarded as 'the one centre of old world gossip left'.[24] From then on theirs developed into one of the most famous literary friendships.

By the middle of May Evelyn was back into his stride and well on his way to finishing *Brideshead*, which he eventually brought to its climax on D-Day, 6 June: 'This morning at breakfast the waiter told me the Second Front had opened. I sat down early to work and wrote a fine passage of Lord Marchmain's death agonies ... I sent for the priest to give Lord Marchmain the last sacraments. I worked through till 4 o'clock and finished the last chapter – the last dialogue poor – took it to the post, walked home by the upper road. There only remains now the epilogue which is easy meat. My only fear is lest the invasion upsets my typist at St. Leonard's, or the posts to him with my manuscript.'[25] Laura came to stay with him for a week while he corrected the typescript, and on 20 June he reported to Peters: 'I have delivered complete ms. "Brideshead Revisited" to Chapman & Hall. Duplicate for yanks is coming to you as soon as a friend in Oxford [Martin D'Arcy] has vetted it for theological howlers.'[26]

With his book finished, Evelyn was now obliged to join up with 2 SAS for training at one of Bill Stirling's shooting lodges in Perthshire, but before leaving he spent a few nights in London where he found himself strangely (for him at least) rattled by the V-1 flying bomb raids prompted by the recent Allied landings in Normandy. 'I heard one flying near and low and for the first and I hope the last time in my life was frightened,' he recorded. 'Thinking this disagreeable experience over I think it was due to weakening my nerves with drink (I was drinking heavily all those days in London) and have therefore resolved today never to be drunk again.'[27] From Scotland he wrote to Laura: 'I have given up drunkenness for life. Are you pleased or sad? It is a cutting of one of the few remaining strands that held me to human society.'[28]

The new commanding officer of 2 SAS, Brian Franks, evidently had qualms about having Evelyn under his command, however by a stroke of luck news promptly arrived that Randolph Churchill wanted Evelyn to join him in Yugoslavia as part of Fitzroy Maclean's military mission to Tito's Partisans. Maclean had no hesitation in endorsing Randolph's idea, having heard reports of Evelyn's bravery in Crete and believing that his early travels further testified to his enterprise and resilience. Besides, he later admitted, 'here, at last, was someone well qualified to contain Randolph, someone whom, with minor adjustments, he might even regard as his social and intellectual equal'.[29] Maclean was keen to send a new mission to Croatia where Tito's guerrillas were especially hard pressed in their resistance against the occupying Germans, and duly gave instructions for Churchill and Waugh to be infiltrated 'soonest'. Randolph told Evelyn that as his second-in-command he was counting on him 'to heal the Great Schism between the Catholic and Orthodox churches', which was proving a hindrance to his war policy.[30] Evelyn 'accepted eagerly', and after saying goodbye to his family at Pixton and his mother in London, on 4 July he set off on a roundabout journey via Gibraltar and Algiers, where he joined a house party at the British Embassy with the 'wonderfully unambassadorial' Coopers. The other guests included Evelyn's old friend Bloggs Baldwin, Victor Rothschild, Virginia Cowles and the journalist

Martha Gellhorn, a great friend of Diana Cooper's who was by then estranged from her husband Ernest Hemingway and according to Evelyn went about 'stark naked most of the day & very repulsive'.[31]

Evelyn read Gellhorn's novel *Liana* on a chaise-longue but pointedly said nothing about it when he had finished; she later called him 'a small and very ugly turd'.[32] His hostess also commented on how glum he was being. It is possible that he had got wind of the fact that Diana and Bloggs had recently begun a 'lighthearted' affair – a rare occurrence in Diana's life – and was slightly jealous. In any event he responded that he had never been happier, having just written a novel he considered to be a masterpiece, in addition to having a wife he adored, four fine children, splendid health and 'an active life calling him to Yugoslavia with his beloved Randolph . . . I said I wished he could reflect his happiness a little more, Diana recalled. 'He said that other people had said the same.'[33]

From Algiers it was on via Catania, Naples and Bari to the island of Vis off Croatia's coast where Evelyn soon had his first and only encounter with Marshal Tito, whom he instinctively disapproved of for his Communism and anti-Catholic stance. Evelyn had also already decided that the marshal was a woman, his favourite of several rumours that had circulated before the mysterious resistance leader's identity became more widely known. Maclean later recalled introducing the two of them a few days later as Tito emerged from the sea in some very brief swimming trunks. 'Will you please ask Captain Waugh why he thinks I am a woman,' said the marshal. Evelyn did not record this slightly awkward encounter in his diary – which he continued to keep in serene disregard of standing instructions – however he later maintained that Tito's 'bathing dress' left him in no doubt about 'her' sex.

Their next destination was the Partisans' Croat headquarters in the rundown little spa of Topusko, amid a patch of liberated hills and woodland on the mainland, to which they flew under cover of night. But as their Dakota transport came in to land Evelyn was conscious in the darkness of it first descending and then shooting upwards, 'and the next thing I knew was that I was walking in a cornfield by the light of the burning aeroplane talking to a strange British officer about the progress of the war in a detached fashion and that he was saying "You'd better sit down for a bit skipper". I had no recollection of the crash nor, at the time, any knowledge of where I was or why, but a confused idea that we had made a forced landing during some retreat.'[34]

Soon after Evelyn came round he saw Randolph in tears as his servant had been among ten of those on board who had been killed instantly. As Randolph later wrote to Laura, it was 'really providential'[35] that he and Evelyn had survived, given that the plane's engines had stalled at about 400 feet and it burst into flames immediately upon hitting the ground. Both of them had been badly burnt, Evelyn on his head and both hands and legs.

Bandaged like mummies, they were eventually transferred to hospital in Bari and soon visited by Hermione Ranfurly, who was amused by their periodic shouting matches and 'arguments about nothing in particular'.[36] Coote Lygon also came from her nearby WAAF base and recalled Randolph 'creating a fine fuss' about his knee and Evelyn telling her about his recently completed novel, *Brideshead Revisited*, the proofs of which he was eagerly awaiting from his publishers: 'It's all about a family whose father lives abroad, as it might be Boom [Coote's father Lord Beauchamp] – but it's not Boom – and a younger son: people will say he's like Hughie, but you'll see he's not really Hughie – and there's a house as it might be Mad, but it isn't really Mad.'[37]

During Evelyn's subsequent convalescence in Rome he was operated on for a painful abscess on the back of his neck and suffered also from homesickness: 'I feel I have been away many months,' he wrote to Laura, 'tho it is less than two, and long to be with you again.'[38] He saw Diana Cooper and Bloggs Baldwin again and otherwise spent his time visiting churches and art galleries and reading. By mid-September he and Randolph had sufficiently recovered to return to Topusko, where they established their mission in a small farm on the edge of the town, looked after by a hard-worked cook-cum-housekeeper called Zora and a bibulous handyman known as Stari, who had lived for some years in America and replied to their every request with a cheery and unreliable 'Sure, Boss, I'll fix it!'[39] The work of the farm, meanwhile, appeared to Evelyn to be 'mainly in the hands of a little girl of five or so'.[40]

Evelyn made sure to get a bedroom to himself, 'away from Randolph,' he told Laura, 'whose rhetoric in his cups I find a little wearisome'. The spa town's medical baths had lost their windows to the war but were otherwise undamaged, and as Evelyn reported, 'we go there daily & sit in radio-active hot water which I find very enervating. The town has been laid out entirely for leisure, with neglected gardens and woodland promenades reminiscent of Matlock. It suits our leisured life well. We do very little & see little company except a partisan liaison officer, the secretary general of the communist party, the leader of the Peasant party & such people. We also arrange for the evacuation of distressed Jews.'[41]

Evelyn was in 'admirable' health, he reported in a subsequent letter home, and 'my nut very clear – so clear that I hunger to rewrite Mag. Op'. The only available alcohol was a local spirit called *rakia* which to Evelyn stank of somewhere between sewage and glue, so he had little difficulty in sticking to the non-drinking pledge he had made in London. He was thus sleeping unusually well by his standards – 10.30 until 6.30 – however at other times the uninterrupted boisterousness of Randolph was proving a considerable strain. 'The good time of day for me,' he told Laura, 'is the first two hours of daylight before Randolph is awake.'

In mid-October they were joined by Freddy Birkenhead, F. E. Smith's son and Winston Churchill's godson, whom Randolph had fagged for at Eton. Evelyn, too, knew him fairly well and described him to his mother as 'an old friend who is always amusing in a surly & sour way'. But 'more than the pleasure of his company I value him as taking Randolph off my hands a bit'.[42]

Birkenhead was accompanied by Major Stephen Clissold, a 'gentle schoolmaster', as Evelyn described him, besides being a fluent Serbo-Croat speaker and expert on the Partisans. Clissold later remembered the sensation on arrival of finding himself 'in the midst of an old boys' reunion, an unexpected house-party in which I felt something of an intruder', however Evelyn proved an unexpectedly 'affable companion, who did what he could to put me at my ease'.[43]

The tension between Evelyn and Randolph was immediately apparent, though. 'There he is!' roared Randolph as Evelyn returned from meeting the newcomers at the airfield. 'There's the little fellow in his camel-hair dressing-gown!' Evelyn gave Randolph a stare 'cold and hostile as the Arctic Ocean', recalled Birkenhead, 'and remarked with poisonous restraint: "You've got drunk very quickly tonight. Don't send any more signals."'[44]

A week or so later they were all awoken early one morning by cries of 'Avion! Avion!' and the menacing drone of German planes overhead.

Though generally as insanely fearless as Evelyn, Randolph on this occasion became hysterical, convinced that they were being deliberately targeted because of his father. As the others all scrambled for cover in a ditch, Evelyn calmly strolled from the farmhouse wearing a white duffel coat that seemed designed to attract fire. 'You bloody little swine, take off that coat!' yelled Randolph. 'TAKE OFF THAT FUCKING COAT! It's an order! It's a military order!'

Evelyn made a point of keeping the coat on and deliberately took his time lowering himself into the trench, pausing as he did so to remark to Randolph: 'I'll tell you what I think of your repulsive manners when the bombardment is over.' Birkenhead later recalled that Evelyn's behaviour 'endangered all of us'[45] as the mission was sprayed with machine-gun fire and bombs dropped near enough to blow its windows out. However Clissold remembered the raid more nonchalantly as a 'rather ineffectual enemy visitation' during which 'no bomb fell near us'.[46]

In any event Randolph soon became anxious to clear the air and apologised to Evelyn for his sharpness. In an echo of his scorn for the wretched Colonel Colvin on Crete, Evelyn replied: 'My dear Randolph, it wasn't your manners I was complaining of: it was your cowardice.'[47] When Randolph pleaded for kinder treatment Evelyn remained unmoved, explaining to his diary that

> in these matters he is simply a flabby bully who rejoices in blustering and shouting down anyone weaker than himself and starts squealing as soon as he meets anyone as strong. In words he can understand, he can dish it out, but he can't take it . . . The facts are that he is a bore – with no intellectual invention or agility. He has a childlike retentive memory and repetition takes the place of thought. He has set himself very low aims and has not the self-control to pursue them steadfastly. He has no independence of character and his engaging affection comes from this. He is not a good companion for a long period, but the conclusion is always the same – that no one else would have chosen me, nor would anyone else have accepted him. We are both at the end of our tether as far as war work is concerned and must make what we can of it.[48]

In a bid to stem the flow of Randolph's incessant chatter, Evelyn and Freddy bet him £20 that he could not read the Bible in a fortnight, however Randolph proceeded to spend the next two weeks noisily reading quotations aloud or, as Evelyn told Nancy Mitford, 'slapping his side & chortling "God, isn't God a shit!"'[49] In the long run, Evelyn and Randolph's friendship would prove remarkably resilient, however at its lowest point at Topusko Evelyn wrote to Laura: 'I have got to stage of disliking Randolph which is really more convenient than thinking I liked him & constantly trying to reconcile myself to his enormities. Now I can regard him as one of the evils of war like Col. Cutler or Tom Churchill or Roger Wakefield and so live with him more harmoniously.'[50]

Evelyn's relations with Birkenhead were ostensibly more harmonious, Birkenhead later recalling Evelyn as 'friendly and charming' towards him and pathetically grateful for the 100 cigars he had brought with him, along with various replacements for items he had lost in the air crash – two pairs of shoes, a pot of shaving cream, a pair of hairbrushes, razor blades, plus a letter from Laura. However Birkenhead shared Randolph's weakness for the bottle and in the uneasy aftermath of the raid he too began to get on the temporarily abstinent Evelyn's nerves.

'At luncheon Randolph and Freddy became jocular,' Evelyn recorded a couple of days afterwards.

> They do not make new jests or even repeat their own. Of conversation as I love it – a fantasy growing in the telling, apt repartee, argument based on accepted postulates, spontaneous reminiscence and quotation – they know nothing. All their noise and laughter is in the retelling of memorable sayings of their respective fathers or other public figures; even with this vast repertoire they repeat themselves every day or two – sometimes within an hour. They also recite with great zest the more hackneyed passages of Macaulay, the poems of John Betjeman, Belloc, and other classics. I remarked how boring it was to be obliged to tell Randolph everything twice – once when he was drunk, once when he was sober.

A couple of weeks later he told Laura: 'Drunkenness is a very sad thing for the sober. Freddy is fuddled most evenings and, I suppose, just as he was in White's when I thought him the wittiest of Worm friends – now I find him repetitive & trite.'[51]

In the essay he wrote about their time together in Yugoslavia for the collection *Evelyn Waugh and His World* (1973), Birkenhead described

Evelyn in generally affectionate terms. However, possibly prompted by the various unflattering references to himself in Evelyn's published letters and diaries, he later told Hugh Trevor-Roper (himself not a great fan of Evelyn's either) that he had actually thought him 'an odious, indeed a psychopathic character', ruefully adding: 'I should have dealt far more hardly with him had his widow not still then been with us, & had I not wished to avoid, perhaps cravenly, the insane malice of his repulsive son.'[52] Birkenhead also thought that Evelyn's virulent hatred of Communism limited his usefulness as a liaison officer to the Partisans; however Clissold offered a different perspective, recalling Evelyn as 'punctilious in carrying out the duties assigned to him' and commenting that his diaries showed 'a good deal of prescience and insight' about the Partisans' lack of real interest in fighting the Germans as opposed to getting on with their own civil war.[53] Fitzroy Maclean, too, was at pains to stress that Evelyn 'did his job very efficiently' and that overall he had been 'very keen on being a good officer and succeeded in that'. But in any event Evelyn had now had quite enough of soldiering and was longing to go home. 'The war seems to me to have rolled itself in blubber like an Eskimo & settled down for the winter,' he wrote to Laura that November. 'I don't see much hope of getting back before the spring.'[54]

Evelyn's homesickness was exacerbated not just by his weariness of Randolph but also the knowledge that fifty privately printed advance copies of *Brideshead Revisited* had been sent out to his family and friends in England. Evelyn begged Nancy Mitford to tell him 'what everyone says behind my back' while more confidently telling his mother that he expected 'a great success' when the public edition eventually came out the next spring.[55]

While the war rolled on interminably in Yugoslavia the least Evelyn required was a respite from Randolph, a feeling that was evidently mutual, with Randolph cabling that he was 'Waugh-weary'. In early December they got their wish when Evelyn was posted to Dubrovnik to mediate between British troops and the Partisans, with permission also from Fitzroy Maclean to write a report on the subject closest to his heart, the local situation of the Roman Catholic Church.

Christmas in his new posting was spent entirely alone, 'which next to being with you,' he wrote to Laura, 'is what I like best'.[56] It was, he told her, 'a joy to be surrounded by first class architecture again', and though his quarters were in 'a slum' he had a jeep at his disposal, 'an excellent Dalmatian cook', two other servants, plenty of wine and an Alsatian dog.

In the new year reactions to *Brideshead* began to arrive, first of all from Nancy, who wrote reassuringly that she thought it 'a great English classic in my humble opinion' and that she was 'literally dazzled with admiration'. A subsequent postcard informed him that 'people are giving luncheon parties to discuss the book & the Windsors have given it to everyone for Xmas. Rather low-brow circles I fear but still!'[57]

Nancy shared Evelyn's gift for writing letters as if in a gossipy conversation. Hers were sharp, provocative and often very funny. It was a talent that would endear her to Evelyn for the rest of his life; however it also served to highlight the fact that Laura was a far from sparkling correspondent. 'Sweet whiskers,' Evelyn wrote to her,

> do try to write me better letters. Your last, dated 19 December received today, so early expected, was a bitter disappointment. Do realize that a letter need not be a bald chronicle of events; I know you lead a dull life now, my heart bleeds for it, though I believe you could make it more interesting if you had the will. But that is no reason to make your letters as dull as your life. I simply am not interested in Bridget's children. Do grasp that. A letter should be a form of conversation; written as though you were talking to me. For instance you say my Christmas presents have arrived and Eddie is pleased. What do you think of the book? Your copy is still binding but you must have seen his. You know I have not seen one. Tell me what it is like. It is dedicated to you. Are you pleased to see it in this form? Are you curious to know what changes I have made in the final proofs. There are many changes in this copy from what you read before. Can you not see how it disappoints me that this book which I regard as my first important one, and have dedicated to you, should have no comment except that Eddie is pleased with it.[58]

After the unbroken solitude of his Christmas, he celebrated the Orthodox equivalent in early January at what was billed as a tea party, although as he told Nancy, 'One never knows what one will get in this country.' Without a word of greeting from their military hosts the guests were soon served with '(a) Green Chartreuse (b) tea and ham sandwiches (c) cakes and cherry brandy & cigarettes (d) two patriotic speeches. Then it seemed reasonable to think the party was over, but no, in came cold mutton & red wine. It is unsettling at my age.'[59] A few days later Evelyn took pity on an elderly sculptor he had met called Mr Paravacini who was short of food and money. Evelyn commissioned a portrait bust of himself in return for £50 and some rations while he was at work: 'I doubt his ever getting the stone or finishing it,' Evelyn wrote in his diary; 'if he does it will be the next best thing to having myself stuffed.'[60] 'It is very masterly,' he told Laura when the bust was under way, 'rather bad tempered in expression but most forceful like Beethoven rather. It will be a beautiful possession for you – indeed a series of possessions for all as I propose to have it cast in bronze and terra cotta & lead & iron & so forth and to travel with it as Gerry Wellesley used to travel with the bust of his great ancestor. You can imagine what an interest & excitement it has been to me.'[61]

Meanwhile, he felt increasingly worn down, surrounded by 'so many unhappy people who look to me for help which I can ill supply,' he told Laura. 'It seems to comfort them to come & tell me how miserable they are; it saddens me. But is it not odd? Would you have thought of me as having a kind nature? I am renowned for my great kindness here.* At our headquarters in Bari however I am looked on as very troublesome and offensive.'[62]†

Evelyn's latest outrage had been to refuse to be transferred to Trebinje on the grounds that he had not finished his investigations into the Dubrovnik clergy and the alleged killing of fifty-two Roman Catholic priests by Partisans. However a few days later he did obey a command to return to Bari, where he then obtained permission to visit Pope Pius XII in Rome to report on what he had discovered, although His Holiness appeared to grasp almost nothing of what he said. 'The sad thing about the Pope,' Evelyn wrote to Laura after his private audience, 'is that he loves talking English and has learned several elegant little speeches by heart parrot-wise & delivers them with practically no accent, but he

---

* After the war, one of those who served with Evelyn in Dubrovnik wrote to his MP from Yugoslavia to say how he was 'known and loved by a surprising number of civilians here, for his efforts on their behalf' (Signalman Leslie John Murphy to Lieutenant-Colonel Sir Thomas Moore, 20 September 1945, cited in Donat Gallagher, *In the Picture*, p. 265).
† Evelyn's immediate superior in Bari, Major John Clarke, later recalled having had his life made hell by Maclean's 'incredibly stupid' decision to send Evelyn to Dubrovnik 'to tickle up the RC clergy' and that he 'stirred up a hornet's nest' (Frank McLynn, *Fitzroy Maclean*, p. 245).

does not understand a word of the language.' When Evelyn had finished expounding on the desperate plight of the Dubrovnik clergy, the Pope 'made a little English speech, inopportunely the one he keeps for sailors telling them how much he enjoyed a naval review at Portsmouth in 1920 something'.[63] A week after his audience Evelyn left Rome with his report on the Church in Croatia half written and flew via Naples to London, arriving there on 15 March.

Evelyn's report on 'Church and State in Liberated Croatia' eventually ran to some 7,500 words. It was first presented to Fitzroy Maclean, who pronounced it to be 'reasonably fair'; however when Evelyn tried to circulate it further the Permanent Under-Secretary of the Foreign Office, Sir Orme Sargent, sternly forbade it, seeing it as blatant propaganda against the British government's policy of support for Marshal Tito. All that Evelyn managed in the end was to get a question asked in the House of Commons in May about what measures were being taken to protect the Croat Catholics, to which the Foreign Secretary, Anthony Eden, replied that such matters fell outside the British government's responsibilities and must remain those of the Yugoslav state.

Observers far more sympathetic to Tito and the Partisans accused Evelyn of bias in his report and of omitting evidence that Catholic priests had collaborated with the Ustaše terrorists who supported the Italians during the fascist occupation of Yugoslavia. Evelyn freely admitted that some Catholic priests had been guilty of horrific crimes, but insisted that such cases were rare. In any event, even allowing for the possibility of bias on his part, the persistent ill-treatment of priests in post-war Yugoslavia would show his diagnosis of Communist persecution of the Catholic Church to be broadly correct. Evelyn meanwhile remained a fierce critic of Tito, and when Eden invited him to Britain on a state visit in 1952 at the height of the Cold War, he wrote an article angrily denouncing 'Our Guest of Dishonour'.

20

....

The Occupation

The war had been frustrating and disillusioning for Evelyn, however the change of habit had at least stimulated him as an artist and he had written two fine novels, the latest of which was about to make him rich ('stinking rich', he assured Laura) and famous. *Brideshead Revisited* was published at the end of May 1945, three weeks after VE Day. Evelyn was quite sure at the time that it was his most important work, his 'magnum opus' as he had called it ever since he started writing it in February 1944. 'For the first time since 1928,' he told Nancy Mitford, 'I am eager about a book.'[1]

Not all his friends enjoyed it, Katharine Asquith being prominent among those who did not, however reactions to his privately bound advance copies were mostly very positive. Like Evelyn, Graham Greene would later revise his opinion, however at first he rated it even better than *Work Suspended*, his previous favourite. Another Catholic friend, Daphne Acton, was 'ecstatic in her praise', Martin D'Arcy reported, while Ronnie Knox was 'at first antagonistic' but later 'in tears over the deathbed scene, & by the last chapter an ardent convert'.[2] The future Catholic convert Penelope Betjeman wrote: 'I think it is as good as Madame Bovary.'[3]

Among non-Catholic friends the unsurprising consensus was that there was 'too much Catholic stuff'.[4] Yet even the irreligious and increasingly egalitarian Henry Yorke,* who confessed to finding *Brideshead*'s subject matter deeply distasteful, could only conclude that 'to my mind you carry

---

* Henry Yorke/Green's most recent novel, *Loving*, published two months before *Brideshead*, was also about the country house in decline yet so different in perspective that Evelyn privately described it as an 'obscene book about domestic servants' and lamented that his friend had become a 'fierce proletarian convert'. 31 March 1945; *EWD*, p. 624; EW to Patrick Kinross, 1 August 1945; AWA.

out what you set out to do better than any English writer now writing'.[5] Meanwhile Nancy reported that Raymond Mortimer had pronounced it a 'Great English classic' and Cyril Connolly had found it 'impossible to put down'.[6]

Connolly, though, was also among those who did not care for some of the 'purple passages', an opinion that Evelyn would later come to share. In his preface to the 1960 edition, he explained that *Brideshead* had been written during 'a bleak period of present privation and threatening disaster – the period of soya beans and Basic English – and in consequence the book is enthused with a kind of gluttony, for food and wine, for the splendours of the recent past, and for rhetorical and ornamental language which now, with a full stomach, I find distasteful'.[7]

After the book was published in May, the first letter of congratulation Evelyn received was a typically extravagant outpouring from Harold Acton, who claimed to have 'slid my paperknife through the still virginal pages like an itching bridegroom and was panting, trembling and exhausted by the time I had finished cutting them'.

After he had caught his breath and begun reading the book, Acton had been

> swept alternatively by pleasure and pain: pleasure at your ever-increasing virtuosity and mastery of our fast-evaporating language, for there are subtler nuances of prose in this than perhaps any of your writings; pain, at the acrid memories of so many old friends you have conjured, with accompanying passion which I am surprised to find still smouldering in my bosom after all those years. It is the only successful evocation of the period that I know. But like the period itself, it leaves a melancholy dirge-like aftertaste. So far one has survived, but for how long and into what?[8]

Among the early newspaper reviews, the *Manchester Guardian* was predictably prejudiced against *Brideshead*'s subject matter while conceding 'the brilliance of his writing'.[9] The *Times Literary Supplement* questioned whether Evelyn had managed to trace the workings of divine purpose with any 'marked clarity' and thought 'the decorations of the tale' were devised to better advantage than the working out of his overall theme. Reservations were also expressed about what seemed to be the author's excessive reverence for the aristocracy. The *New Statesman* found

Brideshead 'deeply moving in its theme and its design' and 'a fine and brilliant book', yet suggested that 'a burden of respect for the peerage and Eton, which those who belong to the former or have been to the latter, seem able to lightly discard, weighs heavily on him'.[10] Even more damning was Edmund Wilson's assessment in *The New Yorker* early the next year: 'Waugh's snobbery, hitherto held in check by his satirical point of view, has here emerged shameless and rampant . . . his cult of high nobility is allowed to become so rapturous and solemn that it finally gives the impression of being the only real religion in the book.'[11]

Wilson was America's pre-eminent critic at the time and had previously singled out Evelyn as 'the only first-class comic genius that has appeared in England since Bernard Shaw'.[12] Given his antipathy towards both Catholicism and conservatism, *Brideshead* was always going to be less to his liking than Evelyn's earlier books; however he may also have felt that he had a score to settle, having been teased mercilessly by Evelyn at Cyril Connolly's table about his failure to find a British publisher for his recent novel on the grounds of obscenity. The next day Evelyn recorded in his diary having 'chucked an appointment to show London to insignificant yank named Edmund Wilson'.[13]

Evelyn shrugged off Wilson's criticisms and in any case could argue that the various aristocratic characters in his book were never sanctified and mostly decidedly flawed. It was also a gratifying irony for him that 'the age of the common man' ushered in by the post-war anti-elitism also fuelled nostalgia for the disappearing aristocratic way of life that made *Brideshead* such a spectacular bestseller. The first edition sold out in the first week of publication in Britain, and in America the book quickly sold more than half a million copies.[14] When it was made America's Book of the Month in July Evelyn calculated that it was worth '£10,000 down and a probable £10,000 from ordinary sales and cinema rights',[15] and he began to look forward to an annual income of at least £25,000 over the next five years.

But the satisfaction he had always taken in making money was soon competing with the fear of losing it in tax, especially after the post-war general election victory of the Labour Party, whose government Evelyn was soon referring to as 'the Attlee terror'[16] or simply 'the Occupation'.[17]

The pleasure he took in things going wrong, particularly for self-important politicians, meant that at first he found much to enjoy in the shock result.* Having failed to persuade Laura to come up from the country for Ann Rothermere's election night party, he reported afterwards that 'although the champagne was exiguous & the vodka watery the spectacle of consternation as details of the massacre spread was a strong intoxicant'.[18] But as the establishment of what he called 'Welfaria' got under way, he began to reflect miserably on what he saw as the new regime's commitment to obliterate all class distinctions, getting rid of a structure which for Evelyn lay at the very heart of English culture and which 'influenced, and often determined, all social and personal relations' and had grown over the centuries 'so complex that no foreigner and few natives could completely comprehend it'.[19] He contended that during his lifetime England had changed from being one of the most beautiful countries in the world to being one of the ugliest, adding that: 'German bombs have made but a negligible addition to the sum of our own destructiveness. It is arguable that the entire process is traceable to the decay of aristocratic domination.'[20]

Among those who had been newly elected as MPs, Evelyn saw Christopher Hollis and Hugh Fraser (with whom he got along better than with his brother Shimi Lovat) as 'the hope of the Catholics';[21] Randolph Churchill, meanwhile, was among those of his friends who had failed to win seats. Unable to move back into Piers Court until September and unwilling to live even temporarily at Pixton, Evelyn arranged to go and stay with Randolph, with whom he was by then reconciled, at Ickleford in Hertfordshire. Evelyn found Randolph 'crestfallen but not crushed' by his election defeat,[22] although he had also recently separated from his wife Pamela and the only furniture in his rented old rectory were odd bits that she had left behind. 'The plan is to stay until White's reopens,' Evelyn noted in his diary, 'but I am not confident that we shall live harmoniously so long.'[23] Anywhere was preferable to living with his in-laws, however, and he remained there on and off throughout August, joined for the last two weeks by Bron, who was just short of his sixth birthday and a potential playmate for Randolph's slightly younger son Winston.

After a few days Evelyn told Laura that his son's visit had been 'an unqualified success', adding that he had so far 'behaved admirably and won

---

* Evelyn never voted himself, explaining: 'I do not aspire to advise my sovereign in her choice of servants.' *The Spectator*, 2 October 1959; *EAR*, p. 537.

golden opinions on every side'. However when he took him to London to stay with his grandmother and show him some sights, Evelyn reported:

> I have regretfully come to the conclusion that the boy Auberon is not yet a suitable companion for me. Yesterday was a day of supreme self-sacrifice. I fetched him from Highgate, took him up the dome of St. Pauls, gave him a packet of triangular stamps, took him to luncheon at the Hyde Park Hotel, took him on the roof of the hotel, took him to Harrods & let him buy vast quantities of toys (down to your account) took him to tea with Maimie who gave him a pound and a box of matches, took him back to Highgate, in a state (myself not the boy) of extreme exhaustion. My mother said 'Have you had a lovely day?' He replied 'A bit dull'. So that is the last time for some years I inconvenience myself for my children. You might rub that in to him.[24]

Evelyn and Laura finally moved back into Piers Court two weeks later after almost exactly six years away, leaving the children at Pixton while they put the house back in order. 'Arrived on a grey, fly-infested, heavy evening with a hangover and the excitement of homecoming contending,' Evelyn recorded. 'At first sight the garden was rank, the paths lost, the trees stunted or overgrown irregularly; inside everything damp but superficially tidy. Slept ill.' The next day he wrote: 'Nuns half out, ourselves half in. Laura saying how perfect everything looked, I detecting losses and damage everywhere.'[25]

Evelyn later admitted to having returned home with 'many sentimental tremors' only to find that 'my love for it was quite dead, as so many soldiers found about their wives but not me thank God'.[26] Yet within a week the tanks were full enough for a hot bath, his library was back in order and he had begun to resume his pre-war routine. 'It is delightful to be writing to you again on Piers Court paper,' he told his mother,

> at my own writing table face to face with Queen Victoria in bronze and George III in paint. We have had an arduous week moving in. The nuns left things superficially clean and in as good condition as one could expect after six years school-use, but all the furniture was misplaced, moths had ravaged carpets, paint has gone and innumerable small breakages come to light daily. The water supply had been diverted from the village and is only

slowly returning; our first two or three days we could not light the boilers and had to carry all water up in buckets from the well. The garden is in poor shape, many paths entirely lost, but the trees & hedges well grown & the quinces, in particular, bearing well. The stables have been repaired after their collapse.[27]

It took several months to reassemble their household staff and for much of that autumn they were reliant on Laura's somewhat erratic cooking and housework, 'vague but pertinacious' as Evelyn described it. 'Little Laura and I live alone here in circumstances of very grave austerity,' he told Maimie. 'We have 27 hens which lay sometimes 3, more often 2 eggs a day and keep L. L. constantly busy cramming them with rich foods. She and I live on dry bread & vintage port . . .'.[28] To Randolph he reported: 'Laura broods despondently over the kitchen range and periodically raises columns of black smoke, announces that our meat ration has been incinerated, and drives me to dinner at a neighbouring inn.'[29]

The return of the butler Ellwood in mid-November was evidently an uplifting event: 'silver, boots, and furniture shine,' purred Evelyn. Less so was the arrival of Teresa and Bron just before Christmas. 'By keeping the children in bed for long periods we managed to have a tolerable day,' Evelyn recorded. 'The children leave for Pixton on the 10th. Meanwhile I have my meals in the library.'[30] Shortly after New Year 1946 he wrote to Diana Cooper:

I have my two eldest children here, a boy and a girl; two girls languish at Pixton; a fifth leaps in the womb. I abhor their company because I can only regard children as defective adults, hate their physical ineptitude, find their jokes flat and monotonous. Both are considered great wits by their contemporaries. The elder girl has a precocious taste for theology which promises well for a career as Abbess; the boy is mindless and obsessed with social success. I will put him into the Blues [the Royal Horse Guards] later, meanwhile he goes to boarding school at the end of the month with the keenest expectation of delight.[31]

Six when he was packed off to prep school, Bron later recalled: 'Papa's best practical joke was played in my first term when I was still very nervous. He told me he proposed to change his name to Stinkbottom. When he had done so, the headmaster would summon the school together and say: "Boys, the person you have hitherto called Waugh will in future be called Stinkbottom." School assembly was held every morning, and every morning I felt a slight tightening of the chest as Mr Dix came forward to make his morning announcements.'[32]

*   *   *

After the war Evelyn had begun working on a new novel about St Helena, the research for which entailed 'a very interesting correspondence with Mrs. Betjeman about horses & sex', he told Nancy Mitford. Evelyn had first met Penelope Chetwode in the early 1930s staying with the Pakenhams in Ireland when she was engaged to John Betjeman. Fresh from his lessons at Captain Hance's equitation academy, Evelyn was very keen to go riding with the gamine Penelope but she had taken the Pakenhams' only good horse and his mount, an unbroken and completely unmanageable bay cob, promptly carted him off at a gallop towards Lough Derravaragh. When Penelope followed she came across the horse grazing calmly by the lake and heard Evelyn calling her from the branch of a tree where he had eventually been deposited. It was the start of a great friendship, admiring of his bravery and literary genius on her part, flirtatious and at times boldly suggestive on his. 'Be a good girl about this,' he wrote from Abyssinia in 1935 when asking for information about the mysterious Mr Rickett, 'and I will reward you with a fine fuck when I get back.'[33]

If this sounds like a joke or at least wishful thinking on Evelyn's part, he was later said to have complained to Osbert Lancaster in a moment of bitterness, 'She always laughs when I come'.[34] For her part Penelope recalled being alarmed when he made advances on her both before and after her marriage, maintaining that 'he never attracted me in the very least'.[35] Years later, shortly before Evelyn died, Auberon asked him whether he had ever been to bed with Lady Betjeman, to which he replied, 'Since you ask, yes.'[36]

Whether or not this was a tease, Evelyn clearly found Penelope attractive and given that John Betjeman almost certainly knew this, Evelyn's letter to him in May 1945, explaining that he was modelling the Empress Helena's early life on the horse-mad Penelope's own 'hipporastic' experiences, bordered on the sadistic: 'She [Helena] is 16, sexy, full of horse

273

fantasies. I want to get this right. Will you tell her [Penelope] to write to me fully about adolescent sex reveries connected with riding. I have no experience of such things, nor has Laura. I make her always the horse & the consummation when the rider subdues her. Is this correct? Please make her explain. And is riding enough or must she be driven? Are spurs important or only leather-work?'[37]

After hearing nothing, Evelyn eventually asked Penelope directly: 'I describe her as hunting in the morning after her wedding night feeling the saddle as comforting her wounded maidenhead. Is that O.K.? After that she has no interest in sex . . .'[38] Penelope had by then read an extract of Evelyn's work in progress in *The Tablet* and replied that she thought the descriptions of Helena hunting 'very good but whatever will Fr Darcy say?'. She further confided that 'my first experiments in horse sex were when I drove my donkey round the pine-woods at Aldershot in father's cavalry bit when I was 11', and that she had 'found it very difficult to separate sex & religion after I married & frequently used to drive a severely-bitted carriage horse in flights of fancy with an Anglo or Roman priest seated at my side. Couldn't the Empress take great pleasure in driving a Druid about in a chariot? . . . Pray consign this to your kitchen boiler when studied.'[39]

Aside from Evelyn's nosy questions about his wife, John Betjeman also had to put up with regular barrages about his own religious views. 'I have been painfully shocked by a brochure named "Five Sermons by Laymen",' Evelyn wrote to him just before Christmas 1946:

Last time I met you you told me you did not believe in the Resurrection. Now I find you expounding Protestant devotional practices from the pulpit. This WILL NOT DO . . . Your ecclesiastical position is entirely without reason. You cannot possibly be right. Marxist Atheists might be. Zealous protestants may be (i.e. it is possible to say that from the word go the Church was all wrong & had misunderstood everything Our Lord told them, & that it required a new Divine Dispensation in the sixteenth century to put people on the right track again. That is just possible.) What is inconceivable is that Christ was made flesh in order to found a Church, that He canalized his Grace in the sacraments, that He gave His promise to abide in the Church to the end of time, that He saw the Church as a human corporation, part of his Mystical Body, one with the Saints triumphant – and then to point to a handful of homosexual curates and say: 'That is the true Church.'[40]

On the point of going over to Rome herself, Penelope Betjeman was as keen as Evelyn was for her husband to convert to Catholicism, however she worried that Evelyn went too far, and in April 1947 she told him that John was 'in a dreadful state he thinks you are the devil and wakes up in the middle of the night and raves and says he will leave me at once if I go over'. Two months later she wrote: 'The ONLY thing is to leave him alone at present. He has dreadful persecution mania where Catholics are concerned . . .'[41] Evelyn replied: 'I am by nature a bully and a scold, and John's pertinacity in error brings out all that is worst in me. I am very sorry. I will lay off him in future.'[42] Two months later, Evelyn recorded in his diary: 'To Farnborough to make my peace with the Betjemans. Successful in this . . . Penelope seems resolved to enter the church in the autumn and John to desert her when she does so.'[43]

* * *

Another long-standing friend who was regularly put through the mill was Cyril Connolly. The commercial success of *Brideshead* meant that Evelyn could now afford to pick and choose what journalism he did, however in the autumn of 1945 when Douglas Woodruff at *The Tablet* asked if he might like to supply a 'trenchant' review of Connolly's *The Unquiet Grave*, Evelyn obliged with a piece which, as he cheerfully told Nancy Mitford, 'shook out a few feathers'[44] and might well have ended their friendship had Connolly not sensibly refrained from reacting.

Evelyn and Connolly had been on-off friends since Oxford. Evelyn greatly admired him as a critic – as well he might, given that Connolly was one of his most consistent champions – was fond of him as a drinking companion and realised they had much in common besides their shared literary, artistic and epicurean interests, both being easily bored, notoriously moody, unpredictable and at times spectacularly rude. Yet Connolly's all too evident wariness of Evelyn also made him the recurrent butt of his bullying, and he was relentlessly teased for his left-wing opinions and castigated for his laziness and lack of religion. 'Connolly has many injuries to revenge,' Evelyn admitted in 1951 when he heard that he was researching a profile of him for *Time* magazine. 'I can't blame him if he takes the opportunity.' But he warned him that when the piece appeared (it never did), 'I shall horse-whip you on the steps of White's'.[45]

Reviewing *Enemies of Promise* in 1938, Evelyn had described Connolly as the only man under forty who showed any signs of raising literary criticism to an art form, yet tore into the book as 'structurally jerry-built'.[46] *The Unquiet Grave* had already been widely acclaimed as a potential classic, however Evelyn, while acknowledging that the book contained sentences 'as beautiful as any passages of modern English prose that I know', suggested that Connolly had been 'duped and distracted by the chatter of psychoanalysts' and that he had given 'full rein to the tosh-horse whose hooves thunder through the penultimate passages'.[47] When Nancy had first sent Evelyn the book in Yugoslavia in 1944, he reported back that the passages about Christianity in particular were 'real twaddle' and concluded that 'Connolly has lived too much with communist young ladies. He <u>must</u> spend more time in White's.'[48]

White's remained the place that Evelyn chose to spend most of his time whenever he was in London, and in March 1946 a friend there, Mervyn Griffith-Jones, a former comrade in No. 8 Commando and now a prosecutor at Nuremberg, invited him to attend the trials as an observer. The ancient Bavarian city had been almost completely destroyed by Allied bombs in the final months of the war and Evelyn found 'a waste of corpse-scented rubble with a handful of middle-aged, middle-class Germans in Homburg hats picking their way through ruins. We drove to the Sports Palace which is intact but probably due for demolition – typical modern functional magnificence designed for mass parades, now full of German Jews in American uniforms photographing one another in the act of giving the Nazi salute from Hitler's rostrum.'[49]

He observed the next day's court proceedings as a VIP, sitting in the front row of the gallery and watching the various high-ranking Nazis as they came and went from the dock. Göring had 'much of Tito's matronly appeal', Evelyn told Randolph Churchill, while Ribbentrop looked 'like a seedy schoolmaster being ragged. He knows he doesn't know the lesson and he knows the boys know.'[50]

Always fascinated by the macabre, after the court rose for the day Evelyn 'went to see the room where a French Jew keeps lampshades of human skin, shrunken heads, soap said to be made of corpses and so forth'. After two days he had had enough of listening to legal arguments and flew on to stay with the Coopers in Paris, where Duff had recently become Ambassador. Evelyn initially surprised everyone with his mellow mood, but soon set about baiting the other guests, treating Julian Huxley as 'a crypto-Communist zoo-keeper with no interest in life beyond the diet of his panda' and describing Peter Quennell to Diana in terms 'so foetid and sinister,' she recalled, 'that it will colour most unfairly my sentiments for him'.[51] 'Poor Wu,' she wrote to Conrad Russell afterwards, '– he does everything he can to alienate himself from the affection he is yearning for.'[52] Also at the embassy was his brother-in-law Auberon Herbert, and when he left for Brussels Diana implored Evelyn to follow him downstairs and tell him that he liked him. 'He believed it,' Evelyn noted in his diary.[53]

In June that year Evelyn went to Spain with Douglas Woodruff to attend a centenary celebration of 'a Thomist philosopher whose name escapes me' (Francisco de Vitoria), the inspiration for his novella *Scott-King's Modern Europe*, arriving back on 2 July two days after Laura had given birth to their sixth (fifth surviving) child, James.

At the end of that year Duckworth published a compilation of Evelyn's travel writing, *When the Going Was Good*, with a preface promising that 'my own travelling days are over'. However there would soon be more expeditions, including to Scandinavia the next year to write two travel pieces for *The Daily Telegraph*, and several visits to the United States. The first of these took place in early 1947 after Metro-Goldwyn-Mayer offered an all-expenses-paid trip for himself and Laura to Hollywood to discuss a possible film treatment of *Brideshead Revisited*. The handsome terms that Peters negotiated on Evelyn's behalf were that he would be paid $2,000 (more than $20,000 in today's money) a week throughout their stay, which in the end lasted over two months, with the promise of an eventual $140,000 ($1.5 million) if a film deal was agreed, minus whatever MGM had already spent.

Peters was understandably nervous at the prospect of Evelyn's visit given his frequently declared hostility to 'the bloody yanks', who embodied so much of what he hated about the modern world. In February 1946 Evelyn had written to Maimie Lygon: 'My book has been a great success in the United States which is upsetting because I thought it in good taste before and now I know it can't be.'[54] Worse than the popular applause was the fan mail that came in its wake. 'I have momentarily become an object of curiosity to Americans,' he wrote in an article that spring for *Life* magazine, 'and I find that they believe that my friendship and confidence are included in the price of my book.' Some of the correspondence was not so friendly: 'An offensive letter from a female American Catholic,' Evelyn noted in his diary in March. 'I returned it to her husband with the note: "I shall be grateful if you will use whatever disciplinary means are customary in your country to refrain your wife from writing impertinent letters to men she does not know."'[55]

The *Life* piece gave Evelyn the opportunity of 'answering collectively all the inquiries I have received', but he also used it as a wider statement of his artistic aims and to respond to a few of the more pointed criticisms, including the charge of snobbery. 'Class-consciousness, particularly in England, has been so much inflamed nowadays that to mention a nobleman is like mentioning a prostitute sixty years ago. The new prudes say, "No doubt such people do exist but we would sooner not hear about them." I reserve the right to deal with the kind of people I know best.'[56]

Before Evelyn set off for America, Peters warned him from New York: 'I must tell you that you have the reputation here – both at M.G.M. and everywhere else – of being a difficult, tetchy, irritating and rude customer. I hope you will surprise and confound them all by behaving like an 18th century ambassador from the Court of St. James's. They are children; and they should receive the tolerance and understanding that you show to children. You would (I hope, will) be surprised by the result.'[57] Evelyn replied calmly that 'I mean to do business with the Californian savages if it is possible . . . I am sure Matson [Evelyn's New York agent] and his fellow countrymen are, as you say, just little boys at heart, but I believe little boys should be very frequently whipped and sent to bed supperless.'[58]

Evelyn and Laura sailed for New York on 25 January 1947 shortly after an unsuccessful operation for piles which put him in a foul mood on arrival, when he was soon inveighing against the 'tasteless' food at the Waldorf Astoria, wine ruined by 'bad cellarage' and electric shocks every time he touched something metal. He objected to the talkative taxi drivers ('It's an outrage to be charged for such boredom')[59], the chewing of gum and the habit of smoking between courses. As for New York's famous tall buildings, he wrote to Diana Cooper: 'They are nothing nothing nothing at their best. At their worst, that is to say when they attempt any kind of ornament they are actively wicked. Compare them with the kind of things you have at your doorstep – Horse Guards Parade, Banqueting House, St Martin-in-the-Fields, Westminster Abbey – or what I have within a five mile radius of Stinkers. Think of the infinity of aesthetic problems which a real architect has to solve every yard – and then of these great booby boxes. Interiors <u>all</u> vile.'[60]

At least Laura appeared to be enjoying herself and she managed to get through $2,000 'in a very few minutes' when let loose in an expensive dress shop. After four days they continued their journey aboard the sumptuous 20th-Century train to Chicago, then onwards to Pasadena, where they arrived on the morning of 6 February to be met by a car from MGM to take them to the Bel Air Hotel. Alec Waugh later described what he had heard of Evelyn's arrival in California: 'The sun was shining, tropical flowers were in bloom, all the young people were dressed in shorts and slacks and open shirts and there was Evelyn in a stiff white collar and a bowler hat, carrying a rolled umbrella.'[61] As Harold Acton, who also happened to be in Los Angeles at the time, observed, adaptability was not among Evelyn's traits.

The next day Evelyn went to the vast MGM studios in Culver City, where he was less than elated to learn that their proposed screenwriter was Keith Winter, whom Evelyn 'last knew as Willie Maugham's catamite at Villefranche' as he ominously noted in his diary.[62] On that occasion in 1931 the twenty-four-year-old Winter had been staying at the same hotel as the two Waugh brothers and when Somerset Maugham asked the three young men to dine, Winter ended up spending the night and returned the next day looking very pleased with himself. 'Willie told him how well he used his fingers,' Alec Waugh recalled, 'which made me think of Strickland in the *Moon and Sixpence*, who often despised the people he was enjoying.'[63] Evelyn had taken a strong dislike to Winter then, refusing to speak to him except through the intermediary of Patrick Balfour, and he appeared to like him no better this time around. 'He wore local costume,' Evelyn disdainfully recorded, 'a kind of loose woollen blazer, matelot's vest, buckled shoes. He has been in Hollywood for years and sees *Brideshead* purely as a love story.'

As none of the Americans showed much interest in the book's theological implications the discussions they had over its filming were, as far as Evelyn was concerned, 'futile',[64] although he found 'something a little luxurious in talking in great detail about every implication of a book which the others are paid to know thoroughly'.[65] There was plenty too that was luxurious about MGM's hospitality, which even Evelyn conceded was 'consistently munificent', so he felt 'well content and, as soon as the danger of the film was disposed of, almost serene also'. Laura, meanwhile, 'grew smarter and younger and more popular daily and was serenely happy'.[66]

Besides Harold Acton, who was visiting his American bachelor uncle and benefactor and chanced to meet Evelyn at the Huntington Museum, they also saw Randolph Churchill, who was in the midst of a hectic lecture tour: 'I thought he could never shock me any more but he did,' Evelyn wrote to Peters. 'Brutishly drunk all the time, soliciting respectable women at luncheon parties etc. His lecture, to which we went at Pasadena, was surprisingly good considering the grave condition he was in.'[67]

By March Evelyn was able to tell Peters they were having a surprisingly agreeable time and, contrary to expectations, had been enjoying a 'gay & refined'[68] social life, having befriended Merle Oberon, visited Walt Disney's studios and been taken to supper with Charlie Chaplin by Iris Tree. 'I was thus able to pay my homage to the two artists [Disney and Chaplin] of the place,' Evelyn noted in his diary.[69]

They also saw a lot of the English portrait painter Simon Elwes, an old friend who was visiting Los Angeles with his wife Golly (Peter Rodd's sister). The Elweses' hostess Andrea Cowdin had the Waughs to lunch or dinner every day, took them with her to parties and introduced them to 'all the most agreeable people at her house', Evelyn recorded.[70] Another member of the English colony, Sir Charles Mendl (married to the decorator Elsie de Wolfe) took them to tea with Anna May Wong and lunch with Aldous Huxley, the latter possibly an awkward encounter given that a decade earlier Evelyn had torn into Huxley's novel *Eyeless in Gaza* in a review in *The Tablet*.[71] But they would at least have been able to discuss their shared fascination with Forest Lawn Memorial Park, a cemetery in Glendale that Evelyn had recently discovered and quickly recognised as 'a deep mine of literary gold'.[72]

'I am entirely obsessed with Forest Lawns,' Evelyn wrote to Peters, 'I go there two or three times a week, am on easy terms with the chief embalmer & next week am to lunch with DR HUBERT EATON [the founder] himself. It is an entirely unique place – the only thing in California that is not a copy of something else. It is wonderful literary raw material. Aldous flirted with it in *After Many A Summer* but only with the superficialities. I am at the heart of it. It will be a *very* good story.'[73]

After numerous visits to this extraordinary 300-acre site Evelyn claimed to have become 'something very like friends' with the embalmer, Mr Howells, 'who gives the "personality smile" to the embalmed corpse',[74] each of which was euphemistically referred to at Forest Lawn as 'the loved one'. Evelyn's rapport with the original of Mr Joyboy at Whispering Glades was such that he had 'seen dozens of loved ones half painted before the bereaved family saw them'.[75] With its sentimental sugaring-over of the reality of death, Forest Lawn was for Evelyn the perfect embodiment of the meaningless paganism and general fakery at the heart of the American dream. And while the $140,000 *Brideshead* film deal never materialised, like Dennis Barlow at the end of *The Loved One* he returned from Holly-wood carrying 'the artist's load, a great, shapeless chunk of experience'.

But although he had found American society unexpectedly charming, not all of American society had been charmed by him. Among the Waughs' hosts in New York had been two of Evelyn's former American agents with whom he had quarrelled in the 1930s, Carl Brandt and his wife Carol, formerly Carol Hill. Carol, whom Evelyn privately deemed 'a woman of no intellectual interests . . . a secretary raised to its highest power',[76] later told Peters that she had found Evelyn 'delightful, gracious and appreciative in every sense of the word. But I must say we seem to be alone in this land of sunshine.' She was by then MGM's New York story editor and accompanied the Waughs to Los Angeles, so knew all about Evelyn's dealings there: 'I truly think that people here have tried to be friendly and gracious,' she wrote, 'both in terms of the usual dinners and in terms of work, but Evelyn has been so constantly arrogant and rude apparently as to have left a trail of bloody but unbowed heads behind him. Some of this, I gather, has been utter mischief on his part and some of it has been complete misunderstanding of his particular variety of humor and wit.'[77]

Among those immune to Evelyn's charms was Billy Wilder's screen-writing partner Charles Brackett, who met him at a party held in his honour by the director George Cukor (later, incidentally, buried at Forest Lawn). Amid a gathering that included Greta Garbo and Olivia de Hav-illand, it was perhaps hardly surprising that Brackett found the Waughs 'very unprepossessing' by comparison, describing them as 'a bank clerk and his snuffly wife, an ill-favoured tailor's dummy with halitosis and a blue-eyed Elsa Lanchester part'. Brackett returned later to Cukor's to find that 'in my absence Waugh had sent his wife home, dismissed her in a rude way which impressed everyone unpleasantly'.[78]

If not perhaps in that instance, Evelyn's rudeness often began as a tease to help liven things up, or else it was a bracingly forthright statement of how he actually felt. But it was not always easy to tell which. Igor Stravinsky had lunch with Evelyn in New York in 1949 and remarked afterwards: 'Whether Mr Waugh was disagreeable, or only preposterously arch, I cannot say.' When Stravinsky attempted found some common ground by talking about his own recent sung Mass, Evelyn replied: 'All music is positively painful to me.'[79] Which happened to be true.

Much of Evelyn's humour clearly did get lost in translation, however even the English colony sometimes failed to appreciate his jokes, David Niven for instance taking strong exception to having his black housekeeper referred to in her presence as 'your native bearer'.[80] Evelyn knew perfectly well that he was rarely at his best with strangers of any nationality, and of how offensive he could be, even to his own wife. When Gilbert Pinfold asks 'Why does everyone except me find it so easy to be nice?',[81] Evelyn was clearly speaking about himself. In Italy Harold Acton recalled his spectacular rudeness in restaurants and his sublime remark to the director of the British Institute, Francis Toye, who had a way of standing too close: 'If you want to kiss me please get it over quickly.' Invited to a tea party as guest of honour, Evelyn spent the entire time handing round the tea and cakes, explaining to his hostess, 'I'd much rather do this than have to talk'. When Baby Jungman told him how much a cousin of hers had enjoyed *Brideshead*, Evelyn thought it best to warn her: 'I am sure you will have fully explained to him how disappointing I am to meet. Writers should be heard and not seen . . . Writers should stay in their burrows. I intend to anyway until the ferrets come for me.'[82]

*　*　*

When they arrived back in England shortly before Easter, Laura headed straight down to Pixton and the children, while Evelyn, evidently less eager for this family reunion, spent five days in London then went with Simon Elwes to Downside for a four-day retreat before eventually joining Laura, Teresa and Bron at Piers Court on Easter Day. Two weeks later Evelyn recorded: 'Laura is busy and happy with agriculture and has lost all her Californian chic.'[83] Shortly afterwards he went to Ireland, where he had been toying with the idea of buying a castle to escape the socialist regime and his boredom with Gloucestershire social life. 'If only country neighbours would talk like Jane Austen characters about gossip & hobbies,' he wrote to Nancy. 'Instead they all want to know about Molotov & de Gaulle . . . I am anxious to emigrate, Laura to remain & face the century of the common man. She is younger, braver & less imaginative than I. If only they would start blowing the place up with their atoms.'[84] By mid-May he was back again at his writing desk at Piers Court.

The first thing he wrote about his Hollywood experiences was 'an article on Death for *Life*',[85] as he described it, 2,500 words on Forest Lawn and its founder Dr Eaton, 'the first man to offer eternal salvation at an inclusive charge as part of his undertaking service', as Evelyn put it.[86] On 21 May he began work on *The Loved One* and by early September he was able to send a first draft to Peters asking his advice on 'what form it should take in its public appearances in USA and England'.[87]

Uncharacteristically po-faced in this instance, Peters replied that 'being perfectly frank' the question was rather 'whether it should make any public appearance at all'. 'I found parts of it very amusing, of course; but parts were to me revolting, and my over-riding conviction when I had finished the story was that it was not worthy of Evelyn Waugh . . . It seems to be one of those ideas that is extremely amusing in conception [but] it is not possible to be funny about corpses for 25,000 words. The humour begins to putrefy and finally leaves a very bad taste in the mouth.'[88]

Evelyn valued his agent more as a negotiator than as a critic and tactfully suggested that 'the tale should not be read as a satire on morticians but as a study of the Anglo-American cultural impasse with the mortuary as a jolly setting'.[89] Still convinced that *The Loved One* was a work of art, Evelyn approached Cyril Connolly – with whom he had made up after having him and 'his concubine'[90] Lys Lubbock to stay in June – asking if he would be prepared to publish it in its entirety in *Horizon*. Connolly replied: 'Est, est, est! as the bishop said! One of your very best I think. I should be honoured . . .'[91]

The Loved One duly made its first appearance in *Horizon*'s February 1948 issue, with a preface by Connolly commending it as 'a Swiftian satire [which] in its attitude to death, and to death's stand-in, failure . . . exposes a materialistic society at its weakest spot'. It was, he suggested, 'one of the most perfect short novels of the last ten years and the most complete of [Waugh's] creations, a story cast in a kind of light but immensely strong aluminium alloy, like the one-piece chassis of a racing car'.[92]

The magazine sold out overnight but there was then an eight-month interval before the hardback, due to the fact that *Scott-King's Modern Europe* had sold 14,000 copies in the run-up to Christmas and was still doing well. Evelyn was keen to publish *The Loved One* in America to capitalise on his popularity there after *Brideshead*, however publishers on both sides of the Atlantic were concerned that Whispering Glades in the novel was too easily recognisable as Forest Lawn Memorial Park and that Dr Eaton might sue for libel.

To allay such fears Evelyn asked his high-spirited friend Lord Stanley of Alderley to add a codicil to his will stipulating that on his death he wished his body to be transported to Los Angeles for burial at Forest Lawn, as he understood that 'this cemetery bore some resemblance to the beautiful one so movingly described by his friend Mr Evelyn Waugh'.[93] Ed Stanley's letter to his solicitor requesting this, presumably written on House of Lords notepaper, was enough to set publishers' minds at rest and the book appeared in Britain and America in November to generally favourable reviews, although Evelyn's old adversary Edmund Wilson spitefully maintained that the 'patrons and proprietors of Whispering Glades seem more sensible and less absurd than the priest-guided Evelyn Waugh'.[94]

The Loved One was dedicated to Nancy Mitford, who received her advance copy in Paris where she had moved in 1946 in pursuit of her elusive Free French colonel, Gaston Palewski, the great love of her life. 'Do try & laugh a little,' wrote Evelyn. 'It is dedicated to you as the hardest hearted well no toughest is the word girl I know.' Nancy replied: 'The *heaven* of *The Loved One* oh you are kind to dedicate it to me, thank you thank you for it. I've been utterly shrieking over it since it arrived, luckily was lunching alone. I must say I couldn't quite do it and the *foie de veau* together . . . but combined it happily with a banana & am now in despair at having finished it . . . Dined with a young American last night & told him your book was to be called *The Loved One*. "What a beautiful name," he said. Poor him.'[95]

Evelyn greatly missed being able to trade gossip with her at Heywood Hill's bookshop, however if anything they got along even better by letter, their jokes often based upon a shared readiness to be mischievous and cruel about others, unlike Cyril Connolly, the occasional butt of their unkindness, who told Evelyn that he did not regard the suffering of his fellow men as a fit subject of humour. As far as Nancy was concerned, Evelyn was not just a highly entertaining friend and faithful confidant but also a much-valued literary sounding board whose talents as a word-smith and prose stylist she conceded were on an altogether different plain – 'your well known knack of one tap on the nail & in it goes, whereas the rest of us hammer & pound for hours' – yet whose advice on matters such as romance and religion she felt free to disregard.

It was he who had suggested the title of *The Pursuit of Love*, her first bestseller, in 1945, and that Uncle Matthew's home Alconleigh should be dominated by 'stark and real' images of death, however as often as not his suggestions went unheeded. 'I long to read your novel & criticize tho what's the good you never take my advice,'[96] Evelyn wrote to her in 1950 when she was at work on *The Blessing*. He nevertheless remained the writer whom Nancy measured herself against most often in her own mind and whose approval she most craved. At the same time her headstrong determination to stick to her guns served to preserve his great fondness and regard for her.

Several others benefited from Evelyn's generosity with literary advice, among them the Scottish writer Moray McLaren, whom Evelyn helped rescue from alcoholic despair and loss of faith, just as he did with his old Oxford friend Alfred Duggan, whose late-flowering career as a bestselling historical novelist owed a huge debt to Evelyn's help and encouragement.* Another whom Evelyn mentored was the Thomas Merton, the talkative Trappist monk from Kentucky whose autobiography *The Seven Storey Mountain* Evelyn edited and cut by a third for its English edition, *Elected Silence*. 'Americans tend to be very long-winded in conversation,' Evelyn explained to the monk, 'and your method is conversational'; he added: 'it is of course much more laborious to write briefly'.

Evelyn first visited Father Merton at his monastery when he went to America for a second time, in November 1948, the result of a shrewdly aimed proposal that he write about the Catholic Church in America for

---

* Evelyn was also an obliging writer of prefaces to lesser known writers whom he admired, including to Eric Newby's *Short Walk in the Hindu Kush* (1958) and to Christie Lawrence's neglected masterpiece, *Irregular Adventure* (1947), recounting the exploits of this 'highly individualistic' former comrade of Evelyn's in No 8 Commando after he was captured on Crete in 1941. 'No one could ask for a better thriller,' Evelyn declared in his introduction, and Lawrence's adventures 'should bring encouragement to all who may be in danger of doubting whether knight-errantry is still possible in the conditions of modern war'.

Life. The magazine's proprietor, Henry Luce, greeted his idea enthusiastic-ally, not least since his wife, the writer Clare Boothe Luce, was an ardent convert like Evelyn who developed a soft spot for her despite initially thinking her rather self-centred. He would go weak at the knees whenever they subsequently met, and when she came over to London the next year he gave a dinner party at Tom Burns's to introduce her to a selection of distinguished British Catholics. As Lady Pamela Berry observed to Nancy Mitford, Clare regarded Evelyn 'in a quaint Catholic light as a noble gentle person who is capable, oh yes, from time to time of spitefulness, but who is on the whole a saintly, good person healed and beatified by the Church. What do you know about that?'[97]

During the 1948 American trip Evelyn also renewed what was to become a lifelong friendship with Anne Fremantle, another convert and now leading Catholic intellectual whom he had known slightly in the 1920s and was reputedly the only woman his old tutor Mr Cruttwell ever proposed to. After plying Anne with caviar and 'comfortable amounts of Bristol Cream' over Sunday lunch, Evelyn described her to Laura as '*very* nice', yet entirely failed to understand her decision to become an American citizen, 'with full consent deliberately committing this horrid act'.[98] Evelyn's brother Alec, who was by then living apart from Joan and spending much of his time in New York, was himself also on the point of taking this incomprehensible step – he became a US 'resident alien' in 1950 – and when he called on Evelyn at his hotel later the same day Evelyn told Laura he was 'greatly taken up with some woman, dressed with inappropriate gaiety, talking in an unusual & unbecoming drawl. Then I felt so ill & sad I went to bed without any dinner.'[99]

Evelyn returned to America early in 1949, this time with Laura, to give a series of lectures on 'Three Vital Writers', G. K. Chesterton, Ronald Knox and Graham Greene, returning home at the end of March. 'I must say I've seen enough of USA to last me fifty years,' he wrote to Nancy when he got back home. 'It is very degrading to be constantly in the company of people you have to "make allowances for".'[100] But after his 6,000-word article 'The American Epoch in the Catholic Church' eventually appeared in *Life* magazine that autumn, there was yet more demand for Evelyn among American Catholics and in the autumn of 1950 he went there again, his arrival coinciding with the publication of *Helena*, which he had eventu-ally finished that spring, some five years after starting it. Evelyn always maintained that this was by far his best book, yet while he was in New York being lavishly entertained yet again by the Luces, an anonymous reviewer in Henry Luce's *Time* magazine remarked that Evelyn's 'sky-blue prose' had on this occasion gone 'purple with emotion'. The critical reaction was no better in England and Evelyn later told Christopher Sykes that the book's reception was 'the greatest disappointment of his whole literary life'.[101]

21

....

Off My Rocker

Three months earlier, on 11 July 1950, Laura had given birth to their seventh and last child, Septimus. Shortly afterwards Evelyn went to stay at Pixton for the boy's christening but fled as soon as he heard that Laura's brother Auberon was also on his way. 'I think the mixture of all the children & him would be intolerable to you,' wrote Laura after Evelyn had gone, '& even though I know you would be polite to him I know I should be in a fever & miserable, feeling that things were not right.'[1] Alone at Piers Court with nothing much to do after finishing *Helena*, Evelyn soon grew bored and listless. 'I miss you unendurably & go whistling about the house & fields never hearing an answer,' he wrote to Laura. 'Let me know if Auberon looks like going and I will come quick.'[2]

Evelyn missed Laura whenever he was away from her for any length of time, his love constantly underpinned by the feeling that she was perhaps the only person who was entirely unafraid of him and able to call him to order. He may have made occasional sharp remarks about her eccentric housekeeping arrangements or dishevelled dress sense, but on the whole they appeared to be remarkably happy together, so unalike in so many ways yet crucially sharing a very similar sense of humour – 'a very *peculiar* sense of humour,' as Gilbert Pinfold's tormentors described it.

Laura was essentially a very private person, content to see no one beyond her family and a few local farming folk, and equally content to let her more gregarious husband disappear periodically up to London to see his friends. Whenever they were both at Piers Court they did the crossword together (he apparently not minding that she was noticeably better at it than he was) but otherwise got on with their own thing, he writing in the library or pottering in the garden or going for long walks or taking in a matinee at Dursley cinema, she looking after her cows. 'She never had more than six or seven of them,' recalled her son Auberon, 'but she loved them extravagantly, as other women love their dogs or, so I have been told, their children.'[3]

In keeping with his own anarchic tendencies, Evelyn was inclined to let his children do as they pleased when they were young so long as they did not disturb his tranquillity in the library. Much of Bron's early childhood was thus spent prowling about the woods around Piers Court with an assortment of weaponry or conducting chemistry experiments in a 'lab' at the back of the house with explosive substances liberally procured by his father. At Downside, Bron once took a confiscated air pistol from the headmaster's desk and shot another boy in the leg, maintaining afterwards that he had intended only to stir up the gravel by the boy's feet.[4] He held the school record of fourteen beatings in a single term.

When Randolph Churchill asked the Waughs to stay in 1953, Evelyn replied: 'Laura, who, alas, will be busy with farm and children all summer, sends her love and regretfully declines your kind invitation. The boy Auberon Alexander is available for little Winston's entertainment. His chief interest is shooting sitting birds with an airgun and making awful smells with chemicals. He is devoid of culture but cheerful and greedy for highly peppered foods. If not watched closely he smokes and drinks. Shall I bring him for the first weekend of August?'[5]

As soon as they were at boarding school the children were allowed through the green baize doors to have lunch with their parents in the dining room – 'very gloomy occasions', according to Bron[6] – and to mark the end of each school holidays there was also a rather jollier family dinner party, waited on by Ellwood, at which they all gave little speeches beginning 'Unaccustomed as I am to public speaking'. In 1956 Evelyn wrote to Bron at Downside: 'I am delighted to hear that, unaccustomed as you are to public speaking, you have won the debating prize and are going to Sherborne with the team.'[7]

As theatrical as his own father in many respects, Evelyn put on white tie and tails for the end-of-holidays dinners, completing the regalia with a display of his military medals. His own speech, before they all moved through for charades and dumb crambo, was invariably 'some variation on the theme of how delighted he was that the holidays were over and his children were going back to school', as Bron recalled.[8] As it was clear that in this instance he was not being funny, his children could find his remarks quite hurtful, and although their devotion increased as they grew older, in early childhood they felt largely indifferent towards their father: 'We held him in awe, certainly,' wrote Bron, 'but not in much affection at this stage.'[9]

Evelyn made no secret of how bored he often was by his children when they were young, just as he was whenever he encountered anyone unable to respond intelligently or at least humorously to what he had to say. However there was an endearing eccentricity about his letters to them when they were at school, usually gossipy, often subversive but almost always affectionate, if idiosyncratically so. When Meg wrote pointing out that the other girls had all been sent Easter eggs by their parents, Evelyn replied: 'I won't send you an Easter egg. You must nibble bits off the other girls'. Perhaps as a reward for your great unselfishness I will send you a little book of devotion instead.'[10] As Bron prepared to celebrate his fifteenth birthday at Downside in 1954, Evelyn sounded a rare note of censure: 'May your sixteenth year start prudently. Give up this nonsense of drinking beer and smoking with local poachers. Eat heavily. Wash down crumpets and cakes with refreshing cups of tea. Keep good company.'[11]

Of all his children, the one generally reckoned to have come off worst from Evelyn's occasional bullying was his middle son James, who had the misfortune to be continually compared with his brother Septimus, the youngest of the family by four years and thus doted on by both parents. 'Your brother James is home dull as ditchwater,' Evelyn wrote to Teresa in 1964, 'your brother Septimus bright as a button.' At one stage Evelyn made James tell a new joke every day in order to remedy what he saw as his defective sense of humour. 'And now my son will tell an amusing story,' Evelyn would announce if there were guests for dinner. Yet despite such ordeals James remembers his childhood as extremely free and on the whole 'very happy', and he cheerfully confesses to have been left with no lasting sense of maltreatment. The youngest three were always 'less privileged', he recalls, 'but we were part of a tribe so it didn't seem to matter'. Septimus, meanwhile, grew up in awe of his father but 'less from fear than from a desire not appear foolish in front of him'. His abiding impression was of 'a gentle melancholic man whose chief pleasure lay in parodying his condition'. As his father grew older, Septimus felt increasingly protective of him. When the house filled with children, Evelyn would wander around chanting: 'Oh the hell of it, Oh the smell of it, Oh the hell of the family life . . .'[12]

* * *

Evelyn continued to travel far afield during the 1950s, partly as an anti-dote to the depression that descended on him in winter, particularly at Christmas, which he always found a uniquely dispiriting time of year. In January 1951 he took Christopher Sykes on a tour of the Holy Land under the renewed patronage of Henry Luce, whose wife had enjoyed *Helena* even if most critics had not. As part of the bargain, Evelyn wrote a long article for Luce's *Life* magazine, which later became a short book, *The Holy Places*, published in 1952 by Ian Fleming's Queen Anne Press, with an extra essay on 'St Helena Empress'. By the summer of 1951, Evelyn had returned to fiction and told Graham Greene that he was writing 'an interminable novel about army life, obsessed by memories of military dialogue'.[13]

Greene was about to visit Piers Court with his mistress Catherine Walston, a beautiful and vivacious American-born Catholic convert whom Evelyn had known since before she and Greene became 'chums' (as Evelyn put it) and always liked. Mrs Walston was married with five children and although she told Evelyn that he had 'always been so good to and about us',[14] she had presumably got wind of his occasional splenetic outbursts against adulterers and wrote to Evelyn beforehand to check that her coming to stay would not 'embarrass' him in any way. Evelyn replied: 'Please believe that I am far too depressed by my own odious, if unromantic, sins to have any concern for other people's. For me it would be a delight to welcome you here.'[15] The visit was a great success and it was largely thanks to her that Evelyn saw much more of Greene over the next few years, cementing a close friendship that constantly defied their countless differences and disagreements.

The book that Evelyn was working on at the time of Greene's 1951 visit was *Men at Arms*, the first of his *Sword of Honour* trilogy based on his ex-periences in the Second World War, more closely autobiographical than any of his work to date and, like *Brideshead Revisited*, having the renewal of Catholic faith as its overall theme. *Sword of Honour* ranks as one of the finest works of fiction produced by the war, however *Men at Arms* had a rather mixed reception on its first publication in September 1952. The most appreciative review appeared in Luce's *Time* magazine, whose anonymous critic compared the experience of reading the novel to 'hearing a full keyboard used by a pianist who has hitherto confined himself to a single octave' and predicted that 'if his trilogy continues as well as it has begun, it will be the best British novel of World War II'.[16]

Evelyn managed to miss the dreaded family Christmas that year by taking himself off on a pilgrimage to Goa, where the relics of the great Jesuit missionary St Francis Xavier were being revealed for the last time on the 400th anniversary of his death: 'One brown stump of toe emerging from white wrapping,' Evelyn noted approvingly. 'Body fully vested, one grey forearm and hand, and grey clay-like skull visible.'[17] If this brings to mind the morticians at Forest Lawn, here Evelyn's attitude was strictly reverential and he postponed his own veneration until he could make it more privately. 'India is very like Stinkers,' he wrote home to Laura, who stayed behind with the children. 'There are cows wandering in all the gardens eating all the flowers. All the lower orders call me "master" which I find very familiar.'[18] When he got back he told Nancy that Goa had been 'heaven', the southern temples 'fascinating and exhilarating', the Indians 'more servile than most foreigners'. 'I can only bear intimacy really,' he added, '& after that formality or servility. The horrible thing is familiarity.'[19]

* * *

In the late spring of 1953, buoyed by the news that *Men at Arms* had won the James Tait Black Memorial Prize, Evelyn published *Love Among the Ruins*, a strange dystopian 'romance of the near future' which he had written the previous year. As usual he sent a special edition of this slim volume to friends, whose opinions he always valued far more than those of professional critics. 'Ta muchly, ole man, for your very generous present,' replied John Betjeman. 'It could not have come at a more appropriate moment, for only last Sunday I visited Stevenage New Town in the rainy afternoon. It was exactly like your book. Three miles of Lionel Brett-style prefabs interrupted by Hugh Casson blocks of flats and two shopping arcades and concrete lampposts throughout and no trees, only muddy

Hertfordshire inclines. I saw through the vast, unprivate ground floor window of a house, a grey-faced woman washing up. My goodness, it was terrifying. And the kiddies' scooters lying out in the rain on the streets and a big vita-glass school on stilts.'[20]

In the same way that their religious differences caused friction between Evelyn and Betjeman, their mutual abhorrence of modern architecture and town planning served as a strong bond, as did their shared liking for Gothic Revival decoration and furniture, although Evelyn's tastes were if anything rather bolder in this regard. For Evelyn's fiftieth birthday in October 1953 Betjeman gave him an elaborate – and as it turned out rather valuable – wash-hand stand that he had found in a junk shop in Lincoln. The stand was designed by William Burges, a follower of Pugin, whose freakish flourishes Betjeman suggested rendered people 'punch-drunk', and he could have been forgiven for thinking that his gift had had just that effect on his friend. 'Well, my dear fellow,' Evelyn wrote thanking him, 'all I can say is I am bowled over. What a present!'[21]*

But Evelyn's dizzy delight soon dissolved when the washstand arrived at Stinchcombe without one of the parts that he so vividly recalled seeing at the home of Patrick Kinross who had stored it temporarily for him in London. 'Sorry to be a bore,' Evelyn wrote to Kinross. 'The Betjeman Benefaction has arrived minus an essential organ – the serpentine bronze pipe which led from the dragon's mouth to the basin. I am making a row with Pickfords. Can you testify that it left your house intact?'[22] He also wrote to Betjeman, including a sketch of what he meant, but Betjeman had not the faintest idea what he was on about. 'Oh no, old boy,' he replied. 'There was never a pipe from the tap to the basin such as you envisaged.'[23] Evelyn wrote back just after New Year: 'I must see an alienist. These delusions are becoming more frequent.'[24]

Friends had for some time noticed that Evelyn was not quite himself. In the spring of 1952 he had asked Christopher Sykes if he would go with him to Sicily, but Sykes this time declined, explaining later: 'I had noticed a change coming over Evelyn lately. He was becoming more arrogant, more quarrelsome, and indulged his horrible delight in needling on sensitive spots more freely than usual ... when we did meet by chance he was

---

* When the young architectural historian Mark Girouard visited Piers Court in 1955 and was shown to his bedroom, he exclaimed 'Burges by God!' when he saw the wash-hand stand. 'Not bad,' wrote Evelyn to Betjeman. EW to IB, 4 July 1955, AWA

invariably unpleasant.'[25] Evelyn had long had a reputation for going a bit far, but now his behaviour seemed somehow even more demonic than before. In November 1952 Barbara Skelton, the celebrated femme fatale then married to Cyril Connolly, recorded Evelyn's wild performance at a party of Ann Fleming's (shortly after her divorce from Lord Rothermere and subsequent marriage to Ian Fleming), 'being rude to everybody, pretending he didn't know who Rosamond Lehmann was when she rushed up to greet him with open arms. Waugh criticised Alan Ross's beard and, when Cecil Beaton approached him when he was sitting on the sofa with Jennifer Ross, Waugh exclaimed, "Here's someone who can tell us all about buggery!" He then had to be carried into a taxi at three in the morning.'[26]

Though capable of periods of abstinence, particularly during Lent, Evelyn continued to drink prodigiously, especially during expeditions to London when even in middle age he was regularly sick before retiring to bed and not infrequently felt obliged to send flowers the next day to hostesses whose guests he had offended, occasionally enlisting the help of friends to atone for his gravest indiscretions. After one spree Evelyn paid a morning call to Diana Cooper, 'portly as an alderman,' as she reported to her son John Julius, 'dressed in loud and shapeless checks. He'd been obstreperous the night before and broken his host's decanters, so I had to dedicate an hour of my brief time to buying *amendes*.'[27]

The hangovers when he finally made it back to Piers Court might last several days, the symptoms invariably 'insomnia, a disordered stomach, weakness at the knees, a trembling hand which becomes evident when I attempt to use a pen'.[28] 'I get so painfully drunk whenever I go there,' he wrote to Nancy after a typical visit to London, '(Champagne, the shortest road out of Welfaria) and nowadays it is not a matter of a headache and an aspirin but of complete collapse, with some clear indications of incipient lunacy. I think I am jolly near being mad & need very careful treatment if I am to survive another decade without the strait straight? jacket.'[29]

All the long lunches and late-night carousing were now taking their toll. Long gone were the days when he felt fit enough to ride to hounds. Shortly after the war, when he went to stay with the Betjemans, he told Penelope he felt too old even to ride any more though he was still in his early forties. Even the various earth-moving operations that used to obsess him in the garden were becoming too strenuous. By 1953 he was spending much of his time in an armchair and feeling increasingly unwell: liverish, lethargic, and suffering intermittently from gout, arthritis, rheumatism and back pain. Like his fictional alter ego Gilbert Pinfold he 'ate less, drank more, and grew corpulent'. He also slept badly. If in the midst of writing something he might 'find the sentences he had written during the day running in his head, the words shifting and changing colour kaleido-scopically, so that he would again and again climb out of bed, pad down to the library, make a minute correction, return to his room, lie in the dark dazzled by the pattern of vocables until obliged once more to descend to the manuscript'.[30]

He developed the habit of getting up in the early hours to shave, having a theory that his smooth face on the smooth pillow induced sleep. But otherwise he relied on a cocktail of chloral and bromide to provide him with the 'six or seven hours of insensibility' he felt he needed to 'face another idle day with something approaching jauntiness'.[31] But the more resistant he became to the sleeping drugs, which he also used as a pain-killer during the day for his rheumatism, the more recklessly he increased the dose, with the result that he began to experience delusions and a memory that even before the Burges washstand episode he told Betjeman was 'not at all hazy – just sharp, detailed and dead wrong'.[32]

During the second half of 1953, Evelyn was also haunted by two inter-views he did for the BBC. The first of these, which according to Auberon Waugh 'eventually drove my father mad',[33] was for broadcast on the Over-seas Service and conducted by a man named Stephen Black in the library at Piers Court in August. Thirteen-year-old Bron listened to it all outside in the recording van and commented afterwards that the interviewer did not seem to like his father very much.[34] In the novel, Gilbert Pinfold has a similarly disagreeable experience at the hands of 'Angel' and his team, and when their BBC van disappears down the drive one of Mr Pinfold's children remarks, 'You didn't like those people much, did you, papa?'[35] But however little Evelyn liked them, for a decent enough fee he was prepared to go through it all again. Hence a few months later he was interviewed for the BBC Home Service's *Frankly Speaking* programme in London, where he was faced by three interviewers, including the same Mr Black. The questions this time were even less friendly, although Evelyn emerged from it with far more credit than his relentlessly po-faced and police-like interrogators. Having been asked about capital punishment and declared that he was in favour of it 'for an enormous number of offences', he was pressed on whether he would be prepared to carry out the executions himself. 'Do you mean actually do the hanging?' asked Evelyn. 'I should think it's very odd to choose a novelist for such tasks.'

Later Evelyn was asked 'in what respect do you as a human being feel that you have primarily failed?', to which he replied: 'I've never learnt French well, and I've never learned any other language at all. I've forgotten most of my classics; I can't often remember people's faces in the streets, and I don't like music. Those are very grave failings.'

'But no others you're conscious of?'

'Those are the ones that worry me most.'[36]

* * *

On New Year's Day 1954 the husband of the woman Evelyn loved more than any other besides Laura died at sea en route to Jamaica. In certain respects, Duff Cooper (who had been created Viscount Norwich in 1952) was quite similar to Evelyn, prone at times to extreme irascibility and uncontrollable rudeness, however as Evelyn had told Diana the previous summer, 'Duff and I have never hit it off.'[37]

There had been some spectacular set-tos over the years, most recently in April 1953 when Evelyn arrived at the Coopers' chateau at Chantilly 'plastered' after drinking a bottle of Burgundy and some brandy on the train, then set about baiting another guest and later said something offensive about Mountbatten at dinner, prompting an explosion from Duff: 'How dare a common little man like you, who happens to have written one or two moderately amusing novels, criticize that great patriot and gentleman? Leave my house at once!'[38]

After some subsequent frank exchanges, the two men eventually made up ('I have apologised to Norwich,' Evelyn told Diana, 'and he has accepted my apology, so that is O.K.')[39] but not before Diana had accused Evelyn of being unable to forgive or forget, and Evelyn had fired off one of his more wounding salvos at her: 'I am very sorry to hear that Duff was surprised and grieved to learn that I have detested him for 23 years. I must have nicer manners than people normally credit me with.'[40]

Duff was already unwell by this time, having suffered his first serious haemorrhage in May, a month after the great row at Chantilly, and the fateful trip at the end of the year had been planned with the idea of completing his convalescence. Even as they boarded Duff was feeling unwell and Diana tried in vain to persuade him that they ought to disembark before leaving Southampton. The next day at noon, New Year's Eve, 'it happened,' as Diana later told Cecil Beaton, 'a rush to the bathroom and a bigger, redder haemorrhage than he'd had before'.[41] He might have survived had he been able to get to a hospital, but on board a ship rolling about in heavy seas it was far more difficult to stem the loss of blood, and he died the following day in Vigo Bay at 3.30 p.m.

'All my prayers are for you and Duff,' Evelyn wrote to Diana when he heard the next day. 'If there is any service anywhere that I can do, command it. If my company would be at all comforting, call for me. Believe in my true, deep love.'[42] Having flown back with Duff's body, Diana could not face the funeral at Belvoir Castle on 6 January, and instead remained in London, where Evelyn spent an hour alone with her, finding her 'wild and witty, full of funny stories',[43] but also hearing a 'detailed account of Cooper's death agonies', as he recorded somewhat coldly in his diary. 'Not such a quick and clean ending as newspapers gave one to think.'[44]

*   *   *

Evelyn was far from well himself at the time, either physically or mentally, and the next month he set off for what was becoming his annual winter getaway, this time taking ship for Ceylon, the start of the terrifying voyage later chronicled in his avowedly autobiographical novel, *The Ordeal of Gilbert Pinfold*. Before leaving he had told Laura that he thought all the chloral might have caused 'problems with my nut' and it can scarcely have reassured her to get a letter from Cape St Vincent proposing to 'come home & lead a luny bin life for a while'.

'It was at 50 that Rossetti's chloral taking involved him in attempted suicide,' Evelyn added cheerfully, 'part blindness & part paralysis. We will avoid all that . . . To add to my balminess there are intermittent bits of 3rd Programme talks played in private cabin and two mentioned me very faintly and my p.m. [persecution mania] took it for other passengers whispering about me.'[45]

The other passengers had already noticed that Evelyn was behaving peculiarly, talking to the table lamps in the dining room and to the toast rack at breakfast, and repeatedly knocking on the cabin door below his and asking for 'Miss Margaret Black'. During a small dance on board, Evelyn complained that the music was driving him mad, and on another occasion he was seen crouching at the top of a flight of stairs in his pyjamas and then suddenly hurling a stool at an imaginary target. When they reached Port Said the captain persuaded him to disembark, and accompany a fellow passenger by car to Cairo. From there Evelyn wrote to Laura to say that he was 'resolved never to go anywhere without you again', and that he had been the victim of an experiment in telepathy 'real and true. A trick the existentialists invented – half mesmerism – which is most alarming when applied without warning or to a sick man.'[46]

From Cairo Evelyn flew on to Colombo, where he despatched another barking letter to Laura and one to Diana Cooper describing 'a group of psychologists a thousand miles away who read every word I write over my shoulder. As I write this I can hear their odious voices repeating it word for word ... It began with an elaborate series of practical jokes during which I was convinced I was insane. My sufferings were exquisite but now I know that it is merely a trick of telepathy.'[47]

Laura had grown increasingly alarmed by Evelyn's letters and after the one from Cairo she asked their neighbour Jack Donaldson, one of the few locals whom Evelyn got on with, if he would go with her to Colombo to help bring Evelyn home. But before they could get the necessary injections, Evelyn was on his way back and Laura travelled up to the Hyde Park Hotel in London to meet him.

Speaking in a 'high, unrecognizable squeak',[48] Evelyn began telling Laura the whole story of how he had been tormented on the voyage by the same Mr Black from the BBC who had recently interviewed him and chanced to be on board with his whole family, all of whom had used the powers of telepathy described in his letters to persecute him; only the daughter had shown any mercy. Evelyn mentioned to Laura that they both knew this Miss Black, having met her with a neighbour of theirs in Gloucestershire to whom she was engaged. 'But Evelyn,' Laura interrupted, suddenly twigging who he meant, 'her name wasn't Black, it was So-and-So, and she had nothing to do with the BBC man.'[49] Evelyn immediately realised that Laura was right and when she subsequently telephoned the BBC she was able to establish that Mr Black could not have been on Evelyn's voyage either as he had been ill in hospital for some weeks. Partially restored to his senses by this, Evelyn agreed that Laura should now summon their friend Father Philip Caraman, editor of the Jesuit periodical the *Month* for which Evelyn wrote. When Caraman arrived at about 7.30 p.m. he was greeted by Evelyn leaning across the dining-room table and pleading to be exorcised of the devils that were tormenting him. Evelyn also passed on some uncomplimentary remarks the voices had made about Caraman, and when Evelyn briefly left the table, the priest asked Laura whether his behaviour might be part of an elaborate joke of the sort he liked to play. Caraman promptly rang his friend Eric Strauss, an eminent Catholic psychiatrist, who came immediately and concluded that Evelyn had most likely been poisoned by his sleeping drugs, but then told him that the first thing he needed was a good night's sleep. He therefore wrote out a prescription for an alternative sedative, the vinegary-smelling paraldehyde which Evelyn would continue taking for the rest of his life despite lamenting that it gave him only four hours' sleep and 'spoils my zest for wine'.[50] A thorough check-up by a London physician later confirmed that Evelyn's hallucinations were indeed due to bromide poisoning, and after a few good nights' sleep he was back to normal.

Evelyn did not always seem to enjoy being the object of amusement, however in this instance, once the cause had been ascertained, he was eager to tell everyone about his spell of lunacy, retrospectively at least relishing the strangeness of the whole experience. 'I have been quite mad,'[51] he wrote to Diana, explaining his deranged letter to her from Ceylon; to Nancy Mitford, 'I've been suffering from a sharp but brief attack of insanity.'[52]* And to Cyril Connolly: 'I have had my first attack of insanity – quite a sharp one.'[53] When Evelyn met Christopher Hollis at Downside and was asked how he had been keeping, he replied: 'Been mad! Absolutely mad. Clean off my onion!'[54]

Not the least satisfying aspect of the whole episode was that it provided Evelyn with 'a hamper to be unpacked of fresh, rich experiences', from which to write what was to be his last comic novel. He began working on it after finishing *Officers and Gentlemen*, the second in the *Sword of Honour* war trilogy, which also coincided with the death of his mother

---

* Nancy had seen Evelyn's breakdown coming in December, telling Raymond Mortimer: 'He might go mad – madder at least.' (12 December 1953; cited in Selina Hastings, *Evelyn Waugh*, p. 558.)

in December at the age of eighty-four. 'Mrs Yaxley [her maid] found her dead in her chair after tea,' Evelyn wrote to his daughter Meg. 'I am afraid you will always remember her as very old & feeble. I wish you had known her when she was young and active.'[55] To Nancy Mitford he wrote that it was a 'happy release' for his mother who had grown tired of being so dependent 'but it fills me with regret for a lifetime of failure in affection & attention'.[56]

Evelyn began what he was soon calling his 'barmy book' early in the new year while on a restorative trip to Jamaica. He spent the first fortnight writing at a plantation house belonging to his old friend Perry Brownlow, recently widowed, remarried and drinking more than ever. Though indebted to Perry for so much hospitality over the years, Evelyn nevertheless found it 'a great intellectual strain to find words simple enough to converse with them. They are indeed a grisly household, gin from ten-thirty on . . . The women concentrate on a smooth sunburn and hairless bronzed shanks. The men lounge and yawn or play cards . . . There was a lady here who went to sleep on a mattress in a red bathing dress and all the vultures thought she was dead and bloody and tried to eat her.'[57] It was a relief to move on to the Flemings at Goldeneye, where Ian (aka 'Thunderbird') was busy working on *Diamonds are Forever,* 'an inspiring hive of industry & health', Evelyn wrote afterwards to Ann.[58]

Evelyn remained intermittently at work on *The Ordeal of Gilbert Pinfold* for the next two years. 'I am full in the middle of writing an account of my going off my rocker,'[59] he told Daphne Fielding in October 1956. Published in 1957, the novel included some of his most candid passages of self-revelation, but although the self-portrait he drew of 'the Artist in Middle Age' was typically funny, subtle and nuanced it effectively cemented his reputation as a grumpy symbol of reaction who abhors 'plastics, Picasso, sun bathing and jazz – everything, in fact, that had happened in his own lifetime'.

[Mr Pinfold] wished no one ill, but he looked at the world sub specie aeternitatis and he found it flat as a map; except when, rather often, personal annoyance intruded. Then he would come tumbling from his exalted point of observation.

Shocked by a bad bottle of wine, an impertinent stranger or a fault in syntax, his mind like a cinema-camera trucked furiously forward to confront the offending object close-up with glaring lens; with the eyes of a drill sergeant inspecting an awkward squad, bulging with wrath that was half-facetious.

He was neither a scholar nor a regular soldier; the part for which he cast himself was a combination of eccentric don and testy colonel and he acted it strenuously, before his children and his cronies, before it came to dominate his whole outward personality. When he ceased to be alone, when he swung into his club or stumped up the nursery stairs, he left half of himself behind and the other half swelled to fill its place. He offered the world a front of pomposity* mitigated by indiscretion, that was as hard, bright, and antiquated as a cuirass.[60]

Besides a few sharply dissenting voices, most critics considered *The Ordeal of Gilbert Pinfold* to be one of Evelyn's finest works. Writing in the *New Statesman*, John Raymond hailed Evelyn as 'the only major writer in English whose work reveals any genuine signs of development' and said that in reverting to his earliest manner he had 'given us one of his wittiest, most humane entertainments'.[61] Philip Toynbee in *The Observer* confessed to being no great admirer of what he saw as the 'mannered precision' of Evelyn as a stylist, yet concluded that 'these are the self-revelations of a remarkably honest and brave man who has allowed us to see that he is a likeable one'.[62]

---

* 'I have grown stouter and worse tempered and more pompous,' Evelyn told Diana Cooper in 1949. 'Women don't understand pomposity. It is nearly always an absolutely private joke – one against the world. The last line of defense.' 21 December 1949; *MWMS*, p. 105.

22

....

Suitably Sequestered

Evelyn had never quite rediscovered his love for Piers Court after returning to live there at the end of the war and had lately grown restless. As
his grandson observes: 'He enjoyed making, decorating and improving
houses, but once these things were done he lost interest.'[1] He was also
alarmed by the imminent threat of development around the local town of
Dursley, two miles away, but the final straw came in June 1955 when the
Daily Express journalist Nancy Spain turned up uninvited on his doorstep one evening shortly before dinner.

An exuberant early television 'personality' known for her mannish
clothes and proudly lesbian love life* – numbering Marlene Dietrich
among her various girlfriends – Miss Spain was also 'a lively, if not very
literary, book critic',[2] as her obituary put it when she died in a plane crash
a decade later, and a 'special' feature writer known for her stunts. She had
telephoned Piers Court earlier in the day to ask if she and her companion,
Lord Noel-Buxton, might come and see Evelyn and been firmly told by
Laura that her husband was 'not at home to the *Daily Express*'.[3] They came
nonetheless, and when Evelyn asked why they had ignored the sign at the
gate stipulating 'No Admittance on Business', Lord Noel-Buxton, a tall,
timid eccentric briefly on the staff of *Farmers' Weekly* and occasionally
in the news for attempting to wade across rivers, spluttered: 'I'm not on
business. I'm a member of the House of Lords.'[4]

Shortly afterwards, Evelyn wrote a piece for *The Spectator* in which he
ruminated on the dotty peer's 'moving and rather mysterious words': 'In

---

* In the more innocent early 1960s, when the *News of the World* hired Nancy Spain as a
columnist, the paper proclaimed: 'She's gay, she's provocative . . . she's going places.'

Lord Noel-Buxton we see the lord predatory. He seems to think that his barony gives him the right to a seat at the dinner-table in any private house in the kingdom.'[5]

Privately, Evelyn had been 'tremulous with rage' all evening after the intrusion, as he recorded in his diary. 'And all next day.'[6] Within two weeks he had put the 'polluted' Piers Court on the market, although not before opening his doors to an American television crew under the misapprehension that they would pay him $100 for his trouble. As Evelyn recalled, it was an 'excruciating' day: 'The impresario kept producing notes from his pocket: "Mr Waugh it says here that you are irascible and reactionary. Will you please say something offensive?"'[7]

On 4 July Evelyn wrote to the estate agents Knight Frank & Rutley: 'You may remember that you came here about nine years ago when I had the idea of moving to Ireland. Now I have the idea of moving anywhere. I am sick of the district . . . I don't want the house advertised. But if you happen to meet a lunatic who wants to live in this ghastly area, please tell him.'[8] Another year passed before they found what they were looking for, a 'cosy, sequestered' house in 'very pretty truly rural surroundings' at Combe Florey, seven miles north-west of Taunton, with, as Evelyn told Nancy Mitford 'possibilities of beautification'. 'If only I were a pansy without family cares I could make it a jewel.'[9]

He regarded Combe Florey as 'a suitable place to end my days'. Among its attractions, he told Ann Fleming, was 'a lunatic asylum bang next door which is valuable (a) for me if I get another go of barminess (b) in providing indefatigable gardeners at slave wages (c) husband for Harriet [Waugh]'.[10] He sold Piers Court for £9,500 in June and three months later paid £7,500 for Combe Florey.

The much-needed surplus which he had earmarked for all the planned improvements was doubled in February 1957, four months after their move, by a tax-free award of £2,000 libel damages. Soon after her visit, Nancy Spain had conveniently published an article suggesting Evelyn was an embittered and unsuccessful writer whose total first edition sales were 'dwarfed' by those of his brother's recent novel *Island in the Sun*, which had sold 60,000 copies 'as a direct result of my *Daily Express* notice', maintained Miss Spain – 'rather overstating the case,' as the judge later remarked. But, as the judge also said in his summing-up, some of her other assertions were 'hopelessly inaccurate',[11] Evelyn's books having sold well over four million copies in Britain and America and his total first edition sales amounting to 180,000. Evelyn nevertheless neurotically convinced himself that he would lose the case and his fears were intensified while the jury was out when his counsel, his old Oxford friend Gerald Gardiner, apologised for 'letting him into a mess' and disconcertingly hinted that he might have to pay costs of £5,000.

'At the end of the first day I would have settled for a fiver,' Evelyn later told Nancy Mitford. 'But I had taken the precaution of telling the Dursley parish priest that he should have 10% of the damages. His prayers were answered in dramatic, Old Testament style. A series of Egyptian plagues fell on Sir Hartley Shawcross from the moment he took up the case, culminating in a well-nigh fatal motor accident to his mother-in-law at the very moment when he had me under cross-examination & was making me feel rather an ass. He had to chuck the case and leave it to an understrapper . . . I had a fine solid jury who were out to fine the Express for their impertinence to the Royal Family, quite irrespective of any rights or wrongs.'[12] The defendant, he told Diana Cooper, had 'perjured herself frequently but behaved in a gentlemanly way afterwards, gripping my hand and saying "better man won"'.[13]

Alec had flown over from Tangier, where he now lived for much of the year, to bolster his brother's case: 'You flitted out of court like a rare tropical butterfly,' Evelyn wrote to him afterwards, '& I assumed you were off to your exotic pleasures. Else I should have sought you out to thank you for your startling loyalty in coming to my chilly island to give evidence on my behalf.'[14]

Evelyn's Combe Florey beautification budget received another valuable boost in April with a further £3,000 damages from the Beaverbrook press, this time over its review of a new edition of *The Meaning of Treason* by Beaverbrook's old flame and Evelyn's old friend Rebecca West, in which she had accused him and Graham Greene of having 'created a climate of cackbrained confusion between virtues and vices . . . a climate in which the traitor flourishes' – a view endorsed by the *Daily Express*'s literary editor in his review. Evelyn's earlier suit against Rebecca West's publishers had resulted in the withdrawal of her book, an outcome for which she never forgave him even though he had mercifully not pressed for damages, and besides which she was scarcely in a position to complain, having herself recently suppressed the autobiographical novel by her illegitimate son with H. G. Wells because of its unflattering portrayal of his parents.*

The libel victories were immensely gratifying for Evelyn, not least since the Beaverbrook press appeared to have been waging a vendetta against him for many years, culminating in various recent sneering profiles and some particularly hostile reviews of *Love Among the Ruins* in 1953. Evelyn's association with Lord Beaverbrook stretched back to his inglorious stint as a cub reporter on the *Daily Express* in 1927 and he first portrayed the power-crazed press baron as Lord Monomark in *Vile Bodies* (his original name, Ottercreek, in the manuscript gave a fairly strong hint as to whom Evelyn had in mind) and more memorably as Lord Copper in *Scoop*, at which point Beaverbrook took Evelyn's publishers to court over the original cover claiming (with good reason) that the lettering the *Daily Beast*'s masthead immediately brought to mind the *Daily Express*. The cover was changed to omit the offending masthead but thereafter Evelyn could not help thinking that his treatment by the Beaverbrook papers was somewhat less than friendly.

The tax-free £5,000 damages were very welcome too, counterbalancing Evelyn's customary extravagance in decorating his new house. 'I have been buying objects like a drunken sailor – candelabra, carpets, fireplaces,' he told Ann Fleming shortly before the first libel award. 'The prodigious sideboard which I bought at Ston Easton has been erected with an infinity of skilled labour.'[15] He had also set aside some of winnings for a luxurious holiday in Monte Carlo with Laura, but his old friend Monsignor Ronald Knox was dying of liver cancer and instead Evelyn agreed that they would accompany him on a depressing trip to the south Devon seaside. Evelyn had known Ronnie Knox as an illustrious and inspirational fellow Catholic convert (and fellow castle creeper, their detractors might add) since the early 1920s and a decade later Knox had been instrumental in persuading Mary Herbert of Evelyn's merits as a potential son-in-law. Their friendship had deepened after the war, when Knox moved from being private chaplain to the Actons at Aldenham Park in Shropshire, where he did the first of his famous Bible translations, to the Asquiths at Mells and became a regular visitor to Piers Court. In 1950 Knox had asked Evelyn to be his literary executor. Evelyn tried to persuade him to come to Monte

---

* *Heritage*, by Anthony West, was published in America in 1955 but Rebecca West's threat to sue anyone who published the book in Britain meant that it only appeared there in 1984, after her death.

Carlo, and failing that Brighton, but Knox was too unwell to travel far so Torquay it had to be. 'Torquay is absolute hell,'[16] Evelyn wrote to Jack Donaldson soon after arriving. 'Poor Ronnie is very infirm & fretful,' he told Ann Fleming, 'can't eat, drink or read. All that gives him any relief is laborious crossword puzzles . . . [he] talks as though he will be on my hands for a month. I love and revere him, but oh dear –.'[17] After a week Laura excused herself in order to greet some new cows while they moved on to Sidmouth. But Evelyn soon found that 'ghastly' too, so he took Knox back for a fortnight to Combe Florey, where his stricken friend wrote most of the Romanes Lecture he was due to give that summer at Oxford, 'On English Translation'. 'It was an extraordinary feat,' Evelyn recorded. 'He was oppressed with lassitude and nausea. He had only his host's modest library to draw on. But the paper is as sharp and sparkling as any written in his youth.'[18]

Ronald Knox died that August, aged sixty-nine, but not before he had agreed to Evelyn's proposal that he should write his biography and, fortified by powerful drugs, triumphantly delivered his lecture at the Sheldonian, an occasion movingly described by Evelyn in his subsequent book: 'When half-way through, to illustrate a point, he [Knox] recited in full Cory's familiar rendering of the Greek epigram, "They told me Heraclitus, they told me you were dead," most of those present recognised those words as his own farewell to Oxford, and some with whom of old he had "tired the sun with talking" did not restrain their tears. The applause at the end was terrific.'[19]

Evelyn had been quick to knuckle down to his biography. 'Ronnie's death has transformed my life,' he told Diana Cooper that November. 'Instead of sitting about bored and idle I am busy all day long.'[20] It helped that he was already well acquainted with two of the people who knew most about Knox's life, Katharine Asquith and Daphne Acton, and he lost no time in tracking down Knox's surviving sister, Lady Peck, in Edinburgh, his old friend and disciple Laurence Eyres at Ampleforth and his confidant and confessor Dom Hubert van Zeller at Downside. Evelyn admitted that he felt out of his depth when it came to tackling Knox's spirituality, however Dom Hubert was reassuring. 'I am sure you are right about keeping off Ronald's religious life,' a relieved Evelyn wrote to him in January 1958, after their talk. 'He knew I knew nothing about it, but he wrote to Daphne that he could think of no one more suitable than me to write his biography. So he plainly wanted to be treated as a man of letters rather than of prayer. But of course a lot of people will say that I miss his essential point and of course they will be right.'[21]

In February 1958 Evelyn went out to stay with the Actons in Rhodesia, where they had emigrated after the war to farm at M'Bebi. There Lady Acton freely told him all about her intense platonic love affair with Knox while he had been preparing her for her conversion to Roman Catholicism in 1937, six years after her marriage to the 3rd Lord Acton, whose family had been Catholics for centuries. She sent Evelyn several bundles of their correspondence and urged him to write the biography 'as if I were dead',[22] despite admitting that while Knox had behaved 'with effortless chastity' throughout their relationship she had 'found it more of a strain'.[23] Evelyn greatly admired Daphne's beauty, intelligence and above all perhaps her candour. Her chaotic household (containing ten children) was 'everything that normally makes Hell,' he told Ann Fleming, except for 'Daphne's serene sanctity radiating supernatural peace'. She was, he added, 'the most remarkable woman I know'.[24]

Arriving back in England after his three-week trip, Evelyn got straight down to work and by June he had completed more than half of his manuscript, doing more research as he went along. 'It is a work of pietas,' he told Harold Acton, 'and I enjoy doing it.'[25] But then came the shocking news that Bron was fighting for his life in Cyprus after inadvertently letting off a machine-gun into his own chest while examining it in the turret of his armoured car. Laura flew out the next day, 11 June, and wrote to Evelyn:

Bron has lost one lung and his spleen. He has a shot through the shoulder and his left hand was badly wounded. The Blues doctor who is very nice and who met me when I arrived said his courage was really wonderful. He is an old Downside boy and he said that Bron's resignation and the way he quietly prayed on the way into the hospital had been an inspiring thing to witness and his bravery through it all. They say the next 48 hours are still very critical but he won't be off the danger list for at least another 10 days as there remains the danger of infection. Originally they thought he had no chance at all of surviving. I went and saw him for about 10 minutes tonight and he was clearly in a good deal of pain, particularly breathing – completely uncomplaining but finding hard to speak owing to lack of breath.[26]

Bron had joined the Royal Horse Guards the previous year, aged only seventeen, after choosing to do his National Service before going up to Oxford, a decision he had come to rue well before his horrific accident. When his parents sent him cakes and books to Caterham, Bron replied: 'I cannot tell you how comforting it is to think that there are benevolent agencies working somewhere outside this wilderness of malice and violence and stupidity.'[27]

But soldiering had seemed a good deal more agreeable since arriving on Cyprus: 'So much happens here that I cannot think where to begin,' he wrote to his parents. 'Life is immensely exciting and unbelievably comfortable.'[28] More ominously, he added: 'I cannot hit a human sized target at 10 yards with 20 shots once with my assured pistol, which I am constantly in fear of losing.'[29] On the day of Bron's accident, Evelyn wrote proudly to Diana Cooper: 'My boy is a cornet of the horse. I hope he has some fighting.'[30] A few days later he replied to her letter of sympathy: 'Details are wanting, but it sounds to me as though he will never completely recover. I shall go out to travel home with Laura if he dies.'[31]

Laura sent regular bulletins home and nine days after the accident Evelyn wrote to Ann Fleming: 'It has been an anxious week, but today the news from Cyprus makes it seem probable that Bron will survive. He stopped six bullets and has had a lung, his spleen, two ribs and part of a hand removed. Few people can have lived after such a fusillade. All done by the unaided and independent action of a new-fangled machine gun. I have known many good soldiers hit by their own side (including a posthumous VC)* and several rather moderate soldiers who shot themselves. This is the first time I have known the weapon take control.'[32]

Evelyn's reaction to Bron's plight was in some ways reminiscent of the striking detachment he had displayed all those years ago when his baby daughter Mary died the day after she had been born. His decision not to accompany Laura to Cyprus to see Bron struck some people as odd, however he seems to have decided that his going would make no difference to his son's recovery. 'Prayer is the only thing,' he told Diana. 'The one good result of newspaper reports is that monks and nuns and priests all over the country are praying for him.'[33]

---

* Evelyn probably had in mind his fellow commando Geoffrey Keyes, VC, killed during the Rommel raid in 1941.

Besides, by staying behind and holding the fort he was able pass on all Laura's farming instructions: 'Will you tell Giovanni* to give one spoonful of cake daily to Magdalen and Desdemona this week and two spoonfuls daily to them from next Monday. Also if Lucy is still giving 40lbs a day of milk she had better be artificially inseminated the next time she comes bulling with the Aberdeen Angus bull. If she is not giving as much as 40lbs I do not want her served at all.'[34]

The same letter carried news that Bron would shortly be coming off the danger list. But Evelyn rightly suspected that his son's recovery would still be long and complicated. Hence he wrote to Bron's old housemaster at Downside, Father Aelred: 'Please continue to pray for him. I am sure it is prayer which has saved him so far.'[35] Similarly to Father Caraman: 'Please don't let any of the kind people who have been praying for him turn to other topics.'[36] Whenever Bron suffered a setback, Evelyn suspected all the nuns and monks and clergy and laity who had been 'praying like mad' of suddenly slackening off. When he made progress, the reverse was assumed to be the case. 'The Novena has worked,' Evelyn wrote to Daphne Acton in August. 'My son has taken a turn for the better. Thanks awfully. It was most obliging of you.'[37]

Bron was eventually flown back to the Queen Alexandra Military Hospital at Millbank in early July. 'Welcome home,' wrote Evelyn. 'I am delighted that you have escaped from the torrid and treacherous island of Cyprus. I wish I could come and greet you but I have a long-standing and very tedious engagement in Germany. It started as a treat for your mother, who now can't come with me. I am being paid to stand up in a theatre in Munich and read aloud for an hour to an audience of Huns who think that such a performance will somehow help celebrate the 800th anniversary of the foundation of their city. I am sure neither the Huns nor I will enjoy it.'[38]

Evelyn finally saw Bron a week later and promptly resolved to have him transferred to the more comfortable King Edward VII's Hospital for Officers (Sister Agnes) in Marylebone. But an abscess on Bron's back promptly developed into a chronic infection of his chest cavity, and he was instead moved to the Westminster Hospital to be cared for by Sir

---

* Giovanni Manfredi was employed at Combe Florey to wait at table as well as acting as cowman; his wife Maria did the cooking.

Clement Price Thomas, 'a noted chest surgeon,' as Bron later recorded, 'who had chiefly distinguished himself by his unsuccessful operation on the late King George VI for lung cancer'.[39]

Desperately ill and afraid once again that he might die, Bron scribbled a letter to his father: 'Dear Papa, Just a line to tell you what for some reason I was never able to show you in my lifetime, that I admire, revere and love you more than any other man in the world. My possessions belong to you in any case, and will obviously be retained, divided or jumble-sold at your discretion, but I should very much like my collection of gramophone records to be given to the Grothiers (that is Vera [the Waughs' nanny] and her husband). Love Bron.'[40] He sent this to his bank in a sealed envelope with instructions that it was to go to his father in the event of his pre-deceasing him.

By early August, Bron was still too weak for the major operation that Sir Clement had planned and so the surgeon suggested that he go to King Edward VII's Hospital after all. 'He is now fattening up in Sister Agnes's home for butchery and is greatly enjoying himself being much pampered by all,' Evelyn told Daphne Acton. 'This is primarily to say stop praying for Bron. I am sure there are more urgent cases waiting for your attention.'[41] As a serving officer Bron was admitted free and Evelyn now informed his son that he was stopping the £25 a month allowance he had been paying him as he was short of money and Bron would not need it in hospital, a decision that caused Bron to weep 'bitter tears of rage' by his own account, although naturally he did not say so in his next letter to his father: 'Far from being upset by your action,' Bron replied, 'I am enormously grateful that you should have been so generous as to continue my allowance up to this moment. I hope that you soon overcome your financial difficulties. Mushroom growing is said to be remunerative or you could open a lodging house.'[42]

But his condition continued to fluctuate: 'The news of him is indecisive,' Evelyn wrote to Father Aelred in October. 'He has been moved back and forth between three hospitals and is now at the Westminster. Sir Somebody Something can't make up his mind when to operate.' He added that the 'pampering' Bron was getting was 'inevitable but regrettable, just when the regiment was making a man of him. Please include in your prayers for his physical welfare prayers for his strength of character, when you are so good as to pray for him.'[43] Evelyn wrote along similar lines to Bron's godmother Maimie Lygon, saying that his character was being undermined by 'well disposed people sitting round his bed and satisfying his every whim ... Perhaps you will go & beat him & rob him and undo all the bad work of others.'[44]

When Bron turned twenty that November, Evelyn wrote to him: 'Many happier returns of the day. It has been a year of triumph and disaster, has it not? I am sure you feel very much more than a year older. To have looked into the throat of death at 19 is an experience not to be sneered at.' In the same letter he encouraged him to give up the idea of reading English at Oxford: 'It is a fatal school for anyone who may, as I hope you will, become a writer ... But you are master of your fate and captain of your soul now you are out of your teens.'[45]

Bron finally left hospital the following March. 'At about this time,' he later wrote, 'I began to be quite fond of my father, never having liked him much in childhood or early youth. As I prepared to leave home and set up my own establishments elsewhere he became more tolerant of my various failings, and in the last five years of his life we enjoyed a distinct cordiality.'[46]

If Evelyn's relations with his eldest son had been strained at times, those with his middle daughter Margaret occasionally bordered on a love affair. Known in the family as Meg, and by Evelyn variously as 'pig', 'disgusting hog' and 'sweet swine', Margaret had been his 'eye-apple' ever since she was about five and prematurely allowed to eat in the dining room to save her from a violent nanny. Before sending her to boarding school aged nine, Evelyn described her to the headmistress as 'very pretty, very stupid, with abounding charm'.[47] She was soon homesick and it was while spending the summer term of 1953 being educated at home by Evelyn that she became 'his official favourite', as she later recalled, 'a position neither resented nor sought by my siblings and one which carried with it the risks of disproportionate disfavour as well as the advantages of privilege'.[48]

The previous year Evelyn had written to Ann Fleming: 'My sexual passion for my ten year old daughter is obsessive, I wonder if you'll come to feel this way about your son. I can't keep my hands off her.'[49] If this was most likely a provacative joke, designed to shock his proudly unshockable friend, Evelyn's bond with Meg was clearly intense and became increasingly so as a result of her unhappiness at school. 'When we meet you must tell me whether you are really unhappy or merely giving way to a silly mood. I love you & will not let you be really unhappy if I can prevent it ... darling little girl.'[50]

Defiant, capricious and intermittently lazy as a teenager, Meg was often in trouble at St Mary's Ascot. Evelyn was invariably reassuring, if not uncritically so. 'Darling Meg,' he wrote shortly before her fifteenth birthday, 'I am sorry you are in hot water. You do not have to tell me that you have not done anything really wicked. I know my pig. I am absolutely confident that you will never be dishonourable, impure or cruel ... the part of your letter I don't like at all is when you say the nuns "hate" you. That is rubbish. And when you run down girls who behave better than you. That is mean. Chuck it, Meg ... You are loved far beyond your deserts, especially by your Papa.'[51]

Eventually Meg and the school had decided they had enough of one another and in 1958, aged 15, a few months before Bron's accident, she had returned home again to be taught by Evelyn. 'Bron has got his commission in the Blues,' Evelyn wrote to Diana Cooper at the time, '– many sons of old Blues failed. He must have some guts. He succeeds. Scholarship at the House [Christ Church, Oxford] and now this. But he's a queer morose boy, sloping round the woods with a gun alone or playing light opera on his gramophone. Teresa has had a dazzling term academically. But Meg for me anytime though she's jolly fat at the moment and eats an abnormal amount.'[52]

To Maime Lygon later that year Evelyn described Meg as 'the joy of my heart, perhaps what you were to Boom only she does not bring me cocktails in my bath'.[53] That Christmas, with Bron still in hospital in London, Evelyn seized the opportunity to spend three days at the Hyde Park Hotel with Meg. 'Our ostensible reason,' he told Ann Fleming, 'is to protect Bron from the worst of the Welfare festivities when he fears a Saturnalia when all the nurses dress up as surgeons and the surgeons as nurses and sing carols. My motive is to escape the Saturnalia at home, Margaret's to visit the theatre and the Cathedral. It will be easier to keep her sober when I have my eye directly on her.'[54]

* * *

Evelyn finally finished his Knox biography in early January 1959 and a few weeks later set off for his annual winter holiday, this year comprising a two-month tour of Central and East Africa. 'I have let myself in for crossing the whole of Darkers,' he wrote to Diana Cooper, 'and writing a sickening account of it when I get home. Damn.'[55] He returned in April feeling greatly rejuvenated and was soon 'half heartedly writing a travel book of ineffable tedium and triviality'[56] to pay for his trip. *A Tourist in Africa* (1960) is as elegantly written as one might expect and has several very funny passages, however it was fair to say, as Cyril Connolly did, that it was 'quite the thinnest piece of book-making that Mr Waugh has undertaken'.[57]

Of far more importance to Evelyn was the reception of his latest magnum opus, *Ronald Knox*, which was published by Chapman & Hall in the autumn of 1959. Just before publication his agent Peters had told Evelyn that he would value his copy of *Knox* above all his books 'because I suspect that you have put into it more care, thought, time and slogging hard work than into anything else you have written. Certainly it is the most difficult task you have ever undertaken. And certainly it is triumphantly achieved.'[58] The critics on the whole agreed, even Graham Greene, who admitted to finding the subject at times 'repellent', and the sales greatly exceeded expectations, surpassing 12,000 copies within a month.

The book was not without inaccuracies, as detailed in a 2,500-word letter to the author from the Archbishop of Westminster, but Evelyn accepted the corrections with good grace and promised to amend the next edition. Rather more embarrassing for him was the identification of someone both he and Knox had carefully disguised in their books as 'C', a young Etonian whom Knox had fallen platonically in love with while tutoring him for an Oxford scholarship. 'The question you asked me about the identity of "C" in *Knox*,' Evelyn wrote to Maurice Bowra, 'has been answered in the newspapers by prize shit Muggeridge, who bluffed the truth out of my aged mother-in-law.'[59] The mystery person was none other than the then Prime Minister, Harold Macmillan, quite a scoop for Malcolm Muggeridge in his *New Statesman* diary and perhaps doubly satisfying (or revenge even) given that two years earlier Evelyn had ostentatiously discarded his ear-trumpet during a speech Muggeridge made at a Foyles' luncheon given in Evelyn's honour.

In January 1960 he set off on another winter jaunt, enjoying 'a ripping time at the expense of the *Daily Mail*'[60] in Venice and Monte Carlo with

Laura, followed almost immediately by a trip with Margaret to Athens to visit his old friend Coote Lygon, who was living there at the time (her family formed a theory that she was a spy), and then Rome, returning to Combe Florey in early March. Two weeks later, for a £250 fee he agreed to appear on *Face to Face*, the TV interview series which had begun the previous year and already featured an array of luminaries ranging from Carl Jung to King Hussein of Jordan.

'Please make it a condition that all letters addressed to me at BBC are returned to senders marked "address unknown",' Evelyn wrote to Peters beforehand. 'I have been greatly annoyed by readers of *Pinfold* who wish to compare their hallucinations with mine.'[61] As his grilling drew nearer he contacted Tom Driberg: 'I have let myself in for cross-examination on Television by a man named Major Freeman who I am told was a colleague of yours in the Working Class Movement. Do you know anything damaging about him that I can introduce into our conversation if he becomes insolent?'[62] But he need not have feared. John Freeman may have been a far shrewder and more penetrating interviewer than Stephen Black, but Evelyn again comfortably had the upper hand, his sharp responses as calm as they were clever and delivered with a gleam in his eyes that suggested only mild bemusement at all the impertinent questions he was being asked to answer. Freeman later described it as his most disappointing interview, perhaps because he was so consistently outmanoeuvred during their exchanges:

'Are you a snob at all?'

'I don't think.'

'Irritability with your family, with strangers?'

'Absolutely everything. Inanimate objects and people, animals, everything.'

'Have you ever brooded on what appeared to you to be unjust or adverse criticism?'

'No. I'm afraid if someone praises me I think "What an ass", and if they abuse me I think "What an ass".'

'And if they say nothing about you at all and take no notice of you?'

'That's the best I can hope for.'

'You like that when it happens?'

'Yes.'

'Why are you appearing in this programme?'
'Poverty. We've both been hired to talk in this deliriously happy way.'

Having spent so much time for so little reward (his advance was £3,000) on the *Knox* biography, Evelyn had good reason to be worried about money. Beset by punitive taxation and with his *Brideshead* royalties having long since virtually dried up, he struggled to maintain the standard of living that he had enjoyed before the war. He had let go of Ellwood, the butler, when they moved to Combe Florey and after Giovanni and Maria Manfredi finally left in early 1961 they had only daily help in the house; later that year they acquired 'an engine for washing plates' which quickly became 'an object of worship like a tractor in an early Bolshevist film'.[63]

Evelyn was in some ways quite relieved to see the Manfredis go. Besides the fact that Laura no longer had to contend with the 'nervous annoyances of their tantrums and avarice',[64] as Evelyn saw it, she also had less to occupy her after selling all her beloved cows, another consequence of their reduced circumstances. 'Laura has at last had to give up her herd of cows and mourns them,' Evelyn told Diana Cooper that Christmas Eve just past. 'They cost as much to keep as a troupe of ballet girls and the horrible politicians made a law that one can no longer charge them against income tax.'[65]

Evelyn was at the time hard at work on *Unconditional Surrender*, the final novel in his war trilogy, which he had begun in April 1960 and would take a year to write. His expected earnings from the book were modest, however he still had his artistic vocation to fulfil, as he explained to his publisher: 'Soon I shall have to jump at every chance of writing the history of insurance companies or prefaces to school text-books. Squire and Belloc warn us of the horrors of longevity. But meanwhile, while I have any vestige of imagination left, I must write novels.'[66]

To add to his expenses, between finishing his book in the spring and publishing it in the autumn of 1961, his two eldest children were married. In her last year at Oxford Teresa had met and fallen in love with a postgraduate Classics scholar from Princeton called John D'Arms, whom she first brought to Combe Florey in the spring of 1959. After a subsequent visit that summer, Evelyn wrote to Bron: 'He is not superficially very American (his father, too, was at Oxford), dresses somberly, parts his hair and speaks in low tones. But he has the basic earnestness of his compatriots which I should find unendurable. However that is Teresa's business, not mine. I am sure he would be a kind and conscientious husband and I shall not have to talk to him.'[67] After receiving John's formal request to marry Teresa in November 1960, Evelyn wrote to congratulate his future son-in-law 'on your successful courtship of my daughter' and 'still more on your resolution to become a Catholic'. 'I am sending you her pedigree,' he added. 'It is not illustrious on my side but it will demonstrate that she has no unacceptable taints in her blood.'[68]

Bron, meanwhile, had lately been seeing a lot of a bright young brunette called Teresa Onslow and in early 1961 they too agreed marry, a decision which Evelyn feared they had come to 'in a mood of irresponsible high spirits which reminds me painfully of my marriage to Evelyn [Gardner],'* as he told Pansy Lamb.[69] Bron and Teresa were both only twenty-one at the time and she declined to convert to Catholicism, however on the plus side she was the daughter of the 6th Earl of Onslow and descended from more British monarchs than George VI, the king at the time of her birth.[70] 'It is very distressing that my son should think of marriage at an age when he should give himself to the education of a *femme du monde de quarante ans*,' Evelyn wrote to Jack Donaldson, 'but, as you remark, in this age of miscegenation it is agreeable that he should have chosen a consort of his own class.'[71] And to his brother Alec: 'Your nephew Auberon Alexander has imprudently become engaged . . . a Protestant alas, but pretty & sharp. I don't know her well but I think he is fortunate.'[72]

The prospect of both weddings filled Evelyn with a mixture of gloom and anxiety. 'My life at the moment is hideously overshadowed & agitated by weddings,' he wrote to Daphne Fielding in May. 'I have a daughter marrying a studious & penniless yank in a fortnight and hard on that a son marrying a pretty, well endowed English girl. But the turmoil & expense are damnable.'[73]

Teresa and John D'Arms were married by Father D'Arcy at a Catholic church in Taunton at the beginning of June, with the reception held at Combe Florey. Evelyn later confided to a Catholic friend that the ring had been placed on Teresa's right hand, adding: 'I hope this will provide grounds for a suit of nullity.'[74] He was not so much against the match

---

* Lady Teresa Onslow was Evelyn Gardner's first cousin twice removed.

as anxious that his daughter should have an escape route (rather in the same way that some nervous parents nowadays insist on a 'prenup') in case anything went wrong – bearing in mind of course the problems he had had disentangling himself from Evelyn Gardner. Evelyn found the prolonged wedding celebrations 'extremely painful', although John's parents, who came over from Massachusetts, turned out to be 'rather a jolly couple and quite indefatigable', their remarkable stamina over several days staying with the Waughs leaving Evelyn 'prostrated',[75] he told Ann Fleming. When they had all gone, he wrote tenderly to his 'dear first-born' daughter: 'I think you have found an exceptionally nice husband and am confident of your happiness.'

By way of a postscript he added: 'Yesterday's *Sunday Times* had an article on paternity by Mr. Mathew M.P. He said it was essential to the happy relations of fathers and children that they should congregate at bath-time. The children should stand around their father's bath. The spectacle of his nakedness and wetness while they are clothed and dry establishes confidence and equality. I am sorry I failed you in this.'[76]

Bron and Teresa's wedding was to take place a month later in London, in the same Warwick Street church where Evelyn and Laura had married, but as the day loomed Evelyn began to look for ways he might possibly wriggle out of it. Bron was alive to the danger, having previously failed to entice Evelyn to either his passing out parade or his twenty-first birthday party at the Hyde Park Hotel, the latter paid for by Chapman & Hall and combined with a book celebration for Bron's first novel *The Foxglove Saga*, which had quickly sold 14,000 copies in hardback. As Alexander Waugh records: 'The party was crowded with important people – the Prime Minister, the Duke and Duchess of Devonshire, Sir Isaiah Berlin and many of Evelyn's closest and oldest friends – but Evelyn and Laura stayed at home.'[77] A week prior to the wedding, Bron wrote to Evelyn: 'I hope you will have the fortitude to remain throughout the reception – at any rate until the hand shaking and photographing are over.'[78] A few days later Evelyn wrote back: 'Your sister Margaret has the grippe [flu]. I may have to stay and nurse her while your mother attends your nuptials.'[79] But Laura made sure he went in the end.

Four days later Evelyn told Meg that he had 'nearly' recovered from the wedding. 'What I have not recovered from is the photograph of myself in the *Sunday Express*. I had no idea how old & gross I had become. As I eat nothing it must be drink. Not a drop of wine, whisky or gin has passed my lips since Sunday. I hope when we next meet you will notice a great change.'[80] Evelyn had lately been getting through half a bottle of spirits and a bottle of wine a day. Once on his austere regime, on which he was soon claiming to have 'shrunk to a little wizened monkey',[81] he found he did not miss it, although as so often when he stopped drinking he became rather silent and depressed. Only this time the gloom would prove harder to dislodge.

23

....

Decline and Fall

'Only when one has lost all curiosity about the future has one reached the age to write an autobiography.'[1] So begins *A Little Learning*, the first of a projected three-part autobiography which Evelyn started shortly after the two weddings, in July 1961. Assured by Peters that the three volumes should bring in 'over £29,000 – say £5,000 a year for six years',[2] Evelyn began by reading a draft of *The Early Years of Alec Waugh*, his brother's memoir which was due out the next year, and afterwards thanked Alec for 'the kind things you say about me'. He tactfully told his brother what 'a deep interest & pleasure' it was to read his book,[3] but later confided to his daughter Meg that it was actually *'not very nice* – a great deal of boasting about his sexual adventures,'[4] and to Diana Mosley that he considered it 'embarrassingly revealing'.[5]

Still on his post-wedding slimming regime, Evelyn was intrigued to learn that Alec was in the habit of 'spending one day in ten in bed totally fasting and so preserves his monkey-like figure'.[6] 'Twice a day I drink a small glass of cider,' he told Ann Fleming the next month. 'I have halved my consumption of cigars. I have become totally silent. Sometimes I sally out with a scythe and after an hour totter back exhausted.'[7]

Towards the end of the summer, knowing that Evelyn would again want to escape the English winter, Peters arranged for him to retrace his steps of twenty-nine years ago in British Guiana, which became a self-governing country after elections that August, five years prior to gaining full independence. The *Daily Mail* agreed to pay £2,000 (to include travel expenses) in return for five articles, and also to cover the expenses of a 'secretary', in which capacity Evelyn proposed taking along his nineteen-year-old daughter Margaret. 'I am taking Meg with me partly for the pleasure of her company,' he told Teresa, by then living in Rome, 'but chiefly to detach her from the young men she spends her evenings with in London.'[8]

After failing to get into Oxford, Margaret had spent the past six months writing pamphlets about martyrs for the Jesuits at Farm Street ('My daughter is a hagiographer by trade,' her father told friends)[9] where Evelyn's old friend Father Philip Caraman quickly became infatuated with her. He assured Evelyn that in her reserve and soundness of judgement, Margaret was 'mature beyond her years'. 'She has an independence and sound sense that owes much to her deep devotion to you.'[10] But Evelyn worried that away from work his daughter led a life of reckless dissipation, 'pub crawling and *smoking* in Notting Hill Gate'.[11] The previous year he had opposed her plan to rent a room off Bron, telling her, 'You are no more ready for "independence" than the Congo,' and after she had an unsettling experience of drunkenness he advised her to 'go straight off & confess it,' and thereafter to be very careful: 'Don't on any account get tight or even noticeably jolly for a long time. What we don't want is for people to say, "There's that Waugh girl drunk again".'[12] On another occasion he wrote to her: 'I am told you drive recklessly. Don't do that, it's vulgar.'[13] When Meg proposed spending the weekend with a boyfriend at a cottage, Evelyn wrote to her: 'I know jolly well that no amount of chaperoning ever prevents those who want to fornicate from doing so. It is a matter of manners not morals. Well born, well brought up girls do not stay away with young men and well born, well brought up young men don't expect them to or respect them if they do.'[14] But the keeping of bad company persisted, in Evelyn's eyes at least, and in the spring of 1961 he told Ann Fleming: 'Meg is making herself obnoxious in London by moving about with a train of riff-raff who break into people's houses & eat all the food in their larders & drink all their whisky.'[15]

Meg often returned to Combe Florey for weekends, but Evelyn could never get enough of her company as she arrived late on Friday, slept all day Saturday and left again on Sunday. Occasionally he sounded needy: 'I gave you good warning that I should lose interest in you if you neglected me,' he wrote to Meg shortly before Teresa's wedding. 'A generous nature wishes to give, not always to take. A prudent nature seeks to keep in favour with those on whom it is dependent. An honourable nature keeps promises.'[16] Subsequently he reminded her: 'When Alec Waugh was your age he wrote to his father every day.'[17] Yet as Evelyn suggested, Meg was as devoted to him as he was to her. 'You know I love you more than anyone else in the world,' she wrote after one slightly cross letter. 'Please don't stop loving me I couldn't bear it . . . Papa I'll give up living in London and come home for good if you like. I don't love any of my friends here one quarter as much as I love you.'[18]

Between the two weddings, with his younger daughter Harriet due to leave school that summer and in need of somewhere to live in London, Evelyn wrote to Diana Cooper enquiring about the basement of her newly acquired house in Little Venice: 'I am anxious to find rooms in London which my daughters Meg & Hatty could share this autumn, where a trusted friend could keep an eye on them. They could, when required, do devoted duty as ladies in waiting.' Diana replied enthusiastically, whereupon Evelyn sent her 'the essential data about the little girls':

Harriet. Aged 17. Low mentality, high character. She has inherited her father's deep love of you. She regards you as a lady of the theatre rather than of fashion or letters or high politics. She is pretty when she smiles which is often; sometimes she lapses into blank sullenness. She has no pleasure in rural life and no knowledge of the town. Strong theatrical interests. Strong sense of humour. Chaste, sober, wants to get married but has exaggerated ideas of her market value thinking only elder sons of old nobility suitable. Clean & economical. She leaves school this term without learning one word of any foreign language and is therefore unsuitable for finishing abroad. She goes with a school-friend whose father is on post there at our embassy, to Beirut for August and first three weeks of September. After that she will be a problem. I believe you might find her quite amusing and useful as understrapper. Can't spell at all. No secretarial qualities.

Meg aged 19 'works' all day with Jesuits at Farm Street. Drinks all night with impecunious young men. Expensive tastes. Snob. Chaste but self-indulgent. Smokes when I am not near. Loving but grasping. Has also inherited her father's love of you. Filthy in habits. Always in debt. At present she lives with her cousin Anne Fraser (60 Drayton Gardens, S.W.10. Fremantle 9000) who now has two babies & wants to be rid of her. I will not let her live alone. She can't find any suitable friend to share with. It would be no good setting her up with Hatty. She would not look after Hatty & Hatty would have nothing to do all day. Meg would enter with enthusiasm into all your undertakings of house arrangement, talk engagingly while others toiled and do nothing herself. I find her company so bright that it compensates for her deplorable failings.'[19]

The plan was postponed due to Diana's delayed return to London and eventually came to nothing, but by that time Evelyn had already conceived the idea of taking Meg with him to Guiana, an idea which Father Caraman fell in with, agreeing 'she is not sufficiently robust to work here during the day and then go to parties four or five evenings during the week, staying up till midnight and after. A long rest is just what she needs.'[20] To Ann Fleming Evelyn wrote: 'It will be good for her [Meg] to switch to rum for a bit. Port is inflaming her nose.'[21]

The final volume of Evelyn's war trilogy *Unconditional Surrender* was published shortly before they left, dedicated 'To my daughter Margaret, Child of the Locust Years'. As ever, Evelyn was more interested in the views of his friends and family than those of the critics, and most seemed to think that it was 'as good as anything you have ever written'.[22] Maurice Bowra rhapsodised about the 'endless variety in the use of words, the shape of the sentences, the adroit vocabulary. How I envy you . . .'.[23] Evelyn's mother-in-law Mary Herbert thought 'the wonderful chapter on Guy's father's death & funeral says all the central things about the heart of Catholic life & also the heart of the passing relationships of country life and squirearchy without any over emphasis'.

Among the published reviews, none was more glowing than Cyril Connolly's in *The Sunday Times*, acclaiming the trilogy as 'unquestionably the finest novel to have come out of the war',[24] a remarkably generous tribute given that Ann Fleming had convinced Connolly that Everard Spruce and *Survival* magazine was an unkind caricature of himself and *Horizon*. 'It is not very like him but sufficiently like him to be offensive,' wrote Bowra to Mrs Fleming. 'It is sad that Evelyn has such an urge to torture him. It must be a form of love.'[25] Fearing that Mrs Fleming's mischievous intervention had endangered what he termed 'a very long, the always slightly precarious, friendship,'[26] Evelyn did his best to mend fences: 'There are of course asses in London, who don't understand the processes of the imagination, whose hobby is to treat fiction as a gossip column,' he wrote to Connolly. 'But what distresses me (if true) is that you should suppose I would publicly caricature a cherished friend.'[27] Connolly remained sceptical: 'I do not think posterity will ever believe in our friendship any more than someone who looked me up in the index to your biography!'[28] As he prepared to set sail for British Guiana at the end of November, Evelyn made one final bid to soothe his half-hated friend with the news 'that the vampire bats of Amazonas are now infected with rabies, so we may not meet again'.[29]

By strange coincidence the ship on which Evelyn and Meg sailed out to the Caribbean was the same *Stella Polaris* on which he and his first wife had voyaged in the Mediterranean in 1929. This trip was far happier: 'Little Meg proved a good travelling companion,' Evelyn wrote to Diana Cooper on their return, 'never sea sick in the smallest ships in the worst storms, never complaining of discomfort but jolly appreciative of occasional bits of luxury. We came back in a lovely frog steamer full of decaying literary gents. Now her pecker is down & she wants to circumnavigate the globe.'[30] To Teresa he wrote: 'Meg met no one under 50 during her travels and is developing a pretty manner with the senile.'[31]

Among their hosts had been the sixty-year-old Lord Hailes, Churchill's former private secretary and by then Governor-General of the soon-to-be defunct Federation of the West Indies. Having stayed happily and luxuriously with the Haileses in Trinidad, Evelyn was taken aback to learn from Ann Fleming that 'the Haileses found Evelyn a great bore', gossip she had gleaned from Clarissa Avon. 'Well I mean to say,'[32] Evelyn wrote to Diana Cooper, convinced at first that Lady Avon must have got the wrong end of the stick. Later, as the reality sunk in, he wrote to Nancy:

> I must explain about boring the Haileses because it has been what young people call 'traumatic'. Hailes was a pretty young politician you may have known as Patrick Buchan-Hepburn. I knew him slightly years ago . . . I had never met his wife but took a liking to her, and they were jolly hospitable to Meg & me. The crucial point is that I was confident they both enjoyed my visit. It made a lovely change, I thought, from most of their official visitors. When I briefly returned to Trinidad they sent ADCs to drag me back. I talked loud & long & they laughed like anything. Now I find I bored them. Well of course everyone is a bore to someone. One recognizes that. But it is a ghastly thing if one loses the consciousness of being a bore. You do see it means I can never go out again.[33]

Evelyn's self-esteem suffered another blow a week or so later after an encounter at White's: 'I was sitting in the hall at 7 p.m. being no trouble to anyone, when a man I know by sight but not by name – older than I, the same build, better dressed, commoner – came up & said: "Why are you alone?" "Because no one wants to speak to me." "I can tell you exactly why. Because you sit there on your arse looking like a stuck pig."'[34]

Nancy was quick to reassure Evelyn that 'whatever else you may be *you are not a bore*' and that he was 'wasted on people like Buchan-Hepburn with whom one would sooner have been seen dead than dancing, in my recollection of old ballroom days'.[35] However she also told him that her sister Debo Devonshire, whom Evelyn had always adored but also man-aged to alienate recently with some drunken rudeness, had 'cause to be offended judging by the things I've heard you say (which I did not pass on but others have)'.[36] The result of all this was to 'produce strong Pinfold feelings of persecution' and although he attempted to get back to work tinkering with his autobiography,* in April he admitted to Meg that he was 'in low spirits and in low water'.[37]

Meg's own spirits had risen considerably since their return from the Caribbean, not least due to the fact that by the time she received Eve-lyn's gloomy letter she had fallen deeply in love. Her new boyfriend was an Irishman called Giles FitzHerbert, who had first met her as a young girl at Pixton in the 1950s but only really registered her when he went to watch the Grand National in March 1962 at the flat she shared with friends Evelyn called 'the scoffers'. Margaret appeared 'quite shy and awkward' at the time but FitzHerbert remembered being struck by her unusual intelligence, even among the scoffers, who included the future Lord Chief Justice Tom Bingham. She was 'incredibly quick with a clear way of talking,' he recalled. 'Everyone noticed. She didn't gush and there was no small talk.'[38] In early August, Margaret and Giles drove down to Combe Florey to ask Evelyn's permission to marry, and afterwards Giles wrote to thank them 'for giving up such a treasure with such rare grace'.[39]

'Well, she has fallen head over heels in love and I can't find it in my heart to forbid consummation,' wrote Evelyn to Nancy. 'He is a penniless Irish stock broker's clerk named FitzHerbert of good family but rather caddish

---

* 'I have reached myself in my autobiography,' he wrote to Ann Fleming in May, 'and you know how boring that is.'

& raffish appearance. 27 years old and has not done a hands turn – his stock-broker's clerkship began on the day of his engagement. A Catholic of not very pious disposition, father killed honorably in the war, a brother I haven't been allowed to see, whom I suspect is a skeleton in cupboard (as is mine, and also Laura's for that matter). She had a number of suitors of the kind an old fashioned father would have preferred, but she must have FitzHerbert, & *so* she shall. She wants children & that is a thing I can't decently provide for her. I expect that in ten years' time she will be back on my doorstep with a brood.'[40]

Ann Fleming commiserated with Evelyn 'because you will miss her dreadfully' and Diana Cooper wrote that it was a time that 'I have so often dreaded for you – a time that I have known myself [her only son John Julius had married aged twenty-two] when one must deliver one's treasure to another with a generous show of approval'.[41] It was indeed 'a bitter pill and ungilded,' Evelyn admitted. 'I would forbid the marriage if I had any other cause than jealousy & snobbery. As it is, I pretend to be complaisant. Little Meg is ripe for the kind of love I can't give her. So I am surrendering with the honours of war – without war indeed . . . You see I feel that with Meg I have exhausted my capacity for finding objects of love. How does one exist without them? I haven't got the gaiety euphoria that makes old men chase tarts.'[42]

The day before writing to Diana Evelyn had begun what would be his last work of fiction, *Basil Seal Rides Again*, a final outing for the hero of *Black Mischief* (1932) and *Put Out More Flags* (1942) who had always contained elements of Evelyn but now, at the age of sixty, came closer than ever to being a self-portrait. Friends could scarcely fail to spot the parallels between Basil's jealousy over his daughter's plan to marry and Evelyn's own feelings about giving up Margaret, nor perhaps the incestuous undertone in the fictional father-daughter relationship: 'Two arms embraced his neck and drew him down, an agile figure inclined over the protuberance of his starched shirt, a cheek was pressed to his and teeth tenderly nibbled the lobe of his ear . . . He disengaged himself and slapped her loudly on the behind.'[43]

Margaret and Giles were married on 20 October at the Catholic Church of St Elizabeth of Portugal in Richmond, with the reception held at the house of their friend John Chancellor in Kew. Meg wore a tea gown from the dressing-up cupboard originally belonging to her great-grandmother

Evelyn de Vesci and 'looked jolly pretty in it,' Evelyn told Daphne Fielding, 'and jolly funny going away in a black velvet hat & red boots'.[44] From
honeymoon in Italy Meg wrote to thank Evelyn for 'behaving so beautifully' at the wedding, having earlier thanked him for 'being so kind about
my engagement'. 'You are the best father anyone can ever have had in the
history of the world – really no flattery or sucking up, I think that. And
there need be no divorce between us – I will come home just as often for
week ends – Giles won't mind.'[45]

Evelyn's life had been 'much disturbed by the superabundance of
weddings,' he told friends, and the marriages of his three eldest children
in such quick succession seemed scarcely compensated for by his younger
ones still being at home. 'There is another six days of James & Septimus's
holidays,' he wrote to Ann Fleming in September. 'Oh the Hell of it.'[46] The
birth of his first granddaughter, Sophia Waugh, that summer, appeared
to spell potential disruption as much as anything else. 'Bron speaks in
a sinister way of quartering his daughter here,' Evelyn wrote to Teresa.[47]

That autumn was spent working on a first draft of his autobiography.
'I am toiling & tinkering away,' he told Daphne Acton. 'The trouble is
that I am (genuinely) not interested in myself & that while my friends
are alive I can't write candidly about them.'[48] To Nancy Mitford he wrote
that he had been contacting 'various men who were at school with me and
asking whether they object to revelations of their delinquencies. I think
it may have caused a seasonable chill in some reformed breasts. There is
a pompous ass called Hot-lunch Molson who I don't suppose you ever
met. I have a full diary of his iniquities in 1921–2. Perhaps he will fly the
country.'[49]

When Evelyn wrote to ask Lord Molson whether he minded his
mentioning that he had been 'tight' on Ascension day at school, Molson
replied that he did not want to be a spoilsport but in view of the fact that
'that weakness of mine has never been wholly overcome' it would 'not
only upset my wife very much but also faithful friends in the High Peak'
– the Derbyshire constituency which he had represented as an MP before
he was made a peer in 1961.[50]

Evelyn's reminiscences of Molson eventually went well beyond Ascen-
sion Day, and although he omitted his real name, the use of the nicknames
'Preters' and 'Hot Lunch' meant that plenty of people, if not perhaps his
Derbyshire constituents, knew perfectly well who he was. When the book

was eventually published, in 1964, John Betjeman wrote to congratulate Evelyn on 'how lovably ridiculous appears Hot Lunch Molson'.[51]

Molson's alarm was shared by his fellow peer, Matthew (by then Lord) Ponsonby, who as a magistrate hardly relished having his drunken arrest in 1925 dredged up. Others, though, seemed remarkably relaxed, none more so than Evelyn's pederastic one-legged colleague at Arnold House, Dick Young, whom Evelyn traced to an almshouse in Winchester: 'By all means "publish-and-be-damned" so far as I am concerned,' Young replied cheerfully. 'I always flatter myself that I was the original Capt. Grimes.'[52] A few days later he wrote again:

> Incidentally, when I say 'publish and be damned', I trust you will mention no scandal that could remotely connect me – in the mind of the Master of St Cross, the 'local vicar' – to you. True, no man is entitled to a better reputation than he has earned. But one is at St. Cross in some slight degree on the word of 'Referees', and it might be extremely awkward to have any 'suspicions' about oneself floating around, tho' I imagine that several of our old Brothers may have incidents in their past to which they would not purposely draw attention![53]

That all said, Young had no objection to having his misdeeds fully recounted in Evelyn's autobiography under the pseudonym 'Captain Grimes', and when he eventually read the book wrote to tell Evelyn that he found it all rather 'nostalgic'.[54]

Snowbound for much of January 1963 at Combe Florey, in February Evelyn and Laura escaped to Menton in the South of France, but returned early so that Evelyn could fulfill a $5,000 commission to write an obituary of the ailing Pope John XXIII, who died in June. That spring both Margaret and Bron's wife Teresa announced they were expecting babies: 'I hope at least some of these grandchildren will be a source of delight to you in your old age,' wrote Bron. 'Will you let them pull your beard?'[55] Just short of his sixtieth birthday in October, Evelyn heard that his daughter Teresa, too, was pregnant and wrote to congratulate her: 'Does John feel strongly that his offspring should be born on American soil?' he asked. If not he offered to pay Teresa's air fare 'so that it might be a subject of our good queen'. 'It could always renounce allegiance on coming of age if it feels strong republican sentiments.'[56]

At the age of fifty-nine, Evelyn already felt like a geriatric, 'very lame,' he told Ann Fleming. 'Carrying too much weight. Can't get down the weight walking because of the lameness. A vicious circle.'[57] As he became increasingly decrepit, the gardener 'Coggins' (real name Walter Coggan) seemed to spend more and more time deferentially imparting his rural wisdom to Laura in the kitchen garden to the point where Evelyn began referring to him as 'my rival, Mr Coggins'. 'Coggins has become complete master of this property,' Evelyn reported at the end of August.[58] In September, feeling increasingly seedy, as he told Meg, Evelyn booked himself into a health clinic in the New Forest: 'Well, Madam,' Coggins was heard to say to Laura when he heard Evelyn was to be away for a fortnight, 'we shall really be able to get down to it then?'[59] Midway through his stint at the health farm, Evelyn wrote to Ann Fleming: 'I have lost 13 lbs and all my good spirits.'[60]

Once past his sixtieth birthday, however, Evelyn began to cheer up, 'content to be old,' he told a cousin. 'No one can now expect me to carry anything.'[61] He was equally content to see no one outside his close family, not even old friends, and he found the fortieth anniversary meeting of the Oxford University Railway Club that November 'ghastly', despite the intriguing presence of Terence Greenidge, who announced that he had had a large part of his brain removed, rendering him 'very cheerful', Evelyn told Alfred Duggan, but devoid of 'most of the idiosyncrasies which used to endear him'.[62]* Christmas at Combe Florey was as usual 'Hell', Evelyn told Meg, but he was at least 'glad to have a grandson in the male line', Bron's wife Teresa having given birth to a son on 30 December 1963, later christened Alexander Evelyn Michael.

A Little Learning was eventually finished at the end of 1963 and published in the autumn of 1964. The critics were largely complimentary, although some found it a little reticent. V. S. Pritchett in the *New Statesman* called Evelyn 'a thoughtful rather than intimate autobiographer . . . He keeps the lid on',[63] a view that Evelyn effectively endorsed in his later admission to Diana Mosley: 'It is truthful in the sense of stating nothing false but, of course, it omits a good deal.'[64] Anthony Burgess delighted in the book's 'Gibbonian classicism' but was convinced 'it is an act, a

---

* Even on that trip he surrounded himself with family, taking along with him Bron and his son-in-law Giles FitzHerbert.

posture, and it derives from the father's more Dickensian histrionics as much as the fictional gift itself'.[65] Alec Waugh, perhaps relieved to be treated so gently, called it 'an important book because it presents and interprets the seedtime of one of the most important writers of our day'.[66] Among Evelyn's friends, Katharine Asquith was predictably dismayed by the passages about Captain Grimes but overall found the book 'of absorbing interest . . . some of it sounded so happy – some so terribly sad, some so funny & all so beautifully told'.[67]

The most unhappy reader was Evelyn's old Lancing sidekick Dudley Carew, whom he had not named but unkindly portrayed in the book as 'a boy in another house' whom he had 'fascinated and dominated'. 'Why on earth you should deliberately spit in the eye of one who has always wished you well passes my comprehension,' Carew wrote to him after reading the book. 'I have long letters of yours over a period of years which give a very different picture of an old friendship from the contemptuous squiggle of a caricature you have drawn of our relationship which relegates me to the position of a half-witted hanger-on you tolerantly patronized for a term or two . . . Many people whose opinion of me I value will have little difficulty, thanks to your gratuitous clues, in identifying me with the grotesque figure of the "boy in another house". As for my private feelings, you have hurt them most damnably.'[68]

In a bid to set the record straight, ten years later Carew published his own memoir (*A Fragment of Friendship: A Memory of Evelyn Waugh When Young*), which described *A Little Learning* as 'the worst book Evelyn ever wrote' yet whose bitter tone only served to strengthen the impression created by Evelyn in his rather savage pen portrait. In any event, by the time *A Little Learning* came out, Evelyn was fast losing his teeth, literally as well as metaphorically. 'When the last go I shall harden my gums with salt and eat soft foods,' he told Diana Cooper in October.[69] But in December he announced: 'I may buy a lot of new teeth in the new year and see if they help. Most of my lack of appetite comes from the boredom of chewing with my few, loose teeth. Not eating drives me to the bottle – both spirits & drugs. One can't sleep hungry.'[70]

'I own a toothbrush but since I have no teeth it is a superfluous possession,' he wrote to Ann Fleming in the new year, 'like the tiaras of ladies who are never asked out.'[71] In March 1965 he had his few remaining wobbly teeth drawn in order to make room for a new set, insisting on going through with the procedure without an anaesthetic as his father had done. 'It would be inconvenient for Laura if I kicked the bucket,' he acknowledged to Nancy Mitford beforehand, 'otherwise no apprehensions.'[72] Two months after the operation he told her: 'Honks [Diana Cooper] tells everyone I am dying. I don't think it's true. But I suffer in dignity & pleasure from my new snappers and I do no work.'[73]

But although they initially pleased him, his new teeth were never entirely successful and some months later he announced: 'I have lost the art of eating.'[74] All in all, the past twelve months had been rather grim for him, beset by death as well as dentistry, beginning with that of Alfred Duggan, followed by Baby Jungman's son Richard Cuthbertson, killed in a car accident, then Harry Ilchester (formerly Stavordale) and Phil Dunne. 'There has not been a fortnight without a funeral,' Evelyn told Nancy in May. 'Ian Fleming [who had died in August 1964] is being posthumously canonized by the intelligentsia. Very rum.'[75]

After going to see Edward Albee's play *Who's Afraid of Virginia Woolf?* in September, Evelyn confessed to Nancy: 'I find I can't follow the plot of any plays or films nowadays, whether it is my decay or theirs I don't know.'[76] By far the greatest of his woes, though, was his dismay at the conclusion of the Second Vatican Council, which had radically reformed the Latin Mass, demystifying the priest's role and replacing Latin with the vernacular, to the point at which Evelyn now hated going to church. 'The buggering up of the Church is a deep sorrow to me and to all I know,' he told Nancy. 'We write letters to the papers. A fat lot of good that does.'[77] 'No one minds more than I,' he wrote to Ann Fleming, '& no one can do less.'[78]

His deepening gloom began to worry friends and family. 'I've never seen you so low as before I went away,' wrote Meg at the beginning of December. 'It seemed a more abiding settled depression than ever before. Darling Papa please don't be unhappy – you may think this an impertinence but it is written in love – I think your trouble is that you don't go to the sacraments often enough. You can't expect your faith to suffer these onslaughts unless you sustain it.'[79]

Evelyn replied: 'You must not worry about my condition. I am growing old and old men suffer from aberrations of one kind of another. Dope is less harmful and less sinful than, say, drink or chasing young girls or boys. It would of course be better to be a saint. God chooses his own. The awful prospect is that I may have more than 20 years ahead. Pray that I "make my soul" in this period. I shall just become more and more boring I fear. Don't let me in my dotage oppress you.'[80]

Margaret now feared that he really was trying to kill himself: 'Please, please Papa see a doctor – a proper specialist. Your stomach has probably shrunk or certainly will & you are growing physically weaker under one's eyes ... If there is no eternity then life is precious & if there is life is just as precious – eternity is forever & ever there is no point in prolonging it.'[81]

Evelyn rallied slightly in the new year of 1966, but responded despairingly when nagged by a publisher about the delivery of a book on the Crusades he had promised the previous year. 'Tell them I have temporarily lost my reason as the result of the Vatican Council,' Evelyn pleaded with Peters. 'Tell them anything. Get them to release me from my foolhardy promise.'[82] He intended instead to concentrate on the second volume of his autobiography; however he gave a fairly clear hint to Christopher Sykes (who was afraid of what it might say about him) that it would never be finished: 'My life is roughly speaking over. I sleep badly except occasionally in the morning. I get up late. I try to read my letters. I try to read the paper. I have some gin. I try to read the paper again. I have some more gin. I try to think about my autobiography. Then I have some more gin and it's lunch time. That's my life. It's ghastly.'[83] His correspondence with friends was littered with oblique references to death: 'Maurice [Bowra] has sent me (unsolicited) the extract from his memoirs that deals with me,' Evelyn told Ann Fleming. 'It is as respectful & affectionate as an obituary.'[84]

On Easter Sunday, 10 April 1966, Evelyn attended a Latin Mass in the Catholic chapel in the small market town of Wiveliscombe, five miles from Combe Florey, accompanied by Laura, Hatty, James, Septimus, and all the FitzHerberts – Margaret, Giles and their two little girls, Emily and Claudia. The service was conducted by Father Philip Caraman, who was staying at Pixton. Evelyn appeared surprisingly cheerful, benign and friendly to everyone, even to Auberon Herbert, who was also in the congregation, along with his mother Mary and sister Bridget. Afterwards they all drove back to Combe Florey, where again Evelyn was in high spirits as they all gathered in the morning room. At some point he left the room to go to the library where a postcard was later found, dated 10 April, addressed to a Catholic academic called Professor Robin Anderson:

'Many thanks for your interesting sympathetic letter. We live in a dark age. I cannot hope to live to see it lighter.'[85]

It was almost certainly the last thing Evelyn wrote. When he failed to reappear for lunch, a search was begun during which Septimus, fifteen at the time, eventually knocked on the door of the downstairs lavatory, which was locked from the inside. Getting no answer, he fetched a ladder so that he could peer in through a high window and saw his father slumped on the floor having suffered a heart attack. In shock he called out to his nineteen-year-old brother James, who managed to climb in through the window and unlock the door. Evelyn was then dragged out into the passageway, where the FitzHerberts' Irish nanny, Maureen Regan (henceforth 'Nurse Regan') attempted mouth-to-mouth resuscitation. Father Caraman, to whom Evelyn had given a cheque that morning for ten guineas for his Mass, administered conditional absolution – 'Si vivis, ego te absolvo a peccatis tuis. In nomine Patris et Filio et Spiritus Sancti, amen'* – before summoning the priest at Wiveliscombe, Father Formosa, to bring his oils to anoint the dead man. Bron and Teresa were living at Hungerford at the time and had been out to a long lunch with friends, leaving their two young children, Sophia and Alexander, at home with their nanny. When they arrived back that evening to find a policeman on their doorstep Bron immediately feared something terrible had happened to his children and it came as a 'conscious relief' to hear that instead his father had died suddenly in Somerset.

On further reflection, he wrote: 'To die on Easter Sunday, after communion, among friends, with no lingering deterioration of the faculties, must be reckoned a merciful death.'[86] Margaret, too, although devastated saw some cause for comfort: 'Don't be too upset about Papa,' she wrote to his great friend Diana Cooper. 'You know how he longed to die and dying as he did on Easter Sunday, when all the liturgy is about death and resurrection, after a Latin mass and holy communion, would be exactly what he wanted. I am sure he had prayed for death at Mass. I am very, very happy for him.'[87]

---

* 'If you are living, I absolve you from your sins. In the name of the Father and of the Son and of the Holy Ghost, amen.'

Epilogue

Evelyn was buried on the Friday after Easter in a special plot on the edge of the Combe Florey garden adjoining the Anglican churchyard of St Peter and St Paul. The funeral at the Catholic church of St Teresa of Lisieux in Taunton was conducted by Father Caraman, who also gave the address at a full Requiem Mass held six days later at Westminster Cathedral, where special dispensation was obtained for the Mass to be said in Latin. The congregation sang six verses of Evelyn's favourite hymn, 'O God, Our Help in Ages Past', which he used to hum to himself while working in the library.

The obituaries paid tribute to the precision of his prose, his wildly comic invention and unique satiric stance, while also recording his deep aversion to the modern world, his staunch Catholic apologetics and his reputation for misanthropy and snobbery. Bron thought the notices 'with few exceptions, extraordinarily grudging',* and indeed they mostly over-looked the more humane side of Evelyn's character, which was left to his friends to record in their letters of condolence to Laura. When news of his death reached Graham Greene in Paris late on Easter Day he promptly sent a note saying he was 'shocked more than I can find it possible to write'. 'As a writer I admired him more than any other living novelist & as a man I loved him. He was a very loyal and patient friend to me. What I loved most in him was that rare quality that he would only say the kind things behind one's back.'†

---

* Responding to the obituaries in an article in *The Spectator* that May, Bron wrote: 'The main point about my father, which might be of interest . . . is not that he was interested in pedigree – it was the tiniest part of his interests. It is not that he was a conservative – politics bored him . . . it is simply that he was the funniest man of his generation.'

† A few days later in *The Times*, Greene described Evelyn as 'the greatest novelist of my generation' and wrote: 'We were deeply divided politically, we were divided even in our conception of the same church, and there were times when certain popular journalists tried

Among the many letters that followed was one from Diana Mosley, who had been estranged from Evelyn for more than thirty years until they were reconciled a few weeks before he died. 'Evelyn was such an extraordinarily gifted, clever and really good person,' she wrote to Laura, 'so unusual – unique – that your loss does not bear thinking about. He is the sort of person one would miss more and more. Even I, who never had the joy of seeing him, feel so sad today.'[2] Her sister Nancy (Mitford) said that she 'loved Evelyn I really think the best of all my friends . . . he was far the best living writer of English without a doubt. For him one can only say he did hate the modern world, which does not become more liveable every day.'[3]

Evelyn's agent Peters called it 'a literary tragedy' that he had not completed his autobiography, and remembered his client as 'unfailingly kind & generous to me during the whole of the forty years that I knew him – never a harsh word or a rebuke, even when I deserved them. The world who did not know him had, I'm afraid, a distorted picture of him which he himself took some trouble to paint. But the real Evelyn was a very fine man. I loved him and I shall miss him for the rest of my life.'[4]

There was much mention in the letters of Evelyn's strength and singularity. For Patrick Kinross, he stood out as 'the most alive, the most consistently his personal self' among his friends. 'Even in his poses he was simply burlesquing some part of himself. What a joy he was to be with, & to hear from and to talk about! Whatever mood he was in, gay or morose, benign or angry – he was always thoroughly positive and in the whollest sense human. What a strong and alive personality. No one so dominated a room by simply being in it. His affections were constant & he was the staunchest of friends & the most outspoken too. His friendship was not only a solace and stimulus, but a challenge. This made him the ideal literary mentor, not only encouraging and praising but criticising sharply.'[5]

Several writers recalled Evelyn's generosity, including P. G. Wodehouse, whom he had long championed as 'the Master' and whose reputation he had staunchly defended after Wodehouse came under attack for broadcasting from Germany during the war. Although they had only met once,

---

to push us into what Indonesians would call a confrontation, but Evelyn had an unshakable loyalty to his friends, even if he may have detested their opinions and sometimes their actions. One could never rely on him for an easy approval or a warm weak complaisance, but when one felt the need of him he was always there.' *The Times*, 15 April 1966.

in New York, Wodehouse had 'always looked on him as one of my dearest friends,' he told Laura, 'and I can never forget all he did for me'.[6] Angus Wilson described Evelyn's praise for his first published short story in 1947 as 'the most exciting thing I can remember to do with my writing' and was equally appreciative of his reviews of his early novels when he felt misunderstood by other critics. 'That this encouragement should have come from someone who differed from me in all social and political questions was only what one had come to expected from somebody who cared so completely about writing for itself. But for me that it should have come from our finest novelist was everything.'[7] Robert Henriques was another who, reading back over the letters Evelyn had written to him over the years, felt 'overwhelmingly what a deeply <u>kind</u> person he was' although he also admitted that he had always been rather afraid of him. 'To me he was a superior kind of person, not just intellectually, and as the best writer of our generation, but morally and in ways I can't define. Yet, while feeling more diffident with him than with anyone else I have ever known, I was always keenly aware of his great concern for his friends. Very few people have seemed to mind as much as he did about how his friends were faring. That, and his generosity and his intense loyalties, were qualities as important to his friends as his wit and brilliance.'[8]

Many sought comfort from the timing of his death and from the fact that, as Daphne Acton wrote, he 'didn't like the way things were going, so he will be happy seeing them from another angle'.[9] Dorothy Lygon remembered Evelyn as 'so much part of our youth & was a focusing point of endless fun & happiness [but] it does seem to have been the sort of end one would wish for oneself & perhaps what he would have chosen too'.[10] Diana Cooper suggested to Laura that Evelyn had died 'too young for you but perhaps right for him who never was closely held by the world & its illusions'. He would mind leaving 'You above all things,' she added, 'for you have loved & served & arranged for him & lived for him as no other woman could have done.'[11]

For John Betjeman, too, it was at least 'a joy to think of how perfectly you [Laura] and he were suited to each other, and that Bron has inherited the family genius'.[12] Penelope said 'what a marvellous wife you have been to him',[13] as did Daphne Acton, who ventured that Evelyn 'must have been a whole-time job for you, which you carried out with all heart'.[14]

With the main focus gone from her life, Laura took increasingly to the sherry and passed the time with crosswords and her cows. Barely three months after Evelyn's death, she put Combe Florey up for sale but later changed her mind and continued to live there until Bron and his family took the house over in 1971, whereupon she moved into a wing at the back. Some years before his death, Evelyn had discussed selling his papers to the University of Texas to help fund his retirement. Laura was wrongly advised that she had been left short of money and agreed to the sale of his entire library, bookshelves and all. Some years later she sold the rights to his diaries to *The Observer* without her or any member of the family having read them. When they were published, first in 1973 as extracts in the newspaper and three years later as a book, the countless disobliging references caused a furore and were widely seen as providing corroboration for those who had come to regard Evelyn as an ogre. Laura was at least spared much of the outcry, having died suddenly from pneumonia shortly after the first extracts appeared. She was buried on her fifty-seventh birthday: 'more deeply mourned,' Bron later wrote, 'than her modest nature would ever have understood.'

Notes

Page references to works cited are to the editions listed in the Bibliography unless otherwise stated.

AWA   Alexander Waugh Archive
BL   British Library
BU   Boston University Library
CU   Columbia University
EAR   *The Essays, Articles and Reviews of Evelyn Waugh*, edited by Donat Gallagher
EWCH   *Evelyn Waugh: The Critical Heritage*, edited by Martin Stannard
EWD   *The Diaries of Evelyn Waugh*, edited by Michael Davie
EWL   *The Letters of Evelyn Waugh*, edited by Mark Amory
GU   Georgetown Univerity
HRC   The Harry Ransom Center, University of Texas at Austin
IWM   Imperial War Museum
LHC   Liddell Hart Centre for Military Archives, King's College, London
LNMEW   *Letters of Nancy Mitford and Evelyn Waugh*, edited by Charlotte Mosley
MWMS   *Mr Wu & Mrs Stitch: the Letters of Evelyn Waugh and Diana Cooper*, edited by Artemis Cooper

1 Second Son

1. *A Little Learning*, p. 28.
2. Ibid.
3. Ibid., p.63.
4. See John Howard Wilson, *Evelyn Waugh: A Literary Biography 1903–1924*, pp. 18 and 180; quoted in Alexander Waugh, *Fathers and Sons*, p. 77.

5. Ibid., p. 77; Alec Waugh, *My Brother Evelyn*, p. 164.

6. Christopher Sykes, *Evelyn Waugh*, p. 7.

7. Alexander Waugh, *Fathers and Sons*, p. 79; Alec Waugh, *My Brother Evelyn*, p. 164.

8. It is not recorded who came up with the nickname. Alexander Waugh suspects it was either Evelyn or his mother.

9. *A Little Learning*, p. 22; Alexander Waugh, *Fathers and Sons*, p. 25.

10. Alec Waugh, *The Early Years of Alec Waugh*, pp. 7–8; Alexander Waugh, *Fathers and Sons*, pp. 24–8; *A Little Learning*, pp. 20–23.

11. *A Little Learning*, p. 22.

12. Arthur Waugh, *One Man's Road*, p. 34.

13. Alexander Waugh, *Fathers and Sons*, p. 24.

14. Alec Waugh, *Early Years*, p. 7.

15. *A Little Learning*, p. 22.

16. Alexander Waugh, *Fathers and Sons*, p. 24.

17. Arthur Waugh, *One Man's Road*, p. 61.

18. Alexander Waugh, *Fathers and Sons*, pp. 90–91; Arthur Waugh, *One Man's Road*, p. 63.

19. Sykes, *Evelyn Waugh*, p. 4.

20. As an example, Evelyn records his 'signally humourless' intended wording (never used) for his planned memorial in the church. See *A Little Learning*, pp. 18 and 20.

21. Auberon Waugh, *Will This Do?*, p. 19.

22. *A Little Learning*, p. 21.

23. Ibid., p. 9.

24. Arthur Waugh, *One Man's Road*, pp. 12–13.

25. *A Little Learning*, p. 21.

26. Alec Waugh, *Early Years*, p. 7.

27. *A Little Learning*, p. 49.

28. Ibid.

29. Ibid., p. 47.

30. Ibid., pp. 44–7.

31. Ibid., p. 48.

32. Arthur Waugh, *One Man's Road*, p. 23.

33. Quoted in Alec Waugh, *Early Years*, p. 9.

34. Alexander Waugh, *Fathers and Sons*, p. 32.

35. *A Little Learning*, p. 69.

36. Alexander Waugh, *Fathers and Sons*, p. 41.

37. Quoted in ibid., p. 42.

38. Arthur Waugh, *One Man's Road*, p. 159.

39. *Nash's Pall Mall Magazine*, March 1937, p. 8.

40. Arthur Waugh, *One Man's Road*, p. 208; *The Times*, 20 October 1892, p. 7: 'Mr Waugh's discriminating judgments have evidently cost time and thought, and proceed from a critical faculty of no mean order.'

41. Arthur Waugh, *One Man's Road*, pp. 217–18.

42. *A Little Learning*, p. 4.

43. Sykes, *Evelyn Waugh*, p. 5.

44. *A Little Learning*, p. 31.

45. Arthur Waugh, *One Man's Road*, p. 218.

46. Selina Hastings, *Evelyn Waugh*, pp. 6–7.

47. *A Little Learning*, p. 31.
48. Alexander Waugh, *Fathers and Sons*, p. 75.
49. Arthur Waugh, *One Man's Road*, p. 218.
50. Arthur Waugh to Alec Waugh, 20 May 1914; BU.
51. Arthur Waugh to Catherine Waugh, 10 July 1993, AWA; quoted in Alexander Waugh, *Fathers and Sons*, p. 116.
52. Ibid., p. 116.
53. *A Little Learning*, p. 31.
54. Ibid., p. 32.
55. Arthur Waugh, *One Man's Road*, pp. 257–9.
56. Alec Waugh, *Early Years*, p. 12.
57. Margot Strickland, Notes on *Catherine Waugh's Diary*, p. 7; AWA
58. Alec Waugh *The Early Years of Alec Waugh*, pp. 13-14.
59. Michael Holroyd, *Bernard Shaw*, Vol. 1, p. 267.
60. Alexander Waugh, *Fathers and Sons*, pp. 50–51.
61. Alec Waugh, *Early Years*, pp. 14–15.
62. Arthur Waugh, *One Man's Road*, p. 290.
63. Ibid., p. 321.
64. Alec Waugh, *My Brother Evelyn*, p. 163.
65. Alexander Waugh, *Fathers and Sons*, pp. 74–5.
66. *A Little Learning*, p. 27.

2 *The Sadism of Youth*

1. Hugh Petrie, *Hendon and Golders Green Past* (Historical Publications, 2005), p. 54.
2. *A Little Learning*, p. 34.
3. Ibid.
4. Ibid., p. 42.
5. Ibid., p. 44.
6. Ibid., p. 78.
7. Ibid., p. 71.
8. Ibid., p. 72.
9. Alec Waugh interview with Michael Davie, December 1972, AWA.
10. *A Little Learning*, p. 43.
11. Ibid., p. 36.
12. Jean Fleming to Selina Hastings, interview transcript, p. 2, AWA.
13. *A Little Learning*, p. 44.
14. Ibid., pp. 47–8.
15. Stella Rhys to Christopher Sykes, 19 April 1974, copy in AWA.
16. *A Little Learning*, p. 41.
17. Ibid.
18. Ibid., p. 30.
19. Stella Rhys to Christopher Sykes, 19 April 1974; Sykes Papers, GU.
20. Jean Fleming to Selina Hastings, 17 March 1991, AWA.
21. *A Little Learning*, p. 43.
22. Diary, Summer 1912; HRC.
23. *A Little Learning*, p. 59.
24. Alec Waugh, *Early Years*, pp. 20–22.

25. J. S. Granville Grenfell to Catherine Waugh, 31 October 1910, BL.
26. *A Little Learning*, p. 81.
27. Ibid.
28. Article entitled 'My Father', *The Sunday Telegraph*, 2 December 1962.
29. September 1911; *EWD*, p. 5.
30. *A Little Learning*, p. 63.
31. Mr Stebbing, Evelyn's form master.
32. Diary, [September–October 1914]; HRC.
33. Mr Hynchcliffe, the Classics master.
34. *A Little Learning*, p. 84.
35. Cecil Beaton, *The Wandering Years*, p. 173.
36. Hugh Burnett (ed.), *Face to Face*, Jonathan Cape (1964), p. 38.
37. *The Spectator*, 21 July 1961.
38. Stella Rhys to Christopher Sykes, 19 April 1974; Sykes Papers, GU.
39. *The Spectator*, 21 July 1961.
40. Alec Waugh, *My Brother Evelyn*, p. 166.
41. Alexander Waugh, *Fathers and Sons*, p. 79.
42. Arthur Waugh to Andrew Waugh, 1933, quoted in Selina Hastings, *Evelyn Waugh*, p. 25.
43. 'My Childhood' by Alec Waugh copy in AWA.
44. Alec Waugh to Evelyn Waugh, 29 March 1908 and 21 March 1909; BL.
45. Alec Waugh, *My Brother Evelyn*, pp. 163–5.
46. Ibid., p. 168.
47. *A Little Learning*, p. 86.
48. Catherine Waugh Diary, 16 June 1912, 17 June 1912, 18 June 1912; BU.
49. *A Little Learning*, pp. 55–6; Catherine Waugh Diary, 7 July 1912; BU.
50. Catherine Waugh Diary, 11 July 1912 to 22 August 1912; BU.
51. *A Little Learning*, pp. 56–7.
52. Ibid., p. 58.
53. Ibid., p. 60.
54. Arthur Waugh, *One Man's Road*, p. 333.
55. *A Little Learning*, p. 60.
56. Arthur Waugh, *One Man's Road*, p. 334.
57. Ibid., p. 338.
58. *A Little Learning*, p. 60.
59. Ibid., pp. 60–61.
60. Ibid., p. 61.
61. 12–13 June 1912; *EWD*, p. 6.
62. *A Little Learning*, p. 91.
63. 'Come Inside' in John A. O'Brien (ed.), *The Road to Damascus*, 1949; *EAR*, pp. 366–8.
64. *A Little Learning*, p. 52.
65. Ibid., pp. 92–3.
66. Ibid., p. 93; *EWD*, p. 9.
67. Jane Ridley, *The Architect and His Wife: A Life of Edwin Lutyens*, pp. 175–6.
68. 'Charles Ryder's Schooldays', in *Work Suspended and Other Stories*, p. 305.
69. Alec Waugh, Notes on Christopher Sykes's Biography of Evelyn Waugh, HRC.
70. *A Little Learning*, p. 92.

71. Aubrey Ensor, notes on proof copy of *A Little Learning*, p. 92, in author's possession.
72. *A Little Learning*, p. 92.
73. Email from Father Alan Walker, Vicar of St Jude's, 16 January 2013. In 1914 Bourchier had gone out to Belgium as a chaplain to the Red Cross, until he was captured by Germans and sentenced to be shot at dawn as a suspected spy, 'the greatest thrill of my life,' he recalled. He was reprieved, though, and instead held prisoner until he returned to the suburb and to St Jude's in March 1916, shortly before Evelyn's confirmation.
74. Alec Waugh, *Early Years*, pp. 43–4.
75. *A Little Learning*, p. 68; Alec Waugh's notes on Christopher Sykes's biography of Evelyn Waugh, attached to Alec's letter to Auberon Waugh, 6 March 1976; AWA. In *Charles Ryder's Schooldays*, Charles's was 'not a God-fearing home' but his father nevertheless 'read family prayers every morning; on the outbreak of war he abruptly stopped the practice, explaining, when asked, that there was now nothing left to pray for'.
76. Arthur Waugh to Kenneth McMaster, 24 August 1916, HRC, quoted Hastings, p.40.
77. Alec Waugh, *My Brother Evelyn*, p. 168.
78. *A Little Learning*, p. 94.

3 Serving Lord Kitchener

1. Arthur Waugh to Kenneth McMaster, 25 August 1914, HRC.
2. *A Little Learning*, p. 87; Aubrey Ensor notes on proof copy of *A Little Learning*, in author's possession.
3. *A Little Learning*, p. 87.
4. Ibid., pp. 87–8.
5. Arthur Waugh to Kenneth McMaster, New Year's Day 1915, HRC.
6. *A Little Learning*, p. 89.
7. Ibid., pp. 94–5.
8. Diary, [*c.* 8–18 October 1914], HRC.
9. Ibid.
10. Ibid., [*c.*12 September–1 October 1914], HRC.
11. *A Little Learning*, p. 88.
12. Diary, [mid-June 1915], HRC.
13. Ibid., [early November 1914]; *EWD*, p. 8.
14. Alec Waugh, *My Brother Evelyn*, p. 168.
15. *The Times*, 26 January 1926.
16. Hugo Vickers, *Cecil Beaton*, p. 15.
17. Aubrey Ensor notes on proof copy of *A Little Learning*, in author's possession.
18. Ibid.
19. Alec Waugh, *My Brother Evelyn*, p. 169.
20. Aubrey Ensor notes on proof copy of *A Little Learning*, in author's possession.
21. Ibid.
22. Ibid.
23. *A Little Learning*, p. 90; Diary, [November–December 1915], HRC.
24. *A Little Learning*, p. 90.
25. Vickers, *Cecil Beaton*, p. 15.

26. *The Times*, 20 July 1925, p. 11.
27. *A Little Learning*, p. 90.
28. Diary, *c*. 2 January 1916, HRC.
29. Ibid., late January 1916.
30. *A Little Learning*, p. 94.
31. Alexander Waugh, *Fathers and Sons*, p. 53.
32. Arthur Waugh to Kenneth McMaster, 13 December 1913, HRC.
33. *A Little Learning*, p. 95.
34. Arthur Waugh to Alec Waugh, 20 May 1914; BU.
35. Arthur Waugh, *One Man's Road*, p. 332.
36. Alexander Waugh, *Fathers and Sons*, p. 76.
37. Catherine Waugh to Alec Waugh, 25 May 1915; BU.
38. Arthur Waugh to Alec Waugh, 19 October 1916; BU.
39. *A Little Learning*, p. 95.
40. Alec Waugh to Hugh Mackintosh, 25 February 1915; BU.
41. Alec Waugh to Hugh Mackintosh, 29 October 1915; BU.
42. Arthur Waugh to Alec Waugh, 5 June 1915, quoted in Alexander Waugh, *Fathers and Sons*, p.69; BU.
43. Catherine Waugh to Alec Waugh, 24 June 1915; BU.
44. Arthur Waugh to Alec Waugh, 21 January 1916; BU.
45. Arthur Waugh to Alec Waugh, 1 February 1917; BU.
46. *A Little Learning*, p. 141.
47. Arthur Waugh, *One Man's Road*, p. 367.

4 A Lesser Place than Eton

1. *A Little Learning*, p. 163.
2. Ibid., pp. 99–100.
3. B. W. T. Handford *Lancing 1848–1930*, p. 247.
4. Dudley Carew, *A Fragment of Friendship*, p. 38.
5. *A Little Learning*, p. 99.
6. Undated note by Roger Fulford; AWA.
7. Handford, *Lancing*, p. 263.
8. *A Little Learning*, p. 99.
9. Transcript of Basil Handford interview with Selina Hastings; AWA.
10. Obituary in *The Times*, 9 February 1940.
11. *A Little Learning*, p. 99.
12. *Daily Express*, 20 March 1929.
13. *Evelyn Waugh in Letters by Terence Greenidge*, p. 24.
14. Arthur Waugh to Kenneth McMaster, 6 January 1927, HRC.
15. *A Little Learning*, p. 101.
16. Undated note by Roger Fulford in AWA.
17. David Pryce-Jones (ed.), *Evelyn Waugh and His World*, p. 17.
18. Alec Waugh to Hugh Mackintosh, 13 October 1917; BU, quoted in Hastings, p. 57.
19. Pryce-Jones, *Evelyn Waugh and His World*, p. 17.
20. *A Little Learning*, p. 107.
21. Catherine Waugh to Alec Waugh, 19 May 1918; BU, quoted in Hastings, p. 57.
22. *A Little Learning*, p. 109.

23. Ibid.
24. Ibid., p. 110.
25. Ibid., p. 113.
26. Transcript of C. L. Chamberlin interview with Selina Hastings, p. 5; AWA.
27. Arthur Waugh, *One Man's Road*, p. 358.
28. *A Little Learning*, p. 120.
29. Alec Waugh to Hugh Mackintosh, 31 January 1919; BU.
30. *A Little Learning*, p. 117.
31. Hastings, *Evelyn Waugh*, p. 54.
32. *A Little Learning*, p. 122.
33. Ibid., p.117.
34. Arthur Waugh to Evelyn Waugh, 6 February 1919; dedicatory letter printed in *Tradition and Change* (1919).
35. Arthur Waugh to Jean Fleming, 14 April 1918; private collection, quoted in Hastings, p. 55; copy in AWA.
36. *A Little Learning*, p. 124.
37. Ibid., p. 125.
38. Ibid.
39. Ibid., p. 130.
40. Ibid., p. 131; Evelyn Waugh to Randolph Churchill, 5 September 1963, *Encounter*, Vol. 31, p. 17.
41. *A Little Learning*, p. 131.
42. Ibid.
43. Ibid., p. 126; 23 September 1919; *EWD*, p. 19.
44. *A Little Learning*, p. 146.
45. Preface to Francis Crease's *Decorative Designs* (1927); *EAR*, p. 23.
46. *A Little Learning*, p. 147.
47. *EWD*, pp. 53 and 54; EW to Arthur Waugh, 29 January 1920, quoted in Alexander Waugh, *Fathers and Sons*, pp. 140–41; AWA.
48. 8 May 1920; *EWD*, p. 74.
49. 29 January 1929; *EWD*, pp. 53–4 and *A Little Learning*, p. 148.
50. Thus billed on Amazon.
51. 5 February 1920; *EWD*, p. 55.
52. Preface . . . *Essays Articles*, p. 24.
53. 25 March 1920, quoted in Hastings, p. 67; copy in AWA.
54. March 1920; *EWD*, pp. 65–6.
55. Introduction by Arthur Waugh to Ian Mackenzie, *The Darkened Ways* (Chapman & Hall, 1919).
56. Philippa Codrington to Selina Hastings, 27 January 1991; AWA.
57. *A Little Learning*, p. 69.
58. Ibid., p. 153.
59. Ibid, p. 150.
60. *EWD*, p. 78.
61. 19 July 1921; *EWD*, p. 132.
62. *A Little Learning*, p. 162.

5 Watertight Compartments

1. Noel Annan, *Roxburgh of Stowe*, p. 47.
2. 26 September 1919; *EWD*, p. 20.
3. Evelyn Waugh's review of Annan's *Roxburgh of Stowe*, *The Observer*, 17 October 1965; *EAR* pp. 638–9.
4. 19–25 October 1920; *EWD*, p. 107.
5. Diary, 23 April 1921; edited version at request of Alec in *EWD*, p. 125.
6. *A Little Learning*, p. 158; EW to Nancy Mitford, 6 January [1951], *EWL*, p. 343.
7. *A Little Learning*, pp. 159–60.
8. 11 October 1921; *EWD*, p. 141 (with Macdonald's name deleted).
9. *A Little Learning*, p. 160.
10. Ibid., p. 161.
11. 25 October 1920; *EWD*, p. 107.
12. Robert Murray Davis, *Evelyn Waugh, Apprentice*, p. 63.
13. Ibid., p. 68.
14. 21 December 1920; *EWD*, p. 108.
15. *A Little Learning*, p. 161.
16. 29 October 1921; *EWD*, p. 144.
17. EW to Arthur Waugh, 13 June [1921]; *EWL*, p. 3.
18. *A Little Learning*, p. 132.
19. 31 March 1921; *EWD*, p. 122; *A Little Learning*, pp. 134–5.
20. 19 July 1921; *EWD*, p. 131.
21. Arthur Waugh to EW, 1 June 1921; BL; *A Little Learning*, p. 136.
22. 3 June 1921; *EWD*, p. 127.
23. *Evelyn Waugh, Apprentice*, p. 114.
24. Arthur Waugh to EW, 17 May 1921; BL.
25. 26 June 1921; *EWD*, p. 129.
26. James Lees-Milne diary, 29 July 1973, *Ancient as the Hills*, p. 66.
27. Christopher Chamberlin to Selina Hastings, interview transcript, AWA
28. Henrietta McCall, *The Life of Max Mallowan*, p. 15.
29. Max Mallowan, *Mallowan's Memoirs*, pp. 19-20.
30. Richard Ollard (ed.), *The Diaries of A. L. Rowse*, p. 414, 'Evelyn had a nasty nature (though also charm when he chose).'
31. EW to Nancy Mitford, [28 December] 1962; LNMEW, p. 471.
32. 2 October 1919; *EWD*, p. 23.
33. 6 May 1921; *EWD*, p. 126.
34. Ollard, *Rowse Diaries*, p. 414.
35. 2 October 1919; *EWD*, p. 23.
36. *A Little Learning*, p. 128.
37. 17 October 1919; *EWD*, p. 23, rating one of his efforts a 'terrible effusion'.
38. 23 October 1919; *EWD*, p. 31.
39. 2 May 1921; *EWD*, p. 126.
40. 27 February 1921; *EWD*, p. 114 (with name deleted).
41. Francis Wheen, *Tom Driberg*, p. 27.
42. 7 November 1919; *EWD*, p. 35.
43. *A Little Learning*, pp. 143–4.
44. Tom Driberg, *Ruling Passions*, p. 49.
45. 13 June 1921; *EWD*, p. 127.

46. Wheen, *Tom Driberg*, pp. 29 and 32–3.
47. Driberg, *Ruling Passions*, p. 49.
48. 15 October 1920; *EWD*, p. 106.
49. *A Little Learning*, p. 135.
50. Luned Hamilton-Jenkins (née Jacobs) to Selina Hastings, December 1991; AWA.
51. Alec Waugh to Hugh Mackintosh, 31 January 1919; BU.
52. 27 September 1919; *EWD*, p. 21.
53. 24 January 1921; *EWD*, p. 109.
54. Luned Hamilton-Jenkins (née Jacobs) to Selina Hastings, December 1991; AWA.
55. 12 August 1920; *EWD*, p. 95.
56. 22–3 April and 31 August 1920; *EWD*, pp. 69, 99.
57. Dudley Carew Diary, 21 August 1921, HRC.
58. 24 January 1921; *EWD*, p. 109.
59. Dudley Carew Diary, 21 August 1921; HRC.
60. Dudley Carew Diary, 12 May 1921; HRC.
61. 27 June 1920; *EWD*, p. 87.
62. Note to Dudley Carew interview with Michael Davie, 17 November 1972; AWA.
63. Dudley Carew Diary, 15 August 1921, HRC.
64. Alec Waugh, *Early Years*, p. 152.
65. Ibid., p. 160.
66. Alec Waugh, *Early Years*, pp. 155–6.
67. Andrew Waugh to Selina Hastings, transcript of interview, p. 7; AWA.
68. Alexander Waugh, *Fathers and Sons*, p. 147.
69. Ibid.
70. Andrew Waugh to Selina Hastings; AWA.
71. *A Little Learning*, p. 138.
72. 16 October 1921; *EWD*, p. 141.
73. *A Little Learning*, p. 138.
74. 16 and 19 October 1921; *EWD*, pp. 141–2.
75. 19 October 1921; *EWD*, p. 142.
76. 29 October 1921; *EWD*, p. 144.
77. 6 December 1921; *EWD*, p. 150.
78. C. R. M. F. Cruttwell to Evelyn Waugh, 14 December 1921; BL.
79. 16 December 1921; *EWD*, p. 154.

6 All That One Dreams

1. Arthur Waugh to EW, 15 December 1921; BL.
2. *A Little Learning*, p. 137.
3. Lancing College report, Christmas Term 1921, AWA.
4. Roxburgh to EW, 12 March 1922; BL.
5. EW to Dudley Carew, undated (c.New Year 1922), HRC.
6. *A Little Learning*, p. 163.
7. Ibid., p. 166.
8. [Early 1922]; *EWL*, p.4.
9. 13 February [1922]; *EWL*, p. 7.
10. *Evelyn Waugh in Letters by Terence Greenidge*, p. 43.
11. *A Little Learning*, p. 191.

12. [1922]; *EWL*, p. 10.
13. EW to Dudley Carew [March 1922], *EWL*, p. 8.
14. Claud Cockburn, 'Evelyn Waugh's Lost Rabbit', *Atlantic Monthly*, December 1973.
15. EW to Dudley Carew, undated (spring 1922), HRC.
16. Christopher Hollis, *Oxford in the Twenties*, p. 76.
17. Martin Stannard, *Evelyn Waugh: The Early Years: 1903–1939*, p. 74.
18. *The Isis*, 8 February 1922, p. 12.
19. *Oxford Magazine*, 23 February 1922, p. 246; 30 November 1922, p. 123; and *The Isis*, 29 November 1922.
20. *A Little Learning*, pp. 180–81.
21. Quoted in Noel Annan, *Our Age*, p. 113.
22. Terence Greenidge, *Degenerate Oxford?*, p. 91.
23. Driberg, *Ruling Passions*, p. 55.
24. Sykes, *Evelyn Waugh*, p. 48.
25. EW to Dudley Carew, 10 March 1922; *EWL*, p. 8.
26. EW to Tom Driberg, 21 May 1922, Christ Church, Oxford; *EWL*, p. 10.
27. EW to Tom Driberg, late May 1922, Christ Church, Oxford.
28. Transcript of Selina Hastings's interview with A. L. Rowse, 17 March 1990; AWA.
29. Cited in Clive Fisher, *Cyril Connolly* (Macmillan, 1995), p. 58.
30. EW to Nancy Mitford, 18 December 1954; *EWL*, p. 435.
31. Christopher Hollis to Cyril Connolly, quoted in Jeremy Lewis, *Cyril Connolly*, p. 111.
32. A. L. Rowse to Selina Hastings, 4 June 1991; AWA.
33. Transcript of Selina Hastings's interview with A. L. Rowse, 17 March 1990; AWA.
34. Richard Pares to EW, undated; BL.
35. Ibid.
36. Ollard, *Rowse Diaries*, p. 414.
37. Isaiah Berlin, *Personal Impressions*, (Hogarth, 1980), p. 92.
38. *A Little Learning*, pp. 191–2.
39. *The Isis*, 3 December 1924.
40. Richard Pares to EW, undated [December/January 1923]; BL.
41. Quoted in David Pryce Jones, *Cyril Connolly: Journal and Memoir*, p. 63.
42. Transcript of *Arena* interview with Anthony Bushell; AWA.
43. Hollis, *Oxford in the Twenties*, p. 79.
44. Stannard, *Evelyn Waugh: The Early Years*, pp. 82–3.
45. EW to Dudley Carew, two undated letters, from spring 1923 and spring/summer 1924.
46. *Brideshead Revisited*, p. 25.
47. Transcript of BBC *Arena* interview with Anthony Bushell, p. 250 (although earlier in the interview, on p. 249, he said the incident was 'pure invention'); copy in AWA.
48. Ibid.
49. Anthony Powell, *Infants of the Spring*, p. 154.
50. James Knox, *Robert Byron*, p. 43.
51. Powell, *Infants of the Spring*, p. 113.
52. Rowse, *A Cornishman at Oxford*, p. 23; Lucy Butler (ed.) *Robert Byron Letters Home*, p. 16; Emlyn Williams, *George: An Early Autobiography*, pp. 315–16.
53. John Rothenstein, *Summer's Lease*, p. 94.
54. Rowse, *Cornishman at Oxford*, p. 24.

55. Marie-Jacqueline Lancaster (ed.) *Brian Howard: Portrait of a Failure*, p. 126.
56. Harold Acton to EW, 23 September 1923; BL.
57. *The New York Times Magazine*, 30 November 1952; *EAR*, pp. 423–4.
58. Harold Acton, *Memoirs of an Aesthete*, p. 126.
59. Ibid., p. 120.
60. Harold Acton to Evelyn Waugh, undated; BL.
61. *A Little Learning*, p. 198.
62. Ibid.
63. Ibid., p. 204; Stannard, *Evelyn Waugh: The Early Years*, p. 89.
64. *A Little Learning*, p. 204.
65. *Put Out More Flags*, p. 19.
66. Sefton Delmer, *Trail Sinister*, pp. 337–443; Evelyn's cousin and Murray's friend Claud Cockburn countered with a more innocent explanation that the ape had inadvertently bitten her host's jugular vein while attempting to rouse him from sleep. See Claud Cockburn, 'Spying in Spain and Elsewhere', *Grand Street*, Vol.1 No. 2 (1982); Paul Preston, *We Saw Spain Die*, pp. 125–6.
67. Alec Waugh, *My Brother Evelyn*, p. 172.
68. *Hertford College Magazine*, No. 78 (1992), p. 12.
69. Cockburn, 'Evelyn Waugh's Lost Rabbit', *Atlantic Monthly*, December 1973.
70. *A Little Learning*, p. 171.
71. Ibid., p. 171–2.
72. Alexander Waugh, *Fathers and Sons*, pp. 177–9.

7 His Poor Dead Heart

1. EW to Tom Driberg, [May 1922]; *EWL*, p. 9.
2. Alexander Waugh, *Fathers and Sons*, p. 169.
3. Hugh Molson recalling what Christopher Hollis told him, *Arena* interview with Lord Molson; AWA.
4. Alec Waugh, *Early Years*, p. 165.
5. Cockburn, 'Evelyn Waugh's Lost Rabbit', *Atlantic Monthly*, December 1973.
6. Alec Waugh, *My Brother Evelyn*, p. 169.
7. Fragment of Vol. 2 of autobiography, 'A Little Hope', HRC, quoted in ibid., p. 170.
8. See for example Arundel del Re in *The Isis*, 20 June 1923, p. 12.
9. Transcript of interview with Lord Molson for *Arena*, copy in AWA.
10. Harold Acton to Christopher Sykes, 16 October 1972, AWA; Introduction by Ann Pasternak Slater to *The Complete Short Stories of Evelyn Waugh*.
11. *Evelyn Waugh in Letters by Terence Greenidge*, p. 7.
12. *A Little Learning*, p. 192.
13. Selina Hastings interview with Anthony Powell; AWA; Duncan Fallowell, *How to Disappear*, p. 175.
14. Harold Acton to Alastair Graham and EW, 8 April 1924; BL.
15. Humphrey Carpenter, *The Brideshead Generation*, p. 85.
16. Fallowell, *How to Disappear*, p. 178.
17. *A Little Learning*, p. 193.
18. Alastair Graham to Michael Davie, 30 October 1975, Michael Davie Papers; AWA.
19. 'I wrote to my father asking to be taken away and sent to Paris to enjoy the full life of [George du Maurier's] *Trilby*', *A Little Learning*, p. 175.

20. EW to Dudley Carew, undated; *EWL*, p. 12, where the date is estimated as 1924, however the letter also refers to EW speaking at the Union and the only instance recorded in *The Isis* of his doing that was in late 1923.
21. Jessie Graham to Brasenose College, 6 November 1923, Brasenose College Archives, Oxford.
22. *A Little Learning*, p. 192.
23. *Brideshead Revisited* (Penguin Classics edition, 2000), p. 25.
24. Catherine Waugh's Diary, 15 December 1923; BU.
25. Alastair Graham to EW, 5 September 1925; BL.
26. *A Little Learning*, p. 208.

8 Pure as Driven Slush

1. EW to Dudley Carew, *c.* 12 June 1924, HRC.
2. 29 July to 30 August 1924; *EWD*, p. 172.
3. C. R. M. F. Cruttwell to EW, undated; BL.
4. *A Little Learning*, p. 210.
5. *EWD*, 25 June 1924.
6. Paula Byrne, *Mad World,* p. 63.
7. Transcript of Selina Hastings's interview with Tamara Talbot Rice; AWA.
8. Harman Grisewood to Selina Hastings, interview transcript; AWA.
9. Powell, *Infants of the Spring*, p. 98.
10. *A Little Learning*, p. 210.
11. Anthony Bushell, *Arena* interview; AWA.
12. 29 October 1924; *EWD*, p. 183.
13. Rothenstein, *Summer's Lease*, p. 110.
14. *A Little Learning*, p. 212.
15. Douglas Goldring, *Odd Man Out*, p. 282.
16. Quoted in Kate Summerscale, *Queen of Whale Cay* (Fourth Estate, 1997), p. 76.
17. 3 July 1924; *EWD*, p. 166.
18. 12 July 1924; *EWD*, p. 169.
19. Anthony and Violet Powell to Selina Hastings, interview transcript; AWA.
20. 9 November 1924, *EWD*, p. 186.
21. *A Little Learning*, p. 213.
22. 12 November 1924; *EWD*, p. 187.
23. 18 November 1924; *EWD*, p. 188.
24. 29 October 1924; *EWD*, p. 183.
25. EW to Harold Acton, [*c.* 15 December 1924]; BL; 19 December 1924; *EWD*, p. 192.
26. Acton, *Memoirs of an Aesthete*, p. 146.
27. The only institutional libraries known to hold copies of *Irais* are the Kinsey Institute, Cornell, and the British Library.
28. 24 December 1924; *EWD*, p. 193–4.
29. *A Little Learning*, pp. 217–18.
30. Dorothea Ponsonby Diary, 28 July 1924, quoted in Taylor, *Bright Young People*, p. 56.
31. Note by Harman Grisewood headed 'Olivia Plunket Greene'; AWA.
32. Harman Grisewood to Selina Hastings, interview transcript; AWA.
33. Harman Grisewood to Christopher Sykes, 2 April 1973, GU.
34. 11 January 1925; *EWD*, p. 197.

35. 21 January 1925; *EWD*, p. 199.
36. 25 January 1925; *EWD*, p. 201.
37. *A Little Learning*, p. 221.
38. EW to Catherine Waugh, undated [*c*.23 January 1925]; BL.
39. 5 May 1925; *EWD*, p. 211.
40. Quoted in Sykes, *Evelyn Waugh*, p. 60.
41. Verschoyle, quoted in ibid., p. 60.
42. *A Little Learning*, p. 224.
43. 2 March 1925; *EWD*, p. 203.
44. 29 March 1925; *EWD*, p. 204.
45. *A Little Learning*, p. 225.
46. Georgiana Russell (later Blakiston) to Patrick Balfour, 22 April 1925, Balfour Papers, Huntington Library.
47. Ibid.
48. *The Daily Telegraph*, 16 April 1925.
49. Georgiana Blakiston to Patrick Balfour, 22 April 1925, Huntington Library.
50. Arthur Ponsonby to Dorothea Ponsonby, 7 April 1925, Shulbrede archives, quoted in Raymond A. Jones, *Arthur Ponsonby*, (Christopher Helm, 1985), p. 161.
51. 20 October 1925; *EWD*, p. 229.
52. 24 April 1925; *EWD*, p. 209.
53. *Evelyn Waugh in Letters by Terence Greenidge*, p. 135.
54. 15 April 1925; *EWD*, pp. 207–8 (with name deleted).
55. Ibid.
56. 18 April 1925; *EWD*, p. 208.
57. Ibid.
58. Alexander Waugh *Fathers and Sons*, p. 192.
59. 14 May 1925; *EWD*, p. 211.
60. *Decline and Fall*, p. 45.
61. *A Little Learning*, pp. 227–8; not recorded in his Diary.
62. 3 July 1925; *EWD*, p. 213.
63. 28 May 1925; *EWD*, p. 212.
64. *A Little Learning*, p. 228.
65. Ibid.
66. 1 July 1925; *EWD*, p. 213.
67. *A Little Learning*, p. 230.

9 Becoming a Man of Letters

1. 28 July 1925; *EWD*, p. 241.
2. EW to Harold Acton, [18 February 1925]; *EWL*, pp. 23–4.
3. 26 August 1925; *EWD*, p. 218.
4. Alastair Graham to EW; 1 September 1925; BL.
5. Alastair Graham to EW; 5 September 1925; BL.
6. 16 and 20 August 1925; *EWD*, pp. 216–7.
7. 23 September 1925; *EWD*, p. 223.
8. 1 and 7 August, 1925; *EWD*, pp. 214–15.
9. 22 December 1925; *EWD*, p. 238.
10. Christmas Day 1925; *EWD*, p. 238.

11. 15 November 1925; *EWD*, p. 234.

12. Note headed 'Olivia Plunket Greene' by Harman Grisewood; AWA.

13. Michael Holroyd, *Augustus John*, Vol. 2, pp. 167–8.

14. 29 December 1925; *EWD*, p. 240.

15. Harman Grisewood to Selina Hastings, transcript of interview, p. 9; AWA.

16. 8 October 1925; *EWD*, p. 226.

17. 26 January 1926; *EWD*, p. 244.

18. 25 February 1926; *EWD*, p. 247.

19. 13 March 1926; *EWD*, p. 248.

20. 20 January 1926; *EWD*, p. 243.

21. 26 January 1926; *EWD*, p. 244.

22. 29 January 1926; *EWD*, p. 244.

23. 30 January 1930; *EWD*, p. 245.

24. *Nash's Pall Mall Magazine*, March 1937, *EAR*, p. 191.

25. Stannard, *Evelyn Waugh: The Early Years*, p. 120.

26. 13 March 1926; *EWD*, p. 249.

27. 10 June 1926; *EWD*, p. 254.

28. 1 April 1926; *EWD*, p. 250.

29. *A Little Learning*, p. 229.

30. 11 January 1926; *EWD*, p. 242.

31. 1 April 1926; *EWD*, p. 250.

32. 8 March 1926; *EWD*, p. 248.

33. 24 July 1926; *EWD*, p. 256.

34. Alastair Graham to Michael Davie, November 1975, AWA. 'It must have been a terrible strain on E's nerves being cooped up with a lot of strangers whom he would never have chosen as companions, and no means of escape.'

35. 25 August 1926; *EWD*, p. 263.

36. Postcript to *PRB* (Dalrymple Press edition, 1982), p. 44.

37. 28 September 1925; *EWD*, p. 225.

38. Alec Waugh, *Early Years*, p. 216.

39. *Manchester Guardian*, 29 October 1926.

40. 30 October 1926; *EWD*, p. 268.

41. *Literary Review*, 9 April 1927, quoted in Robert Murray Davis, *Evelyn Waugh, Writer*.

42. EW to Henry Yorke [1926], *EWL*, p. 24; the book was published before Yorke left Oxford without a degree that Christmas.

43. 22 September 1926; *EWD*, p. 265.

44. 2 October 1926; *EWD*, p. 266.

45. 6 December 1926; *EWD*, p. 272.

46. James Knox, *Robert Byron*, p. 101.

47. Fallowell, *How to Disappear*, pp. 177–8.

48. Andrew Sinclair, *Francis Bacon: His Life and Violent Times*, p. 42.

49. 1 January 1927; *EWD*, p. 275.

50. 7 January 1927; *EWD*, p. 277.

51. 4 January 1927; *EWD*, p. 276.

52. Sykes, *Evelyn Waugh*, p. 71.

53. 20 February 1927; *EWD*, p. 281.

54. Ibid.

55. 21 February 1927; *EWD*, p. 281.
56. Edmund to EW [dated from postmark 21 February 1927]; BL.
57. 7 March 1927; *EWD*, p. 282.
58. 28 February 1927; *EWD*, p. 281.
59. Ibid.
60. Bill Egan, *Florence Mills: Harlem Jazz Queen*, (Scarecrow Press, 2004), p. 174.
61. 28 February 1927; *EWD*, p. 281.
62. 15 March 1926; *EWD*, p. 249.
63. Note headed 'Olivia Plunket Greene' by Harman Grisewood; AWA.

10 Shevelyn

1. 23 May 1927; *EWD*, p. 284.
2. Unpublished, untitled manuscript by Evelyn Gardner 'about my marriage to Evelyn Waugh and its break-up'; copy in AWA.
3. *The Times*, 29 September 1933.
4. Note by Lady Mary Clive headed 'Evelyn Gardner' (1987); AWA.
5. 1 July 1927; *EWD*, p. 284–5.
6. 'Careers for our Sons: The Complete Journalist', *Passing Show*, 26 January 1929; *EAR*, p. 48.
7. Alastair Graham to Michael Davie, November 1975; AWA.
8. Evelyn Gardner to John Maxse, 21 November 1927, Columbia University, cited in Selina Hastings, *Evelyn Waugh*, p. 166.
9. Ibid, p. 162.
10. Evelyn Gardner interview with Michael Davie, 24 February 1973; AWA.
11. Evelyn Gardner to John Maxse, November 1927; CU.
12. Lady Pansy Pakenham to John Maxse, 29 December 1927; CU.
13. Ibid.
14. Evelyn Gardner interview with Michael Davie, 24 February 1973; AWA.
15. 3 September 1927; *EWD*, p. 249.
16. Evelyn Gardner to Mrs Arthur Waugh, 28 December 1927; HRC.
17. Evelyn Gardner to John Maxse, November 1927; CU.
18. Alexander Waugh, *Fathers and Sons*, p. 200.
19. EW to Nancy Mitford, 8 January 1952; *EWL*, p. 364.
20. See Donat Gallagher, 'Evelyn Waugh and the Vatican Divorce', in Alain Blayac (ed.), *Evelyn Waugh: New Directions*, p. 73.
21. Evelyn Gardner to John Maxse, 4 May 1928; CU.
22. Pansy Pakenham to John Maxse, 8 May 1928; CU.
23. Evelyn Gardner to John Maxse, 2 May 1928; CU.
24. Pansy Pakenham to John Maxse, 8 May 1928; CU.
25. EW to TLS, 17 May 1928; EWL, p. 28.
26. *EWCH*, p. 79.
27. Anthony Powell, *Messengers of Day*, p. 22.
28. Carew, *Fragment of Friendship*, pp. 81–2.
29. Evelyn Gardner to John Maxse, 2 February 1928; CU.
30. Evelyn Gardner to John Maxse, 28 March and 18 July 1928; CU.
31. Pansy Pakenham to John Maxse, 19 March 1928; CU.
32. Pansy Pakenham to John Maxse, 12 June 1928; CU.

33. 27 June 1928; *EWD*, p. 295.

11   *A Common Experience, I'm Told*

1. Unpublished, untitled manuscript by Evelyn Gardner 'about my marriage to Evelyn Waugh and its break-up'; copy in AWA; Evelyn Gardner to John Maxse, 18 July 1928, CU.
2. Acton, *Memoirs of an Aesthete*, p. 202.
3. 25 June 1928, *Robert Byron Letters Home*, p. 103.
4. Catherine Waugh Diary, 27 June 1928; BU.
5. Evelyn Gardner interview with Michael Davie, 24 February 1973; AWA.
6. Nancy Mitford to Heywood Hill, 22 May 1966, *The Bookshop at 10 Curzon Street*, pp. 117–18.
7. Evelyn Gardner to John Maxse, 18 July 1928; CU; 6 July 1928; *EWD*, p. 295.
8. EW to Tom Balston, [*c.* 27 January 1929], copy in AWA.
9. Saturday, 14 July 1928; *EWD*, p. 295.
10. *The Observer*, 23 September 1928; *EWCH*, p. 81.
11. *Evening Standard*, 11 October 1928; *EWCH*, p. 82.
12. Naomi Mitchison to EW, undated letter [autumn 1928]; BL.
13. Derwent May (ed.), *Good Talk: An Anthology from BBC Radio*, p. 15.
14. *Evening News*, 2 November 1928, *EWCH*, p. 84.
15. *New Statesman*, 3 November 1928, *EWCH*, p. 85.
16. Hollis, *Oxford in the Twenties*, pp. 105–6.
17. Hugh Massingberd in The Antony Powell Society Newsletter, Issue 3, Summer 2001.
18. Harold Acton to EW, 18 September 1928; BL.
19. 8 October 1928; *EWD*, p. 295.
20. *Decline and Fall*, p. 120 (Penguin Modern Classics edition).
21. 18 October 1924; *EWD*, p. 295.
22. Wheen, *Tom Driberg*, p. 258.
23. *Decline and Fall*, p. 120 (Penguin Modern Classics edition).
24. EW to Thomas Balston, 1 October 1928; BL.
25. *Good Talk*, p. 16.
26. Acton, *Memoirs of an Aesthete*, p. 204.
27. Unpublished, untitled manuscript by Evelyn Gardner 'about my marriage to Evelyn Waugh and its break-up'; copy in AWA.
28. 8 October 1928; *EWD*, p. 297.
29. 12 October 1928; *EWD*, p. 298.
30. EW to A. D. Peters, undated; *EWL*, p. 30.
31. 25 October 1928; *EWD*, p. 300.
32. See 'Margot, I Presume' by Duncan McLaren, www.evelynwaugh.org.uk.
33. 27 October 1928; *EWD*, p. 300.
34. Note by Lady Mary Clive on Evelyn Gardner (1987); AWA.
35. *Daily Express*, 13 February 1929, p. 19.
36. *Labels*, pp. 45–6.
37. Unpublished, untitled manuscript by Evelyn Gardner 'about my marriage to Evelyn Waugh and its break-up', copy in AWA.
38. EW to Thomas Balston, [*c.* 27 January 1929]; copy in AWA.

39. *Labels*, pp. 29–30.
40. Ibid., p. 69.
41. Evelyn Gardner interview with Michael Davie, 24 February 1973; AWA.
42. EW to Thomas Balston, [*c.* 10 March 1929]; copy in AWA.
43. EW to Harold Acton, [*c.* 7 March 1929]; *EWL*, p. 31.
44. EW to Henry Yorke (the writer Henry Green) [19 March 1929]; AWA.
45. EW to Arthur Waugh, undated; BU.
46. EW to Thomas Balston, 18 March 1929; BL; EW to Arthur Waugh, undated; BU.
47. Evelyn Gardner interview with Michael Davie, 24 February 1973; AWA. NB in that interview and in her written account she said Evelyn's trip had been to Cyprus, but all the other evidence points to his having gone to Cairo.
48. EW to Harold Acton, 31 March 1929; copy in AWA.
49. EW to Henry Yorke, 4 May 1929; *EWL*, pp. 33–4.
50. EW to Harold Acton, *c.* 10 May 1929; copy in AWA.
51. Ibid.
52. Ibid.
53. Evelyn Gardner to John Maxse, 26 May 1929; CU.
54. *Labels*, p. 206.
55. Evelyn Gardner to John Maxse, [May 1929; CU.
56. EW to Henry Yorke, *c.* 2 June 1929; *EWL*, pp. 35–6.
57. Powell, *Messengers of Day*, p. 99.
58. Ibid., p. 101.
59. Ibid., p. 99.
60. Unpublished, untitled manuscript by Evelyn Gardner 'about my marriage to Evelyn Waugh and its break-up', copy in AWA.
61. 'My Friend Evelyn Waugh' in Nancy Mitford, *A Talent to Annoy*, p. 177.
62. *Daily Express*, 12 June 1929.
63. Note of telephone interview between Eleanor Campbell-Orde and Selina Hastings, March 1990; AWA.
64. Unpublished, untitled manuscript by Evelyn Gardner 'about my marriage to Evelyn Waugh and its break-up'; copy in AWA.
65. EW to Henry Yorke, 20 June 1929; copy in AWA.
66. Sir John Heygate to Michael Davie, 11 February 1975; AWA.
67. *The Tatler*, 3 July 1929, p. 46; *Sketch*, 3 July 1929; see also 'Those Parties Again' by Duncan McLaren in www.evelynwaugh.org.uk.
68. Powell, *Messengers of Day*, p. 126.
69. Elizabeth Montagu, *Honourable Rebel*, p. 105.
70. Powell, *Messengers of Day*, p. 128.
71. Ibid.; the telegram was dated about 26 July, Powell remembered. See 'The Tatler's Role in Waugh's Downfall' by Jacqueline McDonnell, *Times Higher Educational Supplement*, 23 June 1989.
72. Sykes, *Evelyn Waugh*, p. 94; Selina Hastings, *Evelyn Waugh*, p. 195.
73. Evelyn Waugh Petition for Divorce, copy in AWA.
74. Alec Waugh, *My Brother Evelyn*, p. 191.
75. *Bystander*, 17 July 1929.
76. Margaret Wyndham to John Maxse, 30 July 1929; CU.
77. Sir John Heygate to Mark Amory, 25 February 1976; AWA.
78. Selina Hastings interview with Eleanor Campbell Orde, 1991; AWA.

79. EW to Tom Balston, undated, copy in AWA.
80. Alec Waugh, *My Brother Evelyn*, p. 191.
81. Ibid., p. 192.
82. EW to Catherine and Arthur Waugh [5 August 1929]; BU.
83. Ibid.
84. Note by Lady Mary Clive on Evelyn Gardner (1987); AWA.
85. EW to Harold Acton, 4 August 1929; *EWL*, pp. 38–9.
86. Harold Acton to EW, 5 August 1929; BL.
87. EW to Henry Yorke, [*c.* 13 September 1929]; *EWL*, p. 40.
88. See note of Selina Hastings's interview with Eleanor Campbell-Orde, 1991; copy in AWA. In a letter Eleanor wrote to John Heygate, she remembered it slightly differently, recalling that she told him that she would 'wait and see'.

12 *Perversion to Rome*

1. Henry Lamb to EW, 14 August 1929; BL.
2. Lady Pansy Lamb to J. H. Maxse, 26 September 1929; CU.
3. Note by Lady Mary Clive on Evelyn Gardner (1987); AWA.
4. 'My Friend Evelyn Waugh' in Nancy Mitford, *A Talent to Annoy*, p. 234; see also Nancy Mitford to Christopher Sykes, undated; Christopher Sykes Papers, Georgetown University.
5. Evelyn Nightingale to Michael Davie, 13 October 1975.
6. Nancy Mitford interview with Christopher Sykes; Sykes Papers, GU.
7. Jessica Mitford, *Hons and Rebels*, p. 34.
8. 18 June 1930; *EWD*, pp. 315–16.
9. Nancy Mitford to Mark Ogilvie-Grant, 1930, quoted in Laura Thompson, *Life in a Cold Climate*, p. 93.
10. *The Independent*, 13 August 2003.
11. EW to Henry Yorke [*c.* 13 September 1929]; *EWL*, p. 39.
12. 30 December 1929, *Love From Nancy: The Letters of Nancy Mitford*, p. 34.
13. Diana Mosley to Christopher Sykes, 30 September 1975, Sykes Papers, GU.
14. EW to Diana Mosley, 30 March 1966, *EWL*, pp. 638–9.
15. Diana Mosley to Christopher Sykes, 30 September 1975, Sykes Papers, GU.
16. Catherine Waugh Diary, 24 December 1929; BU.
17. EW to Bryan and Diana Guinness, 4 January 1930, copy in AWA.
18. *Evening Standard*, 30 January 1930.
19. *Paris Review*, Vol. 30 (1963), p. 77.
20. BBC TV *Face to Face* interview with John Freeman, June 1960.
21. *Daily Mirror*, 7 February 1931.
22. J. F. Roxburgh to EW, 11 July 1930; BL.
23. 26 May 1930; *EWD*, p. 311.
24. EW to Lionel Fielden, 7 July 1930; copy in AWA.
25. Lionel Fielden to EW, 10 July 1930; BL.
26. 5 July 1930; *EWD*, p. 320.
27. EW to Diana Guinness, 17 July 1930; copy in AWA.
28. Bryan Guinness to EW, 23 July 1930.
29. EW to Diana Mosley, 9 March 1966; copy in AWA.
30. Cited in Hastings, *Evelyn Waugh*, p. 219.

31. Diana Mosley, *Loved Ones*, p. 54.
32. Alec Waugh, *The Best Wine Last*, p.45; Alec Waugh to Michael Davie, 1972; AWA.
33. Arthur Waugh Diary, 29 April 1930; BU.
34. 29 May 1930; *EWD*, p. 312.
35. 12 June 1930; *EWD*, p. 314.
36. 19 June 1930; *EWD*, p. 316.
37. *John Bull*, 23 August 1930; *EAR*, pp. 94–5.
38. Alec Waugh, *My Brother Evelyn*, pp. 191–2.
39. *Face to Face* interview, 1960.
40. Quoted in Sykes, *Evelyn Waugh*, p. 107.
41. Pryce-Jones, *Evelyn Waugh and His World*, p. 62.
42. 'Come Inside', in John A. O'Brien (ed.), *The Road to Damascus* (1962); *EAR*, p. 367.
43. *Face to Face* interview, 1960.
44. EW to Martin D'Arcy [21 August 1930]; AWA.
45. Pryce-Jones, *Evelyn Waugh and His World*, p. 64.
46. Alexander Waugh, *Fathers and Sons*, p. 217.
47. *Evelyn Waugh in Letters to Terence Greenidge.*

13 The Dutch Girl

1. Loelia, Duchess of Westminster, *Grace and Favour*, p. 117.
2. *The Times*, 16 August 1935.
3. *Grace and Favour*, p. 117.
4. Cecil Beaton, *Book of Beauty* (Duckworth, 1930), p. 35.
5. Teresa Cuthbertson obituary in *The Times*, 15 June 2010.
6. Jacqueline Mcdonnell, *Waugh on Women*, p. 21.
7. Interview with Jacqueline Mcdonnell in 1984, cited in ibid., p. 23.
8. Hastings, *Evelyn Waugh*, p. 222.
9. 1 June 1930; *EWD*, p. 313.
10. *Daily Mail*, 14 June 1930; *EAR*, pp. 78–80.
11. Teresa Jungman to EW, undated; BL.
12. Lord Longford to Selina Hastings, undated interview transcript; AWA.
13. Sarah Bradford, *Sacheverell Sitwell*, p. 217.
14. *Daily Mail*, 12 July 1930, cited in Hastings, *Evelyn Waugh*, p. 213.
15. [2–12 September 1930]; *EWD*, p. 328.
16. Christine Longford, unpublished memoirs, cited in Bevis Hillier, *Young Betjeman*, p. 309.
17. Elizabeth Longford, *The Pebbled Shore*, pp. 105–6.
18. EWD [2–12 September 1930]; *EWD*, p. 328 (omitting the sentence about Frank and Elizabeth).
19. Bradford, *Sacheverell Sitwell*, p. 201.
20. Elizabeth Longford later recalled: 'I rarely saw Evelyn on this visit except in the company of Alastair.' *Pebbled Shore*, p. 105.
21. EW to Patrick Balfour, 25 September 1931; Balfour Papers, Huntington Library.
22. Alastair Graham to Michael Davie, undated; AWA.
23. Fallowell, *How to Disappear*, p. 218.
24. Ibid., p. 202.
25. David N. Thomas, *Dylan Thomas: A Farm, Two Mansions and a Bungalow*, p. 86.

26. Paul Ferris, *Dylan Thomas: The Collected Letters*, (Dent, 2000) p. 603.
27. Fallowell, *How to Disappear*, p. 165.
28. Ibid., pp. 170–73.
29. EW to Catherine and Arthur Waugh, 16 November 1930; AWA.
30. EW to Teresa Jungman [1 February 1931]; private collection, copy in AWA.
31. Alec Waugh, *A Year to Remember*, p. 95.
32. Ibid., p. 96.
33. Arthur Waugh, *One Man's Road*, p. 372.
34. Alexander Waugh, *Fathers and Sons*, p. 216.
35. Alec Waugh, *A Year to Remember*, p. 190.
36. John Farrar to Bernice Baumgarten, 9 October 1931, HRC, cited in Hastings, *Evelyn Waugh*, p. 247.
37. Alec Waugh to Patrick Balfour, 15 July 1931, Huntington Library.
38. Alec Waugh, *A Year to Remember*, p. 123.
39. EW to Patrick Balfour [26 July 1931], Huntington Library.
40. Alec Waugh, *A Year to Remember*, p. 123.
41. Ibid., p. 124.
42. EW to Patrick Balfour [3 August 1931], Huntington Library.
43. Cited in Paula Byrne, *Mad World*, p. 144.
44. Alec Waugh, *A Year to Remember*, p. 106.
45. Jane Mulvagh, *Madresfield*, p. 23.
46. Pryce-Jones, *Evelyn Waugh and His World*, p. 50.
47. *A Little Learning*, pp. 205–6.
48. EW to Teresa Jungman [*c.* 24 October 1931]; private collection, copy in AWA.
49. EW to Patrick Balfour, [27 October 1931]; Balfour Papers, Huntington Library.
50. EW to Lady Sibell, Lady Mary and Lady Dorothy Lygon, 5 November [1931]; *EWL*, p. 59.
51. EW to Mary and Dorothy Lygon, 14/15 November 1931; copy in AWA.
52. EW to Teresa Jungman, 11 November 1931; private collection, copy in AWA.
53. EW to Teresa Jungman [*c.* 13 November 1931]; private collection, copy in AWA.
54. EW to Teresa Jungman, 3 December 1931; private collection, copy in AWA.
55. EW to Teresa Jungman, [*c.* 6 January 1932]; private collection, copy in AWA.
56. EW to Arthur Windham Baldwin, 14 January [1932]; *EWL*, p. 61.
57. *EWL*, p. 649.
58. EW to Teresa Jungman, 29 February 1932; private collection, copy in AWA.
59. EW to Teresa Jungman, [*c.* 7 March 1932]; private collection, copy in AWA.
60. EW to Teresa Jungman, 16 April 1932; private collection, copy in AWA.
61. EW to Arthur Windham Baldwin [16 April 1932]; *EWL*, p. 63.
62. EW to W. N. Roughead [*c.* 8 May 1932]; copy in AWA.
63. EW to Lady Dorothy Lygon [April 1932]; copy in AWA.
64. Referred to in his open letter to Archbishop Francis Bourne, 15 May 1933.
65. See James Fox, *White Mischief*, (Cape, 1982), p. 50; the de Traffords' eventual divorce was recorded in *The Times*, 26 October 1937.
66. EW to Lady Dorothy Lygon [*c.* 20 April 1932]; *EWL*, p. 64.
67. EW to Teresa Jungman, 23 May 1932; private collection, copy in AWA.
68. Cited in Byrne, *Mad World*, p. 192.
69. *Brideshead Revisited*, p. 92.
70. Philip Ziegler, *Diana Cooper*, p. 150.

71. Ibid., p. 160.
72. Diana Cooper, *The Light of Common Day*, p. 112
73. Ziegler, *Diana Cooper*, p. 150.
74. *The Spectator*, 1 October 1932.
75. *The Listener*, 19 October 1932.
76. *Bookman*, November 1932.
77. Eileen Agar, *A Look at My Life*, pp. 103–5.
78. Clare Mackenzie to EW, undated; BL.
79. Joyce Gill to EW, undated; BL.
80. EW to Teresa Jungman, 28 September 1932; private collection, copy in AWA.
81. EW to Teresa Jungman, 23 October 1932; private collection, copy in AWA.
82. EW to Teresa Jungman, 20 November 1932; private collection, copy in AWA.
83. EW to Lady Diana Cooper [2 December 1932]; *MWMS*, p. 20.

14 *Off to the Forest*

1. EW to Lady Diana Cooper, [8 November 1932]; *MWMS*, p. 19.
2. EW to Teresa Jungman, 4–8 December 1932; private collection, copy in AWA.
3. *Ninety-Two Days*, pp. 3, 5.
4. 4 December 1932; *EWD*, p. 355.
5. Ibid.
6. Pryce-Jones, *Evelyn Waugh and His World*, p. 89.
7. EW to Lady Mary Lygon. [*c.* 20 December]; copy in AWA.
8. 4 December 1932; *EWD*, p. 356.
9. EW to Lady Mary Lygon, [*c.* 20 December]; copy in AWA.
10. EW to Teresa Jungman, 1 December 1932; private collection, copy in AWA.
11. EW to Teresa Jungman, 2 December 1932; private collection, copy in AWA.
12. EW to Teresa Jungman, 4–8 December 1932; private collection, copy in AWA.
13. *Ninety-Two Days*, p. 20 (Serif edition, 2007).
14. 20 December 1932; *EWD*, p. 359.
15. Ibid.
16. 20 December 1932; *EWD*, p. 359–60.
17. 20 December 1932; *EWD*, p. 360.
18. Christmas Day 1932; *EWD*, p. 360.
19. EW to Teresa Jungman, 31 December 1932; private collection, copy in AWA.
20. EW to Lady Diana Cooper [2 January 1933]; *MWMS*, p. 19.
21. *Ninety-Two Days*, p. 30 (Serif edition, 2007).
22. *Ninety-Two Days*, p. 50 (Serif edition 2007)
23. 11 January 1933; *EWD*, p. 364.
24. *Ninety-Two Days*, p. 61.
25. EW to Lady Diana Cooper, 28 January [1933]; *MWMS*, p. 23.
26. *Ninety-Two Days*, pp. 71–2.
27. Ibid., p. 67.
28. Ibid., p. 74.
29. Ibid., p. 88.
30. Ibid., p. 87.
31. EW to Lady Diana Cooper, 10 February 1933; *MWMS*, pp. 25–6.

32. EW to Teresa Jungman, Ash Wednesday [1 March 1933]; private collection, copy in AWA.
33. EW to Lady Diana Cooper, 2 March [1933]; *MWMS*, p. 27.
34. EW to Teresa Jungman, Ash Wednesday [1 March 1933]; private collection, copy in AWA.
35. EW to Teresa Jungman, 7 April 1933; private collection, copy in AWA.
36. EW to Teresa Jungman [c. 8 May 1933]; private collection, copy in AWA.
37. Ibid.
38. EW to Teresa Jungman [c. 21 May 1933]; private collection, copy in AWA.
39. Ibid.
40. EW to Teresa Jungman, 23 July 1933; private collection, copy in AWA.
41. EW to Lady Diana Cooper [c. 29 July 1933]; *MWMS*, p. 38.
42. EW to Teresa Jungman, 31 July 1933; private collection, copy in AWA.
43. Teresa Jungman to EW, undated [c. July 1933]; BL.
44. Teresa Jungman to EW, undated [c. July 1933]; BL.
45. EW to Teresa Jungman, 2 August 1933; private collection, copy in AWA.
46. EW to Teresa Jungman, 31 July 1933, private collection, copy in AWA
47. EW to Teresa Jungman, 2 August 1933; private collection, copy in AWA.
48. EW to Nancy Mitford [4 August 1933]; copy in AWA.
49. Teresa Jungman to EW [c. 7 August 1933]; BL.
50. EW to Teresa Jungman, 16 August 1933; private collection, copy in AWA.
51. Ibid.
52. EW to Lady Diana Cooper, [September/October 1933]; *MWMS*, p. 35.
53. Diary of Katharine Asquith, quoted in Hastings, *Evelyn Waugh*, p. 286.
54. EW to Lady Diana Cooper, [September/October 1933]; *MWMS*, p. 35.
55. EW to Teresa Jungman, 1 September 1933 [and c. 28 August 1933]; private collection, copy in AWA.
56. EW to Teresa Jungman, 1 September 1933; private collection, copy in AWA.
57. Hollis, *Oxford in the Twenties*, p. 84.
58. EW to Teresa Jungman [c. 3 July 1933]; private collection, copy in AWA.
59. Unpublished, untitled manuscript by Evelyn Gardner 'about my marriage to Evelyn Waugh and its break-up'; copy in AWA.
60. EW to Lady Dorothy Lygon, [c. 20 Oct 1933]; copy in AWA.
61. Unpublished, untitled manuscript by Evelyn Gardner 'about my marriage to Evelyn Waugh and its break-up'; copy in AWA.
62. See Gallagher, 'Evelyn Waugh and the Vatican Divorce' in Blayac (ed.), *Evelyn Waugh: New Directions*, pp. 62–84.
63. Ibid. pp. 73–4.
64. Ibid., p. 74.
65. EW to Lady Mary Lygon [October 1933]; *EWL*, p. 81.

15 *I Can't Advise You in My Favour*

1. EW to Teresa, [c. 16 November 1933]; private collection, copy in AWA.
2. EW to Lady Dorothy Lygon, [c. 19 October 1933]; copy in AWA.
3. EW to Lady Mary Lygon [31 October 1933]; copy in AWA.
4. EW to Teresa Jungman, 6 November 1933; private collection, copy in AWA.
5. EW to Teresa Jungman, 3 December 1933; private collection, copy in AWA.

6. EW to Teresa Jungman, 24 December 1933; private collection, copy in AWA.
7. EW to Teresa Jungman, 29 December 1933; private collection, copy in AWA.
8. EW to Katharine Asquith [January 1934]; *EWL*, pp. 83–4.
9. EW to Lady Mary and Lady Dorothy Lygon [*c.* 4 January 1934]; *EWL*, p. 82.
10. EW to Lady Mary Lygon [*c.* 20 January 1934]; *EWL*, p. 82.
11. 'Fan-Fare', *Life* magazine, 8 April 1946; *EAR*, p. 303.
12. EW to Katharine Asquith [January 1934]; *EWL*, pp. 83–4.
13. EW to Katharine Asquith, [*c.* 9 February 1934]; *EWL*, p. 85.
14. Henry Yorke to EW, 2 September 1934; BL.
15. EW to Henry Yorke, [*c.* 3 September 1934]; *EWL*, p. 88.
16. EW to Lady Diana Cooper [*c.* 11 February 1934]; *MWMS*, p. 43.
17. EW to A. D. Peters [*c.* 30 April 1934]; HRC, copy in AWA.
18. 6 July 1934; *EWD*, p. 386.
19. EW to Teresa Jungman, 7 July 1934; private collection, copy in AWA.
20. 9 July 1934; *EWD*, p. 388.
21. EW to Lady Diana Cooper, [13 July 1934]; *MWMS*, p. 45.
22. 17 July 1934; *EWD*, p. 390.
23. 'The First Time I Went To The North: Fiasco in The Arctic', published in the anthology *The First Time I . . .* ed. by Theodora Benson (1935); *EAR*, p. 146.
24. 'The First Time I Went To The North'; *EAR*, pp. 144–9.
25. 'The First Time I Went To The North'; *EAR*, p. 148.
26. Sir Alexander Glen to Selina Hastings, Hastings, *Evelyn Waugh*, p. 306.
27. EW to Tom Driberg [late August 1934], Christ Church, Oxford; copy in AWA.
28. *NYTBR*, 27 May 1934; *EWCH*, pp. 146–8.
29. *New Statesman*, 15 September 1934; *EWCH*, pp. 154–7.
30. EW to Lady Mary Lygon [*c.* 8 September 1934]; *EWL*, p. 89.
31. EW to Lady Dorothy Lygon [*c.* 26 October 1934]; *EWL*, pp. 90–91.
32. Nicola Beauman, *Cynthia Asquith*, (Hamish Hamilton, 1987), p. 314.
33. EW to Lady Mary Lygon [*c.* 10 January 1935]; *EWL*, p. 92.
34. James Lees-Milne, *Ancestral Voices*, p. 184.
35. A. N. Wilson, *Hilaire Belloc* (Hamish Hamilton, 1984), p. 325.
36. EW to Lady Mary Lygon [*c.* 8 February 1935]; *EWL*, p. 93.
37. EW to Laura Herbert [3 May 1935]; *EWL*, p. 94.
38. EW to Katharine Asquith [24 June 1935]; *EWL*, p. 95.
39. EW to Laura Herbert [*c.* late July 1935?]
40. Laura Herbert to EW [8 August 1935]; BL.
41. EW to Laura Herbert [*c.* 9 August 1935]; *EWL*, p. 95.
42. *Evening Standard*, 13 February 1935; *EAR*, p. 163.
43. *Waugh in Abyssinia*, (Penguin Modern Classics edition, 2000), p. 41.
44. W. F. Deedes, *At War With Waugh*, p. 116.
45. Ibid., pp. 90–91.
46. Ibid., p. 35.
47. *Waugh in Abyssinia*, pp. 44–5.
48. EW to Diana Cooper, 13 September [1935]; *MWMS*, p. 52.
49. EW to Laura Herbert, 24 August [1935]; *EWL*, p. 97–8.
50. EW to Laura Waugh 26 October [1935]; AWA.
51. Arthur Waugh Diary, 3 February 1936; BU.
52. Laura Herbert to EW, 28 January 1936; BL.

53. EW to Lady Mary Lygon, 15 April 1936; *EWL*, p. 105.
54. EW to Laura Herbert, 28 April 1936; *EWL*, p. 104.

16 *Goodness She is a Decent Girl*

1. EW to Diana Cooper [June 1936]; *MWMS*, p. 60.
2. *The Spectator*, 1 November 1935; *EWCH*, p. 165.
3. Henry Yorke to EW, 18 June 1936; BL.
4. EW to Henry Yorke, 20 June 1936; copy in AWA.
5. *The Spectator*, 10 July 1936, *EWCH*, pp. 183–4.
6. EW to Katharine Asquith, 4 August 1936; copy in AWA.
7. 18 August 1936; *EWD*, p. 398.
8. *Waugh in Abyssinia*, p. 167.
9. EW to Laura Herbert, 4 August 1936; *EWL*, p. 109.
10. EW to Laura Herbert, 5 August 1936; *EWL*, p. 110.
11. EW to Lady Mary Lygon, 6 August 1936; copy in AWA.
12. 10 September 1936; *EWD*, p. 405.
13. Laura Herbert to EW, August 1936; BL.
14. *The Times*, 20 August 1936.
15. EW to Lady Mary Lygon, 12 September 1936; *EWL*, pp. 110–11.
16. Arthur Waugh Diary, 23 September 1936; BU.
17. EW to Arthur Waugh, 29 September 1936; AWA.
18. Arthur Waugh Diary, 6 October 1936; BU.
19. Arthur Waugh Diary, 7 October 1936; BU.
20. EW to Teresa Jungman, 1 October 1936; private collection, copy in AWA.
21. 15 October 1936; *EWD*, p. 409.
22. 5 November 1936; *EWD*, p. 412.
23. 21 December 1936; *EWD*, p. 417.
24. EW to Lady Diana Cooper [*c.* 21 December 1936]; *MWMS*, p. 62.
25. EW to Laura Herbert [February 1937]; AWA.
26. 21 December 1936; *EWD*, p. 417.
27. 'General Conversation Myself', *Nash's Pall Mall Magazine*, March 1937; *EAR*, p. 190; the fire itself is recorded in Arthur Waugh Diary, 29 January 1935; BU.
28. Arthur Waugh Diary, 31 December 1936; BU.
29. Arthur Waugh Diary, 26 February 1936; BU.
30. Alec Waugh, *The Best Wine Last*, p. 48.
31. Alexander Waugh, *Fathers and Sons*, p. 242.
32. EW to Laura Herbert, February 1937; AWA.
33. EW to Laura Herbert, February 1937; AWA.
34. 4 February 1937; *EWD*, p. 420.
35. EW to Diana Cooper [*c.* 18 July 1937]; *MWMS*, p. 64.
36. Hastings, *Evelyn Waugh*, p. 364.
37. Arthur Waugh Diary, 17 April 1937; BU.
38. 18 April 1937; *EWD*, p. 422.
39. EW to Katharine Asquith, May 1937; copy in AWA.
40. EW to W. N. Roughead, 7 July 1937; copy in AWA.
41. Patrick Balfour to Caroline Kinross, 15 December 1937, National Library of Scotland; cited in Hastings, *Evelyn Waugh*, p. 366.

42. EW to Vivien Greene, 8 March [1938]; *EWL*, p. 116.
43. 8 July 1939; *EWD*, p. 432.
44. 27 November 1937; *EWD*, p. 428.
45. 28 June 1939; *EWD*, p. 431.
46. 17 and 24 November 1937; *EWD*, pp. 426–7.
47. 26 November 1937; *EWD*, p. 428.
48. Arthur Waugh Diary, 25 February 1938, BU
49. EW to A. D. Peters, 10 March 1938; HRC.
50. EW to Thomas Balston, 11 March 1938; copy in AWA.
51. EW to Teresa Jungman, 12 March 1938; private collection, copy in AWA.
52. EW to Teresa Jungman, 17 March 1938; private collection, copy in AWA.
53. Introduction to new Penguin paperback edition of *Scoop* (2000).
54. 7 May 1938; *EWCH*, p. 194.
55. 7 May 1938; *EWCH*, p. 195.
56. 13 May 1938; *EWCH*, p. 199.
57. *The Spectator*, 13 May 1938; *EWCH*, pp. 200-202.
58. Arthur Waugh Diary, 7 July 1938; BU.
59. Alec Waugh, *The Best Wine Last*, p. 58.
60. Arthur Waugh Diary, 8 July 1938; BU.
61. EW to A. D. Peters [*c.* 16 May 1938]; HRC.
62. EW to Mary Herbert, 17 August [1938]; copy in AWA.
63. 28 July 1939; *EWCH*, p. 204.
64. 19 November 1939; *EWCH*, p. 207.
65. EW to Teresa Jungman, 1 January 1939.
66. 23 August 1939; *EWD*, p. 437.
67. Diana Cooper to EW [July 1939]; *MWMS*, p. 68.
68. *The Times*, 5 September 1939, p. 1.

17 A War to End Waugh

1. Catherine Waugh to EW, 5 September 1939; BL.
2. 27 August 1939; *EWD*, p. 438.
3. 1 October 1939; *EWD*, p. 444.
4. Henry Yorke to EW, 14 October 1939, BL.
5. 21 October 1939; *EWD*, p. 447.
6. Carol Mather, *When the Grass Stops Growing*, (Leo Cooper, 1997), p. 35.
7. 18 October 1939; *EWD*, p. 447.
8. EW to Laura Waugh, 23 October 1939; AWA.
9. EW to Laura Waugh [*c.* 25 October 1939]; AWA.
10. All Saints [1 November], 1939; *EWD*, p. 448.
11. EW to Mary Lygon [*c.* 18 November 1939].
12. EW to Laura Waugh [*c.* 30 November 1939].
13. 26 October 1939; *EWD*, p. 437.
14. 23 November 1939; *EWD*, p. 437.
15. 24 November 1939; *EWD*, p. 437.
16. Ibid.
17. EW to Laura Waugh [10 December 1939]; AWA.
18. EW to Laura Waugh, 18 December 1939; AWA.

19. Diana Cooper, *Trumpets from the Steep*, p. 36.
20. John St John, *To the War with Waugh* (The Whittington Press, 1973), p. 6.
21. EW to Helen Asquith, 27 December 1939; copy in AWA.
22. EW to Laura Waugh, 7 January 1940; *EWL*, p. 133.
23. Obituary of Teresa Cuthbertson, *The Daily Telegraph*, 12 June 2010.
24. EW to Teresa Cuthbertson, 1 August 1940, private collection, copy in AWA.
25. EW to Laura Waugh, 14 January 1940; AWA.
26. Major-General R. D. Houghton to Selina Hastings, interview transcript, side 2, page 1; AWA.
27. 15 January 1940; *EWD*, p. 461.
28. EW to Laura Waugh, 25 February 1940; AWA.
29. Evelyn told Laura that Betjeman had been 'registered insane' after the RAF medical exam.
30. EW to John Betjeman, 24 January and 15 February 1940; copies in AWA.
31. EW to Laura Waugh [April 1940]; *EWL*, p. 139.
32. Major-General R. D. Houghton to Selina Hastings, interview transcript, side 1, page 6; copy in AWA.
33. EW to Laura Waugh, 31 March 1940; AWA.
34. EW to Laura Waugh, 2 April 1940; AWA.
35. Admiralty Form S 206 b, signed by Lieutenant-Colonel G. E. Wildman-Lushington (18 May 1940) and Brigadier St Clair-Morford (25 May 1940), cited in Gallagher, *In the Picture*, p. 139.
36. EW to Laura Waugh, 26 September [1940]; *EWL*, p. 141.
37. EW to Arthur Waugh, 5 November 1940; AWA.
38. See Sushila Anand, *Daisy: The Life and Loves of the Countess of Warwick* (Piatkus, 2008).
39. 'Commando Raid On Bardia', *Life* magazine, 17 November 1941; *EAR*, p. 263.
40. David Niven, *The Moon's A Balloon* (Coronet Books, 1972), p. 220.
41. Typed draft of 'A History of the Commandos' by R. E Laycock, Laycock Papers 6/28, Liddell Hart Centre for Military Archives, cited in Gallagher, *In The Picture*, p. 142.
42. Robert Laycock, unpublished memoir, private collection.
43. 13 November 1940; *EWD*, pp. 487–8.
44. EW to Laura Waugh, 21 November 1941; AWA.
45. 'Memorandum on Layforce; July 1940–July 1941', *EWD*, p. 491.
46. EW to Laura Waugh, 15 November 1940; AWA.
47. EW to Laura Waugh, 20 November 1940; AWA.
48. Mather, *When the Grass Stops Growing*, pp. 30–31.
49. EW to Catherine Waugh, 2 December 1940, AWA.
50. Excerpts quoted in a letter from Arthur Waugh to Joan Waugh, 6 December 1940; AWA.
51. Alexander Waugh, *Fathers and Sons*, p. 252.
52. 3 December 1940; *EWD*, p. 437.
53. EW to Laura Waugh [*c.* 8 December 1940]; AWA.
54. EW to Laura Waugh, 25 December 1940; *EWL*, p. 149.
55. Christopher Sykes and Ann Pasternak Slater think it would have been better; Douglas Lane Patey disagrees.
56. 3 February 1941, cited in James Owen, *Commando*, p. 29.

57. EW to Laura Waugh, 8 February 1941; AWA.
58. EW to Laura Waugh, 23 February 1941; *EWL*, p. 150.
59. EW to Laura Waugh, 6 March 1941; AWA.
60. 'I was Evelyn Waugh's Batman', *Punch*, 19 November 1975.
61. Conversation between Dr R. E. S. Tanner and Antony Beevor, 2 December 1990, copy of transcript in AWA.
62. 'I was Evelyn Waugh's Batman', *Punch*, 19 November 1975.
63. 'Memorandum on Layforce; July 1940–July 1941'; *EWD*, p. 494.
64. Ibid.; *EWD*, p. 495.
65. A. D. Peters to EW, 23 September 1941, cited in Douglas Lane Patey, *The life of Evelyn Waugh*, p. 189.
66. 'Memorandum on Layforce; July 1940–July 1941'; *EWD*, p. 496.
67. Ibid., p. 498.
68. Ibid., p. 499.
69. Ibid., p. 500.
70. Account by Laycock; National Archives, DEFE 2/699.
71. 'Memorandum on Layforce; July 1940–July 1941'; *EWD*, p. 502.
72. Ibid., p. 503.
73. Ibid., p. 504.
74. Major F. C. C. Graham, 'Cretan Crazy Week', p. 5, IWM 76/180/1.
75. 'Memorandum on Layforce; July 1940–July 1941'; *EWD*, p. 507.
76. EW's reply, dated 4 July 1955; Mark Amory (ed.), *The Letters of Ann Fleming*, p. 155.
77. 6 July 1955; *EWD*, p. 728.
78. Layforce Diary, National Archives, WO 218/186.
79. Major-General Sir Robert Laycock, unpublished memoir.
80. 'Memorandum on Layforce; July 1940–July 1941'; *EWD*, p. 509.
81. Layforce Diary, National Archives, WO 218/186.
82. Antony Beevor, 'The First Casualty of Waugh', *The Spectator*, 5 April 1991, p. 26.
83. Journal of Major R. W. Madoc, pp. 101–02, IWM, cited in Gallagher, *In the Picture*, p. 207.
84. Letter to Nicholls's mother in Papers of Captain F. R. J Nicholls, IWM 93/17/1.
85. F. C. C. Graham to Michael Davie, 9 June 1976, IWM 76/180/1.
86. Laycock, unpublished memoir, p. 380.
87. Ibid., pp. 380–81.
88. Ibid., p. 388.
89. Ibid.
90. Antony Beevor, *Crete 1941* (Introduction to Penguin edition, 2014), p. xv.
91. Conversation between Dr R. E. S. Tanner and Antony Beevor, 2 December 1990, copy of transcript in AWA.
92. Ibid.
93. Colonel E. E. Rich, 'The Campaign in Crete', National Archives, CAB 44/121; cited in Gallagher, *In the Picture*, p. 86.

18 Head Unbloodied but Bowed

1. EW to Laura Waugh, 28 September 1941; AWA.
2. Arthur Waugh Diary, 27 September 1941; BU.
3. EW to Laura Waugh, 28 September 1941; AWA.

4. Cited in Selina Hastings, *Evelyn Waugh*, p. 422.
5. EW to Laura Waugh, 30 September 1941; AWA.
6. EW to Laura Waugh, 28 September 1941; AWA.
7. EW to Laura Waugh [*c*. November 1941]; AWA.
8. EW to Laura Waugh, 16 November 1941; *EWL*, p. 157.
9. EW to Laura Waugh [January 1942]; AWA.
10. Diary, 5 January–7 February 1942; *EWD*, p. 518.
11. '[H]eroic and chivalrous disguise', *Scott-King's Modern Europe*, p. 5; 'Do you understand . . .', EW to Diana Cooper, [Spring 1942], *MWMS*; 'I wish I were back with you', EW to Laycock, 23 March 1942, copy in AWA; 'It seems unlikely . . .', *EWD*, p. 517; EW to Laura Waugh [May 1942]; AWA.
12. EW to Lady Dorothy Lygon, 17 May 1942; copy in AWA.
13. EW to Laura Waugh, 31 May 1942; *EWL*, p. 161.
14. Arthur Waugh to EW [25 April 1942]; BL.
15. Laycock to EW, 26 June 1942; BL.
16. 26 October 1942; *EWD*, p. 530.
17. EW to Laura Waugh, 27 October [1942]; *EWL*, p. 164.
18. EW to Laura Waugh 27 December 1942; *EWL*, pp. 164–5.
19. 28 October 1942; *EWD*, p. 530.
20. EW to Laura Waugh [28 September 1943]; *EWL*, p. 172.
21. 27 August 1942; *EWD*, p. 525.
22. EW to Laura Waugh, 24 October [1942]; AWA.
23. EW to Laura Waugh [*c*. 10 December 1942]; AWA.
24. EW to Laura Waugh [26 July 1943]; AWA.
25. Lord Lovat, *March Past*, p. 233.
26. EW to Tom Driberg [*c*. 1 July 1943]; Christ Church, Oxford.
27. EW to Alec Waugh, 8 July 1943; BU.
28. EW to Lord Lovat, 12 July 1943, *EWD*, p. 541.
29. Lord Lovat to EW, 13 July 1943, *EWD*, p. 542.
30. Lieutenant-Colonel A. F. Austen to Auberon Waugh, November 1978; AWA.
31. Gen. Haydon to Laycock, 31 July 1943, Laycock Papers 6/20, Liddell Hart Centre.
32. Jakie Astor to Christopher Sykes, cited in Sykes, *Evelyn Waugh*, p. 228.
33. Laycock Papers, Box 6/15, Liddell Hart Centre; cited in Owen, *Commando*, p. 312.
34. Brigadier Antony Head to Laycock, 9 September 1942, Laycock Papers, 6/4, LHC, cited in Gallagher *In the Picture*, p. 227.
35. Laycock to Lovat, 12 September 1942; Laycock Papers, 6/13, LHC, cited in ibid., p. 227.
36. Laura Waugh to Alec Waugh, 3 July 1943, cited in Alexander Waugh, *Fathers and Sons*, p. 265.
37. EW to Brigadier R. E. Laycock, 19 July 1943, *EWD*, p. 543.
38. 10 August 1943; *EWD*, p. 545.
39. 29 August 1943; *EWD*, p. 548.
40. EW to Laura Waugh [6 December 1943]; *EWL*, p. 174.
41. Evelyn Waugh, *Sword of Honour*, p. 533 (Penguin Classics edition).
42. 13 October 1943; *EWD*, pp. 552–3.
43. EW to Colonel A. H. Ferguson, 24 January 1944; copy in AWA.
44. EW to Laura Waugh, 25 January 1944; *EWL*, p. 176.

19 A Book to Bring Tears

1. EW to Laura Waugh, 2 February 1944; *EWL*, p. 176.
2. EW to A. D. Peters, 8 February 1944; *EWL*, p. 177.
3. 13 February 1944; *EWD*, p. 558.
4. 2 March 1944; *EWD*, p. 559.
5. EW to Laura Waugh, 2 March [1944]; *EWL*, p. 179.
6. EW to Lady Dorothy Lygon, 23 March 1944; *EWL*, p. 180.
7. Ibid.
8. EW to Laura Waugh [26 March 1944]; AWA.
9. EW to Laura Waugh, 19 September 1943; *EWL*, p. 169.
10. Auberon Waugh, *Will This Do?*, p. 29.
11. EW to Laura Waugh, 6 December 1941; AWA.
12. EW to Laura Waugh, [*c.* 15 December 1942]; AWA.
13. EW to Laura Waugh, 19 September 1943; *EWL*, p. 170.
14. EW to Laura Waugh [*c.* 13 February 1944]; AWA.
15. EW to Laura Waugh, 2 June 1941; *EWL*, p. 179.
16. 1 April 1944; *EWD*, p. 561.
17. 3 April 1944; *EWD*, p. 561.
18. 16 April 1944; *EWD*, p. 561.
19. 4 May 1944; *EWD*, p. 562.
20. Ibid.; *EWD*, p. 564.
21. 9 March 1944; *EWD*, pp. 564–5.
22. Auberon Waugh, *Will This Do?*, pp. 13–14.
23. Evelyn Waugh to Nancy Mitford, 18 May [1944]; *LNMEW*, p. 4.
24. EW to Lady Dorothy Lygon, 23 March 1944; *EWL*, p. 182.
25. 6 June 1944; *EWD*, pp. 567–8.
26. EW to A. D. Peters, 20 June 1944; HRC.
27. 24 June 1944; *EWD*, p. 568.
28. EW to Laura Waugh, 25 June 1944; AWA.
29. Fitzroy Maclean, 'Captain Waugh', in Pryce-Jones, *Evelyn Waugh and His World*, p. 134.
30. 2 July 1944; *EWD*, pp. 568–9.
31. EW to Laura Waugh, 6 July 1944; AWA.
32. Nicholas Shakespeare, 'A Life Less Ordinary', *The Independent*, 21 September 2011.
33. Diana Cooper, *Trumpets from the Steep*, p. 201. John Julius Norwich, *Trying to Please*, p. 99.
34. 16 July 1944; *EWD*, p. 573.
35. Randoplh Churchill to Laura Waugh, 26 July 1944; AWA.
36. 31 July 1944; Hermione Ranfurly, *To War with Whittaker*, (Heinemann, 1994), p. 260.
37. Pryce-Jones, *Evelyn Waugh and His World*, p. 53.
38. EW to Laura Waugh, 17 August [1944]; *EWL*, p. 182.
39. Stephen Clissold, 'Civil Waugh in Croatia', *The South Slav Journal*, Vol. 3, No. 3, September 1980.
40. 16 September 1944; *EWD*, p. 579.
41. EW to Laura Waugh, 16 September 1944; *EWL*, p. 182.
42. EW to Catherine Waugh, 17 October 1944; AWA.
43. Clissold, 'Civil Waugh in Croatia', *The South Slav Journal*, Vol. 3, No. 3, September 1980.

44. Pryce-Jones, *Evelyn Waugh and His World*, p. 143.
45. The Earl of Birkenhead, 'Fiery Particles', in ibid., p. 152.
46. Clissold, 'Civil Waugh in Croatia', *The South Slav Journal*, Vol. 3, No. 3, September 1980.
47. The Earl of Birkenhead, 'Fiery Particles', in Pryce-Jones, *Evelyn Waugh and His World*, pp. 151–3.
48. 27 October 1944; *EWD*, p. 587.
49. EW to Nancy Mitford, 12 November [194]; *LNMEW*, p. 7.
50. EW to Laura Waugh, 2 November [1944]; *EWL*, p. 192.
51. EW to Laura Waugh, 5 November [1944]; *EWL*, pp. 192–3.
52. The Earl of Birkenhead to Hugh Trevor-Roper, 29 October 1973; *Evelyn Waugh Newsletter*, Vol. 43, No. 3.
53. Clissold, 'Civil Waugh in Croatia', *The South Slav Journal*, Vol. 3, No. 3, September 1980.
54. EW to Laura Waugh, 5 November 1944; *EWL*, p. 192–3.
55. EW to Catherine Waugh, 11 December [1944]; AWA.
56. EW to Laura Waugh, 25 December 1944; AWA.
57. EW to Nancy Mitford, 4 January 1945; AWA.
58. EW to Laura Waugh, 7 January 1945; *EWL*, p. 195.
59. EW to Nancy Mitford, 7 January 1945; *EWL*, p. 196.
60. 12 January 1945; *EWD*, p. 608.
61. EW to Laura Waugh, 5 January 1945; AWA.
62. EW to Laura Waugh, 10 February 1945; *EWL*, p. 201.
63. EW to Laura Waugh, 8 March 1945; *EWL*, p. 202.

20 *The Occupation*

1. EW to Nancy Mitford, 7 January 1945; *LNMEW*, p. 14.
2. Martin D'Arcy to EW, 21 April 1945; BL.
3. Penelope Betjeman to EW, 23 January 1945; BL.
4. Nancy Mitford to EW, 17 January 1945; BL.
5. Henry Yorke to EW, Christmas Day 1944; BL.
6. Nancy Mitford to EW, 17 January 1945; BL.
7. Preface to 1960 edition of *Brideshead Revisited* (Chapman & Hall).
8. Harold Acton to EW, 30 May 1945; BL.
9. *Manchester Guardian*, 1 June 1945; *EWCH*, p. 233.
10. 23 June 1945; *EWCH*, p. 239.
11. 5 January 1946, *EWCH*, p. 245.
12. *EWL*, p. 219n.
13. 12 April 1945; *EWD*, p. 625.
14. EW to Douglas Woodruff, 12 January 1946; copy in AWA.
15. 1 July 1945; *EWD*, p. 608.
16. EW to Alfred Gilbey, 31 October 1945; copy in AWA.
17. *The Daily Telegraph*, 11 November 1947, *EAR*, p. 339.
18. EW to Laura Waugh, 28 July 1945; AWA.
19. 'What To Do With the Upper Classes', *Town and Country*, September 1946, *EAR*, p. 312.
20. Ibid.

21. 28 July 1945; *EWD*, p. 629.
22. EW to Laura Waugh, 28 July 1945; AWA.
23. 28 July 1945; *EWD*, p. 629.
24. EW to Laura Waugh, 25 August 1945; *EWL*, p. 211.
25. 11 September 1945; *EWD*, p. 608.
26. EW to Lady Diana Cooper, 12 January 1947; *MWMS*, p. 93.
27. EW to Catherine Waugh, 19 September 1945; AWA.
28. EW to Lady Mary Lygon, 12 October 1945; copy in AWA.
29. EW to Randolph Churchill, 8 October 1945; *EWL*, p. 213.
30. 26 December 1945; *EWD*, p. 608.
31. EW to Lady Diana Cooper, 3 January 1946; *MWMS*, p. 82.
32. Auberon Waugh, *Will This Do?* p. 65.
33. EW to Penelope Betjeman [August 1935]; edited version in *EWL*, pp. 96–7.
34. Richard Ingrams to Auberon Waugh, January 1987, cited in Bevis Hillier, John Betjeman: New Fame New Love, 2002, p. 661.
35. Penelope Betjeman to Martin Stannard, cited in Stannard, *Evelyn Waugh*, p. 282.
36. Auberon Waugh, *Literary Review*, December 1986.
37. EW to John Betjeman, 27 May 1945; *EWL*, p. 207.
38. EW to Penelope Betjeman, 15 January 1946; *EWL*, pp. 217–18.
39. Penelope Betjeman to EW, 23 January 1946; BL.
40. EW to John Betjeman, 22 September 1946; copy in AWA.
41. Penelope Betjeman to EW, 1 June 1947; BL.
42. EW to Penelope Betjeman, 4 June [1947]; *EWL*, pp. 252–3.
43. Diary, 4 August 1947; edited version in *EWD*, p. 608.
44. EW to Nancy Mitford, 7 August [1946]; *LNMEW*, p. 46.
45. EW to Graham Greene, 21 August 1951; *EWL*, p. 353. EW to Nancy Mitford, 29 October 1951; *LNMEW*, p. 244.
46. *The Tablet*, 3 December 1938, *EAR*, pp. 238–41.
47. *The Tablet*, 10 November 1945, *EAR*, pp. 281–3.
48. EW to Nancy Mitford, 7 January 1945; *LNMEW*, p. 14.
49. 31 March 1946; *EWD*, p. 645.
50. 'Notes on Nuremberg'; EW to Randolph Churchill [April 1946], *EWL*, p. 226.
51. Philip Ziegler, *Diana Cooper*, p. 241.
52. Diana Cooper to Conrad Russell, 7 April 1946, cited in Ziegler, p. 241.
53. 1–2 April 1946; *EWD*, p. 647.
54. EW to Lady Mary Lygon, 4 February 1946; *EWL*, p. 233.
55. 6 March 1946; *EWD*, p. 643.
56. 'Fan-Fare', *Life*, 8 April 1946, *EAR*, pp. 300–304.
57. A. D. Peters to EW, 15 November 1946; HRC.
58. EW to A. D. Peters, 21 November 1946; HRC.
59. Harold Acton, *More Memoirs of an Aesthete*, p. 225.
60. EW to Lady Diana Cooper [c.2 February 1947]; *MWMS*, p. 94.
61. Alec Waugh to Catherine Waugh, 22 February 1948; BU.
62. Diary, 7 February 1947 (omitted from *EWD*).
63. Selina Hastings, *The Secret Lives of Somerset Maugham*, p. 381.
64. EW to A. D. Peters, 19 February 1947; HRC.
65. 7 February 1947; *EWD*, p. 673.
66. 7 April 1947; *EWD*, p. 675.

67. EW to A. D. Peters, 6 March [1947]; HRC.
68. Ibid.
69. 7 April 1947; *EWD*, p. 675.
70. Ibid.
71. *The Tablet*, 17 July 1936.
72. 7 April 1947; *EWD*, p. 675.
73. EW to A. D. Peters, 6 March [1947]; HRC.
74. EW to Lady Diana Cooper, 10 May [1947]; *MWMS*, pp. 95–6.
75. EW to A. D. Peters, 6 March [1947]; HRC.
76. 1 February 1947; *EWD*, p. 670.
77. Carol Brandt to A. D. Peters, 18 March 1947, HRC, cited in Hastings, *Evelyn Waugh*, p. 517.
78. Anthony Slide (ed.), *'It's the Pictures That Got Small': Charles Brackett on Billy Wilder and Hollywood's Golden Age* (2014), 16 February 1947, p. 304.
79. Cited in Craig Brown, *One on One*, (Fourth Estate, 2011), p. 53.
80. Hastings, *Evelyn Waugh*, p. 517.
81. *The Ordeal of Gilbert Pinfold*, p. 23 (Penguin Modern Classics edition).
82. EW's remark to Toye is in Michael Swan to Maurice Cranston, 16 July [1952], Cranston Papers, HRC. His warning to Baby is in EW to Teresa Cuthbertson, 4 January 1946; private collection, copy in AWA.
83. 19 April 1947; *EWD*, p. 675.
84. EW to Nancy Mitford, 16 October [1946]; *EWL*, p. 246.
85. EW to Margaret Stephens, 26 May 1947; AWA.
86. 'Half in Love with Easeful Death: An Examination of Californian Burial Customs', *Life*, 29 September 1947, *The Tablet*, 18 October 1947, *EAR*, pp. 331–7.
87. EW to A. D. Peters, 11 September 1947; HRC.
88. A. D. Peters to EW, 13 September 1947; HRC.
89. EW to A. D. Peters, 14 September [1947]; HRC.
90. 29 June 1947; *EWD*, p. 681.
91. Cyril Connolly to EW, [2 September 1947]; BL.
92. *Horizon*, February 1948, pp. 76–7; *EAR*, pp. 299–300.
93. Sykes, *Evelyn Waugh*, p. 312.
94. Cited in Jeffrey Meyers, *Edmund Wilson*, (Houghton Mifflin, 1995), p. 271.
95. Nancy Mitford to EW, 9 February 1948; *LNMEW*, p. 90.
96. EW to Nancy Mitford [December 1950]; *LNMEW*, p. 207.
97. Lady Pamela Berry to Nancy Mitford, 27 November 1949, cited in Hastings, *Evelyn Waugh*, pp. 537–8.
98. *EWL*, pp. 288–9n.
99. EW to Laura Waugh, 9 November [1948]; *EWL*, p. 288.
100. EW to Nancy Mitford, 2 April [1949]; *LNMEW*, p. 121.
101. Sykes, *Evelyn Waugh*, p. 337.

21 *Off My Rocker*

1. Laura Waugh to EW [July 1950]; BL.
2. EW to Laura Waugh, 30 July and 31 July 1950; *EWL*, p. 334 and AWA.
3. Auberon Waugh, *Will This Do?*, p. 46.
4. Alexander Waugh, *Fathers and Sons*, p. 312.

5. Ibid., pp. 312–13.
6. Auberon Waugh, *Will This Do?*, p. 41.
7. EW to Auberon Waugh, 20 February 1956, *EWL*, p. 466.
8. Auberon Waugh, *Will This Do?*, p. 41.
9. Auberon Waugh, *Will This Do?*, p. 41; Auberon Waugh to Nicholas Shakespeare, *Arena* interview.
10. Cited in Alexander Waugh, *Fathers and Sons*, p. 308.
11. Alexander Waugh, *Fathers and Sons*, p. 310.
12. EW to Teresa D'Arms 17 April 1964; AWA; James Waugh to author, February 2016; 'Let Evelyn Waugh back into Combe Florey churchyard' by Septimus Waugh, *The Spectator*, 26 March 2016.
13. EW to Graham Greene, 18 August 1951; *EWL*, p. 353.
14. Catherine Walston to EW [24 August 1951]; BL.
15. EW to Catherine Walston, 25 August 1951; *EWL*, p. 355.
16. *Time*, 27 October 1952, *EWCH*, pp. 341–3.
17. 19 December 1952, *EWD*, p. 705.
18. EW to Laura Waugh, 5 January 1953; *EWL*, p. 389.
19. EW to Nancy Mitford, 10 February 1953; *LNMEW*, p. 300.
20. John Betjeman to EW, 24 May 1953; Candida Lycett Green (ed.)., *John Betjeman Letters*, Vol. 2 (Methuen, 1995), p. 42.
21. Cited in A. N. Wilson, *Betjeman*, p. 209.
22. EW to Lord Kinross [1953]; *EWL*, p. 416.
23. John Betjeman to EW, 31 December 1953, *John Betjeman Letters*, Vol. 2, p. 47.
24. EW to John Betjeman, 2 January 1954; coopy in AWA.
25. Sykes, *Evelyn Waugh*, p. 472.
26. Barbara Skelton, *Tears Before Bedtime* (Hamish Hamilton, 1987), pp. 135–6.
27. John Julius Norwich (ed.), *Darling Monster: The Letters of Lady Diana Cooper to her son John Julius Norwich, 1939–1952*, p. 229.
28. 29 July 1947; *EWD*, p. 682.
29. EW to Nancy Mitford, 5 December [1949]; *LNMEW*, p. 158.
30. *The Ordeal of Gilbert Pinfold*, pp.11–12.
31. Ibid., p. 12.
32. EW to John Betjeman, 17 September 1953, *EWL*, p. 410.
33. Auberon Waugh to Martin Stannard, 9 February 1989; Stannard, *Evelyn Waugh: The Later Years 1939–1966*, p. 334.
34. Ibid.
35. *The Ordeal of Gilbert Pinfold*, p. 15.
36. *Frankly Speaking*, cited in Appendix to Penguin edition of *The Ordeal of Gilbert Pinfold*.
37. EW to Diana Cooper, 7 August [1953]; *MWMS*, p. 179.
38. Philip Ziegler, *Diana Cooper*, p. 266.
39. EW to Diana Cooper, 19 September [1953]; *MWMS*, p. 183.
40. EW to Diana Cooper, 19 August [1953]; *MWMS*, p. 178.
41. Ziegler, *Diana Cooper*, p. 277.
42. EW to Diana Cooper, 2 January 1954; *MWMS*, p. 186.
43. 6 January 1954; *EWD*, p. 724.
44. 6 January 1954; ibid.
45. EW to Laura Waugh, 3 February [1954]; *EWL*, p. 418.

46. EW to Laura Waugh, 8 February [1954]; ibid.
47. EW to Diana Cooper, 18 February [1954]; *MWMS*, p. 187–8.
48. Frances Donaldson, *Evelyn Waugh: Portrait of a Country Neighbour*, p. 59.
49. Ibid., p. 60.
50. EW to Cyril Connolly, 13 March 1954; copy in AWA.
51. EW to Diana Cooper, 6 March 1954; *MWMS*, p. 189.
52. EW to Nancy Mitford, 5 March 1954; *LNMEW*, p. 332.
53. EW to Cyril Connolly, 13 March 1954; copy in AWA.
54. Hollis, *Oxford in the Twenties*, p. 82.
55. EW to Margaret Waugh, 11 December 1954; *EWL*, p. 434.
56. EW to Nancy Mitford, 18 December 1954; *LNMEW*, p. 332.
57. EW to Ann Fleming, 1955; quoted in Matthew Parker, *Goldeneye* (Hutchinson, 2014), p. 188.
58. EW to Ann Fleming, 6 March [1955]; copy in AWA.
59. EW to Daphne Fielding, 2 October [1956]; *EWL*, p. 476.
60. *The Ordeal of Gilbert Pinfold*, pp. 9–10 (Penguin Modern Classics edition, 2006).
61. 20 July 1957, *EWCH*, pp. 384–6.
62. 21 July 1957, *EWCH*, pp. 386–7.

22 Suitably Sequestered

1. Alexander Waugh, *Fathers and Sons*, p. 338.
2. *The Times*, 23 March 1964.
3. Nancy Spain, 'My Pilgrimage to See Mr Waugh', *Daily Express*, 23 June 1955.
4. 'Awake My Soul! It Is A Lord', *The Spectator*, 8 July 1955.
5. Ibid.
6. 21 and 22 June 1955; *EWD*, p. 725.
7. Diary, 30 June 1955; *EWD*, p. 726.
8. EW to Oldfield, 4 July 1955, *EWL*, p. 443.
9. EW to Nancy Mitford, 14 October 1956; *LNMEW*, p. 397.
10. EW to Ann Fleming, 13 September [1956], Amory (ed.), *Letters of Ann Fleming*, pp. 186–7.
11. *The Times*, 20 and 21 February 1957.
12. EW to Nancy Mitford [5 March] 1957, *LNMEW*, p. 405.
13. EW to Diana Cooper, 24 February [1957]; *MWMS*, p. 237.
14. EW to Alec Waugh, 23 February 1957; BU.
15. EW to Ann Fleming, 28 January 1957, *EWL*, p. 484.
16. EW to Jack Donaldson, 12 March [1957]; copy in AWA.
17. Cited in Sykes, *Evelyn Waugh*, pp. 390–91.
18. *Ronald Knox*, p. 286.
19. Ibid., p. 329.
20. EW to Diana Cooper, 20 November [1957], *MWMS*, p. 245.
21. EW to Dom Hubert van Zeller, 23 January 1958; copy in AWA.
22. Daphne Acton to EW, 25 August 1958; BL.
23. Ibid.
24. EW to Ann Fleming, 10 March 1958, *EWL*, p. 505.
25. EW to Harold Acton, 4 December 1958; copy in AWA.
26. Laura Waugh to EW, 11 June 1958; BL.

27. Cited in Alexander Waugh, *Fathers and Sons*, p. 353.
28. Auberon Waugh to EW, 27 April, 1958; ibid., p. 354.
29. Auberon Waugh to EW, May 1958, ibid., p. 356.
30. EW to Diana Cooper, 9 June 1958, *MWMS*, p. 254.
31. EW to Diana Cooper, 13 June [1958], ibid., p. 255.
32. EW to Ann Fleming, 18 June 1958; private collection, copy in AWA.
33. EW to Diana Cooper, 13 June [1958], *MWMS*, p. 255.
34. Laura Waugh to EW, 18 June 1958; AWA.
35. EW to Father Aelred Watkin, 17 June 1958; copy in AWA.
36. EW to Father Philip Caraman, 29 June 1958; copy in AWA.
37. EW to Daphne Acton, 21 August 1958; *EWL*, p. 512.
38. EW to Auberon Waugh, 8 July 1958; *EWL*, p. 510.
39. Auberon Waugh, *Will This Do?*, p. 109.
40. Auberon Waugh, to EW, 21 July 1958; BL.
41. EW to Daphne Acton, 21 August 1958; copy in AWA.
42. Auberon Waugh to EW [September] 1958; BL.
43. EW to Father Aelred [c. 8 October 1958]; copy in AWA.
44. EW to Lady Mary Lygon, 26 August 1958; copy in AWA.
45. EW to Auberon Waugh, 14 November 1958, Alexander Waugh, *Fathers and Sons*, p. 373.
46. Auberon Waugh, *Will This Do?*, p. 112.
47. EW to Mother Ignatius, 2 August 1950, *EWL*, p. 334.
48. Christopher Sykes, *Evelyn Waugh*, p. 452.
49. EW to Ann Fleming, 1 September [1952]; *EWL*, p. 380.
50. EW to Margaret Waugh, Whitsun 1953; AWA.
51. EW to Margaret Waugh, 3 June [1957], *EWL* pp. 489-490.
52. EW to Diana Cooper, 29 March 1958, *MWMS*, p. 250.
53. EW to Mary Lygon, 26 August 1958; copy in AWA.
54. EW to Ann Fleming, 3 December 1958; Amory (ed.) *Letters of Ann Fleming*, p. 224.
55. EW to Diana Cooper, 14 January 1959, *MWMS*, p. 262.
56. EW to Ann Fremantle, 31 July 1959, copy in AWA.
57. *The Sunday Times*, 25 September 1960, *EWCH*, p. 415.
58. A. D. Peters to EW, 7 October 1959; BL.
59. EW to Maurice Bowra, 22 October 1959, *EWL*, p. 530.
60. EW to Ann Fleming, 17 February 1960, *EWL*, p. 533.
61. EW to A. D. Peters, 17 March 1960, HRC.
62. EW to Tom Driberg, 11 June 1960, Christ Church, Oxford.
63. EW to Teresa D'Arms, 16 September 1961; AWA.
64. EW to Margaret Waugh, 20 February 1961; AWA.
65. EW to Diana Cooper, 24 December 1960, *MWMS*, p. 282.
66. EW to Jack MacDougall, 18 April 1958, *EWL*, p. 507.
67. EW to Auberon Waugh, 28 July 1959; AWA.
68. EW to John D'Arms, 11 November 1960; copy in AWA.
69. EW to Pansy Lamb, 18 July 1961; copy in AWA.
70. Alexander Waugh, *Fathers and Sons*, p. 394.
71. EW to John Donaldson [24 April 1961], copy in AWA.
72. EW to Alec Waugh, 22 March 1961; BU.
73. EW to Daphne Fielding, 22 May 1961; *EWL*, p. 566.

74. EW to Christopher Sykes, 5 June 1961, Sykes Papers, GU.
75. EW to Ann Fleming, 13 June 1961; copy in AWA.
76. EW to Teresa D'Arms, 5 June 1961; copy in AWA.
77. Alexander Waugh, *Fathers and Sons*, p. 399.
78. Auberon Waugh to EW, 24 June 1961; BL.
79. EW to Auberon Waugh, 29 June 1961; AWA.
80. EW to Margaret Waugh, 5 July [1961]; AWA.
81. EW to Ann Fleming, 17 July 1961; copy in AWA.

23 Decline and Fall

1. *A Little Learning*, p. 1.
2. A. D. Peters to EW, 27 April 1961; HRC.
3. EW to Alec Waugh, 19 July 1961; BU.
4. EW to Margaret Waugh, 20 July 1961; AWA.
5. EW to Diana Mosley, 9 March 1966; *EWL*, p. 638.
6. EW to Margaret Waugh, 20 July 1961; AWA.
7. EW to Ann Fleming, 8 August 1961; copy in AWA.
8. EW to Teresa D'Arms, 16 September 1961; copy in AWA.
9. EW to Pamela Berry, 30 October [1961]; copy in AWA.
10. Philip Caraman to EW, 21 April 1961; BL.
11. EW to Ann Fleming, 19 October [1960]; copy in AWA.
12. EW to Margaret Waugh, 7 December 1960; AWA.
13. EW to Margaret Waugh, 20 July 1961; AWA.
14. EW to Margaret Waugh, 12 March 1961; AWA.
15. EW to Ann Fleming, 27 March 1961; *EWL*, p. 563.
16. EW to Margaret Waugh, 24 May 1961; AWA.
17. EW to Margaret Waugh, 20 July 1961; AWA.
18. Margaret Waugh to EW, 6 April 1961; BL.
19. EW to Diana Cooper, 22 June 1961, *MWMS*, p. 288.
20. Philip Caraman to EW, 15 September 1961; BL.
21. EW to Ann Fleming, 30 August 1961; copy in AWA.
22. Christopher Sykes to EW, 21 October 1961; BL.
23. Maurice Bowra to EW, 15 October 1961; BL.
24. *The Sunday Times*, 29 October 1961; *EWCH*, p. 430.
25. Amory (ed.), *Letters of Ann Fleming*, p. 295.
26. EW to Teresa D'Arms, 28 October 1961; copy in AWA.
27. EW to Cyril Connolly, 23 October 1961; copy in AWA.
28. Cyril Connolly to EW, 30 October 1961; BL.
29. EW to Cyril Connolly, 20 November 1961; copy in AWA.
30. EW to Diana Cooper, 30 June 1962, *MWMS*, p. 291.
31. EW to Teresa D'Arms, 19 February 1962; copy in AWA.
32. EW to Diana Cooper, 30 March 1962; *MWMS*, p. 291.
33. EW to Nancy Mitford, 1 April 1962, *LNMEW*, pp. 449–50.
34. EW to Nancy Mitford, 27 March 1962; ibid., p. 447.
35. Nancy Mitford to EW, 10 April 1962; ibid., p. 450.
36. Nancy Mitford to EW, 29 March 1962; ibid., p. 449.
37. EW to Margaret Waugh, 12 April [1962]; copy in AWA.

38. Giles FitzHerbert to the author, December 2013.
39. Giles FitzHerbert to EW, 6 August 1962; BL.
40. EW to Nancy Mitford [*c.* 22 August 1962]; *LNMEW*, p. 457.
41. Diana Cooper to EW [25 August 1962]; *MWMS*, p. 293.
42. EW to Diana Cooper, 28 August 1962; ibid., p. 293.
43. *Basil Seal Rides Again*, p. 13.
44. EW to Daphne Fielding, 25 October 1962; copy in AWA.
45. Margaret Waugh to EW, 7 August 1962; BL.
46. EW to Ann Fleming, 19 September 1962; copy in AWA.
47. EW to Teresa D'Arms, 27 June 1962; copy in AWA.
48. EW to Daphne Acton, 10 June 1963; copy in AWA.
49. EW to Nancy Mitford, 28 December 1962; *LNMEW*, p. 471.
50. Hugh Molson to EW, 2 January 1962; BL.
51. John Betjeman to EW, September 1964; Lycett Green (ed.), *John Betjeman Letters*, Vol. 2, p. 279.
52. W. R. B. Young to EW, 21 November 1963; BL.
53. W. R B Young to EW, 27 November 1963; BL.
54. EW to Teresa D'Arms, 29 October 1964; copy in AWA.
55. Auberon Waugh to EW, 8 June 1963; BL.
56. EW to Teresa D'Arms, 14 October 1963; copy in AWA.
57. EW to Ann Fleming, 13 March 1963; *EWL*, p. 601.
58. EW to Teresa D'Arms, 28 August 1963; copy in AWA.
59. EW to Margaret FitzHerbert, 22 September 1963; copy in AWA.
60. EW to Ann Fleming, 10 October 1963; copy in AWA.
61. EW to Zarita Mattay, 20 November 1963; copy in AWA.
62. EW to Alfred Duggan, 18 November 1963; copy in AWA.
63. *New Statesman*, September 1964; *EWCH*, p. 461.
64. EW to Diana Mosley, 9 March 1966; *EWL*, p. 638.
65. *Encounter*, December 1964; *EWCH*, p. 471.
66. *Cosmopolitan*, November 1964; *EWCH*, pp. 469–70.
67. Katherine Asquith to EW, 9 September 1964; BL.
68. Dudley Carew to EW, 4 September 1964; BL.
69. EW to Diana Cooper, 24 October [1964]; *MWMS*, p. 311.
70. EW to Diana Cooper, 20 December 1964, ibid., p. 315.
71. EW to Ann Fleming, 27 January 1965, *EWL*, p. 630.
72. EW to Nancy Mitford, [2 March] 1965, *LNMEW*, p. 497.
73. EW to Nancy Mitford, 29 May 1965; *EWL*, p. 631.
74. EW to Nancy Mitford, 25 January 1966; *LNMEW*, p. 503.
75. EW to Nancy Mitford, 29 May 1965; *EWL*, p. 631.
76. EW to Nancy Mitford 5 September 1965; *EWL*, p. 633.
77. Ibid.
78. EW to Ann Fleming, 3 January 1966; copy in AWA.
79. Margaret FitzHerbert to EW [4 December 1965]; BL.
80. EW to Margaret FitzHerbert, 6 December 1965; *EWL*, p. 635.
81. Margaret FitzHerbert to EW, 19 December 1965; copy in AWA.
82. EW to A. D. Peters, 29 January 1966; HRC.
83. Sykes, *Evelyn Waugh*, p. 445.
84. EW to Ann Fleming [31 January 1966]; copy in AWA.

85. EW to Professor Robin Anderson, 10 April 1966; copy in AWA.
86. Auberon Waugh, *Will This Do?*, pp. 184–5.
87. Margaret FitzHerbert to Diana Cooper, [April 1966]; *MWMS*, p. 326.

Epilogue

1. Graham Greene to Laura Waugh, 10 April 1966; BL.
2. Diana Mosley to Laura Waugh, 11 April 1966; BL.
3. Nancy Mitford to Laura Waugh, 11 April 1966; BL.
4. A. D. Peters to Laura Waugh, 12 April 1966; BL.
5. Patrick Kinross to Laura Waugh, 17 April 1966; BL.
6. P. G. Wodehouse to Laura Waugh, 11 April 1966; BL.
7. Angus Wilson to Laura Waugh, 13 April 1966; BL.
8. Robert Henriques to Laura Waugh, 12 August 1966; BL.
9. Daphne Acton to Laura Waugh, 13 April 1966; BL.
10. Lady Dorothy Lygon to Laura Waugh, 12 April 1966; BL.
11. Diana Cooper to Laura Waugh, 12 April 1966; BL.
12. John Betjeman to Laura Waugh, 16 April 196; BL.
13. Penelope Betjeman to Laura Waugh, 18 April 1966; BL.
14. Daphne Acton to Laura Waugh, 13 April 1966; BL.

Select Bibliography

Works by Evelyn Waugh

PRB: An Essay on the Pre-Raphaelite Brotherhood, 1847–54, privately printed, 1926.
Rossetti: His Life and Works, Duckworth, 1928.
Decline and Fall: An Illustrated Novelette, Chapman & Hall, 1928.
Vile Bodies, Chapman & Hall, 1930.
Labels, A Mediterranean Journey, Duckworth, 1930; US edition: *A Bachelor Abroad*, J. Cape & H. Smith, 1930.
Remote People, Duckworth, 1931; US edition: *They Were Still Dancing*, Farrar & Rinehart, 1932.
Black Mischief, Chapman & Hall, 1932.
Ninety-Two Days, Duckworth, 1934.
A Handful of Dust, Chapman & Hall, 1934.
Edmund Campion, Longman, 1935.
Mr Loveday's Little Outing and Other Sad Stories, Chapman & Hall, 1936.
Waugh in Abyssinia, Longman Green & Co, 1936.
Scoop: A Novel About Journalists, Chapman & Hall, 1938.
Robbery Under Law, Chapman & Hall, 1939; US edition: *Mexico: An Object Lesson*, Little, Brown, 1939.
Put Out More Flags, Chapman & Hall, 1942.
Work Suspended, Chapman & Hall, 1942.
Brideshead Revisited: The Sacred and Profane Memories of Captain Charles Ryder, Chapman & Hall, 1945.
Scott-King's Modern Europe, Chapman & Hall, 1947.
The Loved One, Chapman & Hall, 1948.
Helena, Chapman & Hall, 1950.
The Holy Places, Queen Anne Press, 1952.

Men at Arms, Chapman & Hall, 1952.

Love Among the Ruins: A Romance of the Near Future, Chapman & Hall, 1953.

Officers and Gentlemen, Chapman & Hall, 1955.

The Ordeal of Gilbert Pinfold, Chapman & Hall, 1957.

The Life of the Right Reverend Ronald Knox, Chapman & Hall, 1959.

A Tourist in Africa, Chapman & Hall, 1960.

Unconditional Surrender, Chapman & Hall, 1961.

Basil Seal Rides Again, Chapman & Hall, 1963.

A Little Learning: The First Volume of An Autobiography, Chapman & Hall, 1964.

Sword of Honour (his final version of the war trilogy *Men at Arms, Officers and Gentlemen* and *Unconditional Surrender*), Chapman & Hall, 1965.

Collected Editions

The Diaries of Evelyn Waugh, edited by Michael Davie, Weidenfeld & Nicolson, 1976 (NB: the 2009 Phoenix paperback edition has a greatly improved index).

The Letters of Evelyn Waugh, edited by Mark Amory, Weidenfeld & Nicolson, 1980.

Evelyn Waugh, A Little Order: A Selection from his Journalism, edited by Donat Gallagher, Eyre Methuen, 1977.

The Essays, Articles and Reviews of Evelyn Waugh, edited by Donat Gallagher, Methuen, 1983.

Mr Wu & Mrs Stitch: The Letters of Evelyn Waugh and Diana Cooper, edited by Artemis Cooper, Hodder & Stoughton, 1991.

The Letters of Nancy Mitford & Evelyn Waugh, edited by Charlotte Mosley, Hodder & Stoughton, 1996.

The Complete Short Stories of Evelyn Waugh, edited by Ann Pasternak Slater, Everyman, 1998.

Other Sources

Acton, Harold, *Memoirs of An Aesthete*, Methuen, 1948.

Acton, Harold, *More Memoirs of An Aesthete*, Methuen, 1970.

Acton, Harold, *Nancy Mitford*, Hamish Hamilton, 1975.

Agar, Eileen, *A Look at My Life*, Methuen, 1988.

Amory, Mark (ed.), *The Letters of Ann Fleming*, Collins Harvill, 1985.

Amory, Mark, *Lord Berners*, Chatto & Windus, 1998.

Annan, Noel, *Roxburgh of Stowe*, Longman, 1964.

Annan, Noel, *Our Age*, Weidenfeld & Nicolson, 1990.

Barber, Michael, *Anthony Powell*, Duckworth, 2004.

Barber, Michael, *Evelyn Waugh*, Hesperus Press, 2013.

Beaton, Cecil, *The Wandering Years: Diaries 1922–1939*, Weidenfeld & Nicolson, 1966.

Beevor, Antony, *Crete: The Battle and the Resistance*, John Murray, 1991; rev. edition: Penguin, 2014.

Blayac, Alain (ed.), *Evelyn Waugh: New Directions*, Macmillan, 1992.

Blondel, Nathalie, *Mary Butts: Scenes from Life*, Kingston, NY, 1998.

Bowra, C. M., *Memories*, Weidenfeld & Nicolson, 1966.

Boyd, William, *Bamboo*, Hamish Hamilton, 2005.

Bradbury, Malcolm, *Evelyn Waugh*, Oliver & Boyd, 1964.

Bradford, Sarah, *Sacheverell Sitwell*, Sinclair-Stevenson, 1993.

Butler, Lucy (ed.), *Robert Byron: Letters Home*, John Murray, 1991.

Byrne, Paula, *Mad World: Evelyn Waugh and the Secrets of Brideshead*, Harper Press, 2009.

Carew, Dudley, *A Fragment of Friendship: A Memory of Evelyn Waugh When Young*, Everest Books, 1974.

Carpenter, Humphrey, *The Brideshead Generation*, Weidenfeld & Nicolson, 1989.

Charteris, Evan (ed.), *The Life and Letters of Edmund Gosse*, William Heinemann, 1931.

Cooper, Diana, *The Rainbow Comes and Goes*, Rupert Hart-Davis, 1958.

Cooper, Diana, *The Light of Common Day*, Rupert Hart-Davis, 1959.

Cooper, Diana, *Trumpets from the Steep*, Rupert Hart-Davis, 1960.

Davis, Robert Murray, *Evelyn Waugh: A Checklist of Primary and Secondary Material*, Whitston, 1972.

Davis, Robert Murray, *A Catalogue of the Evelyn Waugh Collection at the Humanities Research Center, The University of Texas at Austin*, Whitston, 1981.

Davis, Robert Murray, *Evelyn Waugh, Writer*, Pilgrim Books, 1981.

Davis, Robert Murray, *Evelyn Waugh, Apprentice*, Pilgrim Books, 1985.

Davis, Robert Murray et al., *A Bibliography of Evelyn Waugh*, Whitston, 1986.

Deedes, W. F., *At War with Waugh: The Real Story of Scoop*, Macmillan, 2003.

Delmer, Sefton, *Trail Sinister*, Secker & Warburg, 1961.

Donaldson, Frances, *Evelyn Waugh: Portrait of a Country Neighbour*, Weidenfeld & Nicolson, 1967.

Driberg, Tom, *Ruling Passions*, Quartet Books, 1978.

Fallowell, Duncan, *How to Disappear: A Memoir for Misfits*, Ditto Press, 2011.

Fussell, Paul, *Abroad: British Literary Traveling Between the Wars*, Oxford University Press, 1980.

Gale, Iain, *Waugh's World: A Guide to the Novels of Evelyn Waugh*, Sidgwick & Jackson, 1990.

Gallagher, Donat, *In the Picture: The Facts Behind the Fiction in Evelyn Waugh's Sword of Honour*, Rodopi, 2014.

Gallagher, Donat, Ann Pasternak Slater and John Howard Wilson (eds), *A Handful of Mischief: New Essays on Evelyn Waugh*, Farleigh Dickinson University Press, 2011.

Goldring, Douglas, *Odd Man Out*, Chapman & Hall, 1935.

Green, Henry (Henry Yorke), *Pack My Bag: a Self-Portrait*, Hogarth Press, 1979.

Green, Martin, *Children of the Sun: A Narrative of 'Decadence' in England After 1918*, Constable, 1977.

Greenidge, Terence, *Degenerate Oxford?*, Chapman & Hall, 1930.

Grisewood, Harman, *One Thing at a Time: An Autobiography*, Hutchinson, 1968.

Handford, B. W. T., *Lancing 1848–1930*, Blackwell, 1933.

Hastings, Selina, *Nancy Mitford*, Hamish Hamilton, 1985.

Hastings, Selina, *Evelyn Waugh: A Biography*, Sinclair-Stevenson, 1994.

Hastings, Selina, *The Secret Lives of Somerset Maugham*, John Murray, 2009.

Heath, Jeffrey, *The Picturesque Prison*, Weidenfeld & Nicolson, 1982.

Hillier, Bevis, *Young Betjeman*, John Murray, 1988.

Hillier, Bevis, *New Fame, New Love*, John Murray, 2002.

Hillier, Bevis, *The Bonus of Laughter*, John Murray, 2004.

Hollis, Christopher, *Evelyn Waugh*, Longman, 1966.

Hollis, Christopher, *The Seven Ages*, Heinemann, 1974.

Hollis, Christopher, *Oxford in the Twenties: Recollections of Five Friends*, Heinemann, 1976.

Holman-Hunt, Diana, *My Grandfather, His Wives & Loves*, Hamish Hamilton, 1969.

Holroyd, Michael, *Augustus John, Vol. 2*, Heinemann, 1975.

Holroyd, Michael, *Bernard Shaw, Vol. 1*, Chatto & Windus, 1989.

Ker, Ian, *The Catholic Revival in English Literature, 1845–1961*, University of Notre Dame Press, 2003.

Knox, James, *Robert Byron*, John Murray, 2003.

Lancaster, Marie-Jacqueline (ed.), *Brian Howard: Portrait of a Failure*, Antony Blond, 1968.

Lees-Milne, James, *Ancestral Voices*, Chatto & Windus, 1975.

Lees-Milne, James, *Ancient as the Hills: Diaries 1973–1974*, John Murray, 1997.

Lewis, Jeremy, *Cyril Connolly*, Jonathan Cape, 1997.

Linck, Charles E., *The Development of Evelyn Waugh's Career*, unpublished PhD thesis, 1962.

Linck, Charles E., *Evelyn Waugh in Letters by Terence Greenidge*, Cow Hill Press, 1994.

Longford, Elizabeth, *The Pebbled Shore*, Weidenfeld & Nicolson, 1986.

Lovat, Lord, *March Past*, Weidenfeld & Nicolson, 1978.

Lycett, Andrew, *Ian Fleming*, Weidenfeld & Nicolson, 1995.

Lycett, Andrew, *Dylan Thomas: A New Life*, Weidenfeld & Nicolson, 2003.

McCall, Henrietta, *The Life of Max Mallowan*, British Museum Press, 2001.

Maclean, Fitzroy, *Eastern Approaches*, Cape 1949.

McDonnell, Jacqueline, *Waugh on Women*, Duckworth, 1986.

McLaren, Duncan, *Evelyn! Rhapsody for an Obsessive Love*, Harbour, 2015; see also his website www.evelynwaugh.org.uk

Mallowan, Max, *Mallowan's Memoirs*, Collins, 1977.

May, Derwent (ed.), *Good Talk: An Anthology from BBC Radio*, Victor Gollancz, 1968.

Mead, Richard, *Commando General: The Life of Major General Sir Robert Laycock*, Pen & Sword, 2016.

Mitford, Jessica, *Hons and Rebels*, Victor Gollancz, 1960.

Mitford, Nancy, *A Talent to Annoy: Essays, Articles and Reviews, 1929–1968*, Hamish Hamilton, 1986.

Montagu, Elizabeth, *Honourable Rebel*, Montagu Ventures, 2003.

Morriss, Margaret and D. J., Dooley, *Evelyn Waugh: A Reference Guide*, G. K. Hall & Co, 1984.

Mosley, Charlotte (ed.), *Love from Nancy: The Letters of Nancy Mitford*, Hodder & Stoughton, 1993.

Mosley, Diana, *A Life of Contrasts*, Hamish Hamilton, 1977.

Mosley, Diana, *Loved Ones*, Sidgwick & Jackson, 1977.

Mosley, Diana, *The Pursuit of Laughter*, Gibson Square, 2009.

Mulvagh, Jane, *Madresfield: The Real Brideshead*, Doubleday, 2008.

Norwich, John Julius, *Trying to Please*, Dovecote, 2008.

Norwich, John Julius, (ed.) *Darling Monster: The Letters of Lady Diana Cooper to her son John Julius Norwich, 1939–1962*, Chatto & Windus, 2013.

Ollard, Richard, *A Man of Contradictions: A Life of A.L. Rowse*, Allen Lane, 1999.

Ollard, Richard (ed.), *The Diaries of A. L. Rowse, 1903–1997*, Allen Lane, 2003.

Owen, James, *Commando: Winning WW2 Behind Enemy Lines*, Little, Brown, 2012.

Pakenham, Frank, *Born to Believe*, Cape, 1953.

Patey, Douglas Lane, *The Life of Evelyn Waugh: A Critical Biography*, Blackwell, 1998.

Powell, Anthony, *Infants of the Spring*, Heinemann, 1976.

Powell, Anthony, *Messengers of Day*, Heinemann, 1978.

Powell, Anthony, *Faces in My Time*, Heinemann, 1980.

Powell, Anthony, *The Strangers All Are Gone*, Heinemann, 1982.

Powell, Anthony, *Journals 1982–1986*, Heinemann, 1995.

Preston, Paul, *We Saw Spain Die: Foreign Correspondents in the Spanish Civil War*, Constable, 2008.

Pryce-Jones, David, *Cyril Connolly: Journal and Memoir*, Collins, 1983.

Pryce-Jones, David (ed.), *Evelyn Waugh and His World*, Weidenfeld & Nicolson, 1973.

Rothenstein, John, *Summer's Lease: Autobiography 1901–1938*, Hamish Hamilton, 1965.

Ridley, Jane, *The Architect and His Wife: A Life of Edwin Lutyens*, Chatto & Windus, 2002.

Rowse, A. L., *A Cornishman at Oxford*, Jonathan Cape, 1965.

Rowse, A. L., *A Cornishman Abroad*, Jonathan Cape, 1976.

Rowse, A. L., *A Man of the Thirties*, Jonathan Cape, 1979.

St John, John, *To the War with Waugh*, Leo Cooper, 1973.

Saumarez Smith, John (ed.), *The Bookshop at 10 Curzon Street: Letters between Nancy Mitford and Heywood Hill, 1952–1973*, Francis Lincoln, 2004.

Shakespeare, Nicholas, *Priscilla: The Hidden Life of an Englishwoman in Wartime France*, Harvill Secker, 2013.

Stannard, Martin, *Evelyn Waugh: The Critical Heritage*, Routledge & Kegan Paul, 1984.

Stannard, Martin, *Evelyn Waugh: The Early Years 1903–1939*, JM Dent & Sons, 1986.

Stannard, Martin, *Evelyn Waugh: No Abiding City 1939–1966*, JM Dent & Sons, 1992.

Stopp, Frederick, *Evelyn Waugh: Portrait of an Artist*, Chapman & Hall, 1958.

Taylor, D. J., *Bright Young People*, Chatto & Windus, 2007.

Thomas, David N., *Dylan Thomas: A Farm, Two Mansions and a Bungalow*, Seren, 2000.

Thompson, Laura, *Love in a Cold Climate: Nancy Mitford – A Portrait of a Contradictory Woman*, Review, 2003.

Thwaite, Ann, *Glimpses of the Wonderful: The Life of Philip Henry Gosse*, Faber & Faber, 2002.

Thwaite, Ann (ed.), *My Oxford*, Robson Books, 1977.

Treglown, Jeremy, *Romancing: The Life and Work of Henry Green*, Faber & Faber, 2000.

Sieveking, Paul (ed.), *Airborne: Scenes from the Life of Lance Sieveking*, Strange Attractor Press, 2013.

Sinclair, Andrew, *Francis Bacon: His Life and Violent Times*, Sinclair-Stevenson, 1993.

Sykes, Christopher, *Evelyn Waugh: A Biography*, William Collins, 1975.

Vickers, Hugo, *Cecil Beaton*, Weidenfeld & Nicolson, 1985.

Vickers, Hugo, *The Unexpurgated Beaton: The Cecil Beaton Diaries as He Wrote Them*, Weidenfeld & Nicolson, 2002.

Waugh, Alec, *The Early Years of Alec Waugh*, Cassell, 1962.

Waugh, Alec, *My Brother Evelyn & Other Profiles*, Cassell, 1967.

Waugh, Alec, *The Fatal Gift*, WH Allen, 1973.

Waugh, Alec, *A Year to Remember: A Reminiscence of 1931*, WH Allen, 1975.

Waugh, Alec, *The Best Wine Last*, WH Allen, 1978.

Waugh, Alexander, *Fathers and Sons: The Autobiography of a Family*, Headline, 2004.

Waugh, Arthur, *Alfred Lord Tennyson*, William Heineman, 1894.

Waugh, Arthur, *One Man's Road*, Chapman & Hall, 1931.

Waugh, Auberon, *Will This Do? The First Fifty Years of Auberon Waugh: An Autobiography*, Century, 1991.

Westminster, Loelia, *Grace and Favour*, Weidenfeld & Nicolson, 1961.

Wheen, Francis, *Tom Driberg: His Life and Indiscretions*, Chatto & Windus, 1990.

Williams, Emlyn, *George: An Early Autobiography*, Hamish Hamilton, 1961.

Wilson, A. N., *Betjeman*, Hutchinson, 2006.

Wilson, John Howard, *Evelyn Waugh: A Literary Biography 1903–1924*, Associated University Presses, 1996.

Wilson, John Howard, *Evelyn A Literary Biography 1924–1966*, Associated University Presses, 2001.

Wykes, David, *Evelyn Waugh: A Literary Life*, Macmillan, 1999.

Ziegler, Philip, *Diana Cooper*, Hamish Hamilton, 1981.

Zinovieff, Sofka, *The Mad Boy, Lord Berners, My Grandmother and Me*, Jonathan Cape, 2014.

Index